About This Preliminary Edition

The authors, working together as the Graphing Calculator Enhanced Algebra Project, have been developing materials that fully integrate graphing calculators into the algebra classroom. In 1993, Key Curriculum Press joined with the Project to produce *Advanced Algebra Through Data Exploration*. Responding to the intense demand from schools that want to begin using the material, Key Curriculum Press is making *Advanced Algebra Through Data Exploration* available in this soft-cover, preliminary edition. The preliminary edition has been thoroughly and successfully classroom tested for four years. The calculator appendices at the back of this preliminary edition will help your students use this text with TI-80, TI-81, TI-82, and TI-85 graphics calculators.

When the final edition is published, these appendices will appear as separate, stand-alone supplements (shortening the student text by 130 pages!), and will be keyed to additional calculator brands. The final edition will be hardcover, illustrated, professionally typeset, indexed, reworked in minor ways, and yes, we will catch 99% of the errors. We do not plan to make major changes to the content of this textbook. However, we welcome your comments and suggestions based on your experience with the preliminary edition. You can write to us at the address above or e-mail us at editorial@keypress.com.

Author Acknowledgments

We want to thank the National Science Foundation for their support of this project. At this point hundreds of teachers have used materials and/or have participated in workshops and summer institutes. We are especially grateful to teachers and students who have worked with us at various stages, providing suggestions, locating manuscript errors, and most of all encouraging us to continue. Initial class-testing of project materials was especially difficult as teachers and schools duplicated materials, taught without teacher resources and many times without any answer or solution key. These teachers and their students are our heroes.

We are high school teachers at Interlochen Arts Academy. We are especially appreciative of the encouragement offered by our school, colleagues, students, and parents. Thanks for your support. Finally, we truly appreciate the confidence, the cooperation, and the contributions offered by everyone at Key Curriculum Press. The project is in good hands.

Advanced Algebra Through Data Exploration:
A Graphing Calculator Approach

Preliminary Edition

Jerald Murdock

Eric Kamischke

Ellen Kamischke

Interlochen Arts Academy
Interlochen, Michigan

KEY CURRICULUM PRESS
Innovators in Mathematics Education

Advanced Algebra
Through Data Exploration:
A Graphing Calculator Approach

Authors: Jerald Murdock, Eric Kamischke, Ellen Kamischke

Editor: Crystal Mills

Editorial Assistance: Caroline Ayres, Cathy Kessel, Karen Wootton, Romy Snyder, Judy Cubillo

Cover Design: Kirk Mills

Key Curriculum Press
P.O. Box 2304
Berkeley, California 94702
510-548-2304
editorial@keypress.com

This material is based upon work supported by the National Science Foundation under award number MDR9154410. Any opinions, findings, and conclusions or recommendations expressed in this publication are those of the authors and do not necessarily reflect the views of the National Science Foundation.

A Note to Students from the Authors

Ultimately, the goal of mathematics education is to develop the mathematical power of all students so that they can participate fully as productive citizens of the world. People, what they do, how they do it, and the world they live in are continually changing. To be useful and relevant in this dynamically changing situation, the algebra and the mathematics they learn must also evolve. Traditional topics, methods, and algorithms no longer provide the necessary skills for today's students.

What's Different About This Course?

You are about to embark on a very exciting mathematical journey, made possible by available technology. In other algebra texts, you develop a tool kit of paper-and-pencil manipulative skills and procedures for later use. Many students wonder, "When will I ever use this?" when they encounter "Simplify these expressions" and "Solve for x" in situations without any real meaning and when they solve irrelevant word problems. Often the use of technology is included with additional alternative investigations, not as an integral part of the curriculum.

Advanced Algebra Through Data Exploration offers you a fundamentally different and contemporary mathematical experience. It will help prepare you to reason mathematically, communicate mathematically, use mathematics to solve problems, and make connections between mathematics and the world around you. You will be encouraged to explore and to make sense of your experiences with mathematics by integrating and linking algebra with statistics, data analysis, functions, discrete mathematics, geometry, probability, and trigonometry.

Advanced Algebra Through Data Exploration allows you to develop your conceptual understanding of mathematics by doing activities embedded in contextual settings. You will collect and generate data, develop and analyze mathematical models, explore patterns and relevant questions, and then make and defend predictions. The emphasis is on interpretation, analysis, and making sense of the problem, the process, and the answer.

Using Technology

Because this text fully integrates graphing calculators into the explorations, activities, and problems, you will not need to learn many obsolete paper-and-pencil routines. Other traditional procedures are de-emphasized while you learn more efficient technologically driven alternatives. You focus on understanding and using mathematics, and on making sense of symbols rather than manipulating symbols. Explorations from multiple perspectives help you simplify and make sense of what were formerly difficult algebraic abstractions. Variables and functions will be more dynamic—you will explore variables that vary and functions that describe real-world phenomena. You will investigate growth and decay applications with function models like $y = ax^b$, looking for patterns, shapes, and implications as the parameters a and b change. Technology, scientific advances, and a need for different mathematical applications mean that it is important for you to study new and different algebra topics: recursively defined routines, parametric representations, data analysis, random process simulations, Markov processes, matrices, and other discrete topics. The graphing calculator, or grapher, allows you to explore and investigate algebra from this new perspective.

Taking Care of Yourself

This book was written with you, the student, in mind. Have you ever thought about the different ways you will use mathematics in your life? Learning how to think mathematically will help you to solve and analyze problems that you encounter almost daily. Interest rates, mortgage payments, dynamics of population growth, the intelligent analysis of consumer information, and the effects of drugs and vitamins on your body are just a few examples of situations you will soon investigate.

You may not be in the habit of reading your math textbook. If this is the case, then you will need to learn how to read a math book. Reading and understanding a mathematics textbook may seem difficult at first, but do not be discouraged. Sometimes you will need to read and think through a particular sentence, paragraph, or problem more than once before you are ready to go on. Reading a passage aloud will often help. You should always read a math textbook with calculator and pencil in hand, ready to work the examples as you read them. Be sure to answer questions asked in the text. These questions and your answers will help you understand the problems that follow.

Working and communicating with others will also strengthen your understanding of the mathematical concepts presented in this book. You are encouraged to work in groups on the activities as well as on the problems. Share your experiences, discoveries, and frustrations with others—your teacher, friends, family members, and classmates.

Don't be afraid to try something new. Remember that often there are many ways to solve the same problem; at times, there may even be different solutions to the same problem. You will work hard in this course, but your reward will be a deeper understanding of mathematics and an appreciation of how mathematics is really used. As authors, editors, and publisher, we encourage and salute your personal commitment to learning.

Learning how to use technology efficiently is one of the most important things you can do to ensure a successful future. Your graphing calculator will help you solve problems, simulate processes, explore and model data, and confirm hypotheses. Your graphing calculator will help you visualize concepts and develop a deeper understanding of the mathematics involved. The complicated computations and complex applications in this text require that you learn to use your calculator efficiently.

Taking Care of Your Graphing Calculator

Graphing calculators are designed for student use. However, there are precautions you should take to ensure that your calculator doesn't get damaged or broken. Be careful when carrying your calculator in a book bag or backpack. If someone steps on your bag, or the bag gets wet, your calculator may suffer. Also, do not leave your calculator in a place subject to extreme temperatures that can destroy the liquid crystal display. Avoid dropping the calculator. Hard surfaces are very hard on calculators. If you have to change the batteries in your calculator, be sure to read the instructions in the manual before doing so. If possible, back up the contents of your calculator before changing the batteries.

Contents

Chapter 0   Introducing the Calculator

0.1   Using the Calculator for Basic Operations 2

0.2   Fractions, Decimals, and Scientific Notation 9

0.3   Using the Grapher 15

Chapter 1   Patterns and Recursion

1.1   Recursively Defined Sequences 22

1.2   Modeling Growth 28

1.3   A First Look at Limits 33

1.4   Graphing Sequences 37

1.5   Recursive Routine for Sequences 41

1.6   A Recursive Look At Series 46

1.7   Chapter Review 50

1.8   Projects 51

Chapter 2   Sequences and Explicit Formulas

2.1   Explicit Formulas for Arithmetic Sequences 56

2.2   Explicit Formulas for Arithmetic Series 62

2.3   Explicit Formulas for Geometric Sequences 66

2.4   Explicit Formulas for Geometric Series 71

2.5   In The Long Run 75

2.6   Fractal Patterns 80

2.7   Chapter Review 84

2.8   Projects 87

Chapter 3   Introduction to Statistics

3.1   Box Plots and Measures of Center 92

3.2   Measures of Variability 102

3.3   Histograms and Percentiles 109

3.4   Chapter Review 120

3.5   Projects 123

Chapter 4   Data Analysis

4.1   The Best-Fit Line..128

4.2   Equation of a Line...132

4.3   Real-World Meanings...136

4.4   The Median-Median Line..142

4.5   The Residuals..149

4.6   The Least-Squares Line...157

4.7   Coefficient of Correlation...163

4.8   Accuracy...172

4.9   Chapter Review...179

4.10   Projects...182

Chapter 5   Functions

5.1   Interpreting Graphs..188

5.2   Connections with Sequences...193

5.3   The Linear Family..199

5.4   The Parabola Family...203

5.5   The Square Root Family...208

5.6   The Absolute Value Family 212

5.7   Stretching a Curve...215

5.8   A Summary..220

5.9   Compositions of Functions...225

5.10   Chapter Review...230

5.11   Projects...232

Chapter 6   Parametric Equations and Trigonometry

6.1   Graphing Parametric Equations...236

6.2   Parametric to Nonparametric..244

6.3   Right Triangle Trigonometry...248

6.4   Geometric Shapes..256

6.5   Wind and River Problems...261

6.6   Using Trigonometry to Set a Course......................................268

6.7   Chapter Review...275

6.8   Projects...278

Chapter 7   Exponential and Logarithmic Functions

7.1   The Exponential Function...282

7.2   Rational Exponents and Roots...289

7.3   Properties of Exponents 294

7.4   Building Inverses of Functions...303

7.5   Equations with Rational Exponents. 311

7.6   The Logarithmic Function 317

7.7   Properties of Logarithms...324

7.8   Applications of Logarithms 330

7.9   Curve Straightening and More Data Analysis...............................337

7.10   Chapter Review 345

7.11   Projects 347

Chapter 8   Discrete Math Topics

8.1   Using Random Numbers...354

8.2   Random Numbers in Two Dimensions 362

8.3   Some Counting Techniques...366

8.4   Waiting and Expected Value...372

8.5   Chromatic Numbering..378

8.6   The Transition Matrix..383

8.7   Matrix Operations..389

8.8   Chapter Review...394

8.9   Projects...398

Chapter 9   Systems of Equations

9.1   Zooming in on Systems..402

9.2   Substitution and Elimination..407

9.3   Number of Solutions..414

9.4   Matrix Solutions of Systems 420

9.5   Linear Inequations and Systems..428

9.6   Linear Programming...433

9.7   Applications of Linear Programming 436

9.8   Determinants and System Classification 440

9.9   Chapter Review...445

9.10   Projects...448

Chapter 10   Polynomials

10.1	Finite Differences	452
10.2	Different Quadratic Forms	458
10.3	Factored Polynomials	463
10.4	The Quadratic Formula	469
10.5	Applications and Algebraic Solutions	477
10.6	Higher Degree Polynomials	482
10.7	No Real Solutions	488
10.8	More About Finding Solutions	492
10.9	Chapter Review	499
10.10	Projects	501

Chapter 11   More Probability and Statistics

11.1	Permutations and Probability	508
11.2	Combinations and Probability	515
11.3	Binomial Theorem	521
11.4	Standard Deviation	527
11.5	Normal Distribution	536
11.6	Using the Normal Curve	543
11.7	Chapter Review	549
11.8	Projects	551

Chapter 12   Functions and Relations

12.1	The Inverse Variation Function	554
12.2	Rational Functions	560
12.3	Refining the Growth Model	566
12.4	Functions Involving Distance	573
12.5	The Circle and Ellipse	579
12.6	The Parabola	587
12.7	The Hyperbola	592
12.8	The General Quadratic	598
12.9	The Rotation Matrix	604
12.10	Chapter Review	609
12.11	Projects	611

Chapter 13 Trigonometric Functions

13.1 Defining the Circular Function 616

13.2 Other Periodic Functions 624

13.3 Combinations of Functions 630

13.4 The Law of Sines and Law of Cosines 636

13.5 Trigonometry Equations and Inverse Functions....................644

13.6 Polar Curves..651

13.7 Polar Coordinates and Complex Numbers.............................658

13.8 Chapter Review..669

13.9 Projects...672

Appendices for TI-80, TI-81, TI-82, and TI-85 Graphics Calculators

Chapter Zero Appendices 676

Chapter One Appendices 691

Chapter Two Appendices 709

Chapter Three Appendices 711

Chapter Four Appendices..723

Chapter Five Appendices 737

Chapter Six Appendices 745

Chapter Seven Appendices 749

Chapter Eight Appendices...760

Chapter Nine Appendices..770

Chapter Ten Appendices..781

Chapter Eleven Appendices...790

(There are no Chapter Twelve Appendices.)

Chapter Thirteen Appendices..799

Selected Answers

Chapter 0...808

Chapter 1...809

Chapter 2...812

Chapter 3...816

Chapter 4...819

Chapter 5...826

Chapter Zero

INTRODUCING THE CALCULATOR

Contents

Section 0.1: Using the Calculator for Basic Operations... 2

                    Rules of the road

Section 0.2: Fractions, Decimals, and Scientific Notation................................. 9

                    Different ways to say the same thing

Section 0.3: Using the Grapher.. 15

                    It's worth 1000 words

Section 0.1: Using the Calculator for Basic Operations

If you were asked to evaluate the expression 4 + 6 − 2, you probably wouldn't reach for your calculator. Many times, it is more efficient to use mental or pencil-and-paper calculations to solve a problem. Sometimes you will need to make decisions about whether or not to use your calculator. Also, you must learn not to blindly trust answers that quickly appear on the calculator display. Take a moment to think about the answer, making sure that it makes sense in the situation. As the operator, you must know how to enter expressions, and what the calculator is doing to the expressions.

How would you evaluate the expression 6 + 4 • 2? If you got 14 as the answer, you are correct. If you got 20 as your answer, you need to review the rules for order of operations. Enter this expression on your calculator to verify that it will give you an answer of 14. The order in which your calculator performs operations can be summarized by the following rules:

Rules for Order of Operations

1. Simplify expressions within parentheses or other grouping symbols.
2. Simplify exponents.
3. Do the implied multiplications.
4. Do multiplications, and/or divisions in order from left to right.
5. Do additions and/or subtractions in order from left to right.

Expressions such as $3n$, 2π, ^-x, and $\frac{2}{5}x$, for example, or use of parentheses, such as 4.5(13.864), indicate **implied multiplication**. Graphing calculators evaluate implied multiplications, like $3n$, 2π, 4.5(13.864), ^-x, and $\frac{2}{5}x$, *before* performing a multiplication or division indicated by an operation sign. This can cause some confusion if you are not careful. Experiment by trying several similar examples. Be sure to think about the order in which your calculator is evaluating the operations.

The expression $(2 + 3)^2 + 3 • 4^2$ does not contain any implied multiplications. Use the rules for order of operations to evaluate this expression. Then enter the expression in your calculator, and confirm both your interpretation of the correct order of operations and your computed answer. Did you get 73? Do you understand the rules?

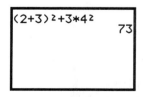

Symbols are an important part of any mathematics course. They are used to denote values, operations, and relationships. When reading a math book, you need to be sure that you understand the symbols used. You will be introduced to many new symbols in this book. Some of the symbols will relate to mathematical concepts; others will be used to denote operations and/or keys on the graphing calculator.

Many of the symbols used in mathematics have an interesting history. Symbols in common use today have come from many different cultures. In 1706, William Jones gave the number π (pi) the name by which we know it today. However, this name did not become popular immediately. Some mathematicians used the symbol π to denote quantities other than the ratio of the circumference of a circle to its radius; some used p or P for that ratio. Eventually, Jones's symbol became accepted. The determination of the value of π also has an interesting history; several books have been written on the subject. About 1650 B.C., the Egyptian scribe Ahmes showed that π is approximately $4 \cdot (8/9)^2 \approx 3.16049$. In A.D. 264, the Chinese mathematician Liu Hui showed that π was approximately 3.14159. Even today, some mathematicians and computer scientists are interested in finding ways to compute more and more digits for π. An approximate value for π is stored in your calculator. See if you can figure out how to access that value.

Example 1: How do you evaluate $3(2 + 7\pi)$?

Solution: First you multiply 7 and π (implied). Then add 2 to the product. Finally, you should multiply by 3 (also implied) to get 71.97344573. . . . If your answer is a rounded approximation, or looks very different from this, check **APPENDIX 0A** for settings.

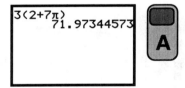

Example 2: How should you enter $\dfrac{27 + 39}{4}$ in the calculator in order to evaluate it?

Solution: If you enter $(27 + 39)/4$, you will get the correct answer, 16.5. The fraction bar is another kind of grouping symbol. Any operations within the numerator and/or the denominator must be performed before the division indicated by a fraction bar.

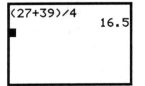

Example 3: How should you enter $\frac{3 + 7^2}{5}$ (12) in the calculator?

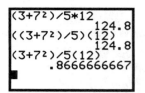

Solution: First use parentheses around the numerator of the fraction to indicate that all of it will be divided by 5. Here are two ways to get 124.8, the correct answer. (See **APPENDIX 0B** if you're not sure how to square a number.)

```
(3+7²)/5*12
            124.8
((3+7²)/5)(12)
            124.8
(3+7²)/5(12)
    .8666666667
■
```

Method 1: Use a multiplication symbol in front of the 12.

$$(3 + 7^2)/5 \cdot 12$$

Method 2: Add another layer of parentheses around the entire fraction.

$$((3 + 7^2)/5)(12)$$

Perhaps you can find another approach to get the same answer. What is wrong with entering the expression as $(3 + 7^2)/5$ (12)? Why doesn't this entry work?

The equal sign is probably the most common symbol used in mathematics. The first use of twin lines for "equals" was by the Welsh physician and mathematician Robert Recorde in 1557. He chose this symbol because "noe .2. thynges, can be moare equalle."

Example 4: Evaluate $2L + 2W$ for the given values.

      a. $L = 7, W = 11$ b. $L = 23, W = 8$

Solution: You can use the replay or last-entry key when you evaluate variable expressions for several different sets of values. This key is helpful because it reprints the previous entry on the screen. (See **APPENDIX 0B**.) Then you can edit the expression by typing over, inserting, or deleting.

Enter the expression using the first set of values for L and W. Enter $2 \cdot 7 + 2 \cdot 11$ to get 36 as the correct answer. To evaluate part b, use the replay key and the arrows to position the cursor on top of the 7. Different combinations of typing over, inserting, and deleting will produce $2 \cdot 23 + 2 \cdot 8$. This should give the answer, 62.

```
2*7+2*11
            36
2*23+2*8
            62
■
```

Using the replay, insert, and delete procedures in this example may seem like more trouble than it's worth. However, these edit functions will be extremely helpful with more complicated expressions.

Example 5: Evaluate $17^2 - 4^3 + 2^5$

Solution: You can enter expressions like this just as they are written. Exponents are entered in two ways: by using special keys for squaring and cubing, or by using keys that allow you to enter any exponent. See **APPENDIX 0B** for specific instructions. Be careful to use the subtract key rather than the (–), *negative of*, key.

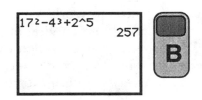

The concepts of positive and negative numbers, and rules for calculating their sums and differences, were introduced in the Chinese *Nine Chapters on the Mathematical Art*, written around the first century A.D. In India, positive and negative numbers first appeared in the work of Brahmegupta in the seventh century. Rules for multiplying and dividing positive and negative numbers appeared around the thirteenth century in China. In the next activity, you will apply these rules as you practice entering expressions on your calculator.

Cross-Number Puzzle Activity

Complete the following cross-number puzzle. Each digit, decimal point, and negative sign will occupy an individual square. Round all answers to the nearest hundredth. If your answer does not fit the squares provided, check your calculation entry and use of parentheses. Learn from your mistakes by working with others in your group, re-entering, editing, and discussing what you might have done incorrectly.

Across

1. $12 + 11 \cdot 10$

5. $6543(132 + 329)$

8. $\sqrt{765^2 + 1836^2}$

9. $\left(\frac{1}{2}\right)^4 + 3.7^3$

10. $\dfrac{(3.6 \cdot 10^6)(2.8 \cdot 10^{10})}{2.4 \cdot 10^{12}}$

11. $6\sqrt{11} + \sqrt[3]{4.4} - 1.83^5$

Down

1. $\dfrac{12 + 3}{7 + 5}$

2. $\dfrac{463}{94} \cdot 47$

3. -320^2

4. $-\sqrt{500(17852 + 1993)}$

6. $\sqrt{337 + 504}$

7. $\dfrac{9710}{15(17)}$

You may be very challenged by the next activity, because it is not a five-minutes-or-less type of problem. One of the objectives of this activity is to help you learn how to work with a group to solve a problem. Your group should try a variety of problem-solving approaches. Brainstorm to generate ideas. Try not make quick judgments. When a group member proposes a strategy and/or solution, it should be considered and explained carefully, so that everyone in the group can verify whether or not it works.

In this activity, and throughout the course, each group member has the following responsibilities:

1. Be cooperative and considerate.

2. Listen carefully, without interrupting, while another is talking.

3. Ask questions of others and ask others for help (when help is needed). If the group is stuck and can't move on, decide as a group to ask for suggestions or help from the teacher.

4. Help others in your group when asked.

5. Work on the problem until every group member understands it and is ready to describe the solution to the class.

Camel Crossing the Desert Activity

A camel is sitting by a stack of 3000 bananas at the edge of a 1000-mile-wide desert. He is going to travel across the desert, carrying as many bananas as he can to the other side. He can carry up to 1000 bananas at any given time, but he eats one banana every mile. What is the maximum number of bananas the camel can get across the desert? How does the camel do it? Be prepared to present your solution to the class. (Hint: The camel doesn't have to go all the way across the desert in one trip.)

Problem Set 0.1

1. Evaluate each expression using your calculator.

   a. $\sqrt{7^2 + 8^2}$

   b. $\dfrac{2\,(18 - 2) + 7}{14 + 2 \cdot 3}$

   c. $\sqrt{12(32 + 43)}$

   d. $\pi \cdot \dfrac{1}{2} \cdot 12.6^2$

2. a. Evaluate $(^-4)^2$ and $^-4^2$ on the calculator. Compare the answers, and explain why they are (or are not) different.

   b. René Descartes (1596–1650) was the first mathematician to use the x^2 notation. Evaluate the expression x^2 for $x = 17$. Write what you entered into the calculator. What is the answer?

   c. Evaluate the expression $^-x^2$ for $x = 24$. Write what you entered into the calculator. What is the answer?

   d. Your calculator can store values for variables. Use this calculator feature to evaluate x^2 and $^-x^2$ for $x = 17$. See **APPENDIX 0B** for specific instructions.

3. a. For each expression below, try to compute the answer in your head.

   i. $12 + \dfrac{3 - \sqrt{169 - 2^3(6)}}{2}$

   ii. $\dfrac{2 + \dfrac{11 - \sqrt{25}}{3}}{\sqrt{6^3 - 20} - \dfrac{18}{2}}$

   b. Write a step-by-step solution showing how to compute the answer without a calculator.

   Example: $3(2 - 5(4 + 1))^2$

   Solution: $3(2 - 5(5))^2$

   $3(2 - 25)^2$

   $3(^-23)^2$

   $3(529)$

   1587

   c. Finally, calculate each answer by entering the expression into your calculator.

   d. Write a note to a friend, (who is absent today), describing each step when evaluating expressions like these in your head, by hand, and with the calculator. Which way is easier? Which way is more reliable? If there is a combination of techniques that makes the process both easier and less susceptible to errors, outline it for your friend.

4. Substitute the given values into each formula and evaluate. If you know what the formula represents, indicate this with your solution.

a. $\frac{1}{2}bh$

   i. $b = 12.3, h = 43.7$

  ii. $b = 0.548, h = 6.21$

 iii. $b = 4.7, h = 2.91$

b. $-16t^2 + vt + s$

   i. $v = 75, t = 3.6, s = 24.75$

  ii. $v = 242.8, t = 7.72, s = 438$

 iii. $v = 28.4, t = 2.6, s = 47$

c. $\dfrac{y_2 - y_1}{x_2 - x_1}$

   i. $x_1 = 7, y_1 = {}^-5.3, x_2 = {}^-7, y_2 = 11.8$

  ii. $x_1 = 12, y_1 = 3.9, x_2 = 12, y_2 = 7.1$

 iii. $x_1 = 4.7, y_1 = 2.8, x_2 = {}^-1.2, y_2 = 6$

5. Insert operations signs and/or parentheses into each string of numbers to create an expression equal to the given answer. You may use the digits as exponents if you desire. However, you must keep them in the same order as originally given. Write an explanation of your answer, which operation is done first, which one is next, and so on.

Example: 3 2 5 7 = 18

Solution: $(3 + 2)(5) - 7 = 18$,

             First add 3 and 2. Then multiply this sum by 5. Finally, subtract 7.

a. 5 3 8 4 = 16   b. 7 5 3 4 = 602

c. 1 2 3 4 = 28   d. 7 3 2 9 = 18   e. 15 3 7 12 = 30

6. a. Enter a decimal followed by at least fourteen 4's; like .44444444444444 ENTER . What shows on your calculator display? What does this mean?

   b. Count the number of digits displayed on your calculator. Call this number n. Enter a decimal point followed by n 4's and several 6's. Press ENTER . What does your calculator display? What does this mean?

   c. Start over again and enter a decimal point followed by n 4's, and at least eight 6's. (Multiply this number by 10, and subtract the number in front of the decimal.) Repeat the procedure in parentheses until you can determine how many digits of a number your calculator actually stores. You can also use this method to *recover* digits of a number that are not displayed on the screen.

Section 0.2: Fractions, Decimal Numbers, and Scientific Notation

"Two-thirds of my third-hour class are girls," "one square foot is $\frac{1}{9}$ of one square yard," "50 minutes is $\frac{5}{6}$ of an hour," and "the probability of two consecutive boys being born into a family is about $\frac{1}{4}$" are just a few illustrations of how fractions and ratios are commonly used in the real world. However, the answers your calculator displays will almost always be in decimal form. In this section, you will review how to change fractions to decimal form, and vice versa. You will also learn about scientific notation, a special way of expressing a number that allows you to write very large and very small numbers efficiently.

Example 1:

a. Convert $\frac{5}{16}$ to decimal form.

b. Convert 42 min to part of an hour.

c. What part of a foot is 3 in.?

d. Which is a better deal: a ten-ounce tube of cheese at $2.85, or a one-pound tube of the same product at $4.25?

Solution:

a. Because a fraction bar is actually a division sign, you divide the numerator by the denominator. So 5 ÷ 16, or 5/16, gives 0.3125.

```
5/16
        .3125
42/60
          .7
3/12
          .25
```

b. Because one hour is 60 min, enter 42 ÷ 60, or 42/60, to get 0.7 hr.

c. Because one foot is 12 in., enter 3/12 to get 0.25 ft.

d. Because one pound contains 16 ounces, $\frac{10}{16} \cdot \$4.25 = \$2.65$ should be the equivalent cost for the smaller tube. The one-pound container has a unit price of $0.266 per ounce, while the ten-ounce container has a unit price of $0.285 per ounce.

```
(10/16)(4.25)
         2.65625
4.25/16
        .265625
2.85/10
          .285
```

Here are two methods you can use when working with mixed numbers. With the first method, you convert the mixed number to an improper fraction, then divide. In the second method, you split the mixed number into an addition problem and a division problem.

Example 2:

a. Convert $3\frac{8}{25}$ to decimal form.

b. Convert 2 hr 24 min to hours.

c. Convert 20 ft 9 inches to feet.

d. Convert the latitude 16°51′ to an equivalent latitude in decimal degrees.

Solution:

a. First change the mixed number to $\frac{83}{25}$. Then divide to get 3.32. Or as an alternative, enter 3 + 8/25 to get 3.32.

b. 2 hr and 24 min, or $2\frac{24}{60}$ hr, is 2 hr $+ \frac{24}{60}$ hr = 2.4 hr.

c. 20 ft and 9 in is 20 ft $+ \frac{9}{12}$ ft or 20.75 ft.

d. $16° + \frac{51}{60}°$ is 16.85°.

In the next example, you will convert each number from its decimal form (without repeating digits) to its fractional equivalent. In the activity that follows, you will discover some techniques to use with decimal numbers when there are repeating digits.

Example 3:

a. Convert 0.275 to a fraction.

b. Convert 12.125 to a fraction.

Solution:

a. 0.275 can also be read as two hundred seventy-five thousandths, so it can be written as $\frac{275}{1000}$. Another form of the answer is $\frac{11}{40}$. To verify that this is indeed the same value, enter 11 ÷ 40 and you will see 0.275. Fractions can also be simplified by dividing the numerator and the denominator by the same number, though you will not often be required to do so in this course.

b. 12.125 is equivalent to 12 + 0.125 or $12 + \frac{125}{1000} =$ $12\frac{1}{8}$ or $\frac{97}{8}$. See **APPENDIX 0B**; your calculator may have a fraction key.

```
              12.125
12+125/1000
              12.125
12+1/8
              12.125
Ans▶Frac
                97/8
■
```

B

Fractions and Decimal Numbers Activity

Though the Babylonians and the Chinese used decimal fractions, the Arabs were the first to use a symbol to indicate a decimal fraction. This symbol first appeared in *The Book of Chapters on Indian Arithmetic*, written by Abul Hassan al-Uqlidisi in Damascus in A.D. 952 or 953.

Every fraction can be written in an equivalent decimal form. In some cases, the digits at the end of the number will terminate; in others, a digit or group of digits will begin repeating. (The digits may start repeating near the end of your display. If you are not certain whether or not there is a repeat, try recovering some digits using the process described in Problem 6 of Section 0.1.)

a. Make up a list of fractions that includes, but isn't limited to, the ones below. Rewrite each in decimal form. If the digits do not appear to end, indicate the repeating unit by placing a bar over those digits that repeat.

$$\left\{ \frac{3}{5}, \frac{7}{16}, \frac{11}{125}, \frac{7}{15}, \frac{8}{13}, \frac{8}{21}, \frac{9}{22}, \frac{11}{30}, \frac{7}{20}, \cdots \right\}$$

  i. List the denominators of all fractions that convert to terminating decimal numbers (numbers without a repeating unit).

  ii. List the denominators of all fractions that convert to decimal numbers with repeating digits.

  iii. Look at the lists of denominators in parts i and ii. Describe how you can predict whether a fraction will convert to a decimal number with digits that terminate or digits that repeat.

b. Use your calculator to convert each number written in decimal form to its fractional equivalent.

  i. Multiply each answer from part a by its original denominator. What happens? (If the original decimal number has repeating digits, enter the repeating unit enough times to fill at least 13 decimal places.)

  ii. $0.\overline{12} \cdot 33 = 4$. Therefore, what fraction is equal to $0.\overline{12}$?

  iii. Convert each number to fractional form. (This may require some exploration, using guess-and-check.)

    1. $0.\overline{18}$ 2. $1.\overline{72}$ 3. $0.3\overline{571428}$

If you evaluate 345^4, your calculator might display 1.416695063E10, which is in **scientific notation**. It means $1.416695063 \cdot 10^{10}$. It is a rounded-off scientific notation version of the exact answer, 14,166,950,625, a number that has too many digits for most calculator screen displays.

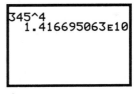

The decimal point in 14,166,950,625 has been moved ten places to the left, so that it is between the first two digits of the number, which means that the calculator divided the number by 10^{10}. Your calculator will roundoff the decimal number so that it is short enough to fit the display screen of your calculator. A number in scientific notation will always have one nonzero digit to the left of the decimal point.

> Any number written as a number between 1 and 10, multiplied by a power of 10, is said to be in **scientific notation**.

The mass of a hydrogen atom is greater than the mass of an electron. However, both masses are tiny!

The mass of a hydrogen atom is 0.00000000000000000000000017 grams.

The mass of an electron is 0.00000000000000000000000000091 grams.

Enter the first number in your calculator and press ENTER. You should get the scientific notation form of the number. Now find the scientific notation form of the mass of an electron. Can you explain the meaning of the numbers indicated on your calculator?

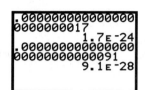

To change a number from normal (decimal) form to scientific notation, you must determine how far and what direction to move the decimal point so that there is exactly one nonzero digit to its left. Make a connection between *how far and what direction* the decimal point moves, and the effect of multiplying by a positive, or negative, power of ten.

Example 4: Write each number using scientific notation:

a. 6,240,000   b. 0.004 819

Solution: Refer to **APPENDIX 0C**.

a. $6.24 \cdot 10^6$ b. $4.819 \cdot 10^{-3}$

Problem Set 0.2

1. Substitute the given values into the appropriate formula and evaluate. Give your answer in scientific notation.

   a. $L\sqrt{1 - \frac{v^2}{c^2}}$

   i. $L = 12{,}345{,}678$, $v = 5{,}000{,}000$, $c = 300{,}000{,}000$

   ii. $L = 1$, $v = 299{,}999{,}999$, $c = 300{,}000{,}000$

   b. $\frac{eVL}{c}$

   i. $e = 1.6 \cdot 10^{-19}$, $V = 40{,}000$, $L = 3.11 \cdot 10^{-11}$, $c = 3 \cdot 10^8$

   ii. $e = 1.6 \cdot 10^{-19}$, $V = 75{,}000$, $L = 2.79 \cdot 10^{-11}$, $c = 3 \cdot 10^8$

2. Convert each expression to normal (decimal) form.

   a. $3.47895 \cdot 10^8$ b. $8.247 \cdot 10^{-12}$ c. $\dfrac{(7.952 \cdot 10^{15})(2.5 \cdot 10^{-3})}{(1.42 \cdot 10^8)}$

3. Write a clear but thorough explanation (for a friend who is about to take a quiz), of how to determine when the scientific notation exponent is positive or negative.

4. The average human brain has about 8 billion neurons. There are about 250 million people in the United States. About how many total neurons do all these people have?

5. You and eight friends have just ordered the biggest pizza available and are deciding how to divide up the food. Frak Shenwize proposes the following scheme: She will take $\frac{1}{9}$ th of the "Lotza Pizza," the next person will take $\frac{1}{8}$ th of the remaining pizza, the next $\frac{1}{7}$ th of the remainder, and so on.

   a. Describe the fairness of this proposal.

   b. How much of the pizza will you get if you are the last one to select?

6. a. Some of your friends claim to have bicycled across the state of Michigan, from Lake Michigan to Lake Erie, at an average speed of 60 ft/sec. Is this possible? Justify your answer. (1 mi = 5280 ft)

   b. A Detroit Tiger game announcer recently claimed that an average baseball player could run the bases in 10 seconds. Was he right? Justify your answer.

   c. The scale on a National Geographic map is listed as 16.2 mi to the inch.

      i.   Give a quick approximation or estimate for the distance between two cities that are 3.9 in. apart on the map.

      ii. Find the actual distance.

      iii. Find the error between the actual distance and your predicted distance.

7. One day it rained 0.1 in. Harve Ester decided to find out how much water fell on his 1 sq mi of farmland.

   a. How many pounds of water fell on his farm? (Water weighs 62.4 lb/ft^3 and 1 ft = 12 in.)

   b. If it rains so that the depth is one inch, will the water weigh ten times as much as in 7a? Write a few sentences that describe why or why not.

8. Which has the greater mass, the hydrogen atom or the electron? How many times greater?

9. What are the advantages of working in groups in your math class? What are the disadvantages? Explain these completely.

Section 0.3: Using the Grapher

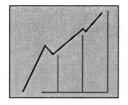

It is said that "a picture is worth a thousand words." The next time you look at a newspaper, magazine, or book, remind yourself of the importance of *visual images* in the real world. Throughout this course, you will communicate information using graphs. This is because a graph can quickly summarize numerical information. As you become more familiar with it, your graphing calculator or grapher will allow you to discover patterns, explore relationships, find particular values, and to generalize.

Before displaying a graph, you need to set the range of values that will be displayed on the graph. This is similar to figuring out how to label the axes on graph paper when graphing by hand. Determine the lowest (minimum) and highest (maximum) values you want to see on both the horizontal (x) and vertical (y) axes. You can also control the scale for each axis, or how often to make marks on the axis. This is the

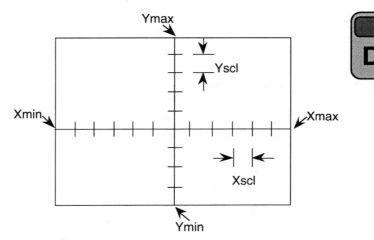

same as determining how many units are represented by one square on graph paper. See **APPENDIX 0D** for details on your particular grapher.

Example 1: Teacher Fay Silitator is designing tables for her classroom. She wants to use trapezoid-shaped table tops so that the longer base length is 48 inches and the table width is 30 inches. If the shorter base is to be less than 48 inches, find a graphing window that displays the relationship between the possible values for the shorter base and the resulting area of the table top.

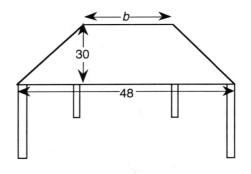

Solution: Recall that the formula for finding the area of a trapezoid is $\frac{1}{2}h(b_1 + b_2)$ where h is the height and b_1 and b_2 represent the lengths of the bases. Because the grapher generally accepts equations in the form $y =$ "an expression involving x," rewrite the equation as $y = 0.5(30)(48 + x) = 15(48 + x)$.

Because x represents the length of the second base, x can be a value between 0 and 48. Set the minimum value of x (Xmin) to 0 and the maximum value of x (Xmax) to 48. This means your calculator will graph (*base, area*) values so that $0 \leq base \leq 48$. Set the scale for x (Xscl) at 2 to provide 24 tic marks. This means the first mark represents 2, the next 4, the next 6, and so on. An Xscl of 1 would produce 48 very crowded tic marks along the axis.

The y-axis represents the area. You can get an idea of a good range for this axis by testing several values for the base (x) of the trapezoid. The table below shows several pairs of (*base, area*) values. Remember, the y-values represent area values. (See **APPENDIX 0D** to see if your grapher has a table function.)

Y1■5(48+X)		X	Y1			WINDOW FORMAT
Y2=		0	720			Xmin=0
Y3=		8	840			Xmax=48
Y4=		16	960			Xscl=2
Y5=		24	1080			Ymin=0
Y6=		32	1200			Ymax=1500
Y7=		40	1320			Yscl=100
Y8=		48	1440			
		Y1■15(48+X)				

As you look at the table values, you might decide to set the minimum value of y (Ymin) at 0, because area can't be negative, and the maximum value of y (Ymax) at 1500. Appropriate marks on this axis could be made in increments of 100, so set the scale for y (Yscl) at 100. Enter this information, and graph the equation to produce a picture like the one provided here.

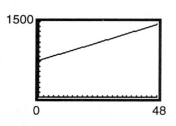

There are other **graphing windows** (Xmin, Xmax, Ymin, and Ymax) that would also work. In the problems, you will practice finding appropriate graphing windows, and see how different windows can change the way a graph looks.

The distance between any point on a line and the point at 0 is a nonnegative number. If x is the coordinate of the point, the distance can be generated using the **absolute value** function. You will be exploring the absolute value function in more detail in the chapter on functions. See **APPENDIX 0E**.

Example 2:   Find the distance between the point at x and the point at 0.

a. If x is 6, then the distance from x to 0 is the absolute value of $6 - 0$, or
$$\left|6 - 0\right| = \left|6\right| = 6$$

b. If x is $^-4$, then the distance is $\left|^-4 - 0\right| = \left|^-4\right| = 4$

c. The set of ordered pairs (x, y) that satisfy the equation $y = \left|x\right|$ generalize the information that is pictured on the above number lines. Enter the equation and interpret the meaning of the table and/or graph pictured. What is the meaning of $x = ^-1.8$ and $y = 1.8$ as pictured on the graph?

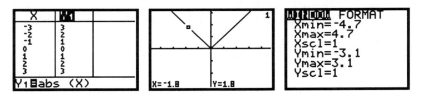

Problem Set 0.3

1. For each set of points, determine values for Xmin, Xmax, Ymin, and Ymax to find an appropriate graphing window for displaying the listed points.

    a. (3, 17), (−2, 21), (0, 5)   b. (1, 12), (0, 0), (3, −4)

2. Dr. Frank Stein, a famous scientist, is studying the growth of the bacteria, *Mathematicus Headachus*. He finds that the population of his test tube bacteria is given by the equation $P = 20 \cdot 2^{(0.21h)}$. You can see the growth in the bacteria population over the first 24 hr by setting the Xmin to 0 and the Xmax to 24. Use the settings for Ymin and Ymax given below, and record a sketch of each graph.

    a. Ymin = 0, Ymax = 2000, Yscl = 100

    b. Ymin = 0, Ymax = 1000, Yscl = 100

    c. Ymin = 0, Ymax = 500, Yscl = 50

    d. Ymin = 0, Ymax = 125, Yscl = 25

    e. Which of the above graphing windows gives the *best* picture of the situation? Why?

3. On one midsummer day in Mathtropolis, the temperature, over the 12-hr period from 8 a.m. to 8 p.m., varied according to the equation $t = -0.91h^2 + 10h + 65$, where t is the temperature and h is the number of hours after 8 a.m. Set Xmin at 0, Xmax at 12, and Xscl at 1. Use the settings for Ymin and Ymax given below, and record a sketch of each graph.

    a. Ymin = 0, Ymax = 80, Yscl = 10

    b. Ymin = 0, Ymax = 160, Yscl = 20

    c. Ymin = 50, Ymax = 100, Yscl = 10

    d. Which of the above graphing windows gives the *best* picture of the situation? Why?

4. Find appropriate values for Ymin and Ymax for each equation. In each case, use Xmin = −10, Xmax = 10, and Xscl = 1. Sketch each graph on paper, and label the graphing window. Describe why you selected the particular Ymin and Ymax values.

    a. $y = 3x + 5$ b. $y = 3x^2 + 5$ c. $y = 3|x - 4|$

5. Substitute the given values into the appropriate formula and evaluate.

   a. $\dfrac{2v + at}{2}$

      i. $a = {}^-16$, $t = 1.2$, $v = 24$

      ii. $a = {}^-16$, $t = 0.28$, $v = 36$

   b. $0.2768|f - i|$

      i. $f = 3.468$, $i = 3.457$

      ii. $f = 4.781 \bullet 10^{-4}$, $i = 4.657 \bullet 10^{-4}$

6. Find values for Xmin, Xmax, Ymin, and Ymax that will position this star in the center of the graphing window. You do not need to draw this graph on your calculator.

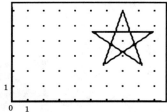

7. Describe a problem that you think will be easier to solve using a graphing calculator than with a simpler calculator. Be clear *why* it will be easier with the graphing calculator.

8. Describe a problem that some people might *think* requires the graphing calculator to solve, but is actually just as easy to solve "by hand," or with a simpler calculator.

Chapter One

PATTERNS AND RECURSION

Contents

Section 1.1: Recursively Defined Sequences 22

     The definition of definition is definition

Section 1.2: Modeling Growth.. 28

     This could get out of control

Section 1.3: A First Look at Limits.. 33

     We all have our limits

Section 1.4: Graphing Sequences 37

     What does a sequence look like, anyway?

Section 1.5: Recursive Routine for Sequences... 41

     Now we're getting automated

Section 1.6: A Recursive Look At Series... 46

     Is this like a soap opera?

Section 1.7: Chapter Review 50

     Assessing yourself

Section 1.8: Projects.. 51

     Taking it one step further

Section 1.1: Recursively Defined Sequences

Look around! You are surrounded by patterns and influenced by how you see, hear, and perceive them. You probably recognize visual patterns in tree leaves, flower petals, floor tiles, and window panes. The sounds of bird calls, barking dogs, dripping faucets, or busy traffic may be familiar noises. In every discipline, at every level, people discover, observe, re-create, explain, generalize, and use patterns. Architects, scientists, athletes, business managers, and musicians all strive to find useful patterns that are attractive, practical, or predictable.

When studying arithmetic, geometry, algebra, and other topics in mathematics, you have seen patterns. Just as artists, architects, and scientists keep an open dialog with the natural world, you, too, can make discoveries and provide appropriate explanations by being alert and observant. As you learn about recursively defined sequences, you will be able to visualize mathematical patterns that help explain natural phenomena.

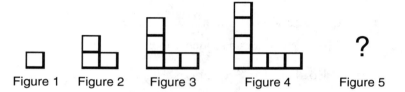

Figure 1   Figure 2   Figure 3   Figure 4   Figure 5

Example 1: Draw or build the figures pictured above. Make some observations about a pattern suggested by the figures, and continue the pattern.

Solution:

a. One observation you can make is that the number of squares in Figure 3 is *two* more than the number of squares in Figure 2. This same pattern describes the connection between Figure 1 and Figure 2, as well as that between Figure 3 and Figure 4.

You can organize the information like this.

Figure 2 = Figure 1 + *two* squares.

Figure 3 = Figure 2 + *two* squares.

Figure 4 = Figure 3 + *two* squares.

If you assume that the same pattern continues, then

Figure 10 = Figure 9 + *two* squares.

In general, the pattern is

Figure n = Figure $(n - 1)$ + *two* squares.

The figures are a visual representation of the sequence $1, 3, 5, 7, 9, \ldots$. A **sequence** is an ordered list. The tenth term of this sequence, u_{10} (pronounced *u sub ten*, or *the tenth term*), can be compared to the preceding term, u_9, by writing $u_{10} = u_9 + 2$. The nth term, u_n, is called the **general term** of the sequence.

b. You can form another pattern by looking at the outer perimeter of each figure.

The perimeter of Figure 1 is 4.

The perimeter of Figure 2 is 4 plus that of Figure 1.

The perimeter of Figure 3 is 4 plus that of Figure 2.

In general, the perimeter of Figure$_n$ equals 4 plus the perimeter of Figure$_{(n-1)}$. This means that if n equals 7, the perimeter of Figure$_7$ equals 4 plus the perimeter of Figure$_6$. The first few terms of the perimeter sequence are $4, 8, 12, 16, 20, 24, \ldots$.

> A **recursive definition** for a sequence is a set of statements that specifies one or more initial terms, and defines the nth term, u_n, in terms of one or more of the preceding terms.

For this perimeter example, $u_1 = 4$ and $u_n = u_{(n-1)} + 4$. This means *the first term is four* and *each subsequent term is equal to the preceding term plus four*. Notice that each new perimeter is described in terms of the previous perimeter. (The notation $u_{(n-1)}$ refers to the preceding term. *It does not mean one less than the term.*)

c. Now consider the total number of segments used to build the shapes. This table display of the sequence is partially completed.

Figure	1	2	3	4	5 ...	12 ...	32	...	n
Segments	4	10	16	22				...	

This sequence also appears to be of the form $u_n = u_{(n-1)} + d$, where d is a constant. The constant difference between successive terms is 6. Do you see where the 6 comes from in the table and in the figures? This means each term is 6 more than the preceding term. Therefore, the sequence representing the total number of segments needed for each figure above is described recursively as $u_1 = 4$, and thereafter as $u_n = u_{(n-1)} + 6$.

> An **arithmetic sequence** is a sequence where each term is equal to the preceding term plus a constant. This constant is called the **common difference**.

Arithmetic sequences are of the form $u_n = u_{(n-1)} + d$, where d is some constant. Another way to think of this is each *answer = preceding answer + d*. Your calculator has an $\boxed{\text{ENTER}}$ key or an $\boxed{\text{EXECUTE}}$ key. Each time you press this key, the calculator computes or executes the last command. Your calculator also has a *last answer function*. (In this text, this function is referred to as **Ans**, although it may be different on your calculator.) The purpose of this function is to allow you to use your last answer in the next calculation, without retyping the number.

With these two commands, you can create a recursive routine

4 $\boxed{\text{ENTER}}$	This establishes, or seeds, the first Ans.
Ans + 6 $\boxed{\text{ENTER}}$	This calculates the second term and makes it Ans.
$\boxed{\text{ENTER}}$	This establishes the third term as the Ans.
$\boxed{\text{ENTER}}$	

and so on.

Shifting Funds Activity

Carlotta "Lotta" Doe has $2000 in a savings account, while Les Cache has only $470 in his account. Criminal Hank Hacker gains access to the bank's computer and begins to shift funds around. On the first night, she creates a new account for herself. Next, she takes $50 from Carlotta's account, puts $40 of it into Les's account, and puts the remaining $10 into her own account. Each night after that, she makes the same dollar shifts. Use three calculators to model this movement of funds in the three accounts. How many nights did Hank work until Les had more money than Carlotta? Hank was arrested the night that Les's balance first became more than twice Carlotta's balance. How much was in Hank's account the night she was arrested? Write down the entries or expressions you used for each calculation.

Example 2: Waclaw Sierpiński (1882–1969) made significant contributions to number theory, set theory, and topology. He was a major figure in the mathematical community in Poland, which flourished between the two world wars. The figure that results from continuing the geometric pattern below is known as the Sierpiński Triangle. Count the number of black triangles at each transition. How many triangles would be in the twentieth such figure?

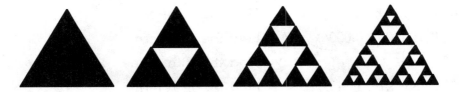

Solution: The sequence which represents the number of black triangles is 1, 3, 9, 27, ... This pattern can be represented with the recursive notation $u_1 = 1$ and $u_n = 3 \cdot u_{(n-1)}$. On the calculator, start the sequence with 1. Then multiply this last answer by 3. Press $\boxed{\text{ENTER}}$ repeatedly, and count to the twentieth term. You will find that $u_{20} = 1,162,261,467$. Check this on your own calculator.

1 $\boxed{\text{ENTER}}$	Establishes or seeds the first Ans.
3 • Ans $\boxed{\text{ENTER}}$	Calculates the second term and makes it Ans.
$\boxed{\text{ENTER}}$	Establishes the third term as the Ans.
and so on.	

The expressions *preceding term*, *Ans*, and $u_{(n-1)}$ are interchangeable. In the example above, each preceding term was *multiplied* by the same constant. This is an example of a geometric sequence.

A **geometric sequence** is a sequence where each term is equal to the preceding term multiplied by a constant, or $u_n = r \cdot u_{(n-1)}$. The constant r is called the **common ratio**.

Problem Set 1.1

1. What sequence is generated by this recursive routine?

    6 $\boxed{\text{ENTER}}$

    1.5 • Ans $\boxed{\text{ENTER}}$

    $\boxed{\text{ENTER}}$

    and so on.

    Is the sequence arithmetic or geometric? What is the 10th term?

2. Write a calculator routine, similar to the one in Problem 1, to generate an arithmetic sequence with a beginning term of 6 and a common difference of 3.2. What is the 10th term?

3. Write a routine, similar to the one in Problem 1, to generate terms in each sequence. Find the indicated term.

   a. 2, 6, 18, 54, . . .   Find the 15th term.

   b. 10, 5, 2.5, 1.25, . . .   Find the 12th term.

   c. 0.4, 0.04, 0.004, 0.0004, . . .   Find the 10th term.

   d. 2, 8, 14, 20, 26, . . .   Find the 30th term.

   e. 1.56, 4.85, 8.14, 11.43, . . .   Find the 14th term.

   f. 6.24, −15.6, 39, −97.5, . . .   Find the 20th term.

4. A 50-gal bathtub contains 20 gal of water, and is being filled at a rate of 2.4 gal/min.

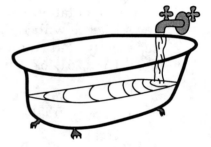

   a. When will the water flow over the top?

   b. Suppose that the bathtub contains 20 gal of water, and is being filled at a rate of 2.4 gal/min. The drain is open, and water is draining out at a rate of 3.1 gal/min. How long will it take until the tub is empty?

   c. Write a single recursive routine that shows the rates of both filling and draining.

5. A car leaves town heading west at 57 kilometers per hour (km/hr).

   a. How far will the car travel in 7 hr?

   b. A second car leaves town 2 hr after the first car, but it is traveling at 72 km/hr. To the nearest hour, when will the second car pass the first?

6. The bathtub in Problem 4 is once again filled to the 20-gal mark. The incoming water is turned off, and the drain allows half of the remaining water to drain out each minute.

   a. How much water will remain after 1 min?

   b. After 5 min?

   c. When will it be totally empty?

7. The week of February 14, store owner J.C. Nickels ordered hundreds of heart-shaped red vacuum cleaners. The next week, he still had hundreds of heart-shaped red vacuum cleaners, so he told his manager to discount the price 25% each week until they were all sold.

   a. The first week the vacuums sold for $80.00. What was the price the second week?

   b. What was the price for the vacuum in the fourth week?

   c. When will the vacuum sell for less than $10?

8. Consider again the bathtub containing 20 gal of water. This time, it is draining half the remaining water each minute and, at the same time, is filling at a constant rate of 2.4 gal/min.

   a. Write a recursive routine that incorporates both of these actions.

   b. Using your model, determine how much water will be in the tub after 1 min.

   c. After 5 min?

   d. After a long time?

Section 1.2: Modeling Growth

Have you ever received a chain letter offering you great financial rewards? Typical letters might offer you thousands of cassette tapes, golf balls, or recipes if you will just follow the simple instructions. They ask that you not break the chain. Actually, chain-letter schemes are illegal, even though they have been quite common, (especially during the 1980s). Carefully read the following letter.

Pyramid Investment Plan Activity

Pyramid Investment Plan

*Become a millionaire! Join the **Pyramid Investment Plan** (PIP). Send only $20, and return this letter to PIP. PIP will send five dollars to the name at the top of the list below. You will receive a new letter with your name added to the bottom of the list, and a set of 200 names and addresses. Make 200 copies of the letter, mail them, and wait to get rich. Each time your letter is advanced, your name advances toward the top of the list. When PIP receives letters with your name at the top, we will start sending you money! A conservative marketing return of 6% projects that you will earn over $1.2 million.*

Here is an example of how this works: When we receive your check, we will send $5 to Chris. Then Katie will be #1, and your name will be in position #6. Each time this process is repeated, the names move up on the list. When your name reaches the top, each of the thousands of people who receive that letter will be sending money to PIP, and you will receive your share.

1. Chris
2. Katie
3. Josh
4. Kanako
5. Dave
6. Miranda

Suppose you have just received this letter, along with several quotes from "ordinary people" who have already become millionaires. In your group, prepare a written analysis of this plan. Use the following questions as an outline for your report.

a. If you send copies of this letter to 200 people, the list of names now reads:
    1. Katie, 2. Josh, 3. Kanako, 4. Dave, 5. Miranda, 6. **Your Name**. According to the plan's "conservative marketing return of 6%," how many of the 200 people receiving the letter will "join" the plan?

Round number	1	2	3	4	5	6
Letters sent	200	?	?	?	?	?
Responded	?	?	?	?	?	?

b. If each new *PIP* investor mails 200 copies of the letter, and 6% of those receiving the letter join *PIP*, how many people will there be in the second round?

c. Continue this process for the third, fourth, fifth, and sixth rounds.

d. Those investors in the sixth round receive a list that may look like this: 1. Your Name, 2. Moira, 3. Elizabeth, 4. Kiku, 5. Bill, 6. Clara. If you receive $5 from each person responding in the sixth round, will you make over $1.2 million? How much will you make?

e. The letter is sent to 200 households in the first round. How many households receive letters in the second round?

f. What is the *total* number of households that receive a letter by the sixth round?

g. Assume that the quotes on the back of the letter are from people who have completed the plan and are no longer on the list. Receiving this letter places you in at least the seventh round of the plan. How many households will receive the letter by the time it reaches the thirteenth round?

h. According to the 1990 census, how many households were there in the United States?

i. What are your conclusions? Why are chain letter and pyramid schemes illegal?

Each sequence you generated in the above activity is a geometric sequence modeling growth. In many growth models (like those in the next activity), it is more useful to treat the first term as *term zero* or u_0. The initial value is usually given at *time zero,* or before the growth begins. However, there are no hard and fast rules. You will have to consider each problem carefully, and decide if you should begin at term one or term zero.

Investing with Meg Abux Activity

Meg Abux deposits $2000 into a bank paying 7% annual interest compounded annually. This means she receives 7% of her bank balance as interest at the end of each year. Let's look at the growth of this money.

Here is a start to the solution.

NEW BAL = OLD BAL + 0.07 • OLD BAL

or NEW BAL = OLD BAL • (1 + 0.07)   By the distributive property.

Use the Ans function on your calculator to compute the sequence. Each result gives a year-end balance.

2000 ENTER — This establishes, or seeds, the first Ans.

Ans • (1 + 0.07) ENTER — This establishes $2140 (the balance after the first year) as the Ans.

ENTER — This establishes $2289.80 (the balance after the second year) as the Ans.

ENTER

and so on.

a. Copy and complete the table below.

Elapsed time (yr)	0	1	2	3	...	7 ...	10 ...	...	n
Balance in $	2000	2140	2289.8	$u_3 =$	...	$u_7 =$	$u_{10} =$	...	$u_n =$

b. How many years will it take for the original deposit to triple in value?

c. Start over with $2000, and change the annual interest rate to 8.5%.

Elapsed time (yr)	0	1	2	3	...	7 ...	10 ...	...	n
Balance in $	2000	$u_1 =$	$u_2 =$	$u_3 =$	...	$u_7 =$	$u_{10} =$	...	$u_n =$

d. Now how many years will it take for the original deposit to triple in value?

e. Describe the difference between the answers to parts b and d.

f. If 8.5% is the annual interest rate, what is a real-world meaning of 0.085/12?

g. Use the recursive routine below to answer each question that follows. (Throughout this course, please label each answer with its proper unit of measurement. For example, these answers could be expressed in dollars, percentages, years, or months.)

2000 ENTER

Ans (1 + 0.085/12) ENTER

and so on.

What is the balance after 1 yr? After 4 yr? After 7 yr? How many years will it take for the original deposit to triple in value? How does this compare with the answer to part d?

Problem Set 1.2

1. Suppose Jill's biological family tree looks like the diagram below, and you assume no common ancestry. No common ancestry is probably an unrealistic assumption, but it provides a pattern that you can model.

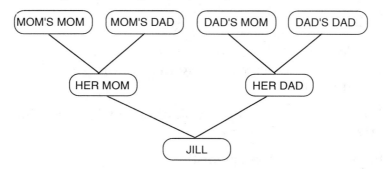

a. Copy and complete a table showing the sequence that represents the number of Jill's ancestors in each generation.

Generations back	0	1	2	3	4	?	n
Ancestors within a generation	$u_0 = 1$	$u_1 = 2$	$u_2 = 4$	$u_3 = ?$	$u_4 = ?$	$u_? = 131{,}072$	$u_n = ?$

b. Describe how to find the number of ancestors within a generation if you know the number in the preceding generation.

c. Name the number of the term of this sequence that is closest to 5,000,000. What is the real-world meaning of this answer?

d. If a new generation is born every 25 yr, approximately when did Jill have 5,000,000 living ancestors?

e. Write a few sentences describing any problems you have with the original assumption of no common ancestors.

2. If the number of people who receive the letter from the Pyramid Investment Plan increases from 200 to 400 at each level, and you still expect 6% of them to respond, will your hypothetical income double? Explain your reasoning.

3. Carbon dating is used to find the age of very old, dead objects. Carbon 14 (C^{14}) is created by the sun and is found naturally in all living things. C^{14} transforms (decays) slowly after death. About 88.55% of it remains after any 1000-yr period of time. Let 100% or 1 be the beginning amount of C^{14}. At what point will less than 5% remain? Write the recursive routine you used.

4. Suppose $500 is deposited into an account that earns 6.5% annually.

   a. If the interest is compounded monthly, what is the monthly rate?

   b. What is the balance after 1 mo?

   c. After 1 yr?

   d. After 29 mo?

   e. What would the annual interest rate (compounded monthly) have to be for the $500 to grow to $600 *during* the 29th month? Write the recursive routine you used.

5. Between 1970 and 1990, the population of Grand Traverse County in Michigan grew from 39,175 to 64,273.

   a. Find the population increase for the 20-yr period.

   b. Find the percent increase over the 20-yr period by computing the fraction:

$$\frac{\text{actual increase}}{\text{original population}}$$

   c. What do you think the *annual* growth rate was during this period?

   d. Check your answer to 5c by writing and using a calculator recursive routine. Explain why that answer does or does not work out to a population of 64,273 people over the period.

   e. Using guess-and-check, find a growth rate, to the nearest 0.1% (0.001), that comes closest to producing the growth experienced.

   f. Use the answer to 5e to estimate the population in 1980. How does this compare with the average of the populations of 1970 and 1990? Why is that?

Section 1.3: A First Look at Limits

The number of Sierpiński Triangles, an increasing bank balance as it is compounded monthly, and increasing arithmetic and geometric sequences have terms that get larger and larger forever. Is there a limit to how tall a tree can grow? Can people continue to build taller buildings, run faster, jump higher? If you were to record the temperature, at one-minute intervals, of your next cup of hot cocoa as it cooled, this sequence of temperatures would approach the temperature of the room. The amount of water in a bathtub, which is draining half of its remaining water each minute, will slowly stop changing as the bathtub empties. Sequences that slowly stop changing are said to have **limits**. The activity below introduces another sequence that has a limit. You will revisit variations of this problem, and the limit concept, throughout the year.

(This activity is based on an article by James Sandefur in the February 1992 *Mathematics Teacher*.)

Color Concentration Activity

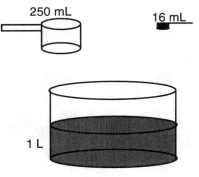

A bowl contains a total of one liter (L) of liquid. All of the liquid is clear water, except for 16 milliliters (mL), which is a colored fluid.

During a fixed time period, 250 mL of liquid is removed from the bowl and replaced with 250 mL of clear water.

a. Record the amount of colored fluid in the bowl over several time periods. Write a recursive routine to describe this sequence. How many time periods will pass before there is less than 1 mL of coloring? What happens in the long run?

b. Start over again with 1 L of clear water that includes 16 mL of coloring. During each time period remove 250 ml of liquid and replace it with a mixture of 234 mL of clear water and 16 mL of coloring. Record the amount of colored fluid in the bowl over several time periods. Write a recursive routine to describe this sequence. Do the contents of the bowl ever turn into pure coloring? What happens in the long run?

This activity illustrates a simplified version of a closed, but changing, or dynamic, system. Medicine and its elimination in the human body, a water supply and pollution control system, or a contaminated lake and cleanup processes, are real-world examples of this activity. Being able to find limits is very important.

Example 1: If $u_0 = 450$ and $u_n = 0.75 \cdot u_{(n-1)} + 210$, find u_1.

Solution:

$u_1 = 0.75 \cdot u_{(1-1)} + 210$ Substitute 1 for n.

$u_1 = 0.75 \cdot u_0 + 210$

$u_1 = 0.75 \cdot 450 + 210$ Substitute 450 for u_0.

$u_1 = 547.50$

Show that you can use this recursive definition by finding the second and third terms. (Your answers for u_2 should be 620.625.) At this point, the sequence 450, 547.50, 620.625, . . . has been identified.

The following notation describes the recursive sequence in Example 1.

$$u_n = \begin{cases} 450 & \text{if } n = 0 \\ 0.75 \cdot u_{(n-1)} + 210 & \text{if } n > 0 \end{cases}$$

It is important that you are able to make sense of this kind of mathematical notation. Can you identify the first term? The second term? Given a term, can you see how to get the next term? Do you see the connection between *Ans* and $u_{(n-1)}$? Rewrite this recursive routine using *Ans*.

Problem Set 1.3

1. a. Find u_5 and u_{10} of the sequence defined by the notation below.

$$u_n = \begin{cases} 450 & \text{if } n = 0 \\ 0.75 \cdot u_{(n-1)} + 210 & \text{if } n > 0 \end{cases}$$

    b. Invent a situation that could be modeled with this recursive routine.

    c. Describe what happens to this sequence over the long run.

2. a. List the first six terms of the sequence defined by the notation below.

$$u_n = \begin{cases} 1 & \text{if } n = 1 \\ n \cdot u_{(n-1)} & \text{if } n > 1 \end{cases}$$

    b. What is u_7? What is u_{14}?

3. Use the notation developed in Problems 1 and 2 to write a recursive definition of each sequence.

    a. 49.06, 50.24, 51.42, 52.6, . . .   b. −4.24, −21.2, −106, −530, . . .

4. On October 1, $24,000 is invested, earning 6.4% annually compounded monthly. Beginning on November 1, a monthly withdrawal of $100 is made, and the withdrawals continue on the first of every month thereafter.

   a. Write a recursive routine for this problem.

   b. List the first five terms of this sequence of balances.

   c. What is the meaning of the fifth term?

   d. What is the balance at the end of one year? at the end of three years?

5. The Forever Green Nursery owns 7000 white pine trees. Each year, the nursery plans to sell 12% of its trees and plant 600 new ones.

   a. Determine the number of pine trees owned by the nursery after ten years.

   b. Determine the number of pine trees owned by the nursery after many years (in the long run), and explain what is occurring.

   c. Try different starting totals in place of the 7000 trees. Describe any changes to the long-run totals.

   d. Rework the problem again, but this time build in a catastrophe of some sort to the nursery in the fifth year. Describe your catastrophe.

   e. How does the solution change?

6. Dr. Jeck L. Hyde takes a capsule containing 20 milligrams (mg) of a prescribed drug early in the morning. By the same time one day later, 25% of the drug has been eliminated from his body. Dr. Hyde doesn't take any more medication, and his body continues to eliminate 25% of the remaining drug each day. Write a recursive routine that provides the daily amount of this drug in Dr. Hyde's body. How long will it be before there is less than 1 mg of the drug present in Dr. Hyde's body?

7. Suppose Jeck's doctor prescribes a 20-mg capsule to be taken every morning. As before, 25% of the drug is eliminated from the body each day. Write a recursive routine that provides the daily accumulation of this drug in his body. To what level will the drug eventually accumulate?

8. Consider part b of the Color Concentration Activity. If you double the amount of colored fluid added each time from 16 mL to 32 mL, but continue to add only 250 mL of fluid, will the final concentration be doubled? Write a convincing argument for your position.

9. Suppose you want to buy a new car and need to finance or borrow $11,000. The new-car-loan annual interest rate is 9.6% of the unpaid balance, compounded monthly.

   a. Write a recursive routine that provides the declining balances of the loan for a monthly payment of $274.

   b. List the first five terms of this sequence.

   c. When is the loan paid off?

   d. What is the total cost of the new car paid over this time period?

10. a. What happens to the balance in Problem 4 if the same interest and withdrawal pattern continues for a long time?

   b. What monthly withdrawal would maintain a constant balance of $24,000?

Section 1.4: Graphing Sequences

Thus far, you have examined several sequences and considered some complicated applications that produce them. By using a recursive routine, you can display a sequence of numbers quickly and efficiently. You can also use your graphing calculator to help you visualize sequences with graphs. These graphs give you a visual spreadsheet of valuable information.

This graph is a visual representation of the first sequence in Section 1.1. Written recursively, this sequence is defined by the notation below.

$$u_n = \begin{cases} 1 & \text{if } n = 1 \\ u_{(n-1)} + 2 & \text{if } n > 1 \end{cases}$$

The position of each point is given by two numbers. The first number, or first coordinate, n, provides the horizontal location of the point. The second number, or second coordinate, u_n, provides the vertical location of the point. For example, $u_4 = 7$ is pictured as the point (4, 7).

Ans is 2nd coordinate

• (5,9)

• (4,7)

• (3,5)

• (2,3)

• (1,1)

n is 1st coordinate

This means the graph of $u_4 = 7$, or (4, 7), is 4 units to the right, and 7 units up, from the point (0, 0), which is called the origin. Each point in the graph is a geometric representation of (n, u_n) for some choice of n. A table of the early points of this sequence looks like this.

n	1	2	3	4	5
u_n	1	3	5	7	9

Set the graphing window of your calculator to the following values: [0, 7, 1, 0, 10, 1].

The Xscl and Yscl are not too important, because they do not change the appearance of any graph. They simply provide reference marks on the axes. Refer to **APPENDIX 1A** to learn how to **Plot** the points from a table of values on your calculator screen. Graphs in this section will be collections of points that are not connected. Graphs of sequences are examples of **discrete graphs**, which means they are separate points and are not connected by a line, segment, or curve.

The points for this sequence should appear to be **linear**, or on the path of a straight line. Do you remember what the slope of a line is? Can you find the slope of the line suggested by this sequence?

You will find graphs are very useful tools in helping you to understand and explain situations. One of the goals of this book is to help you understand mathematics by providing opportunities for you to "see," or visualize, the mathematics. When you make a graph or look at a graph, look for connections between the graph and the mathematics used to create the graph. Sometimes this will be clear and obvious, and sometimes you will need to look at the graph in a new way to see the connections.

What variable (units) belongs on the horizontal axis? What are the smallest and largest values for this variable? What variable (units) belongs on the vertical axis? What are the smallest and largest values for this variable?

Uncle Scrooge's Investment Activity

An investment plan contains a clause that states that any money in an investment account with a balance over $1000 cannot be withdrawn all at once. The clause further states that no more than the larger of 20% of the investment, or $1000, can be removed in any calendar year. Uncle Scrooge has $50,000 invested in the plan and would like to withdraw his funds. To make the problem simpler, make an assumption that the money remaining in the investment account will not earn any interest. With your group, make a graph of this situation. Be certain to "play" with the problem a little bit before you decide what kind of graphing window you will need. Use your graph and a clear mathematical explanation to help your uncle understand why he cannot have all of his money within five years. Explain how many years it will take him to withdraw all of his money. Explain how the $1000 limit works, and why this is important. Show on the graph when the $1000 limit "kicks in."

Time	Now	After 1 years	After 2 years	. . .
Balance	$50,000	?	?	. . .

What would happen if the balance in the account continued to earn 8% interest? Create another graph of the account balance over time. This graph should show that he withdraws 20% at the beginning of each year as above, and that the remaining balance in the account earns 8%. Be sure to note on the graph when the $1000 limit kicks in. Now explain how long it will take him to withdraw all of his money.

Problem Set 1.4

1. a. Copy and complete a table of values generated by this sequence.

$$u_n = \begin{cases} 2.5 & \text{if } n = 1 \\ u_{(n-1)} + 1.5 & \text{if } n > 1 \end{cases}$$

1st coordinate						
2nd coordinate						

   b. Provide graphing-window values that give a good picture of these terms. [Xmin, Xmax, Xscl, Ymin, Ymax, Yscl]

   c. Plot the points on your calculator screen.

   d. Sketch the graph of the sequence on paper. Remember, this is a discrete graph.

2. The sequence below models the population growth of the U.S. each decade since 1790.

$$u_n = \begin{cases} 3929000 & \text{if } n = 0 \\ (1 + 0.24) \cdot u_{(n-1)} & \text{if } n > 0 \end{cases}$$

   a. Copy and complete a table of values for the first six terms of the sequence.

n (decades)	0	1	2	3	4	5
u_n						

   b. What is the meaning of 3,929,000?

   c. What is the growth rate over each decade?

   d. Is this an arithmetic or geometric sequence, or neither?

   e. Using the graphing window provided, list the window dimensions, scatter-plot the points on your calculator screen, and carefully sketch the graph into your homework.

   Graphing window: [0, 6, 1, 0, 15000000, 5000000]. See **APPENDIX 1B**.

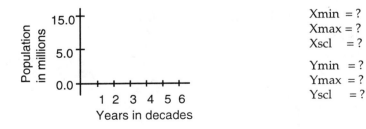

Xmin = ?
Xmax = ?
Xscl = ?

Ymin = ?
Ymax = ?
Yscl   = ?

3. Extend Problem 2 so that the graphing window can handle the first 200 years of the sequence of populations.

   a. Name a graphing window that provides a good picture of the sequence, and sketch a graph of the points involved.

   b. Do the points appear to be linear?

   c. What is the 200-year growth rate? Show how you found this.

4. If the original amount of money in the investment described in the Uncle Scrooge Investment Activity is doubled, will this double the amount of time needed to withdraw all of it? Write a short note to convince your uncle of your position.

5. Draw a graph or make a scatter plot of the sequence generated in the White Pine Tree Problem (Problem 5, Section 1.3).

   Name the graphing window you used.

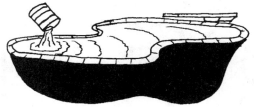

6. The ideal concentration of chlorine in a swimming pool is between 1 and 2 parts per million (ppm). If the concentration gets as high as 3 ppm, the pool is safe, but swimmers are a bit uncomfortable with burning eyes. If the concentration is less than 1 ppm, slime takes over. Suppose 15% of the chlorine present in the pool dissipates (disappears naturally) during a period of one day. Use a graph to answer each question.

   a. If the chlorine content is at 3 ppm, how long will it be before the slime takes over?

   b. If the chlorine content starts out at 3 ppm, and 0.5 ppm is added daily, will the concentration be increasing or decreasing? Will the pool ever be pure chlorine? Explain.

   c. Suppose the original content is 3 ppm, and 0.1 ppm is added daily. Describe what happens.

   d. How much do you need to add daily for the chlorine content to stabilize at 1.5 ppm?

Section 1.5: A Recursive Routine for Sequences

Finding the first six terms of the sequence produced by the calculator recursive routine shown below is easy.

3   ENTER

2 Ans   ENTER

             ENTER , and so on.

However, many of the longer sequences have probably taxed your patience. Physically pressing the ENTER key 48 or 120 times helps you understand what a recursive routine is, but is not really necessary, because the graphics calculator is a hand-held computer. When routines are not included as features of the calculator, then, as with all computers, routines can be written, edited, stored, and executed when needed. These routines are called programs.

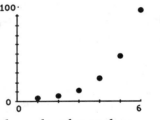

See **APPENDIX 1C** for help in entering a program that will execute a recursive routine in your calculator. The example in the appendix will seed 3 as the starting term, provide for exactly six terms, and display the results as 3, 6, 12, 24, 48, 96. The display can be a listing of the terms, the plotted points, or both. As with any graph, the graphing window must be set to show what you are interested in seeing. You will need to think carefully about the role of x and y, and how they relate to n and u_n.

Entering, executing, adjusting, and understanding a new recursive program may be the most complicated process you have undertaken with your calculator. Do not become frustrated if it doesn't work the first or second time you try. The more you experiment with the calculator, the better you will understand what it is doing.

> Example 1: Use your new recursive routine to find the balance after 60 mo if $500 is deposited in an account earning 6.5% annual interest compounded monthly.
>
> Solution: These important changes are required in the program to get $691.41.
>
> **1st:** The starting value is $500.
>
> **2nd:** Start the sequence at u_0.
>
> **3rd:** The recursive routine is Ans(1 + 0.065/12).
>
> **4th:** The sequence should end at u_{60}.

The Tower of Hanoi Activity

Ancient legend has it that Brahma stacked 64 gold disks in order from largest to smallest. According to the legend, the world will end when his priests have transferred all the disks from one tower to another. They are guided by the rules that only one disk can be moved at a time and larger disks cannot be placed on top of smaller disks.

Frequently this problem appears as the Tower of Hanoi Puzzle with 7 disks stacked on a tower. If you don't have an  actual tower puzzle, you might want to use coins to model the solution. To find a recursive solution, first reduce it to a simpler problem.

1. How many moves would you need with just 1 disk? With 2 disks?

2. How do you solve the puzzle with 4 disks if you know how to solve the puzzle with 3 disks? How do you solve it with 5 disks if you know how many moves were required with 4 disks? How do you solve the puzzle with n disks if you know how many moves were required with $n - 1$ disks?

Prepare a report explaining how your group solved this problem. Here are some suggestions and some questions to be answered. You could begin by defining a sequence representing the number of moves required depending on the number of disks.

Number of disks	1	2	3	4	5	6	7
Number of moves	?	?	?	?	?	?	?

a. What is the fewest number of moves required with 3 disks? With 7 disks?

b. Write a recursive routine and use it to continue this sequence, so you won't have to push the [ENTER] key repeatedly. Record your start value and your routine.

c. What is the fewest number of moves required with 64 disks?

Suppose the top gold disk has a diameter of 3 in., and the diameter of each lower disk increases by 2 in. from that of the disk above it.

d. List a few terms to represent the sequence of diameters.

e. What is the diameter of the 64th disk?

f. What do you consider to be a reasonable average length of time to move an average disk?

g. Using your last answer, figure out how long it would take to complete the task.

h. If the priests started in 3000 B.C. and worked in 24-hour-a-day shifts, in what year will the world end, according to this legend?

> The Tower of Hanoi Puzzle was actually invented by François Édouard Anatole Lucas (1842–1891) in 1883. He worked at the Paris Observatory and taught high school. He did most of his mathematical research in the field of number theory. He is also responsible for inventing the "legend" about the priests and the end of the world.

Problem Set 1.5

1. Find the first 30 terms of the sequence 2, 8, 14, 20, 26, ... Write the 10th, 20th, and 30th terms.

2. Find the value of a $1000 investment, at an annual rate of 6.5% compounded quarterly, for each time period.

    a. 10 yr   b. 20 yr   c. 30 yr

3. Use what you have learned in this section to solve the White Pine Tree Problem again (Problem 5, Section 1.3).

    a. Draw a graph that represents the number of trees each year during the first ten years and indicate the graphing window used. (See **APPENDIX 1C**.) Sketch this graph on paper.

    b. Draw graphs for 20 yr and 30 yr.

    c. Describe what happens in the long run.

4. The atmospheric pressure is 14.7 pounds per square inch (psi) at sea level. An increase in altitude of one mile produces a 20% decrease in the atmospheric pressure.

   a. Write a recursive routine that will provide atmospheric pressures at different altitudes.

   b. Draw a graph that pictures the relationship between altitude and pressure.

   c. What values do (n, u_n) have when the altitude is 7 mi?

   d. At what altitude does the atmospheric pressure drop below 1.5 psi?

5. Suppose a benevolent grandparent deposits $5000 in an account for a ten-year-old grandchild. The account pays interest at an annual rate of 8.5% compounded monthly.

   a. What regular monthly deposits are needed to assure that the account will be worth $1,000,000 by the time the youngster is 55 yr old? Write a recursive routine, and use guess-and-check to find the amount of the monthly deposit needed.

   b. Sketch the graph of increasing balances, and indicate the graphing window used.

6. Meg Abux wants to buy a new house and must finance $60,000 at 9.6% annual interest compounded monthly on the unpaid balance.

   a. What monthly payment is needed to pay off the loan in 25 yr?

   b. Sketch the graph of the unpaid balances, and indicate the graphing window used.

7. Each year, 5% of Americans move to California, and 10% of Californians move to other states. In 1986, there were 20 million Americans living in California, and 220 million living in other states.

   a. Calculate the number of people who left California during 1986.

   b. Calculate the number of people moving into California during 1986.

   c. From these two answers, give the population of California in 1987.

   d. Assume the United States population stays at a constant 240 million. What was the population outside of California in 1987?

   e. How is this value expressed in terms of California's population?

   f. If this trend continues, how many people should be living in California in 1990? In 1995? What happens in the long run?

8. Suppose a sequence is defined as below.

$$u_n = \begin{cases} 1 & \text{if } n = 1 \\ 1 & \text{if } n = 2 \\ u_{(n-1)} + u_{(n-2)} & \text{if } n > 2 \end{cases}$$

   a. List the first ten terms of this sequence.

   b. Consider the sequence of ratios of the above terms: $\frac{u_2}{u_1}, \frac{u_3}{u_2}, \frac{u_4}{u_3}, \frac{u_5}{u_4}$, and so on. List a few terms of this sequence in decimal form. Describe what is happening.

9. In the previous chapter, you were asked to think about the purpose of working in groups in your classroom. Now, think about the role you played in your group while working on the activity. Were you a leader? A follower? Were you satisfied with the way you participated in your group? Will you change your role? Does it matter? Be clear and explain your response.

Section 1.6: A Recursive Look at Series

Up to 50 tons of garbage has been left by climbers along the routes to the summit of Mount Everest since the first successful climb in 1953. Does this make Mount Everest the world's tallest trash dump? If you think that's a lot of garbage, consider that an average U.S. resident produces 0.75 tons of solid waste trash each year. At this rate, a community of less than 70 people produces over 50 tons of garbage in just one year. A community of 25,000 Americans produces over 50 tons of solid waste garbage in one day.

According to the *1994 Information Please Environmental Almanac*, each American produced 2.7 lb/day in 1960; this increased to 4.3 lb/day in 1990. Despite attempts to recycle and conserve, our garbage is accumulating. In fact, over a 30 yr period, the sum $2.7 + 2.753 + 2.806 + \cdots + 4.29 = 108.345$ provides this accumulated total. What does this number mean?

The expression $u_1 + u_2 + u_3 + \cdots + u_6 = S_6$ indicates the sum of the first six terms of a sequence. The series $1 + 3 + 5 + 7 + 9$ is a simple example where S_5 represents the sum of the first five terms of the sequence of odd integers. A decimal like 0.44444, a more difficult example, shows how the geometric series

$$S_5 = 0.4 + 0.04 + 0.004 + 0.0004 + 0.00004$$

is formed by combining five consecutive terms of a geometric sequence with a common ratio $\frac{1}{10}$.

A **series** is formed when the terms of a sequence are added.

In general, the sum of n terms in a series is written

$$u_1 + u_2 + u_3 + \cdots + u_n = S_n.$$

Finding the sum of a series has been a problem that has intrigued mathematicians throughout history. Chu Shih-chieh, a thirteenth-century Chinese mathematician and professional mathematics educator, would call the sum $1 + 2 + 3 + \ldots + n$ a "pile of reeds" because it can be pictured like the diagram shown at the right.

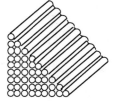

When the famous mathematician Karl Friedrich Gauss (1777–1855) was nine years old, his teacher asked the class to find the sum of the numbers from 1 to 100. Historical accounts indicate the teacher was hoping to take a break from his students (things haven't really changed that much since) and expected the students to add the terms one by one. Karl didn't have a calculator (and didn't need one, as you will see later). You can write the terms of the series involved as:

$S_n = 0 + 1 + 2 + \ldots + n$, where $n = 100$.

Or, using recursive notation, you could write:

$S_n = u_n + S_{(n-1)}$, where, in this case, u_n is just n.

The sum $u_n + S_{(n-1)}$, for $n = 100$, means "100 plus the sum of the first 99 terms."

In **APPENDIX 1D,** you will find directions to modify the recursive routine so that you can sum terms and display the nth sum, or the **partial sum** (the accumulated sum through that term). Refer to the appendix for help on this example.

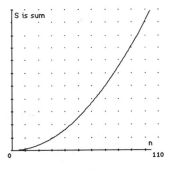

Example 1

Find the answer to the Gauss Problem and make a graph of the partial sums. Be sure to set the graphing window at [0, 110, 10, 0, 5500, 500].

Solution: The points are so dense that they appear to form a solid curve, but this is a discrete set of 100 points representing each partial sum from S_1 through S_{100}. Each point is (n, S_n) for integer values of n, $1 \le n \le 100$. The sum of the first 100 terms is $S_{100} = 5050$.

Wheat on a Chessboard Activity

Part 1: A very old Arab legend, recounted by al-Yaqubi in the ninth century, begins, "It is related by the wise men of India that when Husiya, the daughter of Balhait, was queen. . . ," then goes on to tell how the game of chess was invented, and how the queen was so delighted that she told the inventor, "Ask what you will." The inventor asked for one grain of wheat on the first square of the chessboard, two grains on the second, four grains on the third, and so on, so that each square contained twice that of the one before.

How many grains are needed for the eighth square? for the first row? for the 64th square? to fill the board and fulfill the wish?

Part 2: With your group, design a series of *eight* containers.

The *first* container should be able to hold all of the grains needed for squares 1 through 8 (row 1).

The *second* container should be able to hold all of the grains needed for squares 1 through 16.

The *third* container should be able to hold all of the grains needed for squares 1 through 24, the *fourth* for squares 1 through 32, the *fifth* for squares 1 through 40, the *sixth* for squares 1 through 48, the *seventh* for squares 1 through 56, and the *eighth* for the grains from the entire board.

Of course, each container will be a different size. Each one should also be a different shape (box, sphere, pyramid, and so on). Assume each grain to be a small box 1 mm × 1 mm × 4 mm.

Problem Set 1.6

1. Find S_1, S_2, S_3, S_4, and S_5 for this sequence: 2, 6, 10, 14, 18.

2. a. Find S_{15} for the sequence 2, 6, 18, 54, ...

   b. Sketch a graph of the partial sums S_1 through S_{15}, and name the graphing window.

3. a. Find the sum S_{10} for the sequence 0.3, 0.03, 0.003, ...

   b. Find S_{15}. Describe any difficulties encountered.

   c. What is another way of indicating the infinite decimal suggested by the sum of the terms of 0.3, 0.03, 0.003, . . . ?

4. a. Find the sum of the first 12 odd positive integers.

   b. Find the sum of the first 20 odd positive integers.

   c. What is the sum of the first n odd positive integers? (Hint: Try several choices for n until you detect a pattern.)

5. Suppose you practiced the piano 45 min on the first day of school and increased your practice time by 5 min each day. How much total time have you devoted to practice, if you are now 15 days into the semester? 35 days?

6. a. Find the sum of the first 1000 positive integers.

   b. Find the sum of the second 1000 positive integers (the numbers from 1001 to 2000).

   c. Make a guess at the sum of the third 1000 positive integers (the numbers from 2001 to 3000).

   d. Now find this sum (the sum indicated in 6c).

   e. Describe a way to find the sum of the third 1000 positive integers (the numbers from 2001 to 3000) if you know the sum of the first 1000 positive integers.

7. As a contest prize, you are given the choice of two prizes. The first choice will provide you with $1,000 for the first hour, $2,000 for the second hour, $3,000 for the third hour, and so on. For one entire year, you will be given one thousand dollars more each hour than you were given during the previous hour. The second choice is 1¢ for the first week, 2¢ for the second week, 4¢ for the third week, and so on. For one entire year you will be given double the amount you received during the previous week. Which of the two plans is more profitable, and by how much?

8. Find the sum S_6 of

$$u_n = \begin{cases} 0.39 & \text{if } n = 1 \\ 0.01 \cdot u_{(n-1)} & \text{if } n > 1 \end{cases}$$

9. There are 650,000 people in a city. Every 15 min, the local media broadcasts an important announcement of a huge downtown fire. During each 15-min time period, 42% of the people who had not yet heard the news become aware of the fire.

   a. How many people have heard the news about the downtown fire after 1 hr? After 2 hr?

   b. Write a news report on the spread of this story through the city's population. Assume the event took place several hours earlier. Be as detailed and as graphic as you wish.

10. Consider again the role of the graphing calculator in this course. Have you discovered new advantages or disadvantages of using the graphing calculator? If so, what are they? Has your perspective or your feelings changed? Be clear and explain your response.

Section 1.7: Chapter Review

Problem Set 1.7

1. a. Mark Ett arranges a display of soup cans as shown in the picture. List the number of cans in the top row, second row, third row, and so on, down to the tenth row.

   b. Write a recursive formula for the terms of the sequence in 1a.

   c. If the cans are to be stacked 47 rows high, how many cans will it take to build the display?

   d. If he uses 6 cases (288 cans), how tall can he make the display?

2. Answer each question based on the arithmetic sequence 3, 7, 11, 15, ...
   a. What is the 128th term?
   b. Which term has the value 159?
   c. Find u_{20}.
   d. Find S_{20}.

3. Answer each question based on the geometric sequence 256, 192, 144, 108, ...
   a. What is the eighth term?
   b. Which term is the first one smaller than 20?
   c. Find u_7.
   d. Find S_7.

4. a. If you invest $500 in a bank that pays 5.5% annual interest compounded quarterly, how much money will you have after 5 yr?

   b. Start over and invest $500 at 5.5% annual interest compounded quarterly, and deposit an additional $50 every month. Now find the balance after 5 yr.

5. The enrollment at the local university is currently 5678. From now on, the university will graduate 24% of its students yearly and add 1250 new ones. What will the enrollment be during the sixth year? What will the enrollment be in the long run?

6. What monthly payment will be required to pay off an $80,000 mortgage at 8.9% interest in 30 yr?

7. List the first five terms of each sequence:

   a. $u_n = \begin{cases} -3 & n = 1 \\ u_{(n-1)} + 1.5 & n > 1 \end{cases}$

   b. $u_n = \begin{cases} 2 & n = 1 \\ 3 \cdot u_{(n-1)} - 2 & n > 1 \end{cases}$

Section 1.8: Projects

Project 1.1: Interest, the Bank, and Rounding-off

Research current interest rates for some local banks and savings institutions, and find out how often they compound the interest. Ask at least one institution manager, "What becomes of fractions of a cent? Is the interest rounded up to the nearest cent, rounded down to the nearest cent, or is some other rule used?" Then, using the appropriate calculator function (round, int or ?), generate a recursive formula that simulates the actual process used by these financial institutions. Compare the different outcomes by calculating the account balances of a $1000 deposit for 1 yr, 2 yr, 3 yr, and so on.

Project 1.2: Automobile Depreciation

Select a particular used automobile that interests you. With help from a car dealer or car collector, gather some data relating the value of the vehicle to its age. Make a graph of your data over the life of the vehicle. Find a good mathematical model for this (*age, value*) relationship. Your model may require more than one function. See the following example.

$$u_n = \begin{cases} \$15,000 & \text{if } n = 0 \\ u_{(n-1)}(1 - 0.25) & \text{if } 1 \le n \le 3 \\ u_{(n-1)}(1 - 0.18) & \text{if } n > 3 \end{cases}$$

Project 1.3: Fibonacci's Rabbits

As you might know, Australia once had a real problem with rabbits! When rabbits were introduced to Australia in the late 1800s, there were no natural enemies on the continent. As a consequence, the number of rabbits quickly grew out of control.

Suppose two rabbits, one male and one female, scampered on board a ship that was anchored at a European port. The ship set sail for Australia; when it anchored in late December, the two rabbits abandoned the ship to make their home on the island continent. Consider the following assumptions:

- The number of young produced in every litter is six, and three of those six are female.

- The original female gives birth to six young on January 1, and produces another litter of six 40 days later, and every 40 days thereafter for as long as she lives.

- Each female born on the island will produce her first litter 120 days after her birth, and then produce another new litter every 40 days thereafter.

- The rabbits are on an island with no natural enemies and plenty of food. Therefore, in this first year, there are only births, and no rabbits die.

What will be the total number of rabbits by the next January 1, including the original pair? A good project will give at least two methods of describing this situation, and a very good project will give more than two methods. If possible, find out and explain what has actually happened to the rabbit population in Australia.

Project 1.4: The Gingerbread Man

In this project, you will investigate the iteration of different points through the function $x_{n+1} = 1 - y_n + |x_n|$, $y_{n+1} = x_n$. All results will be graphed in the window $-5 \le x \le 10, -5 \le y \le 10$.

a. Begin with the point $(0, 0)$ and plot the points resulting from iterating this function on graph paper. Describe what happens as you continue to iterate the function. Points like this are called **periodic.** These points have period 6.

b. Begin with the point $(3, -1)$ and plot the points resulting from iterating this function on graph paper. What is the period for these points?

c. Begin with the point $(2.5, -1)$ and iterate by hand. Plot the points on graph paper. What is the period for these points?

d. Enter the program in **APPENDIX 1E**. The program will automatically iterate the function and plot each point. Set the window to $-5 \le x \le 10, -5 \le y \le 10$. Turn off all functions and statplots before running the program.

e. Use the program to iterate the function, using each given point as the starting point. Do not clear the screen between runs of the program.

    i. $(3, 0.5)$ ii. $(1.5, -0.2)$ iii. $(1.3, 0.1)$ iv. $(-0.13, 0)$

    v. $(1, -1.8)$ vi. (π, π) vii. $(\sqrt{2}, -0.1)$

Describe how the resulting picture relates to the graphs in parts a, b, and c.

f. Use the program to investigate what happens when points within the "belly" are iterated. Describe the periods of these points, and any patterns you observe.

g. Use the program to investigate what happens when points within the "head" and "limb" regions are iterated. Describe the periods of these points, and any patterns you observe.

h. The points in the shaded region of the gingerbread man have periods of all possible values. Some points never repeat their locations, or have infinite periods. Investigate what happens when you iterate points just outside the gingerbread man. You may need to iterate several points without clearing the screen to see any pattern. Describe what you see.

Project 1.5: Recursive Midpoint Games

Game 1. Draw a large equilateral triangle on a sheet of paper. Label the vertices A, B, and C. Read the rules of the game and predict the outcome before you play.

Start by choosing one of the vertices. Roll a die and move according to this plan:

die result is 1 or 2   move halfway to A and plot a point

die result is 3 or 4   move halfway to B and plot a point

die result is 5 or 6   move halfway to C and plot a point

Connect this new point to the previous point. Starting from this midpoint, roll the die and repeat the procedure.

What do you think your picture will look like after 50 moves?

Play the game and see if your prediction was correct.

Game 2. This is exactly like Game 1, but you will not connect the midpoints. Record your prediction for the outcome of this game.

Play the game and make at least 50 moves, (more if possible). Describe your result as completely as possible.

The calculator is capable of measuring and plotting points much more quickly than you. Enter the program in **APPENDIX 1F** to automate this procedure.

The program uses the window $0 \le x \le 10$ and $0 \le y \le 7$. After running the program once, change the window to view only the top large triangle, and run again. How does this picture compare to the one you saw in the full-size window? Zoom in again by changing the window to view only the top large triangle of this new picture and run the program. You may need to modify the program to plot more points, because many of the points will be plotted outside of the visible window. What do you see? Would the picture change if you had zoomed in on the triangle at the bottom left? How many times can you zoom in and see the same effect? Use these questions to explain what you think the term **self-similarity** means.

Create your own shape which has this same property of self-similarity.

Chapter Two

SEQUENCES AND EXPLICIT FORMULAS

Contents

Section 2.1: Explicit Formulas for Arithmetic Sequences 56

    Here's a different way to look at things

Section 2.2: Explicit Formulas for Arithmetic Series 62

    Ever heard the expression "same difference"?

Section 2.3: Explicit Formulas for Geometric Sequences 66

    That's the way the ball bounces

Section 2.4: Explicit Formulas for Geometric Series 71

    Now things are really adding up

Section 2.5: In The Long Run 75

    All good things come to an end, maybe

Section 2.6: Fractal Patterns 80

    As if there wasn't enough chaos

Section 2.7: Chapter Review... 84

    Assessing yourself

Section 2.8: Projects.. 87

    Taking it one step further

Section 2.1: Explicit Formulas for Arithmetic Sequences

 Matias wants to call his aunt in Chile on her birthday. He learned that the first minute costs $2.27, and each additional minute costs $1.37. How much would it cost to talk for 30 minutes?

If you're thinking recursively, it's easy: It costs $2.27 for 1 minute; $1.37 more, or $3.64, for 2 minutes; $5.01 for 3 minutes; and so on. Just keep adding $1.37. It's an arithmetic sequence with a first term of 2.27, and a common difference of 1.37. But you don't want to carry that sequence all the way out to 30 terms. So what does the recursive definition tell you about the 30th term of the sequence? Only that it's 1.37 more than the 29th term—not much help if you don't know the 29th term. But you can find the 29th term: it's 1.37 more than the 28th term, and that's . . . hmm. Can you see the limitations of a recursive definition? You want to be able to find the value of *any* term in the sequence without having to start at (or work back to) the beginning of the sequence. Explicit formulas allow you to do that.

> The **explicit formula** for a sequence defines u_n with an expression that does not involve previous terms. Individual terms are defined in terms of n, where n is a nonnegative integer.

Fortunately, Matias found a way to calculate the cost of a 30-minute call directly. He figured he'd pay $2.27 for the first minute, and $1.37 for each of the next 29 minutes. So he calculated $2.27 + (29)(1.37)$. The call would cost $42. You could use this method to find the cost of a phone call of any length. Can you write an expression for calculating the cost of an n-minute call?

You may find some patterns easier to define explicitly than recursively. Consider the sequence 1, 4, 9, 16, 25, . . . , 225. There is no *common difference,* so the sequence is not arithmetic. It isn't geometric, because consecutive terms have no *common ratio*. This sequence isn't even a combination of the two. Yet, chances are you can see a pattern, and you can find the missing terms between 25 and 225. In this case, you can easily relate the term number (or index) n and the term value u_n.

n	1	2	3	4	5	6	7
u_n	1	4	9	16	25		

To find the term value, just square the index. So $u_8 = 8^2 = 64$, and $u_{15} = 15^2 = 225$. What is u_{10}? Find the index n so that $u_n = 289$.

The formula $u_n = n^2$ is an example of an explicit formula for a sequence. You can calculate any term by substituting that particular index number for n. You don't need to know any previous terms, as you would with a recursive definition.

Example 1: Complete a table of values for the sequence defined by the explicit formula $u_n = 2(1 + 3n)$.

n	1	2	3	4 . . .	11		n
u_n						. . . 152	$2(1 + 3n)$

Solution: The solution involves substitution, which is typical of most explicit-formula work. To find u_1, substitute 1 for n in the formula and simplify.

$$u_1 = 2(1 + 3 \cdot 1)$$

$$u_1 = 2(4)$$

$$u_1 = 8 \qquad \text{likewise for } n = 2, 3, 4, \text{ and } 11$$

Finding the missing value of n when $u_n = 152$ also involves substitution.

$$152 = u_n$$

$$152 = 2(1 + 3n) \qquad \text{substituting } 2(1 + 3n) \text{ for } u_n$$

$$76 = 1 + 3n \qquad \text{divide by 2}$$

$$75 = 3n \qquad \text{subtract 1}$$

$$25 = n \qquad \text{divide by 3}$$

This means that $u_{25} = 152$.

The greatest difficulty occurs when the formula is unknown, and you are to describe a relation between n and u_n. Some relations will require creative solutions. Here is an unusual sequence. Can you complete it?

n	1	2	3	4	5	6 . . .	10	. . .	18	19
u_n	O	T	T	F	F	S		. . . E		

Try this next one.

n	1	2	3	4 . . .	11	. . .	. . . n
u_n	2	5	10	17		. . . 401	

Hint: The formula involves squaring.

The real purpose of this section, however, is for you to learn to write and use explicit formulas for *arithmetic sequences* like the phone call example. Although you can use creative thinking or guessing to find these formulas, you can also use what you know about writing equations for lines.

Example 2: Find an explicit formula for the arithmetic sequence 2, 8, 14, 20, 26, . . . , and use it to find u_{22} and the value of n to make $u_n = 86$.

Solution: Notice that the common difference is 6. First create a data set representing the sequence as pairs of numbers, with n representing the number of the term and u_n representing the term itself.

n	1	2	3	4	5 . . .	22		. . . n
u_n	2	8	14	20	26		. . . 86	

Graph the sequence. The graphing window pictured is [0, 7, 1, 0, 30, 5].

The common difference between terms is 6. The points appear to be linear. What is the slope (rate of increase) of this line?

The vertical intercept of this line would be −4. Do you see why?

The explicit formula of the sequence using the slope and vertical intercept is $u_n = 6n - 4$.

u_n

(5,26)

(4,20)

(3,14)

(2,8)

(1,2)

n

Now you can use this formula to find u_{22}. By substitution, $u_{22} = 6 \cdot 22 - 4$. Therefore, $u_{22} = 84$. (See **APPENDIX 2A**.)

Find n when $u_n = 86$. Again, by substituting in the formula $86 = 6n - 4$, you get $n = 15$.

The equation of the line $y = 6x - 4$ will also contain all of the points in the sequence.

What is the relationship between the common difference of an arithmetic sequence, and the slope of the line that connects the points representing the sequence? Will the graph of every arithmetic sequence be linear? Why or why not?

Problem Set 2.1

1. a. Find the first five terms for the sequence whose nth term (the **generator**) is given by $u_n = \dfrac{n(n + 1)(2n + 3)}{6}$.

    b. Is this sequence arithmetic, geometric, or neither?

2. Complete the table and write an explicit formula for the sequence. (Hint: Experiment with different calculator keys.)

n	1	2	3	4	5	6 . . .		n
u_n	1	1.41	1.73	2	2.24		3.87	

3. a. Graph the sequence $u_n = \begin{cases} 18 & \text{if } n = 1 \\ u_{(n-1)} - 3 & \text{if } 1 < n \le 6 \end{cases}$

    b. What is the common difference?

    c. What is the slope of the line that contains the points?

    d. What is the vertical or u_n-intercept?

    e. Write the explicit formula for the sequence.

    f. Use this formula to find u_{10}.

    g. Write the equation of the line that contains these points.

4. a. What are the terms of the sequence pictured?

    b. What is u_3?

    c. What is the common difference?

    d. If the pattern is continued, what is u_5? What is u_0?

    e. What is the slope of the line through the points?

    f. What is the u_n-intercept?

    g. Write the explicit formula for the sequence.

    h. Write the equation of the line that contains these points.

5. Find the four arithmetic means between 7 and 27. This suggests the sequence is arithmetic and looks like 7, ____, ____, ____, ____, 27.

    a. Name two points on the graph of this sequence, (, 7) and (, 27).

    b. Plot the two points you named in 5a, and find the slope of the line connecting the points. (You can assume the points lie on a line, because the sequence is arithmetic.)

    c. Use the slope to find the missing terms and the term just prior to the 7.

d. Plot all the points, and write the equation of the line that contains them.

e. What equation gives the explicit formula for the sequence u_n?

f. What is the connection between the slope and the common difference in this sequence?

6. a. Write an explicit formula for an arithmetic sequence with a first term of 6.3 and a common difference of 2.5.

   b. Use the formula to figure out which term is 78.8.

7. Suppose you drive from Interlochen, (which is 15 miles from Traverse City), toward Detroit, at a steady 54 mi/hr.

   a. What is your distance from Traverse City after driving for 4 hours?

   b. Write an equation that represents your distance from Traverse City after x hours.

   c. Graph the equation.

   d. Does this equation model an arithmetic sequence? Why or why not?

8. Les Cache's older brother, Noah, sells cars for a living. If he sells only 3 cars, he is still in debt by $2050. If Noah sells 7 cars, he makes a profit of $1550. Assume that d (the number of dollars of profit) is related to c (the number of cars sold), and that the possible profits form an arithmetic sequence.

   a. List a few terms of this sequence of profits.

   b. Sketch a graph of possible profits.

   c. What is the real-world meaning of the common difference?

   d. What is the real-world meaning of the slope of a line drawn through the points?

   e. What is the real-world meaning of the horizontal and vertical intercepts?

   f. What is the explicit formula relating profit to cars sold?

9. The points on this graph represent the first five terms of an arithmetic sequence. The height of each point can be described as its distance from the x-axis, or the value of the second coordinate of the point.

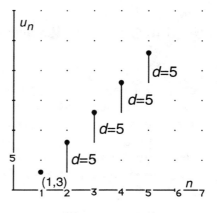

a. Find u_0, the second coordinate of the point preceding those given.

b. How many common differences (d's) are needed to get from the height of $(0, u_0)$ to the height of $(5, u_5)$?

c. How many d's would be needed to get from the height of $(0, u_0)$ to the height of $(7, u_7)$?

d. Explain why the height from the x-axis to $(7, u_7)$ can be found using the equation $u_7 = u_0 + 7d$.

e. The height of $(13, u_{13})$ is $u_{13} = u_0 + \_\_d$.

f. In general, for an arithmetic sequence, $u_n = ?$

10. a. Which is better for a new company employee, a starting salary of $18,400 with annual raises of $2000, or a starting salary of $17,900 with semi-annual raises of $500?

b. Is there ever a time when one choice is better than the other? Explain.

Section 2.2: Explicit Formulas for Arithmetic Series

Suppose a family friend just told you the story of her life and the history of her current job, again! You remember her original, or first-year, salary was $18,400, with annual raises averaging about $2000. How much did she make during the first 15 years? The series $S_{15} = 18,400 + 20,400 + 22,400 + \ldots$ provides this income total. One disadvantage of computing this sum recursively is that you, or the calculator, must compute each of the individual salaries. Is there any way to compute this sum without finding all 15 numbers and adding?

If you can find an explicit formula, you will be able to compute the sum directly. Explicit formulas allow you to compute sums very quickly, and the process involved helps you develop more mathematical power. The following example and activities will give you an opportunity to discover at least one explicit formula for summing terms of an arithmetic series.

Example 1: Recall the problem given to Gauss when he was 9 years old. He was asked to find the sum of the first 100 counting numbers.

$$1 + 2 + 3 + \ldots + 98 + 99 + 100 = S \text{ (the total sum)}$$

Solution: His ingenious solution was to add the terms in pairs. Consider the series written normally and written backwards.

$$1 \quad + \quad 2 \quad + \quad 3 + \ldots + 98 \quad + \quad 99 \quad + 100 \quad = S_{100}$$

$$100 \quad + \quad 99 \quad + \quad 98 + \ldots + 3 \quad + \quad 2 \quad + \quad 1 \quad = S_{100}$$

$$\overline{}$$

$$101 \quad + 101 \quad + 101 + \ldots + 101 \quad + 101 \quad + 101 \quad = 2S_{100}$$

The sum of each column shown is 101. In fact, the sum of *every* column is 101. There are 100 columns. Thus, the sum of the integers, 1 through 100 is $\dfrac{100 \cdot 101}{2}$. The 2 as a divisor is the tricky part; it is necessary because the series was added twice (forward and backward).

Arithmetic Series Formula Activity

Each member of the group should follow the steps below. Then, based on the individual results, work together to develop a formula for the sum of an arithmetic series.

a. Define an arithmetic series. Select a start value, a common difference, and the number of terms (between 10 and 20). These selections should be different for each member of the group.

b. Use Gauss's method, as shown in Example 1, to compute the sum of your series.

c. Check your sum by using a method from Chapter One.

d. Determine what you need to know in order to calculate the sum using Gauss's method.

e. Combine your efforts with those of other members of your group to develop a formula for the sum of an arithmetic series. Test your formula by finding $S_{15} = 18{,}400 + 20{,}400 + 22{,}400 + \ldots$. (Your answer should be \$486,000.)

The summation expression $\sum_{n=1}^{15}(18{,}400 + 2000(n-1))$ is another way of writing the sum of the terms, $u_1 + u_2 + \ldots + u_{15}$, of a sequence. The notation means that you should substitute the values $\{1, 2, 3, \ldots, 15\}$ for n in the expression $u_n = 18{,}400 + 2000(n-1)$, and then sum the 15 resulting values.

Toothpick Trapezoids Activity

It takes five toothpicks to build the top trapezoid figure pictured here. Nine toothpicks are enough to build a two-in-a-row configuration of trapezoids, because the two trapezoids share one edge. Thirteen toothpicks are needed to build a three-in-a-row configuration of trapezoids. Build several more rows of trapezoids, each containing one more trapezoid than the preceding row. If 1000 toothpicks are available, how many trapezoids will be in the last row? How many rows are there? How many toothpicks are used? Use the numbers in this activity to carefully describe the difference between a sequence and a series.

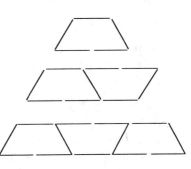

There are times when adding individual terms or numbers together is questionable. For example, consider this sign posted at the city limits of a small town.

Spiritville	
Population	256
Elevation	425
Year Founded	1850
Total	2531

Problem Set 2.2

1. Find the sum of the first 50 multiples of 6. (Hint: $6 + 12 + 18 + \cdots + u_{50}$)

2. Find the sum of the first 75 even numbers, starting with 2.

3. a. Find u_{75} if $u_n = 2n - 1$.

   b. Find $\displaystyle\sum_{n=1}^{75}(2n - 1)$

4. Find S_{67} for the sequence $125.3 + 118.5 + 111.7 + 104.9 + \ldots$.

5. a. What is the 46th term of the pictured sequence?

   b. Write a general expression for u_n.

   c. Find the total sum of the heights from the horizontal axis of the first 46 points of the sequence pictured.

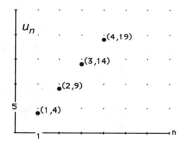

6. A large barrel contained 12.4 gallons of oil 18 minutes after a drain was opened. How many gallons of oil were in the barrel initially, if it drained at 4.2 gallons per minute?

7. Make several different graph sketches, each representing a generic arithmetic sequence. What graph shapes are possible? (Hint: Use what you know about different kinds of slopes.)

8. Your friend buys you a concert ticket for seat 995 in a concert hall with 65 seats in row one, 67 seats in row two, 69 seats in row three, and so on. The seats are numbered left to right, so the first seat in row one is 1, the first seat in row two is 66, and so on. The concert hall has 40 rows of seats.

   a. How many seats are in the last row?

   b. How many seats are in the concert hall?

   c. Describe the location of your seat.

9. a. Find the area of the trapezoid bounded by the x-axis, vertical segments at $x = 5$ and $x = 6$, and the line containing points of the sequence $u_n = 1.8n + 2.6$.

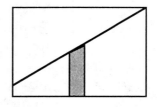

  b. Find the total area between the line pictured through the sequence points, and the x-axis from $x = 0$ to $x = 10$.

  c. Explain how you can find the area from 9b using a series of ten terms.

Section 2.3: Explicit Formulas for Geometric Sequences

Have you and your classmates tried linking calculators, or transferring data from one calculator to another using some electronic method? Suppose there are a sufficient number of link cables in a classroom, and that it takes 20 seconds to link and then transfer a program from one calculator to another. During the first time period, the program is transferred to one calculator; during the second time period, to two more calculators; during the third time period, to four more calculators, and so on. How long before everyone in a class of 25 students has the program? How long before everyone in a lecture hall of 250 students has the program? You could answer these questions very quickly if you knew an explicit formula for the sequence involved.

Over uniform time periods (like 20 seconds, 1 day, 1 year, or 1 decade), many increasing populations produce a sequence that is very close to geometric.

Decade	0	1	2	3	4	5	6	7
California	1.213	1.485	2.378	3.427	5.677	6.907	10.586	15.717

[p. 282 of *The 1994 Universal Almanac*]

This table of figures lists California's census populations (in millions of people) for the years 1890, 1900, 1910, . . . , 1960. (If you investigate the growth after 1960, you will find a different pattern.) You can model this growth in successive decades by finding a common ratio and multiplying.

1.213	u_0 or the initial population (in 1890)
1.213 • 1.45	population 1 decade later = 1.759 (approx)
$(1.213 • 1.45) • 1.45 = 1.213 • 1.45^2$	population 2 decades later = 2.550 (approx)
$(1.213 • 1.45^2) • 1.45 = 1.213 • 1.45^3$	population 3 decades later = 3.698 (approx)

and so on.

Can you write a similar expression for u_7 (the population 7 decades later)? The 1.45 used in the solution is the average ratio of any two consecutive populations, $\dfrac{\text{next decade population}}{\text{present decade population}}$, found in the table.

Bouncing a Super Ball Activity

In this activity, you will work with your group to gather data from an experiment. Your group needs to decide upon a good experimental procedure. Try to collect data which is as accurate as possible. Because of the equipment and conditions, your group may have to be imaginative and creative to obtain accurate measurements. Do not oversimplify the experiment by making assumptions that you have not tested.

Carefully drop a super ball from a starting height of 200 cm. Record the heights of the 1st rebound, 2nd rebound, . . . , 6th rebound. Repeat the experiment 10 times. Copy and complete a table like the one following showing the results of all 10 trials.

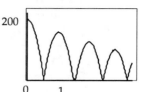

Trial 1		Trial 2		. . .	Trial 10	
Rebound Number	Height	Rebound Number	Height		Rebound Number	Height
0	200	0	200		0	200
1		1			1	
2		2			2	
3		3			3	
4		4			4	
5		5			5	
6		6			6	

a. Find and record the average of all the 1st rebounds in the 10 trials. Do the same for the 2nd rebounds, the 3rd rebounds, and so on.

b. Compute the rebound ratio, the fraction representing $\dfrac{\text{height of rebound}}{\text{distance of previous fall}}$, for the ball you are using. Call this fraction r for ratio.

c. Describe some of the factors that might affect the ratio in this experiment.

Rebound Number	Average Height	Ratio
0	200	████
1		
2		
3		
4		
5		
6		

Make the original height term zero. This makes the index, n, equal the number of rebounds. For example, u_0 is after no rebounds, u_5 is after 5 rebounds.

Ideally, the ratios in your table should be the same for each rebound. Write a recursive formula that uses this common ratio. The value for the 1st term should be nearly equal to 200 • r. How would you express the value of the 2nd term, using only 200 and your value of r? How could you express the value of the 5th term (the height of the 5th rebound), using only 200 and r? How would you express the value of the nth term, using only 200 and r? How would you write an explicit formula using only u_0 and the variable r?

Example 1: An automobile depreciates as it gets older. This means it becomes less valuable. Suppose that every year it loses one-fifth of its value (or maintains four-fifths of its value). Find the value of a six-year-old automobile that initially cost $14,000.

Solution: This geometric sequence of annual values represents the car's depreciation.

Original value	Value after one year	Value after two years
$14,000	$14,000(0.8)	$14,000(0.8)²

Therefore, the six-year-old car has a value of $14,000(0.8)^6$, or $3670.02.

Problem Set 2.3

1. Use an explicit formula to find the 15th term of the sequence 2, 6, 18, 54, ...

2. Suppose $1500 is deposited in an account earning 5.5% annually, compounded annually. What is the balance after 8 years? (Remember that the multiplier must be bigger than 1 for the balance to grow.) How long before the balance is at least $5000?

3. What could be a real-world meaning for these expressions? Use the value of the expression in a sentence.

   a. $4000(1 + 0.072)^{10}$

   b. $4000\left(1 + \dfrac{0.072}{12}\right)^{48}$

   c. Write an explicit formula for the solution to Problem 2.

4. Without using your calculator, match each sequence in the second column to an explicit formula in the first column. After you have done this, check your answer with your calculator.

   a. $u_n = 2(5)^n$ i. $7, 9, 11, 13, 15, \ldots$

   b. $u_n = 2 + 5n$ ii. $10, 20, 40, 80, \ldots$

   c. $u_n = 5(2)^n$ iii. $7, 12, 17, 22, 27, \ldots$

   d. $u_n = 5 + 2n$ iv. $10, 50, 250, 1250, \ldots$

5. Try different values of r in the expression $u_n = 60 \cdot r^n$. Try negative numbers, fractions, 0, 1, and -1. Make sketches of the different graphs that are possible as n gets larger. Write a paragraph describing at least two discoveries you made.

6. Without using your calculator, match each explicit formula to a graph. After you have done this, check your answers by graphing each equation on your calculator.

   a. $u_n = 10(0.75)^n$ b. $u_n = 10(1.25)^n$ c. $u_n = 10(1.00)^n$

   i.   ii.   iii.

7. Suppose the rebound heights (in inches) of an ideal rebounding ball are 80, 64, 51.2, 40.96, ... The initial height from which the ball is dropped is 100 in.

   a. What is the height of the 10th rebound?

   b. How far in the sequence do you have to go until the height becomes less than 1 in.? Less than 0.1 in.?

8. The week of February 14, store owner J.C. Nickels ordered hundreds of heart-shaped red vacuum cleaners. The next week, he still had hundreds of heart-shaped red vacuum cleaners, so he told his manager to discount the price 25% each week until they were all sold. The first week they sold for $80.00.

   a. Write an explicit formula you can use to find the price of the vacuum cleaners in successive weeks.

   b. What was the price in the second week?

   c. What was the price for the vacuums in the fourth week?

   d. When will the vacuum sell for less than $10? (You may need to use guess-and-check to answer this question.)

9. Suppose $u_n = \begin{cases} 0.39 & \text{if } n = 1 \\ 0.01 \cdot u_{(n-1)} & \text{if } n > 1 \end{cases}$

   Find $\displaystyle\sum_{n=1}^{6} u_n$.

Section 2.4: Explicit Formulas for Geometric Series

In the last section, you were asked, "How long before everyone in a lecture hall of 250 students has the program, if a pair of calculators can be linked and a program transferred from one calculator to the other in 20 sec?" During the first time period, the program is transferred to one calculator; during the second time period, to two calculators; during the third time period, to four more calculators, and so on . Do you see that the problem involves determining the maximum value of n before $S_n = 1 + 2 + 4 + \ldots$ exceeds 250?

You have developed recursive tools for finding the sum of geometric series. For some series, those involving a large number of terms, an explicit formula is very accurate, and faster to compute. This activity will help you develop an explicit formula for summing terms of geometric sequences.

Explicit Geometric Series Activity

Let the month you were born be called r, and the day you were born be called u_1. (Note: If you were born in January, choose any number between 2 and 12 for r.)

a. List the first six terms of the geometric sequence defined by u_1 and r.

b. Multiply each term of this sequence by r, and write a new sequence.

c. Cancel any values that appear in both lists.

d. Subtract those terms remaining in the sequence you wrote in part b from those remaining in the sequence in part a.

e. Find the value of $(1 - r)$, and divide this into the answer from part d.

f. Find the sum of the original six numbers.

g. Working together with your group members, write an explanation for what happened. Find an explicit formula that gives the sum of the terms of a geometric series. Test your formula on another group member's series.

h. Why will this method not work when r is equal to one?

There are many ways to express the explicit formula for the sum of a geometric series. It is useful to recognize and translate between different symbolic forms, because often the information you have gathered is not the same information needed in the formula. In Example 1 below, the formula uses only three pieces of information—the first term, the common ratio, and the number of terms. This explicit formula may look different from your version, but it does not require you to find any other terms before you find the sum.

Example 1: Find S_{10} for the series defined by $16 + 24 + 36 + \ldots$.

Solution: The first term, u_1, equals 16, the common ratio, r, equals 1.5, and the number of terms, n, equals 10.

$$S_{10} = \frac{16(1 - 1.5^{10})}{1 - 1.5} = 1813.28125$$

Try using this formula to find S_6 in the Explicit Geometric Series Activity.

Example 2: Each day, the now-extinct Caterpillarsaurus would eat 25% more leaves than it did the day before. If a 30-day-old Caterpillarsaurus has eaten 151,677 leaves in its brief lifetime, how many will it eat the next day?

Solution: In this problem the first term is unknown, but $r = (1 + 0.25) = 1.25$, and $n = 30$. This means

$$151{,}677 = \frac{u_1(1 - 1.25^{30})}{1 - 1.25}$$

$$151{,}677 = 3227.17u_1$$

$$u_1 = \frac{151{,}677}{3227.17} = 47$$

Knowing this, you can predict that on its thirty-first day the Caterpillarsaurus will consume no less than $47(1.25)^{30} = 37{,}966$ leaves.

Problem Set 2.4

1. Find the missing value in each set of numbers. This may require some guess-and-check work.

   a. $u_1 = 3$ $r = 2$ $n = 10$ $S_{10} = ?$

   b. $u_1 = 4$ $r = 0.6$ $n = ?$ $S_? = 9.999868378$

   c. $u_1 = ?$ $r = 1.4$ $n = 15$ $S_{15} = 1081.976669$

   d. $u_1 = 5.5$ $r = ?$ $n = 18$ $S_{18} = 66.30642497$

2. Sue Pertendant has been offered a seven-year contract totaling 2.7 million dollars. Her first-year salary is $200,000. Assume she is to get the same percentage raise each year. What is that percentage?

3. Consider the geometric series $5 + 10 + 20 + 40 + \ldots$.

   a. Create a table of the first seven partial sums, $S_1, S_2, S_3, \ldots, S_7$.

   b. Are the terms found in 3a also a geometric sequence?

   c. For what values of u_1 and/or r would the terms of a partial sum form a geometric sequence?

4. Find each sum for $u_n = \begin{cases} 40 & \text{if } n = 1 \\ 0.60u_{(n-1)} & \text{if } n > 1 \end{cases}$

   a. S_5 b. S_{15} c. S_{25}

5. $\dfrac{1}{1} + \dfrac{1}{2} + \dfrac{1}{3} + \dfrac{1}{4} + \ldots + \dfrac{1}{8} = \displaystyle\sum_{n=1}^{8} \dfrac{1}{n}$. (Notice that $1, 2, 3, \ldots, 8$ replace n in the

   expression $\dfrac{1}{n}$ to form the series.)

   a. Is this series arithmetic, geometric, or neither?

   b. Find the sum of this series.

6. a. List the terms of the series indicated by $\displaystyle\sum_{n=1}^{7} n^2$ and find the sum.

   b. List the terms of the series indicated by $\displaystyle\sum_{n=3}^{7} n^2$ and find the sum.

7. Remember the chess inventor and his wish?

    a. How many grains of wheat are on that 64th square?

    b. How many grains of wheat are there on the entire chessboard?

    c. Write the series using sigma (Σ) notation.

8. Suppose $u_n = \begin{cases} 8 & \text{if } n = 1 \\ 0.5 \cdot u_{(n-1)} & \text{if } n > 1 \end{cases}$

    a. Find $\displaystyle\sum_{n=1}^{10} u_n$.

    b. Find $\displaystyle\sum_{n=1}^{20} u_n$.   c. Find $\displaystyle\sum_{n=1}^{30} u_n$.

    d. Explain what is happening to these partial sums as you add more terms.

Section 2.5: In the Long Run

In preceding sections, you developed some useful explicit formulas for sequences and series. These formulas are expressed in more formal mathematical notation below.

The **explicit formula for the general term of an arithmetic sequence** is $u_n = u_0 + nd$, where d represents the common difference between the terms and $n = 1, 2, 3, \ldots$, or the explicit formula can also be given as $u_n = u_1 + (n - 1)d$.

The **sum of an arithmetic series** is given by the formula
$$S_n = \frac{n \cdot (u_1 + u_n)}{2}$$
where n is the number of terms, u_1 is the first term, and u_n is the last term.

The **explicit formula for the general term of a geometric sequence** is $u_n = u_0 \cdot r^n$, where r represents the common ratio between the terms and $n = 1, 2, 3, \ldots$, or the explicit formula can also be given as $u_n = u_1 \cdot r^{(n - 1)}$

The **sum of a geometric series** is given by the formula
$$S_n = \frac{u_1[1 - r^n]}{1 - r}$$
where u_1 is the first term, r is the common ratio ($r \neq 1$), and n is the number of terms.

These formulas work when you have a specific number of terms. But what happens "in the long run"? How can you find out what would happen if n, the number of terms, grew without bound?

Later in this chapter, you will consider the **Sierpiński Triangle**. This figure begins as an equilateral triangle with each segment one unit in length. The recursive procedure is to replace the triangle with three equal and smaller equilateral triangles such that each smaller triangle shares a vertex with the larger triangle. What do you expect the area to become in the long run? What is the long-run sum of the segments? Some sequences and series have a **limiting value**, and some do not.

In this section, you will find more long-run answers and make some initial classifications.

Counting Beans Activity

Begin this activity by assigning tasks in your group. There are four jobs that need to be done. They are bean counter, bean taker, bean giver, and recorder. Your group will be given some beans to be kept in the "bank."

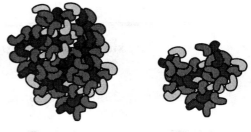

The Bank   **The Pile**

- On each turn, it is the task of the *bean taker* to take 20% of the bean counter's beans (rounded off to the nearest bean), and return them to the bank.

- It is the job of the *bean giver* to give the bean counter 10 beans from the bank, after the bean taker has taken the correct share.

- It is the job of the *bean counter* to keep careful count of all the beans not in the bank.

- It is the job of the *recorder* to record all transactions and inventories in a table.

a. Give the bean counter 10 beans from the bank to start with, and begin the activity. Repeat until the values stop changing, or it becomes obvious that they will never stop changing.

b. Now start over. This time, the bean counter should begin with 150 beans. Repeat the activity as before.

If the bean taker did not round off, what values do you think you would have had for these two runs? Does rounding-off affect the final outcome? How did you know that the value would not start changing again when you stopped the activity? The remainder of this activity can be done either with beans or with the calculator simulating the movements. Do not be concerned with whether or not you round off the numbers.

c. Begin again with 10 beans and repeat the activity, but this time the bean giver should give only 5 beans.

d. For the fourth run, start with 150 beans. The bean taker takes 20%, and the bean giver gives 5 beans.

e. Start again with 10 beans. The bean giver gives 10 beans, but the bean taker removes 25%.

Analyze your information, and try to summarize your findings in a way that allows you to predict what will happen with any start value, take percentage, and give value. Present this as a formula or a procedure in your activity conclusion.

Consider the ideal bouncing ball again. If the distances the ball falls can be represented by 200, 200(0.80) , 200(0.80)^2, 200(0.80)^3, and so on, then the distance it falls after the 10th bounce is 200(0.80)^{10}, or almost 11 inches. What about after the 25th bounce? How long before the molecules are just shrugging their shoulders? Mathematicians say the **limiting value** of this sequence is zero (as n gets larger), because the term values are getting closer and closer to zero.

What will be the impact on the total sum of all the distances? Do you agree that the total grows? Try bigger and bigger values of n in the formula

$$S_n = \frac{u_1[1 - r^n]}{1 - r} = \frac{200\,[1- (0.80)^n]}{1 - 0.80}$$

What limiting value does this sum seem to approach for larger and larger values of n? Can you make it larger than that value?

Problem Set 2.5

1. Consider the geometric sequence with $u_1 = 6$ and $r = 1$. What is the sum of the first 10 terms? The first n terms? An infinite number of terms?

2. a. Consider the infinite geometric sequence with $u_1 = 4$ and $r = 0.7$. What is the sum of the first 10 terms? The first 40 terms?

    b. Change r to 1.3 and answer the same questions.

    c. Change r to 1 and answer the same questions.

    d. Sketch a graph of each of the partial sums described in parts a–c.

    e. For what values of r does the sum appear to approach a limiting value?

3. Use the results of the activity to find the limiting value of the series in the White Pine Problem (Problem Set 1.3, Problem 5).

4. a. What is the sum of the first five terms of $\frac{1}{10} + \frac{1}{30} + \frac{1}{90} + \frac{1}{270} + \ldots$?

   b. The first ten terms?

   c. The first n terms, as n gets larger than the biggest number your math teacher can name?

   d. Give an argument why the limiting value for the partial sums of an infinite geometric series is $S = \frac{u_1}{1-r}$ when the value of r is between 1 and −1 (that is, when $|r| < 1$).

5. A math conference descends upon a city, and the teachers spend $1,000,000 "on the town." The money is received by the "townies," and they spend 90% of it in their city. Suppose 90% of that amount is again spent in the city, and so on. Show that the total impact is ten times as great as the original amount.

6. A flea jumps $\frac{1}{2}$ ft, then $\frac{1}{4}$ ft, then $\frac{1}{8}$ ft, and so on . Its first jump was to the right, its second jump left from that point, then right, and so on.

   a. Which way and how far is its seventh jump?

   b. Which way and how far is its eighteenth jump?

   c. What point is the flea zooming in on?

0   1/4   1/2

7. Two trains are 60 mi apart and heading toward each other on the same track. Each train is traveling at 30 mi/hr. A bee buzzes back and forth between them at 50 mi/hr until it is squished by the two trains. How far did the bee travel?

60 mi

8. Prudence and Charity are identical 20-yr-old twins with identical jobs and identical salaries, and they receive identical bonuses of $2000 yearly.

Prudence is immediately concerned with saving. She invests her $2000 bonus each year at 9% interest compounded annually. At age 30, she decides it is time to see the world, and spends her annual bonus on a trip from that point on.

Charity is immediately concerned with saving the world. She gives her $2000 bonus to charitable causes every year until she reaches 30. On her 30th birthday, her friends start telling her stories about what happens to people who haven't saved any money for their retirement. She gets so worried about what will happen when she retires that she starts saving her bonus money at 9% compounded annually.

How much will they each have when they are 30 yr old? Compare the value of each investment account when Prudence and Charity are 65 yr old.

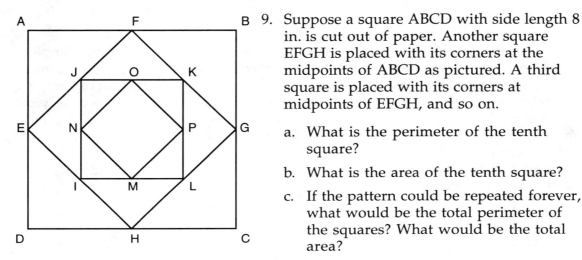

9. Suppose a square ABCD with side length 8 in. is cut out of paper. Another square EFGH is placed with its corners at the midpoints of ABCD as pictured. A third square is placed with its corners at midpoints of EFGH, and so on.

a. What is the perimeter of the tenth square?

b. What is the area of the tenth square?

c. If the pattern could be repeated forever, what would be the total perimeter of the squares? What would be the total area?

10. a. List the terms of: $\displaystyle\sum_{n=1}^{12} 96(0.25)^{n-1}$

b. Find the sum of: $\displaystyle\sum_{n=1}^{12} 96(0.25)^{n-1}$

c. Find the sum of: $\displaystyle\sum_{n=1}^{\infty} 96(0.25)^{n-1}$. This sum has an infinite number of terms.

d. Draw a sketch of the graph of partial sums for $n \geq 1$ in 10b.

Section 2.6: Fractal Patterns

A major highway map of the United States is a fairly complex drawing. If you concentrate your view on only one of the states pictured on this map, the drawing seems less complex. A part of the map showing a rural county of that state would be simpler yet. This phenomenon is typical of most of the graphs you will investigate this year. That is, if you look at some small portion of the total graph, it looks much simpler and probably does not look much like a larger view of the graph.

However, the graphs you will investigate in this section do not become simpler as you move or zoom in. These graphs are called **fractals**. When you take a very close look at some small area of a fractal graph, you find that it is just as complex as the greater view, and that there is a marked similarity between this close view and the total view. In the problems, you will explore some very interesting and mysterious patterns. Each figure in this section is generated by applying a recursive transformation to a given figure. Like sequences, some of these patterns will grow larger and larger forever, and some of them will shrink at each step of the recursion.

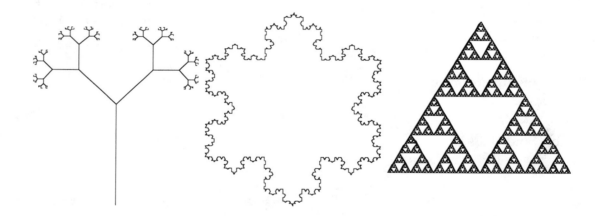

Preliminary Edition

Problem Set 2.6

1. **GeomeTree:** This figure begins as a vertical segment one unit in length. The recursive procedure is to take each segment and create two new segments that are each half as long, and rotated 135° clockwise and counterclockwise, respectively, from the end of the figure. Copy the table below into your homework, and fill in each missing value. It may be helpful to draw each figure accurately, and to measure carefully to verify your results.

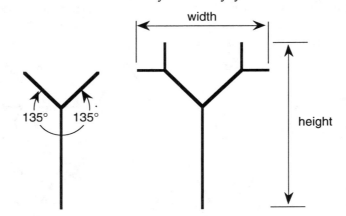

   a. The length of each of the last two segments drawn at each stage.

   b. The total length of each path, beginning at the base of the tree and proceeding to the end of a branch.

   c. The total number of segments that make up the tree.

   d. The sum of the lengths of all segments in the tree.

   e. The height of the tree from the base to the topmost branch. (Hint: The formula for n may have two forms, depending on whether n is even or odd.)

   f. The width of the tree at its widest point. (See the diagram above.)

	1	2	3	4 . . .	n	∞
a. Length of the last segment	1					
b. Length of the path	1					
c. Total number of segments	1					
d. Sum of the lengths of all segments	1					
e. Height of the tree	1				■	
f. Width of the tree	0				■	

2. **Koch Snowflake:** Helge von Koch (1870–1924) was a Swedish mathematician. His principal research involved problems of infinitely many linear equations in infinitely many unknowns. (You will learn about linear equations with finitely many unknowns in Chapter 9.) He invented the Koch curve at the University of Stockholm in 1904. This figure begins as an equilateral triangle, with each segment one unit in length. The recursive procedure is to trisect each segment and replace the middle segment with two sides of an equilateral triangle. Copy the table below into your homework, and fill in each missing value. It may be helpful to draw each figure accurately, and to measure carefully to verify your results.

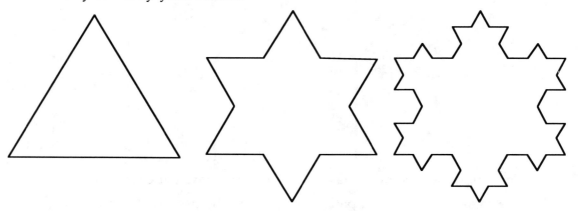

a. The length of each segment.

b. The total number of segments.

c. The perimeter, or sum of the lengths of all segments in the snowflake.

d. The area enclosed by the snowflake.

	1	2	3	4 . . .	n	∞
a. Length of each segment	1					
b. Total number of segments	3					
c. Perimeter	3					
d. Area	0.43301					

3. **Sierpiński Triangle:** This figure begins as an equilateral triangle, with each segment one unit in length. The recursive procedure is to replace the triangle with three equal and smaller equilateral triangles such that each smaller triangle shares a vertex with the larger triangle. Copy the table below into your homework, draw each figure, and carefully measure.

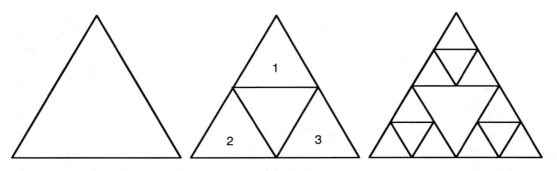

a. The length of each side of the triangle drawn at any recursion.

b. The number of new triangles drawn at each stage.

c. The perimeter of each new triangle.

d. The area of each new triangle.

e. The total perimeter of all new triangles.

f. The total area of all triangles.

		1	2	3	4 . . .	n	. . . ∞
a.	Length of each side	1					
b.	Number of triangles	1	3				
c.	Perimeter of each Δ	3					
d.	Area of each Δ	$\frac{\sqrt{3}}{4}$					
e.	Sum of perimeters	3					
f.	Sum of areas	$\frac{\sqrt{3}}{4}$					

4. Create your own recursively defined pattern. Choose a simple polygon. Define some type of procedure to copy the figure (or the sides of the figure) to new locations, new lengths, or new orientations. Construct several stages. It may be very difficult to create a figure that does not grow incredibly large very quickly, or shrink out of existence too fast. Give it your best effort. Keep it simple. Identify at least two sequences formed by your pattern, such as length and area.

Section 2.7: Chapter Review

Problem Set 2.7

In these problems, unless you are asked to do otherwise, use explicit formulas.

1. a. Mark Ett must arrange a display of soup cans as in the picture. List the number of cans in the top row, second row, third row, and so on to the tenth row.

   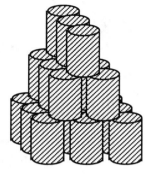

   b. Write a recursive formula for the terms of the sequence from 1a.

   c. Write an explicit formula for the terms of the sequence from 1a.

   d. How many cans will it take to make a display that is 47 layers high?

   e. If he must use 6 cases (288 cans), how many layers will be in the display?

2. Answer each question based on the arithmetic sequence 3, 7, 11, 15, ...

   a. What is the 128th term?

   b. Which term has the value 159?

   c. Find u_{20}.

   d. Find S_{20}.

3. Given plenty of food and space, the biological specimen *Grossus Buggus* will reproduce geometrically, with each pair hatching 24 young every 5 days. Initially, there are 12 bugs.

   a. How many are born in 5 days? In 10 days? In 15 days? In 35 days?

   b. Write a recursive formula for the terms of the sequence from 3a.

   c. Write an explicit formula for the terms of the sequence from 3a.

   d. Find the *total* number of bugs after 60 days.

4. Consider the geometric sequence 256, 192, 144, 108, ...

   a. What is the 8th term?

   b. What is the term number of the first term smaller then 20?

   c. Find u_7.

   d. Find S_7.

   e. What happens to S_n as n gets very large?

5. a. If you invest $500 in a bank that pays 5.5% annual interest compounded quarterly, how much money will you have after 5 yr?

    b. Start over and invest $500 at 5.5% annual interest compounded quarterly, and deposit an additional $50 every month. What will the balance be after 5 yr?

6. A university enrollment is currently 5678. From now on, they will graduate 24% of their students yearly, and add 1250 new students.

    a. What will be the university enrollment after 5 yr?

    b. What will be the enrollment in the long run?

7. A super duper ball will rebound to 95% of the height from which it is dropped.

    a. If it is originally dropped from a height of 200 cm, how high will it bounce on the 7th bounce?

    b. Considering only the downward trips made by the ball, what will be the total distance traveled in 7 falls?

    c. What will be the total falling distance traveled in the long run?

8. Birdie Parr's golf ball is lying 12 ft away from the 18th hole on the golf course. She putts and unfortunately, the ball rolls to the other side of the hole, two-thirds as far away as it was. On her next putt, the same thing happens. If this pattern continues, how far will her ball travel in 7 strokes? How far will it travel in the long run?

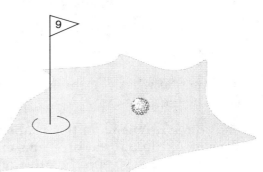

9. What monthly payment will be required to pay off an $80,000 mortgage at 8.9% interest in 30 yr?

10. Georg Cantor (1845–1918) was born in St. Petersburg, Russia, to parents who had migrated from Denmark. When Cantor was eleven, he and his family moved to Germany, where Cantor spent most of his life. His mathematical work led him to establish a new mathematical discipline, the field of set theory. One of his contributions is a set of numbers called the Cantor Set. To generate this set, consider a line segment between 0 and 1, inclusive. Call this line segment C_1.

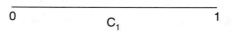

0   1
                         C_1

Remove the middle third of the line segment (and the numbers) to get C_2.

0   1/3   2/3   1
                C_2

Remove the middle third of each line segment in C_2 to get C_3.

0   ?   ? 1/3   2/3 ?   ? 1
                C_3

a. Name the sequence of numbers that represents the sum of the segment lengths for $C_1, C_2, C_3, \ldots$.

b. What is the long-run sum of these segment lengths?

11. a. Use your calculator to find the sequence of partial sums $S_{10}, S_{20}, S_{30}, \ldots, S_{90}$ for the sequence $u_n = \dfrac{1}{n}$.

b. Describe what you think is happening to this sequence of partial sums over the long run.

12. Find three problems in this chapter that you feel are representative of the chapter. Write out the problems and the solutions. For each problem, explain why you feel it is representative of the chapter.

Section 2.8: Projects

Project 2.1: Sierpiṅsky Carpet

To create a Sierpiṅsky carpet, you begin with a square. A 27-by-27 square grid on graph paper works well. Divide the whole into nine equal-sized squares, and remove the center square. (See the middle diagram.) Divide each of the remaining eight squares into nine parts and remove their centers. There are several patterns involved if you continue this process. Find mathematical expressions that generate these patterns of numbers. Be sure to look at the remaining carpet area, the perimeter, and the area removed at each stage. You can even look for other patterns that emerge. Make predictions about what will happen to these patterns after n stages, and in the long run. Your project should include a drawing of the next stage of this carpet, an explanation of all mathematical expressions you find, and a prediction of what the final carpet would look like if the process continued forever.

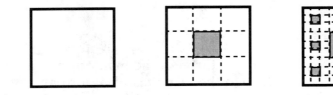

Project 2.2: AIDS Epidemic

You have seen many applications involving geometric or exponential growth. Actually, many types of growth that appear geometric cannot continue forever, because they run out of room, or people, or resources. As you get close to this limit, things change and the percent increase begins to decline.

The data given here is the number of new cases of AIDS diagnosed each year since 1980. Use x-values of 0 through 13 as you put this data into your calculator. Find a window that includes all the points. Sketch this graph on your graph paper. Try using an arithmetic or geometric sequence to fit the data as best you can. Experiment with different starting values and rates until the graph contains at least one point near the beginning and one point near the end. Make separate graphs with each of these two sequences. (Use the same window as your first sketch.) If you connect the points of the sequence and the points of the data, you should find that neither of these two models really fit the data very well.

Year	Cases
1980	114
1981	352
1982	1,254
1983	3,670
1984	7,534
1985	14,701
1986	27,444
1987	53,226
1988	78,266
1989	107,728
1990	131,734
1991	163,502
1992	175,279
1993	194,668

The particular model described in the first paragraph is called a logistics model. A recursive form of this sequence looks like this:

$$u_n = u_{(n-1)}\left(1 + P\frac{(L - u_{(n-1)})}{L}\right)$$

You can see that this is like a geometric sequence, $u_n = u_{(n-1)}(1 + P)$, showing P percent growth. In the logistic sequence, this percent is multiplied by a factor that changes with the values of the sequence. Now you need to experiment with starting values, P, and L to match this sequence to the data. This will not be easy, so be organized and patient. If you are, you will eventually be successful. Make a sketch of your answer. Finally, try to find meanings for the values of P and L that relate to the data and the situation. What are the long-run implications of your model? What will happen 2 yr, 5 yr, and 10 yr into the future? Unfortunately, there is no way to follow up on this data, because by 1994 the medical community had gained a much better understanding of the disease and consequently redefined what it means to have AIDS. Therefore, the numbers from 1994 on do not include the same group of people.

Project 2.3: Instant Money

Recently, an ad came through the mail offering a low-payment loan. The ad claimed the loan was ideal for paying off high-interest-rate credit card debts, or for consolidating all debts. The promoters claimed to offer low monthly payments, which are always 2% of the loan balance. With even a mediocre credit history, an interested individual could borrow up to $5,000 instantly. The first monthly payment would only be $100, and the dollar amount of each payment after that would decrease, as long as you didn't borrow more money. The loan had no initial fees (another "plus"), and charged an annual percentage interest rate of 21.9% compounded monthly. Analyze the proposal mathematically and offer your own conclusions about whether or not this is a good offer. Be very detailed in your analysis (as if you were writing to someone who is not very knowledgeable about loans and interest).

Project 2.4: Living in the City

In a recent article, Sonya Ross of the Associated Press stated, "The world's big cities are growing by a million people a week and will hold more than half the Earth's population within a decade. . . . Urban populations are growing by 3.8 percent a year, and it is projected that

by 2020, 3.6 billion people will inhabit urban areas while about 3 billion will remain in rural areas. . . . In 1990, there were 1.4 billion people living in the world's urban areas." There are several statements here about the population of large cities. Some of them contradict each other, and some just don't work out. Write a response to these statements showing the formulas you used and the conclusions that you reached based on the facts and predictions here. Try viewing the information from different perspectives. Use two or three "facts" from the article to set up equations and find the other information.

Chapter Three

INTRODUCTION TO STATISTICS

Contents

Section 3.1: Box Plots and Measures of Center 92

Different ways to compare data

Section 3.2: Measures of Variability 102

Getting a sense of spread

Section 3.3: Histograms and Percentiles 109

Numbers into pictures

Section 3.4: Chapter Review 120

Assessing yourself

Section 3.5: Projects 123

Taking it one step further

Section 3.1: Box Plots and Measures of Center

Gottfried Achenwall, a professor at the universities of Gottingen and Marbough, invented the word *statistics* ("state arithmetic") in 1749. What he meant by "state arithmetic" was counting and calculating activities, such as census-taking, which governments find useful. John Sinclair was the first English writer to use the term. He had just completed a survey of Scotland in 1791. In the preface, he wrote that while statistics in Germany were concerned with political strength, he was more interested in

> . . . the quantum of happiness enjoyed by the inhabitants and the means of its improvement; yet as I thought a new word (statistics) might attract more public attention, I resolved to adopt it.

Today, newspapers, magazines, the evening news, commercials, government bulletins, almanacs, and sports publications bombard you daily with data and statistics. If you are to be an informed citizen who makes intelligent decisions, you will need to be able to interpret this information. Studying statistics will help you learn how to collect, organize, analyze, and interpret data. In this chapter, you will learn how to make several kinds of graphs that picture data. In addition, you will study some numerical measures of data, which also help you to better understand what the numbers are telling you.

The following table lists twenty toothpaste brands. They are ranked according to a 100-point scale based on their ability to clean stained teeth. A score of 100 indicates perfectly clean unstained teeth. The cost per month is an estimate based on brushing twice a day with one-half inch of toothpaste.

Product	Size in oz	Price	$ per month	Cleaning
Ultra brite Original	6.0	1.56	0.58	86
Gleem	7.0	2.23	0.66	79
Caffree Regular	5.9	2.96	1.02	77
Crest Tartar Control Mint Gel	6.4	1.99	0.53	75
Colgate Tartar Control Gel	6.4	2.04	0.57	74
Crest Tartar Control Original	6.4	2.00	0.53	72
Ultra brite Gel Cool Mint	6.0	1.53	0.52	72
Colgate Clear Blue Gel	6.4	2.06	0.71	71
Crest Cool Mint Gel	6.4	1.99	0.55	70
Crest Regular	6.4	2.01	0.59	69
Crest Sparkle	6.4	2.03	0.51	64
Close-Up Tartar Control Gel	6.4	1.94	0.67	63
Close-up Anti-Plaque	6.4	1.97	0.62	62
Colgate Tartar Control Paste	6.4	2.04	0.66	62
Tom's of Maine Cinnamint	6.0	3.29	1.07	62
Aquafresh Tartar Control	6.0	1.97	0.80	60
Aim Anti-Tartar Gel	6.4	2.24	0.79	58
Aim Extra-Strength Gel	6.4	1.70	0.44	57
Slimer Gel	3.0	1.79	1.04	57
A & H Baking Soda Mint	6.3	3.26	1.12	55

Source: September, 1992 Consumer Reports.

First, you might want to see if your favorite toothpaste is listed, and how it compares with others. Most people seek out useful information when they are changing products, making a purchase, or trying to influence the decisions of others. Sometimes it's easy to find information about a particular product, but patterns, relationships, tendencies, and general observations are frequently hidden in a large table of numbers like this one.

This set of data clearly does not include every type and brand of toothpaste. You have to be careful when drawing conclusions from a set of data. Summaries of data like this may not tell much about toothpaste in general. In order to draw general conclusions from a set of data, you must have data that represent a random sample. The following activity will help you understand something about random sampling.

Random Samples Activity

You will need a standard deck of playing cards, with the aces removed. For this activity, Jacks, Queens, and Kings are each valued at ten, and other cards are valued according to their number. First show mathematically that the average value of all the cards is seven. Now shuffle the deck well and select ten cards at random. Find the average of these ten cards. Return the cards to the deck and repeat five more times the process of finding the average of ten cards. What is the average of the ten lowest value cards? What is the average of the ten highest? How does the average value of all the cards compare to the average of your random samples? In a sentence or two, make a statement about the average value of a random sample, based on this activity.

If you assume the table of toothpaste data is from a random sample of *all* toothpaste brands, then you can make some statements about all brands with some degree of accuracy. What is the typical toothpaste tube size? Is there a single number that can serve as the representative tube size for the population? The size that occurs most frequently, the **mode**, is 6.4 oz. Karl Pearson was the first to use the term "mode." In 1895 he wrote, "I have found it convenient to use the term *mode* for the abscissa corresponding to the ordinate of maximum frequency." The **median** is another single number that can be used to represent an average value. Francis Galton used the concept of the median as early as 1869, but he didn't start using the term "median" until 1883. Gustav Fechner called this measure *der Centralworth* and gave a complete treatment of its properties and computation in 1874.

> The **median** is the middle number in a set that is listed in order (ascending or descending). If the set has an even number of elements, then the *median* is the average of the two middle values.

Because there are 20 values, the median tube size is the average of the 10th and 11th values, $\frac{6.4 + 6.4}{2} = 6.4$. See **APPENDIX 3A** for help with entering the data into the calculator, and **APPENDIX 3B** for help with finding the median.

$$3.0, 5.9, 6.0, 6.0, 6.0, 6.0, 6.3, 6.4, 6.4, \boxed{6.4, 6.4}, 6.4, 6.4, 6.4, 6.4, 6.4, 6.4, 6.4, 6.4, 7.0$$

If you consider the cost per month, you will find two modes at \$0.53 and \$0.66 (each occurs twice), and a median cost per month of \$0.64. Remember to arrange the data in order (either ascending, or descending) to find the median.

The **box and whisker plot** (or box plot) provides a visual tool for analyzing information about a set of data. It was first introduced by John Tukey in his 1977 book *Exploratory Data Analysis*. This plot gives you a good idea of how the data are distributed or spread, and how symmetric the distribution is. The lines emanating from the **box** are called **whiskers**. Five summary values are needed to construct a box plot.

The whisker endpoints at A and E identify the smallest and largest values of the data. The median, point C, of the data is at the vertical line within the box. The left edge of the box, B, is the median of all the values below C; and D, the right edge of the box, is the median of the values above C. The value B marks the **first** or **lower quartile**, the value C marks the **middle** or **second quartile**, and the value D marks the **upper** or **third quartile**. Explain why 50% of the data is contained in the box See **APPENDIX 3C** to learn how to create a box plot on your calculator.

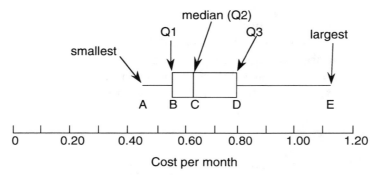

Example 1:

a. What percent of the toothpaste data is represented by the lower whisker?

b. What are the values for the first, second, and third quartiles?

c. What are the five summary values for this data?

Solution:

a. One-quarter, or 25% of the data is represented by the lower whisker. As a matter of fact, one-quarter of the data is represented by the upper whisker, one-quarter is represented by the upper part of the box, and one-quarter is represented by the lower part of the box.

b. The first quartile is the average of the 5th and 6th values, or $0.54, the median is the average of the 10th and 11th values, or $0.64, and the third quartile is the average of the 15th and 16th values, or $0.795.

c. The five summary values {minimum, 1st quartile, median, 3rd quartile, maximum} are {0.44, 0.54, 0.64, 0.795, 1.12}.

A balance point, called the **mean**, is another single number used to represent the typical data value in a set of data. **APPENDIX 3B** explains how you can find the mean using your calculator.

> The **mean**, represented by the symbol $\bar{x}$, is the ratio
>
> $$\frac{\text{sum of the data values}}{\text{number of values}}$$

Frequently the symbol Σ, (sigma), is used to indicate a sum. Σ means to sum the individual values. So

$$\frac{\sum_{i=1}^{n} x_i}{n}$$

would represent the mean, where n is the number of values, and $x_1, x_2, x_3, \ldots, x_i, \ldots, x_n$ are the individual data values. Of the three measures of central tendency (mean, median, mode), the mean is the most sensitive to individual values, because every value in the list is used to compute it. You will investigate the effect of individual values on the mean in the problems.

Pulse Rates Activity

Each member of the class needs to measure and record their resting pulse rate for one minute. Then exercise for two minutes by doing jumping jacks or running in place. Afterwards, measure and record your pulse rate again. Collect the data from  each student and prepare a box plot picturing the resting pulse rate measurements, and a box plot of the pulse rates after exercising. Analyze, interpret, and compare the graphs, measures of central tendency, and measures of spread. Write a few sentences that summarize your results.

Problem Set 3.1

1. Fay Cilitator uses a variety of methods to assess her students. The lists below represent scores for various assignments that she has recorded for two of her students during a semester.

   Connie Sistant 82, 86, 82, 84, 85, 84, 85
   Ozzie Laiting 72, 94, 76, 96, 90, 76, 84

Find the median and mean for each set of scores, and explain why they do not tell the whole story about the differences between Connie and Ozzie's scores.

2. The two box plots below represent Connie's and Ozzie's scores.

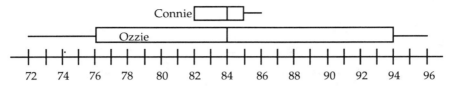

Write a paragraph describing the information pictured in the box plots. Use the plots to help you to draw some statistical conclusions. Include in your description answers to questions like: What does it mean that the second box plot is longer? Where is the left whisker of the top box plot? What does it mean when the median isn't in the middle of the box? What does it mean that the left whisker is longer for Ozzie's scores than the right whisker?

3. a. Homer Unn has played in the minor leagues for eleven years. His home run totals, in order, for each of those years are: 56, 62, 49, 65, 58, 52, 68, 72, 25, 51, and 64. Construct a box plot showing this data.

    b. List the five summary values.

    c. Find $\dfrac{\sum\limits_{i=1}^{n} x_i}{n}$.

    d. How many home runs would he need to hit next season to have a twelve-year mean of 60?

4. The difference between the lower and upper quartiles (the length of the box) is called the **interquartile range**. Sometimes there are one or more data points that are extremely different from the others. If the distance of a data point from the box is more than 1.5 times the length of the box, that point is called an **outlier**. This definition is somewhat arbitrary, and other texts may use a slightly different definition. But the basic idea is that an outlier is a value that lies far away from the majority of the values.

    a. Look at the box plots shown in Problem 2. Do there appear to be any outliers? What high and low scores would be outliers for Connie? For Ozzie?

    b. Show that there is only one outlier (using our definition) with Homer's home run data in Problem 3.

5. Refer to the toothpaste data listed at the beginning of this section.

  a. Compute the mean toothpaste cost per month.

  b. Draw the graph below on your own paper. Draw a vertical line at the mean cost per month.

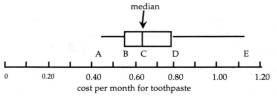

  c. Compare the mean and median values for the data. Which is larger? Explain why it is larger.

6. It is estimated that a person spends between 25% and 35% of his income for shelter. This can be in the form of rent or a mortgage payment. In Chapters One and Two, when learning about sequences, you explored how to compute mortgage payments. Although interest rates are usually fairly uniform throughout the United States, the price of a home varies considerably. The data in the list below gives the median price of a home in various metropolitan areas in the United States.

City	Median home price	City	Median home price
Atlanta, GA	93,200	Milwaukee, WI	106,500
Baltimore, MD	115,700	Minneapolis-St.Paul, MN	100,000
Boston, MA	170,600	New York City, NY	170,300
Chicago, IL	135,500	Philadelphia, PA	116,800
Cincinnati, OH	93,600	Phoenix, AZ	89,200
Cleveland, OH	94,200	Pittsburgh, PA	80,000
Dallas, TX	95,100	St. Louis, MO	83,100
Denver, CO	111,200	San Diego, CA	177,800
Detroit, MI	84,500	San Francisco Bay Area, CA	246,900
Houston, TX	84,800	Seattle-Tacoma, WA	152,900
Kansas City, MO, KS	84,900	Tampa-St. Petersburg, FL	74,300
Los Angeles, CA	188,500	Washington, D.C.	154,900
Miami-Hialeah, FL	105,000		

  a. Make a box plot and list the summary values for all the data. Are there any outliers? Explain why or why not.

  b. Make another box plot after eliminating all of the median home prices greater than 135,000. List the summary values.

  c. Divide the data into two lists and construct a box plot for each list. You decide what criteria to use for dividing the list. You could choose metropolitan areas east of the Mississippi and areas west of the Mississippi. Another possibility might be metropolitan areas in coastal states and those not in coastal states. Describe any similarities and/or differences you observe.

7. While it is difficult to actually count the number of homeless people in the United States, the federal government, as well as independent agencies, have made attempts to do so. The estimates range from 50,000 to a million or more. One night during the 1990 census, census workers did attempt to count as many homeless people as they could, by visiting shelters and street sites. On that night, a total of 228,621 homeless persons were counted. The list below contains estimates of the total number of homeless persons in selected cities in 1990. The second column indicates how many persons out of the total number sleep in official shelters.

City	Total number of homeless people	Number in shelters
New York	33,830	23,383
Los Angeles	7,706	4,597
Chicago	6,764	5,180
San Francisco	5,569	4,003
San Diego	4,947	2,846
Washington, D.C.	4,813	4,682
Philadelphia	4,485	3,416
Newark	2,816	1,974
Seattle	2,539	2,170
Atlanta	2,491	2,431
Boston	2,463	2,245
Houston	1,931	1,780
Phoenix	1,786	1,710
Portland	1,702	1,553
Sacramento	1,552	1,287
Baltimore	1,531	1,144
Dallas	1,493	1,200
Denver	1,269	1,169
Oklahoma City	1,250	1,016
Minneapolis	1,080	1,052

a. What is the mean number of homeless persons in these cities? What is the median number? Which cities, if any, are outliers?

b. Omit the number of homeless persons in New York City and recompute the mean and the median. Was the mean or the median affected more by this one extreme score?

c. Give an argument for using the median score when discussing the average number of homeless persons in major cities. Give an argument for using the mean score.

d. How would the mean and median values be affected if 1000 more were added to each number in the list?

e. Calculate the percentage of homeless people in each of these cities who stay in shelters. Make a box plot of these percentages. Write a paragraph describing the results. Be sure to include a discussion of the median and mean in your description.

8. a. Invent a data set with seven values and a mean of 12. (This is more interesting if the values aren't all 12.)

   b. Invent a data set with seven values, a mode of 70 and a median of 65.

   c. Invent a data set with seven values that will create this box plot.

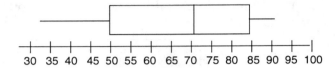

9. It is said that there are three things that you can always count on in life—you are born, you die, and you pay taxes. The table below shows the average amount of taxes paid by each person in the countries listed. These numbers include national, local, and social security taxes.

Country	Per capita taxes		Country	Per capita taxes
Australia	5,050		Luxembourg	11,976
Austria	8,830		Netherlands	9,064
Belgium	8,985		New Zealand	4,481
Canada	8,190		Norway	11,701
Denmark	12,219		Portugal	2,487
Finland	9,366		Spain	4,693
France	9,255		Sweden	14,628
Germany	8,279		Switzerland	10,489
Greece	2,635		Turkey	549
Ireland	4,623		United Kingdom	6,341
Italy	7,907		United States	6,550
Japan	8,419			

   a. Make a box plot of these tax amounts.

   b. Are there any outliers? If so, what are they? If not, what tax amounts would be outliers? What does it mean to be an outlier (as written from the perspective of an outlier)?

   c. What are the mode, median, and mean tax amounts?

   d. In what quartile is the United States?

10. a. Find the median and mean toothpaste price, and the median and mean cleaning rank, for the products listed at the beginning of this section.

    b. Create two box plots: one representing the toothpaste prices, and another representing the cleaning ranks.

    c. Based on the information in the table, write a brief review or analysis of these toothpaste products. Use the vocabulary developed in this section in your review.

Section 3.2: Measures of Variability

If you ask two or more people to describe their recollections of events or places, their descriptions will usually differ. People vary in their interests, their habits, and in the way they perceive things. When two people independently measure the same object, their measurements will probably vary. In this section, you will investigate different ways to measure and describe variability.

A Typical Student Activity

Choose three body measurements, such as height, length of an ear, and wrist circumference. Each group should choose a different set of measurements. Collect this data from each member of your class. Determine the median and mean values of each measurement. Use the results from all of the groups to write a description of the "mean student" and the "median student" in your class. Do you think there is any one person that fits either description? Why or why not? Which do you think is a better description of a "typical or average" student in your class? Is your class representative of every class in your school? Carefully explain your procedures and conclusions.

A box plot is a visual display of the way data vary. There are also ways to obtain numerical measures of data that indicate inconsistency, variation, or spread within data. One way to do this is to find the **deviation**, or directed distance from each data value to the mean.

Example 1: Connie and Ozzie volunteered for an experiment in biology class. Every other Wednesday for fourteen weeks, they had their cholesterol level checked. Find the difference (deviation) between each data point and the mean of the data, for both Connie and Ozzie.

Connie Sistant 182, 186, 182, 184, 185, 184, 185

Ozzie Laiting 152, 194, 166, 216, 200, 176, 184

Solution: The mean for each student is 184. The individual deviations, $x_i - \bar{x}$, for each data value x_i, are in the table below.

Connie	Level	Deviation	Ozzie	Level	Deviation
x_1	182	$182 - 184 = {}^-2$	x_1	152	$152 - 184 = {}^-32$
x_2	186	$186 - 184 = 2$	x_2	194	$194 - 184 = 10$
x_3	182	$182 - 184 = {}^-2$	x_3	166	$166 - 184 = {}^-18$
x_4	184	$184 - 184 = 0$	x_4	216	$216 - 184 = 32$
x_5	185	$185 - 184 = 1$	x_5	200	$200 - 184 = 16$
x_6	184	$184 - 184 = 0$	x_6	176	$176 - 184 = {}^-8$
x_7	185	$185 - 184 = 1$	x_7	184	$184 - 184 = 0$

These deviations indicate more variation in Ozzie's levels than Connie's. Do you think the sum of Ozzie's deviations should be larger than the sum of Connie's? If you think of the mean as a balance point in a data set, what do you expect will happen when you sum the positive and negative deviations for either Connie or Ozzie?

$$\text{Connie's deviation sum} = {}^-2 + 2 + {}^-2 + 0 + 1 + 0 + 1 = 0$$

$$\text{Ozzie's deviation sum} = {}^-32 + 10 + {}^-18 + 32 + 16 + {}^-8 + 0 = 0$$

The deviation sum for both students is zero. Therefore, the average deviation in both lists is also equal to zero.

$$\frac{{}^-2 + 2 + {}^-2 + 0 + 1 + 0 + 1}{7} = 0 \text{ and } \frac{{}^-32 + 10 + {}^-18 + 32 + 16 + {}^-8 + 0}{7} = 0$$

Because the mean is a balance point in a list of values, the deviation sum, or average deviation, doesn't reflect the variation differences, or the spread in the two lists. Look at the table below. It suggests another possibility that provides a numerical approach to variability, or spread, in data.

Connie Sistant				**Ozzie Laiting**		
Level	Deviation	Absolute deviation		Level	Deviation	Absolute deviation
182	−2	2		152	−32	32
186	2	2		194	10	10
182	−2	2		166	−18	18
184	0	0		216	32	32
185	1	1		200	16	16
184	0	0		176	−8	8
185	1	1		184	0	0
Sum		8				116
Mean		1.14				16.57

Did you notice that, instead of summing the deviations, you can sum the absolute values of the deviations, and that the sum is no longer zero? The sum of the absolute values of the deviations, divided by the number of values, is called the average absolute deviation or **mean absolute deviation** (**MAD**), and it provides one way to judge the "average difference" between data values and the mean.

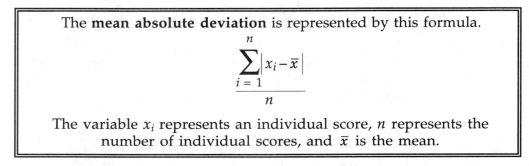

The **mean absolute deviation** is represented by this formula.

$$\frac{\sum_{i=1}^{n}\left|x_i - \bar{x}\right|}{n}$$

The variable x_i represents an individual score, n represents the number of individual scores, and $\bar{x}$ is the mean.

The larger mean absolute deviation for Ozzie indicates that his levels generally lie much further from the mean than do Connie's. A large value for the mean absolute deviation tells you that the data values are not as tightly packed around the mean. As a general rule, a distribution with more data near the mean will have less spread and a smaller mean absolute deviation.

Example 2: The following data represents the student-to-teacher ratio for elementary and secondary schools, listed by regions, of the continental United States:

Northeast		Midwest		South		West	
ME	13.9	MI	19.8	VA	15.7	WA	20.1
NH	16.2	WI	16.2	NC	16.9	OR	18.5
VT	13.2	MN	17.3	SC	16.8	CA	22.8
MA	15.4	OH	17.2	GA	18.3	NV	19.4
RI	15.4	IN	17.5	FL	17.2	ID	19.6
CN	13.6	IL	16.7	AL	19.9	UT	25.0
NY	14.6	IA	15.6	MS	17.9	AZ	19.4
PA	17.0	MO	15.5	TN	19.2	MT	15.9
NJ	15.6	KY	19.9	AR	16.8	WY	14.5
DE	13.6	ND	15.5	LA	18.6	CO	17.8
MD	16.8	SD	15.2	OK	15.6	NM	18.1
WV	16.5	NE	14.6	TX	15.4	KA	15.0

Calculate the mean and mean absolute deviation for each region. What does this tell you about the distribution of each set of ratios? Which region has the most consistent ratios?

Solution: The mean student-teacher ratios of the regions are 15.15, 16.75, 17.36, and 18.84, in the order listed above. The mean absolute deviation of the Northeast is 1.14, of the Midwest is 1.33, of the South is 1.18, and the mean absolute deviation of the West is 2.21 students per teacher. (See **APPENDIX 3D** to find out how to find the mean absolute deviation using your calculator.) There are many conjectures and questions that you can propose. The greater spread of the values in the West compared to those in the other three regions reflects a wider variety of student-teacher ratios in that region of the country.

Problem Set 3.2:

1. The average (mean) diameter measurement of a Purdy Goode Compact Disc is 12 cm, with a mean absolute deviation of 0.12 cm. No CDs can be shipped that are more than one mean absolute deviation from the mean. What does this imply from the perspective of the Quality Control Engineer?

2. Invent a data set of seven lengths with both mean and median of 84 cm, a range of 23 cm, and an interquartile range of 12 cm.

3. Without calculating, use the mean and mean absolute deviation to sketch what you think a graph of the four box plots for Example 2 would look like. Find the five summary values and draw the actual box plots on a graph.

4. The following information was collected during a math lab by a group of students. The mean measurement was 46.3 cm and the deviations of the eight individual measurements were 0.8 cm, −0.4 cm, 1.6 cm, 1.1 cm, −1.2 cm, −0.3 cm, −0.6 cm, and −1.0 cm.

   a. What were the actual eight measurements collected?

   b. Find the mean absolute deviation of the actual measurements.

   c. Which measurements were more than one mean absolute deviation from the mean?

5. The students in four classes recorded their pulse rates. The class averages and mean absolute deviations are given below. Each class has an equal number of students.

Class	Mean	Mean Absolute Deviation
1st period	79.4	3.2
3rd period	74.6	5.6
5th period	78.2	4.1
6th period	80.2	7.6

   a. Which class has students with pulse rates most alike? How can you tell?

b. Can you tell which class has the students with the fastest pulses? Why or why not?

c. Using the same scale, sketch your best estimate of a box plot for each class.

6. Each year there are many tornadoes in the United States. Even though a tornado may have wind speeds between 100 and 300 miles per hour, many of them do not do significant damage or endanger lives, because they don't touch ground in populated areas. However, when they do strike a populated area, they cause significant damage and often loss of life. The table below gives the number of tornadoes recorded, and the number of deaths that resulted, in various years from 1980 to 1992.

Year	Number of tornadoes	Number of fatalities
1980	866	28
1985	684	94
1986	764	15
1987	656	59
1988	702	35
1989	856	49
1990	1,133	53
1991	1,132	39
1992	1,303	396

a. What is the mean number of deaths for this data? Describe how to find it without using the special calculator key that automatically calculates the mean.

b. What is the mean absolute deviation for this data? Describe how to find it.

c. Draw the figure at the right and label the mean. Point A and point B indicate distances of one mean absolute deviation from the mean; point C and point D indicate distances of two mean absolute deviations from the mean. Find the numerical value for each of the points A, B, C, and D.

d. Identify each year in which the death total fell within one mean absolute deviation of the mean.

e. Identify each year that the death total was at least two mean absolute deviations away from the mean.

7. Use the data in Problem 6 to answer these questions.

a. What is the mean number of tornadoes per year, according to this data?

b. What is the mean absolute deviation for this data?

c. Draw the figure at right and label the mean. Point A and point B indicate distances of one mean absolute deviation from the mean; point C and point D indicate distances of two mean absolute deviations from the mean. Find the numerical value for each of the points A, B, C, and D.

  d. Were there any years in which the number of tornadoes was at least two mean absolute deviations away from the mean? If so, identify them.

  e. Why do you think the number of tornadoes seemed to increase in 1990? Was it because of a dramatic change in weather patterns, or is there another explanation?

8. The normal monthly temperatures for Juneau, Alaska and New York, New York are given below.

Month	Juneau	New York
January	22	32
February	28	33
March	31	41
April	39	53
May	46	62
June	53	71
July	56	77
August	55	75
September	49	68
October	42	58
November	33	47
December	27	36

Draw a box plot for each city and find each mean absolute deviation. Which city has more consistent temperatures? Justify your conclusion.

9. Members of the school math club sold packages of hot chocolate mix to raise funds for their club activities. The numbers of packages sold by individual members are given below.

65	76	100	67	44
147	82	94	92	79
158	77	62	85	71
69	88	80	63	75
62	68	71	73	74

  a. Find the median and interquartile range for this set of numbers.

  b. Find the mean and mean absolute deviation for the individual sales numbers.

  c. Draw a box plot for this set. Name any numbers that are outliers.

  d. Draw another box plot, for the set of numbers without the outliers.

  e. With the outliers removed, recalculate (i) the mean and mean absolute deviation, and (ii) the median and interquartile range.

f. Which is more affected by outliers, the mean or the median? The mean absolute deviation or the interquartile range? Explain why you think this is so.

Section 3.3: Histograms and Percentiles

A box plot gives you a good picture of the data distribution, but in some cases you might want to see other information and details that a box plot doesn't show. The term histogram was introduced by Karl Pearson in an 1895 lecture, in which he described it as, "a common form of graphical representation, that is, by columns marking as areas the frequency corresponding to the range of their base." Histograms give vivid pictures of distribution features, clusters of values, or gaps in data. They are especially useful for displaying large amounts of data.

City	1980 Population	1990 Population	+%	City	1980 Population	1990 Population	+%
Mesa, AZ	152,404	288,091	89.0	Glendale, AZ	97,172	148,134	52.4
Cucamonga, CA	55,250	101,409	83.5	Mesquite, TX	67,053	101,484	51.3
Plano, TX	72,331	128,713	77.9	Ontario, CA	88,820	133,179	49.9
Irvine, CA	62,134	110,330	77.6	Virginia Beach, VA	262,199	393,069	49.9
Escondido, CA	64,355	108,635	68.8	Scottsdale, AZ	88,622	130,069	46.8
Oceanside, CA	76,698	128,398	67.4	Santa Ana, CA	204,023	293,742	44.0
Bakersfield, CA	105,611	174,820	65.5	Stockton, CA	148,283	210,943	42.3
Arlington, TX	160,113	261,721	63.5	Pomona, CA	92,742	131,723	42.0
Fresno, CA	217,491	354,202	62.9	Irving, TX	109,943	155,037	41.0
Chula Vista, CA	83,927	135,163	61.0	Aurora, CO	158,588	222,103	40.1
Las Vegas, NV	164,674	258,295	56.9	Raleigh, N.C.	150,255	207,951	38.4
Modesto, CA	106,963	164,730	54.0	San Bernardino, CA	118,794	164,164	38.2
Tallahassee, FL	81,548	124,773	53.0				

Source: The Universal Almanac 1994, page 188

This histogram pictures the 25 fastest-growing major cities in the United States between 1980 and 1990. Growth rates for these cities range from 38.2% for San Bernardino, CA to 89% for Mesa, AZ. The width of each bar is 5%. The gap between 70% and 75% means no major United States city grew at a rate between 70% and 75%. How can you know the graph accounts for all 25 cities?

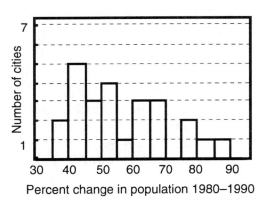

Percent change in population 1980–1990

The individual bar width is arbitrary. However, each bar should have the same width in any particular histogram. You can see that a histogram with bar widths of 10% presents a different look than one with bar widths of 5%. Notice the columns are taller in this graph because each category is made up of two categories from the previous graph. Use the information in the table above to create the same graphs on your calculator. (See **APPENDIX 3E.**)

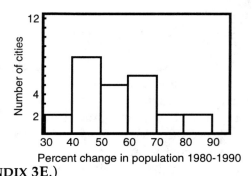

Percent change in population 1980-1990

Example 1: The annual tuition costs of attending fifty different public colleges are shown in the histogram below. This distribution is said to be stretched or **skewed** to the right towards the outliers.

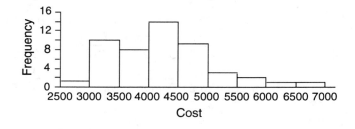

Cost

a. How many colleges represented in this graph have tuitions that are between $3,000 and $3,500?

b. In what interval is the median tuition?

c. What percent of these tuitions are less than $5,000?

Solution:

a. The height of the second bar from the left indicates that 10 of the 50 college tuitions are between $3,000 and $3,500.

b. This histogram represents fifty college tuitions. (Find the sum of the bar heights.) The median, which is between the 25th and 26th number, is found by adding up the frequencies, or heights, of each column from the left until you get to 25. The median must be in the $4,000 to $4,500 range, but it can't be determined any more closely than this. You do know that 50% of all the values in a data set are below or at the median value.

c. The college tuitions in 43 of the 50 colleges are less than $5,000. These 43 represent $\frac{43}{50} \cdot 100$, or 86% of the schools. This means $5,000 has a **percentile rank** of about 86, because 86% of the school tuitions are less than $5,000. Percentile ranks are frequently used for very large distributions.

Francis Galton originated the term "percentile" around 1885. His definition was, "The value that is un-reached by *n* per cent of any large group of measurements, and surpassed by 100 − *n* of them, is called the *n*th per-centile." You can use the somewhat simpler definition below.

> The **percentile rank** of a data value in a large distribution is the percent of scores that are below the given value.

Suppose a large number of students take a standardized test like the SAT. Students at point A are at the 30th percentile, because their scores are better than 30% of the tested students.

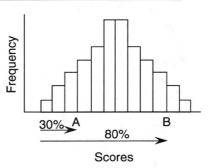

Likewise, students at point B are at the 80th percentile, because 80% of the tested students have results that are lower.

A percentile rank gives a good indication of how one individual's SAT score compares to other scores across the country. So many individual scores are involved that it would be impossible to look at all of the actual numbers.

Example 2: Make a histogram of the flight duration for space flights between 1961 and 1972. Round off each flight time to the nearest hour.

Date	Mission name	Duration (hours)	Date	Mission name	Duration (hours)
4/12/61	Vostok 1	1.8	11/11/66	Gemini-Titan XII	94.6
8/6/61	Vostok 2	25.3	4/23/67	Soyuz 1	26.7
2/20/62	Mercury-Atlas 6	4.9	10/11/68	Apollo-Saturn 7	260.2
5/24/62	Mercury-Atlas 7	4.9	10/26/68	Soyuz 3	94.9
8/11/62	Vostok 3	94.4	12/21/68	Apollo-Saturn 8	146.0
8/12/62	Vostok 4	71.0	1/14/69	Soyuz 4	71.2
10/3/62	Mercury-Atlas 8	9.2	1/15/69	Soyuz 5	72.7
5/15/63	Mercury-Atlas 9	34.3	3/3/69	Apollo-Saturn 9	241.0
6/14/63	Vostok 5	119.1	5/18/69	Apollo-Saturn 10	192.1
6/16/63	Vostok 6	70.8	7/16/69	Apollo-Saturn 11	195.3
10/12/64	Voskhod 1	24.3	10/11/69	Soyuz 6	118.7
3/18/65	Voskhod 2	29.0	10/12/69	Soyuz 7	118.7
3/23/65	Gemini-Titan III	4.9	11/14/69	Apollo-Saturn 12	244.6
6/3/65	Gemini-Titan IV	97.9	4/11/70	Apollo-Saturn 13	142.9
8/21/65	Gemini-Titan V	190.9	1/31/71	Apollo-Saturn 14	216.0
12/4/65	Gemini-Titan VII	330.6	6/6/71	Soyuz 11	569.7
12/15/65	Gemini-Titan VI-A	25.9	7/26/71	Apollo-Saturn 15	295.9
3/16/66	Gemini-Titan VIII	10.7	4/16/72	Apollo-Saturn 16	265.9
6/3/66	Gemini-Titan IX-A	72.4	12/7/72	Apollo-Saturn 17	301.9
7/18/66	Gemini-Titan XI	71.3			

Solution: There is not necessarily one right way to group these numbers, but you want to divide them so that there won't be too many columns. If you group them by forty-eights, then each column will show a time period of two days. The first column will show the number of flights from 0 to 47 hours, the next from 48 to 95 hours, and so on. If you are drawing the graph on your calculator, you'll need to estimate the maximum bar height in order to determine the value for Ymax.

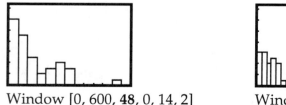

Window [0, 600, **48**, 0, 14, 2]　　　Window [0, 600, **24**, 0, 8, 1]

In the histogram on the right, each bar represents an interval of twenty-four hours, which gives a slightly different perspective of the totals. There are 25 flights of less than 120 hours. Therefore, 120 hours is at the $\frac{25}{39} \cdot 100 = 64$th percentile.

Fast Food Activity

How conscious are you of good nutrition? Do you often eat at a fast-food restaurant? If you do, this activity may help you become more aware of what you are eating and whether it is good for you.

Most adults require about 1,800 to 2,400 calories per day. It is generally recommended that 50 to 60 percent of your calories be from carbohydrate food sources. Your diet should include approximately 63 grams of protein per day, if you are an adult male over the age of 25. For a female, the recommendation is 50 grams of protein per day. Less than 30 percent of your daily intake of calories should come from fat. Cholesterol should be limited to between 13 and 20 grams per day. Your daily intake of sodium should not exceed 3,000 milligrams (about one-and-a-half teaspoons). That's a lot to think about when planning your diet.

Examine the information given below about the nutritional content of fast foods. (All items are sandwiches unless noted by an asterisk.) With your group, select either a type of food (burger, chicken, or fish) *or* one of the nutritional elements (calories, carbohydrates, fat, protein, cholesterol, or sodium). If your group chooses a type of food, then investigate the nutritional elements of that type of food. If your group chooses a nutritional element, then compare the amount of that element in the burger, chicken, or fish items. Prepare a report that uses box plots and histograms. Use each of the measures of central tendency and each of the measures of spread in your investigation. Draw attention to items that might be classified as outliers. Write a report discussing your conclusions. Prepare a short oral presentation for the class to accompany your report.

Company	Food	Serving size (oz)	Total Calories	Carbohydrate (gm)	Protein (gm)	Fat (gm)	Cholesterol (mg)	Sodium (mg)
Arby's	Roast Beef	5.5	383	35	22	18	43	936
Burger King	Whopper Jr.	4.7	300	29	14	15	35	500
Carl's Jr	Carl's Original Hamburger	6.8	460	46	25	20	50	810
Dairy Queen	Hamburger	5	310	29	17	13	45	580
Hardee's	Big Deluxe Burger	7.6	500	32	27	30	70	760
Jack in the Box	Hamburger	3.4	267	28	13	11	26	556
McDonald's	Hamburger	3.6	255	30	12	9	37	490
Rax	Regular Rax	4.7	262	25	18	10	15	707
Wendy's	Single Hamburger	4.7	350	31	25	15	70	510
Whataburger	Whataburger Jr.	5.4	304	31	15	12	30	684
Arby's	Chicken Breast Fillet	7.2	445	42	22	23	45	958
Burger King	Chicken	8	620	57	26	32	45	1430
Carl's Jr.	Charbroiler BBQ Chicken	11	310	34	25	6	30	680
Chick-Fil-A	Chick-Fil-A Deluxe	7.5	369	30	41	9	66	1178
Church's Fried Chicken	Fried Chicken Breast	2.8	200	4	19	12	65	510
Dairy Queen	Grilled Chicken Fillet	6.5	300	33	25	8	50	800
Hardee's	Chicken Fillet	6	370	44	19	13	55	1060
Jack in the Box	Chicken and Mushroom	7.8	438	40	28	18	61	1340
KFC	Original Recipe Breast*	3.6	260	8	25	14	92	609
Long John Silver's	Batter-dipped Chicken	4.5	280	39	14	8	15	790
McDonald's	McChicken	6.5	415	39	19	20	50	830
Popeyes	Chicken Breast	3.7	270	9	23	16	60	660
Rax	Grilled Chicken	6.9	402	26	25	23	69	872
Wendy's	Grilled Chicken	6.25	290	35	24	7	60	360
Whataburger	Whatachicken	10	671	61	35	32	71	1460
Arby's	Fish Fillet	7.8	526	50	23	27	44	872
Carl's Jr.	Carl's Catch	7.5	560	54	17	30	5	1220
Dairy Queen	Fish Fillet	6	370	39	16	16	45	630
Hardee's	Fisherman's Fillet	7.5	480	50	23	21	70	1210
Jack in the Box	Fish Supreme	7.7	510	44	24	27	55	1040
Long John Silver's	Batter-dipped Fish	5.6	340	40	18	13	30	890
McDonald's	Fillet-O-Fish	5	370	38	14	18	50	730
Wendy's	Fish	6.4	460	42	18	25	55	780
Whataburger	Whatacatch	6.2	475	43	14	27	34	722

Source: *Fast Food Facts, Marion J. Franz, Chronimed Publishing*

Problem Set 3.3

1. Recently Fay Cilitator's students spent the class period rolling pairs of dice and recording the results. They kept track of the sum of the two dice on each of 1000 rolls. The number of times (**frequency**) each different sum came up is listed below.

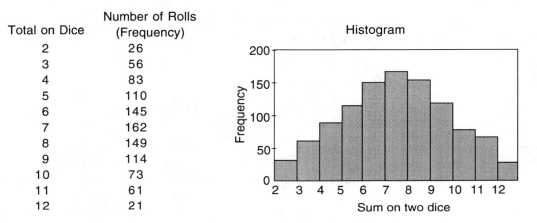

Total on Dice	Number of Rolls (Frequency)
2	26
3	56
4	83
5	110
6	145
7	162
8	149
9	114
10	73
11	61
12	21

Histogram

a. Graph this histogram on your calculator. List the window values needed for it to look like the histogram pictured. See **APPENDIX 3E** for help.

b. Explain why the histogram has a mound-like shape.

c. Describe how you would find the mean sum and median sum for the pairs of dice rolled.

2. Rita and Noah are working on a report for their economics class. They surveyed ninety-five farmers in their county to see how many acres of sweet corn the farmers had planted. The results are summarized in this histogram.

a. The distribution is skewed to the right. Explain what this means.

b. Graph this histogram on your calculator.

c. Describe what you think a box plot of this information would look like, and then check your conjecture with your calculator.

3. Describe a situation and sketch a histogram, reflecting each condition named below.

a. mound-shaped and quite symmetric

b. skewed to the left

c. skewed to the right

d. rectangular

4. At a large university, 1500 students took a final exam in chemistry. Frank Stein learned that his score of 76 (out of 100) placed him at the 88th percentile.

   a. How many students had lower scores than Frank? How many had higher scores?

   b. Mary Curie had a score of 82, which placed her at the 95th percentile. Describe how Mary's performance compared to that of others in the class.

   c. What percentile is associated with the best test score of 91?

   d. If every student who scored above the 90th percentile received an A, how many students earned this grade?

5. Ozzie kept a log of the time he spent doing homework and watching television during twenty days in October.

October date	3	4	5	6	7	8	10	11	12	13	14	15	17	18	19	20	21	22	24	25
HW (min)	4	10	40	11	55	46	46	23	57	28	65	58	52	38	38	39	45	27	41	44
TV (min)	78	30	15	72	25	30	90	40	35	56	12	5	95	27	38	50	10	42	60	34

   a. Draw two box plots: one showing time spent doing homework, and one showing time watching television. Name the five summary values for each. Which distribution has the greatest spread? What is the spread value of each?

   b. Make an educated guess at the histogram shape for each set of data. Will either, or both, be skewed or mound-shaped? Describe what you think each will look like. Confirm your guess by constructing each histogram.

6. The deviations from the mean for Penny Saved's bank account during the last eight months are 0, −40, −78, −71, 33, 36, 42, and 91. Find (i) the mean absolute deviation, (ii) the actual data values, (iii) the median, and (iv) the interquartile range for each given mean value.

   a. The mean value is 747.   b. The mean value is 850.

   c. Write a paragraph describing what you discovered in this problem.

7. Penny Spendfree received five different Gold Cards shortly after graduating from college. Within a month, she had furnished her apartment with new furniture, high tech appliances, and the latest in audio and video equipment. She used each of the cards to its maximum credit limit, and soon found that she owed $20,000 at 21.5% annual interest. Penny then locked up all the cards and began to make $546.71 payments each month, so that she would be out of debt in five years.

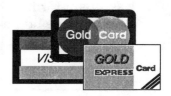

a. List the unpaid balances for the 60 months as data in the calculator. What is the average unpaid balance during the 60 months?

b. Graph a histogram of unpaid balances.

c. Explain what information the shape of the histogram in 7b gives you.

d. What is the total interest cost on the loans?

e. Use the mean unpaid balance to approximate the answer to 7d.

8. Use this information about major league baseball stadium capacities, 1992 average home attendance, and the year the stadium was built, when answering the questions that follow the table.

Team	Stadium	Built	Capacity	1992 Average Attendance
Baltimore	Orioles Park	1992	48,041	44,598
Boston	Fenway Park	1912	34,142	31,648
California	Anaheim Stadium	1966	64,593	25,499
Chicago	Comiskey Park	1991	44,702	33,101
Cleveland	Cleveland Stadium	1931	74,483	15,694
Detroit	Tiger Stadium	1912	52,416	18,256
Kansas City	Royals Stadium	1973	40,625	23,642
Milwaukee	County Stadium	1953	53,192	23,511
Minnesota	H.H.H. Metrodome	1982	55,883	30,647
New York	Yankee Stadium	1923	57,545	21,859
Oakland	Coliseum	1966	47,313	30,792
Seattle	The Kingdome	1976	59,702	20,387
Texas	Arlington Stadium	1965	43,521	27,478
Toronto	SkyDome	1989	50,516	49,732
Atlanta	County Stadium	1965	52,007	38,468
Chicago	Wrigley Field	1914	38,710	26,584
Cincinnati	Riverfront Stadium	1970	52,952	28,949
Colorado	Mile High Stadium	1948	76,100	N.A.
Florida	Joe Robbie Stadium	1987	48,000	N.A.
Houston	The Astrodome	1965	54,816	14,956
Los Angeles	Dodger Stadium	1962	56,000	32,120
Montreal	Olympic Stadium	1976	43,739	20,864
New York	Shea Stadium	1964	55,601	23,415
Philadelphia	Veterans Stadium	1971	62,382	24,711
Pittsburgh	Three Rivers Stadium	1970	58,729	22,585
St. Louis	Busch Stadium	1966	56,227	30,231
San Diego	Jack Murphy Stadium	1967	59,700	21,252
San Francisco	Candlestick Park	1960	62,000	19,759

Source: *The 1993 Information Please Sports Almanac, page 476 and page 76*

a. Compute the mean absolute deviations of both the stadium capacities and the average attendance. Which has the larger mean absolute deviation? In your own words, explain what this means.

b. How does knowledge about the mean absolute deviation help you predict the shape of a histogram? A box plot?

c. Based on your answer to 8b, predict what the two box plots and two histograms will look like. Confirm your predictions by drawing each of the four graphs on your calculator.

d. Write a short paragraph to a sports-minded friend about something that interests you in this table. Support your writing with statistical information.

9. Find a problem in this chapter, or in an earlier chapter, that you cannot solve. Write out the problem and as much of the solution as you can. Then, clearly explain what is keeping you from solving the problem. Be as specific and clear as you can.

10. Since the beginning of the school year, you have been working with your group, or perhaps you have worked with several different groups. How has your attitude toward group work changed since the beginning of the school year? Has your role in your group changed? Explain completely.

Section 3.4: Chapter Review

Problem Set 3.4

1. Which box plot has the larger mean absolute deviation? Support and explain your answer.

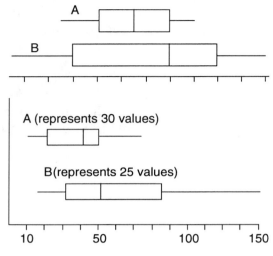

2. a. Draw two different histograms that might represent the information pictured in these two box plots.

   b. How many data values are in each lower whisker? How many are in the upper whisker in plot B?

   c. Which plot represents the data set with the larger mean absolute deviation? Explain how you know this.

3. The following are recorded extreme temperatures (in degrees Fahrenheit) for each of the seven continents. Find the mean and the mean absolute deviation of the extreme high temperatures. Then find the mean and mean absolute deviation of the extreme low temperatures. Which values, if any, are more than two mean absolute deviations from the mean?

Continent	High	Low
Africa	136	−11
Antarctica	59	−129
Asia	129	−90
Australia	128	−8
Europe	122	−67
North America	134	−87
South America	120	−27

4. a. Create a histogram that has a mean absolute deviation close to zero.

   b. Create a histogram with the same number of values as in 4a, but with a mean absolute deviation of about 5.

5. Enter the space flight data from Example 2 in Section 3.3 into your calculator. You may round off the duration to the nearest hour.

   a. Make a prediction as to which is longer, the median flight duration or the mean flight duration. List some reasons for your prediction. Then use the calculator to compute each statistic.

   b. Divide the data into two lists—one representing Soviet space flights and one representing United States space flights. Construct a histogram for each list.

   c. Predict which data set—the United States flights or the Soviet flights—will have the greater mean absolute deviation. Check your prediction using your calculator.

6. The 1991 United States plant passenger car production totals are shown below.

Plymouth	143,963	Cadillac	228,419	Dodge	275,613
Saturn	95,821	Ford	771,354	Honda	451,199
Lincoln-Mercury	400,326	Mazda	165,314	Chevrolet	786,012
Nissan	133,505	Pontiac	509,080	Subaru	57,945
Oldsmobile	439,752	Toyota	298,847	Buick	436,922

The 1993 World Almanac and Book of Facts, page 667

   a. Make a box plot of the production totals.

   b. Make a histogram using a bar width that provides meaningful information about the data.

   c. Write a short news article describing information in this data.

   d. Suppose the total number of cars produced in a different year is 400,000 greater than the 1991 total. Describe how this could affect the shape of your box plot and histogram.

7. Examine the information in the following table about the percent of the population over five years old in the United States that is non-English-speaking.

   a. Prepare a histogram and box plot that best pictures the information. Describe what information you can get from looking at the graphs.

   b. Prepare histograms and box plots that compare information from states east of the Mississippi with those west of the Mississippi. Describe and explain the similarities and differences between the two regions.

   c. Compare histograms and box plots of data from different geographic regions of the United States as defined in Example 2 of Section 3.2.

   d. Prepare a report that uses box plots, histograms, and each of the measures of central tendency and spread. What information could you provide to someone who is making a decision related to this data? Prepare a short oral presentation to the class to accompany your report.

Percent of Population over Five Years Old in the United States that is Non-English Speaking

State	Percent non-English	State	Percent non-English
Alabama	2.9	Montana	5.0
Alaska	12.1	Nebraska	4.8
Arizona	20.8	Nevada	13.2
Arkansas	2.8	New Hampshire	8.7
California	31.5	New Jersey	19.5
Colorado	10.5	New Mexico	35.5
Connecticut	15.2	New York	23.3
Delaware	6.9	North Carolina	3.9
Florida	17.3	North Dakota	7.9
Georgia	4.8	Ohio	5.4
Hawaii	24.8	Oklahoma	5.0
Idaho	6.4	Oregon	7.3
Illinois	14.2	Pennsylvania	7.3
Indiana	4.8	Rhode Island	17.0
Iowa	3.9	South Carolina	3.5
Kansas	5.7	South Dakota	6.5
Kentucky	2.5	Tennessee	2.9
Louisiana	10.1	Texas	25.4
Maine	9.2	Utah	7.8
Maryland	8.9	Vermont	5.8
Massachusetts	15.2	Virginia	7.3
Michigan	6.6	Washington	9.0
Minnesota	5.6	West Virginia	2.6
Mississippi	2.8	Wisconsin	5.8
Missouri	3.8	Wyoming	5.7

The World Almanac and Book of Facts 1994, page 580.

Section 3.5: Projects

Project 3.1 Adding Graphs

Find an article in your city newspaper that uses a great deal of data and statistics, but contains no graphs. Rewrite the article representing as much of the information as you can graphically (that is, with histograms, box plots, and so on). Conclude your article by describing the insights you have gained from the graphs. Indicate to the reader what graph and where to look in order to "see" your conclusions. Submit a copy of the original article with your improved version.

Project 3.2 Collecting Data

Collecting your own data can be very interesting, but poorly collected data is meaningless. Good scientific procedure requires many things. You must record the data neatly and clearly, labeling variables and units. You should describe in detail the method used for collecting the data. You also need to explain the factors you considered when setting up the experiment. Note as many other possible variables, no matter how unlikely they seem to you, such as the temperature, the day and time the data was collected, and other factors that you think may or may not have bearing on the data. When summarizing the results of your experiment, use graphs and statistical measures which look at the data in different ways. In your conclusions, provide some analysis of the data and interpretation of the results. Finally, draw some generalizations from the experiment and explain any outliers. The list below contains possible ideas for collecting data. If you have another idea, be sure to check with your teacher before you begin.

- For how many seconds can you balance a ball on your head?

- How far can you roll a penny before it falls over?

- Roll a die once and record the outcome. How many more rolls does it take for you to get the same number?

- Conduct a study and ratings survey of a selection of radio stations in your area. The study should list the type of music for each station. Ratings should be determined for different age groups.

Project 3.3: Standard Deviation

You will need a meter stick and a string a little longer than 1.5 m. Ask between 30 and 50 people to measure the cord as accurately as they can, and to give you its length in centimeters. Enter this data into your calculator and construct several histograms using different interval widths. Decide which interval width gives the best picture of the data and make a sketch of this histogram. Find the mean value of the data set and the

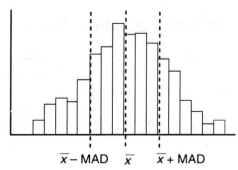

deviation of each measurement from the mean. Calculate the mean absolute deviation, MAD. Add three vertical lines to your sketch—one at the mean, one at one mean absolute deviation above the mean, and one at one mean absolute deviation below the mean.

Square each deviation instead of taking the absolute value. The mean value of the squares of the deviations is called the **variance** of the data. The units of the variance for this activity are centimeters squared, which is a little confusing because it is not a measure of area, but a squared measure of length. The square root of the variance is called the **standard deviation** of the data. The units of the standard deviation for this activity are centimeters. Find the standard deviation for this data and add two more vertical lines to your sketch—one that is one standard deviation above the mean, and another that is one standard deviation below the mean.

One advantage of the standard deviation is that it is a built-in function in many calculators, computer spreadsheets, and other analysis tools. (See **APPENDIX 11E** for instructions on how to calculate standard deviation on your calculator.) The lower case Greek letter *sigma* (σ) is used for standard deviation. Research and identify other advantages to using standard deviation.

The **variance** of a data set is the mean of the sum of the squares of the deviations from the mean of the data.

$$\sigma^2 = \frac{\sum_{i=1}^{n}(x_i - \bar{x})^2}{n}$$

The square root of the variance is called the **standard deviation**, and it is a measure of spread used for data sets.

$$\sigma = \sqrt{\frac{\sum_{i=1}^{n}(x_i - \bar{x})^2}{n}}$$

Project 3.4:   Stem and Leaf Plots

The Stem and Leaf Plot offers another way to represent one-variable data. Something like a sideways histogram, it is more detailed because individual data values can be found in the graph. Consider the scores that your good friends Connie and Ozzie got in their math class.

| Connie Sistant | 82, 86, 82, 84, 85, 84, 85 |
| Ozzie Laiting | 72, 94, 76, 96, 90, 76, 84 |

Two different Stem and Leaf graphs of these data are given here.

```
     Connie      Ozzie                  Connie      Ozzie

               7 | 2 6 6                        7 | 2
 6 5 5 4 4 2   8 | 4                             • | 6 6
               9 | 0 4                   4 4 2   8 | 4
                                           6 5 5 | •
            key  | 7 | 2 = 72                    9 | 0 4
```

To create the display, first order the data, and then divide it into groups (similar to histogram displays). The left graph is divided into ranges of ten points and the right graph is divided into ranges of five points. A key must be provided for the graph in order to interpret the magnitude of the data. In other cases, 7|2 could mean 7200, 7.2, or even 0.0072.

Not all of the accuracy can always be maintained. For example, consider how this data set of calories—320, 340, 410, 344, 570, 614, 500, 935—appears in each of these displays.

3	2 4 4
4	1
5	0 7
6	1
7	
8	
9	3 Key 3|2 = 320

3	20 40 44
4	10
5	00 70
6	14
7	
8	
9	35 Key 3|20 = 320

The left plot shows that there are two values in the 340s, but we cannot see that one is 340 and one is 344. Both options are correct. You must decide whether that level of accuracy is important, or whether the information is clearer without it.

Create a Stem and Leaf Plots for the data given in the Problem 6, Section 11.4. Remember to give a key. Explain how the data has been organized and what insight can be obtained from your Stem and Leaf Plots.

Chapter Four

DATA ANALYSIS

Contents

Section 4.1: The Best-Fit Line. 128

Drawing lines that look good

Section 4.2: Equation of a Line. 132

The point-slope formula

Section 4.3: Real-World Meanings 136

Units, interpolation, and extrapolation

Section 4.4: The Median-Median Line 142

The process

Section 4.5: The Residuals 149

More on median-median lines

Section 4.6: The Least-Squares Line 157

The other method

Section 4.7: Coefficient of Correlation 163

More on least-squares

Section 4.8: Accuracy 172

How do you measure the meaning?

Section 4.9: Chapter Review 179

Assessing yourself

Section 4.10: Projects 183

Taking it one step further

Section 4.1: The Best-Fit Line

Data is a name for numeric information. You can make a graph to display data, and many times you can find a **mathematical model** to describe the data. **Data analysis** is a process of describing a relationship that may closely fit your data. Once you define the relationship, you may be able to extract other information from the data. Data analysis is not an exact science, however, and often there is more than one way to find a mathematical model; sometimes there may be several different models that appear to fit the data. In this chapter, you will look at different methods for finding models, and you will also explore methods for determining how good a model is.

Suppose you collect data from several thousand adult males selected at random. You make a table showing the height of each man (in inches) and his weight (in pounds). From your information, you might determine that a man's weight increases by about 3.7 pounds for each inch of increase in height. But is this enough to tell the whole story? Your data probably does not follow the pattern exactly, so you know that height is only one of the factors that influence a man's weight. What other factors might influence a man's weight? How can you hope to find a complete relationship with only some pieces of the puzzle? The challenge is to find the most important factors, and make a mathematical model that fits these factors, however loosely. The next step is to look at other factors and refine your model.

Car Data Activity

With members of your group, measure the lengths and widths of at least 12 cars. Be sure to measure cars that are all the same type, such as 2-door sedans, pick up trucks, or station wagons. Record this information in a table like the one at the right. You do not have to record the make or model of each car. Next, plot on graph paper the points representing these pairs of numbers. Draw a line that seems to fit your data.

length of car	width of car

How would you describe the **best-fit line** for a set of data? When finding the **best-fit line** there are many things to consider. Ideally, you might want every point to lie on the line, but in real life this will rarely occur, (and you probably should be suspicious if it does happen). There is no single list of rules that will obtain the *best* line in every instance, but, by observing the following guidelines, you will usually end up with a reasonably good fit.

- The line should show the direction of the points. The smallest rectangle that contains the points shows the general direction of the line.

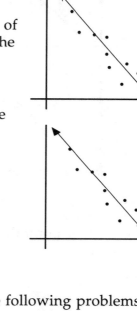

- The line should divide the points equally. There should be nearly as many points above the line as below the line. Connect each point to the line and measure the lengths of these vertical "connectors." The sum of the lengths of the connectors above the line should be nearly equal to the sum of those below the line.

- As many points as possible should be *on* the line, but the previous two guidelines are more important.

- The points above the line should not be concentrated at one end, nor should the points below the line.

These four guidelines may seem confusing at first, but the following problems should help you clarify their meaning.

Problem Set 4.1

1. Look at each graph below, and choose the *one* with the line that best satisfies the guidelines above. (That was the easy part.) For each of the other graphs, explain which guidelines were violated.

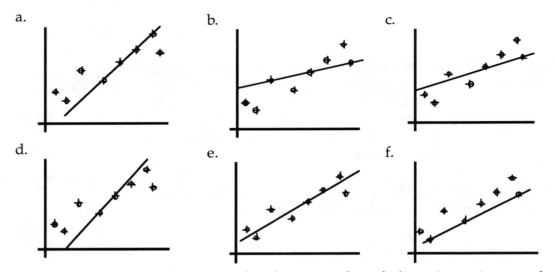

2. For each graph below, lay your ruler along your best-fit line. Assuming a scale of 1 on both axes, give an approximate value for the *y*-intercept, and name one other point that the line goes through (it need not be one of the given points).

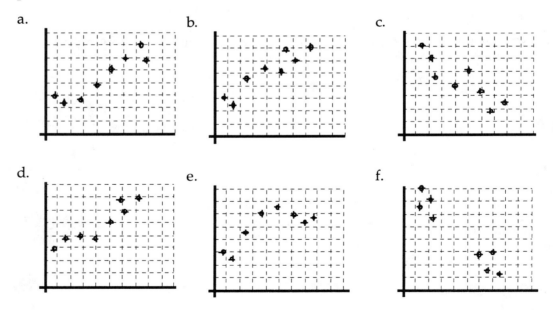

For Problems 3 and 4, graph the data and draw your best-fit line.

3.

Planet	Mean distance from sun	Time of one revolution
Mercury	0.387	0.241
Venus	0.723	0.615
Earth	1.000	1.000
Mars	1.523	1.881
Jupiter	5.203	11.861
Saturn	9.541	29.457
Uranus	19.190	84.008
Neptune	30.086	164.784
Pluto	39.507	248.350

Distances measured in astronomical units (AU);
1 AU ≈ 93,000,000 miles. Time measured in years.

4.

Taxable income	Regular tax
12,000	2,260
16,000	3,260
20,000	4,380
24,000	5,660
28,000	7,100
32,000	8,660

5. Look at the line of best fit you drew in the Car Data Activity. Analyze your line using the four guidelines given in this section. Does your line satisfy these guidelines? If you think you can draw a line that fits better, do so.

6. Listed below are the dimensions (in inches) used by pattern manufacturers. These are supposed to represent the measurements of an average adult woman.

Misses size	6	8	10	12	14	16	18	20
Bust	$30\frac{1}{2}$	$31\frac{1}{2}$	$32\frac{1}{2}$	34	36	38	40	42
Waist	23	24	25	$26\frac{1}{2}$	28	30	32	34
Hips	$32\frac{1}{2}$	$33\frac{1}{2}$	$34\frac{1}{2}$	36	38	40	42	44

a. How many graphs are needed to show all of the possible relationships between the data?

b. Choose two of these relationships, and plot them on separate graphs.

7. Have you discovered any new advantages of working in groups in your math class? New disadvantages? Explain these completely.

Section 4.2: Equation of a Line

Suppose you are taking a long trip in your car. At 5 p.m., you notice that the odometer reads 45,623 miles. At 9 p.m., you note that it reads 45,831. What was your average speed during that time period? The answer, 52 miles per hour, is a rate. If you graph the information, 52 is the slope of the line connecting the two points. You use the definition of slope when you calculate the speed.

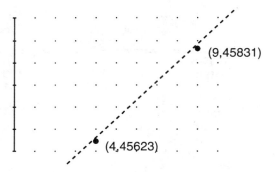

(9,45831)

(4,45623)

$$\text{Average speed} = \frac{45{,}831 - 45{,}623}{9 - 5} \quad \text{or} \quad \frac{d_2 - d_1}{t_2 - t_1}$$

Slope is one of the most important mathematical concepts that you will study. In trigonometry, it is used to help find the heights of objects like trees and buildings, and the distances across lakes or canyons. In calculus, it is used to determine how fast populations are growing, or to help in designing soda cans with the least cost. Slope is just as important in physics and chemistry. In application problems, slope is often called **rate of change**.

> The formula for the **slope** from point 1 (x_1, y_1) to point 2 (x_2, y_2) is
>
> $$m = \frac{y_2 - y_1}{x_2 - x_1}$$

The letter m is used for slope (because all the other good letters were being used for something else at the time a name was needed). The ratio of *the change in the y-values* over *the change in the x-values* will be constant for any two points selected on the line containing this segment. This means that the ratio is invariant on a line. In other words, a line has only one slope.

Example 1: Find the slope of the line.

Solution: First, identify two points on the line, such as the points (−3, −3) and (3, 1). Then, use the formula to find the slope.

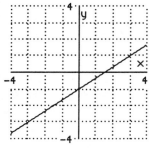

$$m = \frac{1 - (^-3)}{3 - (^-3)} = \frac{2}{3}$$

In many cases, you may not be able to identify points as easily as in the example above. To increase accuracy, choose your points carefully, and select them from opposite sides of the graph. Then choose a third point, and find the slope between it and one of the first two points, to serve as a check of your work.

$$\text{Check: Points } (0, -1) \text{ and } (3, 1): \frac{1-(-1)}{3-0} = \frac{2}{3}$$

You can use the slope formula to find the equation of a line containing two points. Select one point, and let the second point be a "generic" point (x, y).

Example 2: In the automobile trip example, the points are (5, 45, 623) and (9, 45, 831). Use the first of these points and the generic point (x, y), to write an equation for the line. You will also need the rate (slope), which is 52 mi/hr.

Solution:

$$\frac{y_2 - y_1}{x_2 - x_1} = m \qquad \qquad \text{Formula for slope.}$$

$$\frac{y - 45623}{x - 5} = 52 \qquad \qquad \text{Substitute } (x, y) \text{ for } (x_2, y_2) \text{ and } (5, 45623) \text{ for } (x_1, y_1).$$

$$y - 45623 = 52(x - 5) \qquad \qquad \text{Multiply both sides by } (x - 5).$$

$$y = 52(x - 5) + 45623 \qquad \qquad \text{Add 45623 to both sides.}$$

(The result can also be rewritten as $y = 52x - 260 + 45623$ or $y = 52x + 45363$.)

The **point-slope form** of the equation of a line
with slope m containing point (x_1, y_1) is

$$y = m(x - x_1) + y_1$$

Example 3: Find the equation of the line pictured.

Solution: Select the points: $(-3, 1)$ and $(3, -2)$.

Find the slope: $m = \dfrac{-2 - 1}{3 - (-3)} = \dfrac{-1}{2}$

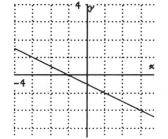

Then choose either of the points and substitute the x- and y-values into the point-slope form. If you choose the first point, $(-3, 1)$, then

$$y = -\frac{1}{2}(x + 3) + 1$$

A Check your answer by repeating the procedure, using the point
(−1, 0). When you simplify, you should get an equivalent equation.
You can do a visual check by graphing the line and the points on
your calculator. (See **APPENDIX 4A** for help in graphing points and
lines.) Another quick check, if your calculator has a table feature, is
to make a table for your equation and see if each point satisfies the
equation.

Car Loan Activity

 You plan to borrow $12,000 to purchase a new car. The bank
advertises an interest rate of 11%. Use the following
method to determine how much your payment needs to be
for you to pay off the loan in 5 years (60 months).

a. Try five different payments. For each one, record
the payment and the balance remaining,
positive or negative, after 60 mo. Make a table
like the one shown.

Payment	Balance remaining

b. Graph these ordered pairs on your calculator, or
on graph paper. What do you observe about the points?

c. Select two points, and find the equation of the line that contains them.

d. Locate the point where the balance (the y-value) is zero. What is the
payment at this point?

e. Try this number as a payment to verify that the balance is zero.

f. What is the y-intercept of your line? What is its real-world meaning?

g. What is the slope of your line? What is its real-world meaning?

Problem Set 4.2

Sketch a graph next to your solution for each of Problems 1–3.

1. Find the slope of the line containing each pair of points:

   a. (3, −4) and (7, 2)   b. (5, 3) and (2, 5)

2. Find the slope of each line.

   a. $y = 3x - 2$ b. $y = 4.2 - 2.8x$ c. $y = 5(x - 3) + 2$

   d. $y - 2.4x = 5$ e. $4.7x + 3.2y = 12.9$

3. Find the equation of the line that passes through each pair of points:

   a. $(4, 0)$ and $(6, 3)$ b. $(-4.33, 7.51)$ and $(1.58, 0.87)$.

4. Find the equation of each line.

   a.　　　　　　　　　　　　　　b.

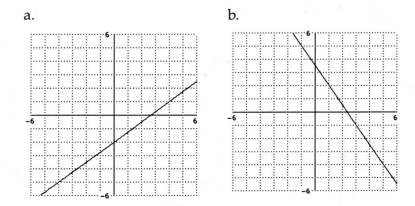

5. Find the equation for the line you drew in Problem 3, Section 4.1.

6. Find the equation for the line you drew in Problem 4, Section 4.1.

7. Find the equation for the line you drew in Problem 5, Section 4.1.

8. Use the method from the activity in this section to find the payment needed to pay off a 25-yr mortgage on a new house, if you must finance $60,000 at 9.6% on the unpaid balance.

Section 4.3: Real-World Meanings

When you find the equation of a line that represents data, you are creating a **mathematical model**. What does this model mean, and why is it valuable? In this section you will explore the answers to these questions.

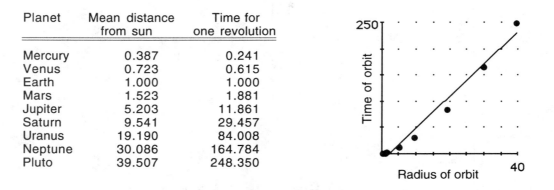

Planet	Mean distance from sun	Time for one revolution
Mercury	0.387	0.241
Venus	0.723	0.615
Earth	1.000	1.000
Mars	1.523	1.881
Jupiter	5.203	11.861
Saturn	9.541	29.457
Uranus	19.190	84.008
Neptune	30.086	164.784
Pluto	39.507	248.350

Distances measured in astronomical units (AU);
1 AU ≈ 93,000,000 mi. Time measured in years.

By analyzing the data, the mean distance from the sun and the time of one revolution, you might find an equation that looks like $y = 6.1x - 12.4$. (Yours might be a bit different, depending on the points you chose.)

Whenever you use measurements, you need to name the unit of measure. Otherwise, the measurements are meaningless. What are the units in this problem? The units of x are astronomical units (AU), and the units of y are years. What are the units of the slope and y-intercept? The y-values represent years, so the y-intercept is 12.4 yr. The slope is the change in y over the change in x. So the slope must be measured in years per astronomical unit, that is, 6.1 yr per astronomical unit. So what does a slope of 6.1 mean in this example?

If you consider Neptune, which is currently orbiting at about 30 AUs from the sun, and move it to 31 AUs, the time for its orbit should change from 164.8 yr to about 170.9 yr, increasing 6.1 yr for an increase of 1 AU.

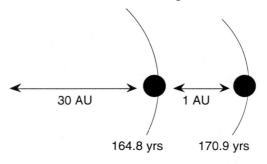

If you were to move it outward another AU, then it should take another 6.1 yr to orbit. So the slope, 6.1, is the increase in the time of revolution for each increase of 1 AU in the radius from the sun.

radius	time
30	164.8
31	170.9
32	177

When you begin to analyze a set of data, you must decide which information will be represented by the x-values, and which will be represented by the y-values. The set of x-values, is called the **domain,** and x is called the **independent** variable. The set of y-values is called the **range,** and y is called the **dependent** variable. The supposed relationship here is that the x-values can be anything within the domain (they are independent), and the y-values must in some way correspond to the chosen x-values (the y-values are dependent).

Domain: The set of values for the independent variable.

Range: The set of values for the dependent variable.

In the example above, radius of orbit is the independent variable, and time of orbit is the dependent variable. Think of it as cause and effect. If you change the radius, the time of orbit will change. The time of orbit cannot change without changing the radius. In the next example, you will deal with the amount of tax you pay compared to the money you earn. Which of these variables depends on the other? It is clear that you have to earn the money before it is taxed, so money earned precedes tax paid. In other cases, the choice may be arbitrary. There is obviously a relationship between the dimensions used by dressmakers for waist measurements and for hip measurements, but does one of these depend on the other? In this case, your choice of x and y may be different from someone else's, but each may be correct.

Example 1: An equation for a best-fit line for the data shown in this table is $y \approx 0.32x - 1820$. If x is dollars earned and y is tax paid, then the slope is 0.32 dollars of tax paid per dollar earned. Another way to think of the slope is $0.32 (or 32¢) paid as tax for each dollar earned.

Taxable Income	Regular tax
12,000	2,260
16,000	3,260
20,000	4,380
24,000	5,660
28,000	7,100
32,000	8,660

a. Figure out the tax you must pay if your expected income is $21,000. Because 21,000 is between 20,000 and 24,000, the tax should be between $4,380 and $5,660, and closer to the lower value. If you use the model and substitute the value $21,000 for x, you find $y = 0.32(21,000) - 1,820 = \$4,900$. Finding a value between those given in a table is called **interpolation.**

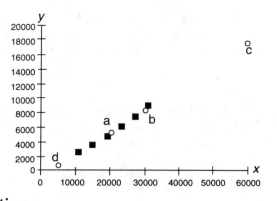

b. Tex Peyar reported that he paid $8,000 in taxes this year. You can estimate his income by interpolating the taxable income with the model. Solving $8,000 = 0.32x - 1,820$ gives you an x-value of about $30,700. (Check this.)

c. What would you expect the tax to be for Noah Cache, whose income was $60,000? This is well beyond the incomes in the table, but, because you have no other information, you will have to assume that the model does not change at higher incomes. This may be a poor assumption, but you have limited information. The equation predicts that he will pay $17,380 in taxes. (Can you find this?) This use of a model to extend beyond the present range of values is called **extrapolation.**

d. When could you expect to pay NO taxes? When $0 = 0.32x - 1,820$, or when your income is about $5,690. The accuracy of extrapolating values far from your data will depend on the accuracy of the data, the accuracy of the model, and the likelihood that no other factors come into play.

The Wave Activity

This is a class activity. The objective is to determine how much time it takes for a given number of people to do "The Wave." The Wave is a sociological phenomenon that sometimes occurs at a sporting event. Each person stands as the person before him sits. As he stands up, he raises both hands above his head, then lowers his hands as he sits down. You will need a watch with a second hand to time each wave. Using different-sized groups, determine the time for each group to complete "The Wave." Collect at least nine pairs of data and put the numbers into a table like the one below.

n	3	5	6	8	. . .	15
t in seconds						

Plot the points and find the equation of a best-fit line. Write a paragraph about your results. Be sure to include the following information:

a. What is the slope of your line, and what is its real-world meaning?

b. What is the y-intercept for your line, and what is its real-world meaning?

c. What is the x-intercept for your equation, and what is its real-world meaning?

d. What is a reasonable domain for this equation? Why? (Keep this data and equation. You will be using them in a later section.)

Problem Set 4.3

Problems 1–4 are review questions about slopes and special types of lines.

1. a. Graph the line $y = 5$.

   b. Identify two points on it.

   c. What is the slope of this line?

2. Write the equation of the line that contains the points $(3, {}^-4)$ and $(-2, {}^-4)$. Write three statements about horizontal lines and their equations.

3. Write the equation of the line that contains the points $(3, 5)$ and $(3, 1)$. Your calculator is a function grapher. A vertical line is not a function. Find a way to graph a vertical line on your calculator. (There is more than one way.)

4. a. Graph the line $x = {}^-3$ on paper.

   b. Identify two points on it.

   c. What is the slope of this line?

   d. What is the y-intercept of this line?

5. The graph at the right shows the relationship between the heights of some tall buildings in Los Angeles and the number of stories in those buildings. The best-fit line drawn has the equation $y = 13.02x + 20.5$.

   a. What is the meaning of the slope?

   b. What is the meaning of the y-intercept?

   c. According to the graph, what is a realistic domain and range?

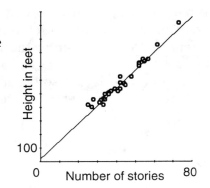

6. Consider the equation used to model the salary of Anita Raze for the last seven years: $y = 847x + 17{,}109$. The variable x is the number of years of experience she has, and y is her salary in dollars.

   a. What did she earn the fifth year?

   b. What is the slope of this line?

   c. What is the real-world meaning of the slope?

   d. What is the y-intercept of this line?

   e. What is the real-world meaning of the y-intercept?

   f. What is a realistic domain for this problem? Justify your answer.

In Problems 7–10 you must choose how to represent x accurately. There may be more than one correct choice. There are many correct answers for each problem. Yours may differ from the answers provided in the Answer Key. If so, graph both your answer and the text answer, and compare. The graphs should look similar.

7. The photography studio offers the following packages to students posing for yearbook photos.

Number of Pictures	44	31	24	15
Total Cost	$19.00	$16.00	$13.00	$10.00

   a. Plot the data, and find an equation of a best-fit line.

   b. Use a complete sentence to explain the real-world meaning of the slope.

   c. Find the point where your line crosses the y-axis.

   d. Use a complete sentence to explain the real-world meaning of the y-intercept.

   e. If the studio offers a 47-print package, what do you think they should charge?

   f. If you have only $14.50, how many prints do you think they should sell you?

When entering data involving years, you can either enter the whole year, such as 1986, or work from a reference year, such as 1900. If you use 1900 as the reference year, then enter the years in the form 86, 87, and so on. You could also use a reference year of 1986, so that 1986 would be entered as 0, 1987 would be 1, 1988 would be 2, and so on. In order to obtain the solutions given in the Answer Key, use 1900 as a reference year unless otherwise noted.

8. In the 1980s and early 1990s, a downward trend was noticed in average SAT verbal scores.

Year	1986	1987	1988	1989	1991
Score	431	430	428	427	422

a. Plot the data, and find the equation of a best-fit line.

b. What are the units of the domain (x-values)?

c. Use complete sentences to explain the real-world meaning of the slope.

d. Use the model to predict the average score last year.

e. Use the model to predict the average score in 1980.

f. How can you explain the fact that in 1980 the average verbal score was actually 424? Make an observation about the data and the use of this model.

9. The percent of American students in grades 9–12 using a computer at home is shown below, for different family incomes.

Family Income	$5,000 to $9,999	$10,000 to $14,999	$15,000 to $19,999	$20,000 to $24,999	$25,000 to $29,999	$30,000 to $34,999	$35,000 to $39,999
Percent Using Computers	4	7	14	14	17	20	25

a. Draw a histogram of this data.

b. Find a best-fit line that represents the trend shown by the histogram.

c. Use complete sentences to explain the real-world meaning of the slope.

d. Use the model to predict the percent of students using a computer at home in families with an income of $62,000.

10. The percent of unmarried males by age group is given in the table below:

Age	15–19	20–24	25–29	30–34
% Unmarried	96.2	73.2	38.2	19.6

a. Plot the data, either as points or as a histogram, and find a best-fit line.

b. What are the units of the dependent variable (the y-values)?

c. Use complete sentences to explain the real-world meaning of the slope.

d. Use the model to predict the percent of men that are not married at age 40.

e. What does this last answer mean?

Section 4.4: The Median-Median Line

Have you noticed that you and your classmates frequently find different equations for the same data? You may be wondering what makes one equation a better (more accurate) model. Answering this question is difficult, and you will spend part of this chapter looking at ways to judge just how well a line represents the data, or if indeed there is any line that fits. First, you will learn a procedure for finding a possible *best-fit* line for a set of data. This will enable each member of the class to get the same equation for the same set of data.

There are a variety of techniques for finding the *best-fit* line. One method, though it may be long, is quite simple in concept and in computation. The procedure for finding the median-median line involves a "chunking" process. Three points are selected to represent the entire data set, and the equation that best fits these three points is taken as the best fit for the entire set of data.

To select the points, you must first order them by their domain value (the *x*-value) and then divide the data into three equal groups. If the number of points is not divisible by three, then split them so that the first and last groups are the same size. For example:

18 data points: split into groups of 6 – 6 – 6

19 data points: split into groups of 6 – 7 – 6

20 data points: split into groups of 7 – 6 – 7

Then order the *y*-values within each of the groups. The representative point for each group has the coordinates of the **median** *x* of that group and the **median** *y* of that group. Carefully study the following example to see how this is done.

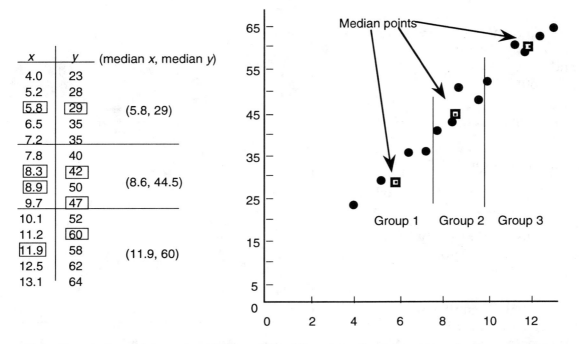

x	y	(median x, median y)
4.0	23	
5.2	28	
5.8	29	(5.8, 29)
6.5	35	
7.2	35	
7.8	40	
8.3	42	
8.9	50	(8.6, 44.5)
9.7	47	
10.1	52	
11.2	60	
11.9	58	(11.9, 60)
12.5	62	
13.1	64	

Note: The median point need *not* be one of the data points. *Don't forget to order the y-values in each group when finding the median y-value.*

Use the first and last of the three representative points to find the slope of the median-median line. To find the intercept, slide the line 1/3 of the way toward the middle point. Study the following example to see how this works.

First find the equation of the line containing the points (5.8, 29) and (11.9, 60).

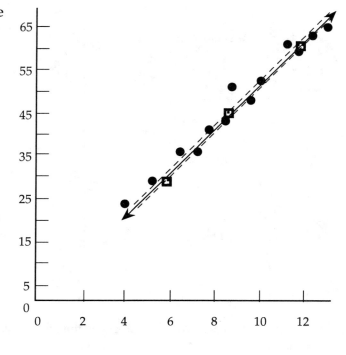

$$\text{slope} = \frac{60 - 29}{11.9 - 5.8} \approx 5.08$$

Using the point (5.8, 29):

$$y = 5.08(x - 5.8) + 29 \text{ or}$$
$$y = 5.08x - 0.46$$

Check to see that you will get the same equation if you use the point (11.9, 60).

A line that is parallel and passes through the middle representative point (8.6, 44.5) is:

$y = 5.08(x - 8.6) + 44.5$ or
$y = 5.08x + 0.81$

The median-median line will be parallel to both of these lines, so it will also have 5.08 as its slope. To find the equation of the line that is 1/3 the distance from the line containing two points, you can average the intercepts for the lines. This is tricky. You have to use the value −0.46 twice, because this line goes through two of the points, (which represent two-thirds of the data).

$$\text{average of the } y\text{-intercepts} = \frac{-0.46 + -0.46 + 0.81}{3} \approx -0.05$$

Therefore, the final median-median equation is $y = 5.08x - 0.05$.

Example 1: In this graph, the original data is not shown, only the three summary points are pictured. Find the equation of the median-median line.

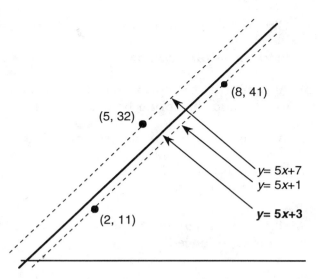

(5, 32)

(8, 41)

y= 5x+7
y= 5x+1

(2, 11)

y= 5x+3

Solution: The first and third points lie on the line $y = 5x + 1$. Parallel (with the same slope) to this line and passing through the second point is the equation $y = 5(x - 5) + 32$ or $y = 5x + 7$. Average the intercepts, $\frac{1 + 1 + 7}{3} = \frac{9}{3} = 3$ and write the equation of the median-median line as $y = 5x + 3$.

The median-median line is closer to the first line, because the line going through two points represents 2/3 of the data.

Spring Experiment Activity

Mass	Length
1.	
2.	
3.	
4.	

Attach a mass holder to a spring. Hang the spring from a spring stand, and the mass holder from the spring. Measure the length of the spring (in centimeters) from the first coil to the last coil.

Add different amounts of mass to the mass holder, recording the corresponding length of the spring each time. Collect about 20 data points.

Graph the data on a separate sheet of graph paper. Calculate and draw the median-median line through the data. Write the equation of this line. Answer the following questions in your write-up of the activity.

1. How much does your measured length for the third point differ from the value given by your equation for that mass?

2. Which two points differ the most from your equation? Can you explain why?

3. Give the real-world meaning for your slope.

4. Find the y-intercept, and give the real-world meaning of this value.

5. Assume that the spring will stretch forever. According to your model, how long would the spring be if you were to hang 4.7 kg from it?

6. What is wrong with the assumption in part 5?

7. What mass should make your spring stretch 20.0 cm? Show how you determined this.

Finally, summarize what you have learned in this activity. List any difficulties that you experienced.

Problem Set 4.4

1. a. How would you divide a set of 31 elements into three groups for the median-median line procedure?

   b. How would you divide a set of 50 elements into three groups for the median-median line procedure?

After completing each problem below, construct the graph for a visual confirmation that your equation is correct. Sketch your graph into your homework beside your solution. See **APPENDIX 4B** if you have forgotten how to graph both data points and lines with your graphing calculator.

2. Find the equation of the line passing through each pair of points:

   a. (8.1, 15.7) and (17.3, 9.5)   b. (3, 47) and (18, 84).

3. Find the equation of the line parallel to $y = 0.75x - 12.2$ that passes through the point (14.4, 0.9).

4. Find the equation of the line 1/3 of the way from $y = -1.8x + 74.1$ to $y = -1.8x + 70.5$.

5. Find the equation of the line 1/3 of the way from $y = 0.65x + 19.3$ to $y = 0.65x + 26.7$.

6. Find the equation of the line 1/3 of the way from $y = 4.7x + 2.8$ to the point (12.8, 64).

7. These questions will help you find the equation for the median-median line for the following data on <u>Male Life Expectancy in the United States</u>. (Enter 20, 25, and so on as *x*-values.)

Year of birth	1920	1925	1930	1935	1940	1945	1950
Life expectancy	53.6	56.3	58.1	59.4	60.8	62.8	65.6

Year of birth	1955	1960	1965	1970	1975	1980	1985	1990
Life expectancy	66.2	66.6	66.8	67.1	68.8	70.0	71.2	72.0

a. How many points are there in each of the three groups?

b. What are the three representative points for this data? Graph these points.

c. Draw the line through the first and third points. What is the slope of this line? Explain what this number means in terms of the information.

d. What is the equation of the line through the first and third points?

e. Draw the line parallel to the line in 7d that passes through the second point. What is the equation of this line?

f. Average the *y*-intercepts and write the equation of the median-median line. Graph this line. (Note: Remember that you have to use one of the *y*-intercepts twice.)

g. The year 1978 is missing from the table. Using your model, what would you predict the life expectancy to be for children born in 1978?

h. Use your model to predict the life expectancy of those children born in 1991, and those born in 1954.

i. Based on this model, when would you predict the life expectancy to exceed 80 years?

8. Find the error for each data point in the spring experiment activity. Display these errors with a histogram or box plot. Using this information, describe how good you think your model is. Justify your conclusion.

9. Refer to your data from the Wave Activity in Section 4.3. and find the equation for the median-median line. (See **APPENDIX 4C** for a way to use your calculator to find this equation.) Compare this equation to the one you found previously. Which equation do you feel is a better model for the data? Why?

10. Use the <u>World Records for the One Mile Run</u> data to answer the questions below.

Year	Runner	Time	Year	Runner	Time
1875	Walter Slade, Britain	4:24.5	1942	Arne Andersson, Sweden	4:06.2
1880	Walter George, Britain	4:23.2	1942	Haegg	4:04.6
1882	George	4:21.4	1943	Andersson	4:02.6
1882	George	4:19.4	1944	Andersson	4:01.6
1884	George	4:18.4	1945	Haegg	4:01.4
1894	Fred Bacon, Scotland	4:18.2	1954	Roger Bannister, Britain	3:59.4
1895	Bacon	4:17.0	1954	John Landry, Australia	3.58.0
1911	Thomas Connett, U. S.	4:15.6	1957	Derek Ibbotson, Britain	3:57.2
1911	John Paul Jones, U. S.	4:15.4	1958	Herb Elliott, Australia	3.54.5
1913	Jones	4:14.6	1962	Peter Snell, New Zealand	3:54.4
1915	Norman Taber, U. S.	4:12.6	1964	Snell	3:54.1
1923	Paavo Nurmi, Finland	4:10.4	1965	Michel Jazy, France	3:53.6
1931	Jules Ladonumegue, France	4:09.2	1966	Jim Ryun, U. S.	3:51.3
1933	Jack Lovelock, New Zealand	4:07.6	1967	Ryun	3:51.1
1934	Glen Cunningham, U. S.	4:06.8	1975	Filbert Bayi, Tanzania	3:51.0
1937	Sydney Wooderson, Britain	4:06.4	1975	John Walker, New Zealand	3:49.4
1942	Gunder Haegg, Sweden	4:06.2			

    a. What is the equation of the median-median line?

    b. What is the real-world meaning of the slope? What are the units of the slope?

    c. Use the equation to predict what new record might have been set in 1992.

    d. Describe some problems you might encounter with this type of extrapolation. Answer in complete sentences.

    e. Has a new world record been set since 1975? Find more recent information on this and compare it to the predictions of your model.

11. The median-median line procedure divides the data into three groups and uses the median x- and y-values. Devise a mean-mean line procedure and use it on the data in Problem 10. Compare this model to the median-median model.

12. Find a problem that you cannot solve (from this chapter or a previous chapter). Write out the problem and as much of the solution as you can. Then, clearly explain what is keeping you from solving the problem. Be as specific and clear as you can.

Section 4.5: The Residuals

The median-median line method is not perfect. In some cases, you can find a more accurate model drawing a line by hand than by following all the steps in the median-median line procedure. However, having a line that "looks better" is not a very convincing argument that it really is better. You must look at the differences between the points in your data set and the points generated by your model.

Look at the point on your line of best fit directly below (or above) each of the data points. The distance between the data point and the point on the line is called the **residual**. The residual is a **signed distance**, that is, it can be positive or negative. This is similar to the deviation from the mean you found in the previous chapter. Positive deviations

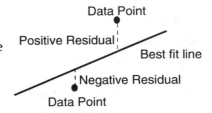

meant the value was above the mean, and negative deviations meant the value was below. Here, a positive residual indicates that the point is above the line and a negative residual indicates that the point is below the line. The line should have nearly as many points above it as below. You can state this more clearly by saying that the sum of the residuals should be near zero.

The manager of Cicero's Pizza must order supplies for the month of November. She looks at her records and finds the sales for the past four years. She decides to use the previous years' November sales figures to guide her purchases. November sales have been 512, 603, 642, and 775 pizzas. She graphs these using x-values of 1 through 4 to represent the last four years, and draws her best-fit line. Her equation is $y = 63.5x + 474$.

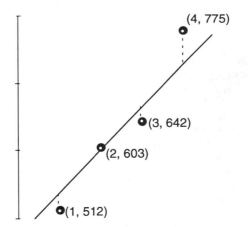

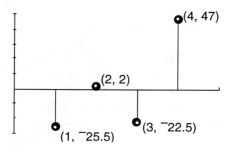

If you evaluate her equation at 1, 2, 3, and 4, you will find y-values of 537.5, 601, 664.5, and 728. The first residual is 512 − 537.5 = −25.5. The remaining residuals are +2, −22.5, and +47, respectively. The sum of these residuals is (−25.5 + 2 − 22.5 + 47) = 1, which is very close to zero. By the way, how many pizzas should she be prepared to sell this November?

By looking at the residual plot, you will sometimes be able to improve the equation of the line. In addition to a sum of nearly zero, you would like to see NO pattern in the residuals. If there is any pattern to the residuals, it is almost certain that there is a better equation that fits the data. You will learn more about this in later chapters. You can use your calculator to make a graph of the residuals. See **APPENDIX 4D** for help with residual plots.

The data below has a median-median line of $y = 0.067x − 2.359$.

Country	Cigarettes per Adult per year	CHD Mortality per 100,000
United States	3900	265
Canada	3350	212
Australia	3220	238
New Zealand	3220	212
United Kingdom	2790	194
Switzerland	2780	160
Ireland	2770	187
Iceland	2290	111
Finland	2160	208
West Germany	1890	150
Netherlands	1810	125
Greece	1800	41
Austria	1770	182
Belgium	1700	118
Mexico	1680	32
Italy	1510	114
Denmark	1500	120
France	1410	60
Sweden	1270	127
Spain	1200	44
Norway	1090	90

Table of Coronary Heart Disease (CHD) per 100,000 people per year ages 35–64.
Source: *American Journal of Public Health*

The residuals for this data are plotted to the right. Notice that the range of the residuals is from −100 to 80. The sum of the residuals is −1.022. In some cases, you might be able to shift the line slightly and get a better distribution of the residuals.

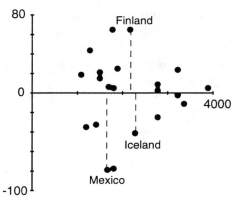

Residuals can also help you find points that are not true to the data. The data below was gathered in a lab by measuring the current through a circuit with constant resistance as the voltage was varied.

Volts	5.000	7.500	10.000	12.500	15.000	17.500	20.000
Milliamps	2.354	3.527	4.698	5.871	7.151	8.225	9.403

On the left is the graph of the data and a best-fit line. On the right is the graph of the residuals.

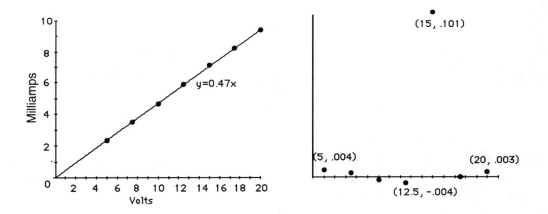

The scale of the y-axis of the first graph is from 0 to 10, while the range of the residuals is from −0.004 to +0.101. From the first graph, you only have confirmation that the line is a good fit. From the second, you can see that six of the seven data points are within 0.004 of a milliamp of the line, but one point is about 25 times as inaccurate as the worst of the others. This point is called an **outlier**; it could indicate that this particular measurement was inaccurate, or that some unusual phenomenon ocurred. Either way, it is worth further investigation back in the lab.

Examining the residuals can help you find a "better" line. The graph on the left shows the residuals for a set of data and a preliminary "best fit" equation. Because most of the residuals are positive, you can improve the fit of the equation by increasing the y-intercept, thus raising the line. The graph on the right shows the result of doing so.

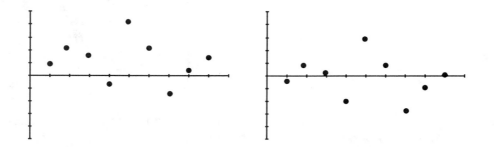

The graph on the left below shows another set of hypothetical residuals for some line. Because there seems to be a definite slope to the residuals, you could change the slope of the line. The middle graph shows the new residuals for an adjusted line with steeper slope. Now a line drawn through the residuals would have a zero slope, but this line needs to be moved down in order to be centered in the points. The graph on the right shows the results of decreasing the y-intercept.

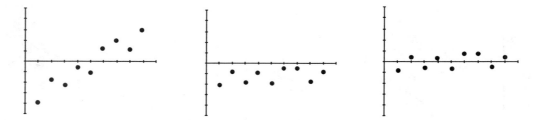

Knowing how to make these changes is a matter of practice. In the problems, you will have the opportunity to improve on some "best-fit" lines. If you think the slope needs to be changed, do this before changing the intercept. Don't try to change both the slope and the y-intercept at the same time.

Preliminary Edition   Chapter 4

Airline Schedules Activity

For this activity, you will need an airline timetable that includes both flight times and distances. You will also need a time zone map.

a. Choose a major city as a starting point.

b. Record the flight times and distances to at least 12 other continental United States cities. Choose only nonstop flights.

c. Plot these as ordered pairs (*time, distance*).

d. Find the median-median line for your data.

e. What is the real-world meaning of the slope?

f. What is the meaning of the *y*-intercept?

g. Find the value of the *x*-intercept and explain its real-world meaning.

h. Next, calculate the residuals by completing a table like the one below. The first two columns are the original data. The third column is found by calculating the *y*-value of the equation for time *x*. The last column is found by subtracting the third column from the second.

From: *Name of City*

Destination	Time	Distance	Computed distance	residual
Name of City	90 minutes	402 miles	**417 miles**	−15 miles

When you have completed the table, find the greatest positive and negative residuals. Check those points again in the airline table. See if a particular flight time is different at other times of day. Are there any flights that would fit your model better? Why do you suppose the times vary?

Problem Set 4.5

1. The median-median line for a set of data is $y = 2.4x + 3.6$. Find the residual for each point.

    a. $(2, 8.2)$ b. $(4, 12.8)$ c. $(10, 28.2)$

2. Return to Problem 7, Section 4.4 (about life expectancy). Using the equation you found for the median-median line, plot the residuals with your calculator.

    a. Describe the residuals.

    b. What must be done to better balance the residuals?

    c. Make a small change in the y-intercept of your equation, to see if you can improve the fit by splitting the data points more evenly.

    d. How much does this change your prediction of the life expectancy of a child born in 1991?

3. The average height in centimeters of United States children from ages 7 to 15 is given below.

Age	7	8	9	10	11	12	13	14	15
Height	119.3	127.0	132.0	137.1	142.2	147.3	152.4	157.5	162.2

    Source: *1990 Physicians Handbook*.

    a. Plot the data and find the median-median line.

    b. Plot the residuals and label the range.

    c. Which points stand out in the residual plot?

    d. Give an argument why the points represented by these residuals do not fit the model.

4. Consider the residuals from Problem 3.

    a. Make a box plot of these values.

    b. Write a paragraph that conveys the information about the residuals that is shown in the box plot.

5. The following readings were taken from a display outside the First River Bank. The display alternated between °F and °C. However, there was an error within the system that calculated the temperatures.

°F	18	33	37	25	40	46	43	49	55	60	57
°C	−6	2	3	−3	5	8	7	10	12	15	13

a. Plot the data and find the median-median line.

b. Plot the residuals.

c. You should see that the residuals are low on the left and high on the right. Adjust the slope of your line first, and then adjust the y-intercept to correct this distortion.

d. Using your new equation, what temperature do you expect to be paired with 85°F? (Remember, the bank will round off temperatures to the nearest degree.)

e. What temperature do you expect to be paired with 0°C on this thermometer?

6. A circle can be circumscribed around any regular polygon. Consider a set of regular polygons whose side lengths are one unit. The lengths of the radii of the circumscribed circles are given in the table.

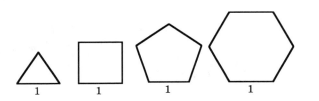

Polygon	n	Radius
Triangle	3	0.577
Square	4	0.707
Pentagon	5	0.851
Hexagon	6	1.000
Heptagon	7	1.152
Octagon	8	1.306
Nonagon	9	1.462
Decagon	10	1.618
Undecagon	11	1.775
Dodecagon	12	1.932

a. Trace each polygon and sketch its circumscribed circle. Draw and label the radius of each circle.

b. Plot the data and find the median-median line.

c. Plot the residuals.

d. Even though the line appears to fit the data, you should see a pattern in the residuals that tells you that, although this line may serve as a rough model, there is a better model that is not a line. Replace the linear equation with

$$y = \frac{0.5}{\sin \frac{180}{x}}$$

and check the residuals again. (Be certain your calculator is in degree mode.) What is the range of the residuals?

e. Use your knowledge of geometry to derive this formula.

7. Each graph below shows the residuals for a linear equation. What does each plot tell you about the use of a linear model for the data?

a.   b.   c.

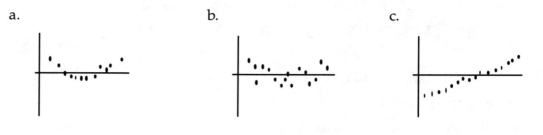

Section 4.6: The Least-Squares Line

Finding the equation of the median-median line is a surprisingly complex procedure for a computer or calculator, because of the decisions that must be made (such as the size of each group, and whether the median is a single number or the average of two numbers). However, there is another commonly-used "best-fit line" called the **least-squares line**, which is more easily done by a machine, because it involves no decisions, (just a lot of number crunching).

Begin with some data points and a line of best fit. Draw the residuals and find the length (value) of each one. Knowing that the sum of the residuals is small may mean the line fits the points well. If the residual sum is a large number, then either the points are not very linear, or the line was not well placed, or both. Still, it is possible for the sum of the residuals to be zero even when the line is a poor fit. (See Figure 1.) However, the **square** of each residual will be a positive number. So, to keep both the sum of the residuals small, and the residuals themselves small, you'll need to find a line where the sum of the squares of the residuals is a small number.

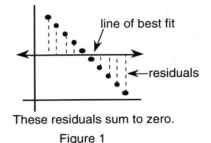

These residuals sum to zero.

Figure 1

Example 1: Determine which of the models, $y_1 = 1 + 2x$ and $y_2 = -3 + 2.5x$, best fits the four-point data sample.

x	y
4	7
6	15
9	17
12	25

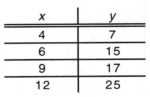

Solution: From the graph at the right, both appear to be good lines of best fit. The table below shows the residuals and their squares for each of these equations. Note that y_2 has the smaller residual sum, but y_1 has the smaller sum of the squared residuals. So y_1 is considered the better of the two models. According to the calculator, the line with the smallest sum of the squared residuals is $y_3 = 0.18 + 2.04x$. Find the sum of the squares of the residuals for y_3. Did you get 10.94?

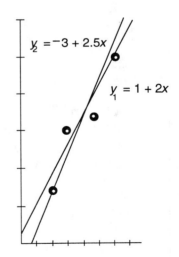

x	y	y_1	Residual	Residual²	y_2	Residual	Residual²
4	7	9	−2	4	7	0	0
6	15	13	2	4	12	3	9
9	17	19	−2	4	19.5	−2.5	6.25
12	25	25	0	0	27	−2	4
Total			−2	12		−1.5	19.25

You can picture the squares of the residuals in a drawing like the one on the right. Imagine summing the areas of all the black squares for each graph. The squares in the graph on the left cover a smaller area than the squares in the other graph.

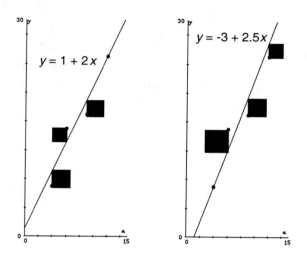

$y = 1 + 2x$

$y = -3 + 2.5x$

Finding the equation where the squares of the residuals have the smallest sum isn't much fun with four points, and becomes unmanageable with more. With the help of some calculus, the procedure can be simplified to a series of basic calculations that provide the equation of the least-squares line. For those of you who wish to know these formulas, see the projects in Section 4.10. Fortunately, your calculator can do these calculations with lightning speed and accuracy.

Example 2: Consider this data used in a previous section. Is the median-median line "better" than the least-squares line?

Volts	5.000	7.500	10.000	12.500	15.000	17.500	20.000
Milliamps	2.354	3.527	4.698	5.871	7.151	8.225	9.403

Solution: Find the least-squares line by entering the data into the calculator. (See **APPENDIX 4E**.) The slope is 0.4714 and the y-intercept is −0.0023. These values are close to, but not the same as, the values for the median-median line ($y = 0.4699x + 0.0017$).

Look at the graph of the residuals for each of the two lines. The median-median line (indicated by circles on the graph) has smaller residuals for all but one point, so it might be considered the better line. The median-median line is sometimes called the **resistant line** because it is not influenced as much by one or two "bad" data points. The least-squares line uses every point in its calculation, so it is affected by outliers.

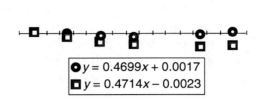

$$y = 0.4699x + 0.0017$$
$$y = 0.4714x - 0.0023$$

Relating Body Lengths Activity

Find 9 to 12 people (including yourself) and measure the lengths of two parts of each of their bodies (for example: the lengths of their ears and the distances from the backs of their knees to the bottoms of their heels).

a. Record the information in a table.

b. Find the median-median line to fit the data.

c. Make a plot of the data and of the residuals for this line.

d. Give the range of your residuals.

e. Find the least-squares line for this data.

f. Make a plot of the residuals for this line and give the range.

g. Compare the two models and write a paragraph summarizing which one is better, and why. Describe the relationship between the body parts measured.

Problem Set 4.6

1. Each graph below shows similar data sets. The graph on the right has two points which are different. These points might be considered outliers for the set. Copy the graphs into your homework. On each grid, identify the three groups of points for the median-median line procedure. Then plot the three representative points. How do these summary points compare in the two graphs? How will the median-median line be affected by the outliers? Will this always be the case when there are outlying points?

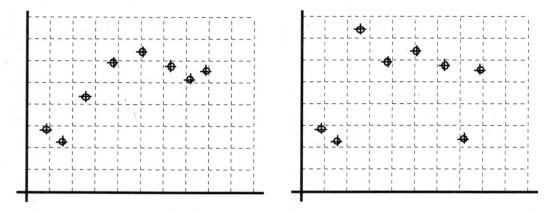

2. What are the major differences (name at least two) between the median-median method and the least-squares line method for finding the line of best fit?

3. Use the data from Example 2 with the outlying point removed, and calculate the new least-squares line. Compare this to the least-squares equation that used all of the data. Calculate a new median-median line. Compare it to the median-median line that used all of the data. Explain what it means to be a *resistant line*, and why the median-median line has this property.

4. Why is it important to minimize the sum of the **squares** of the residuals? Try to think of another option you could use to find a best-fit line. Explain what advantage or disadvantage the squares of the residuals have over other options?

5. Use the data in Problem 3, Section 4.5.

   a. Find the equation of the least-squares line.

   b. Verify that the least-squares line passes through the mean x and mean y values.

   c. Decide which of the two equations, the median-median line or the least-squares line, is a better model, and write a paragraph defending your choice.

6. Use the data in Problem 5, Section 4.5.

   a. Find the equation of the least-squares line.

   b. Verify that the least-squares line passes through the mean x and mean y values.

   c. Decide which of the two equations, the median-median line or the least-squares line, is a better model, and write a paragraph defending your choice.

7. A 20-yr $60,000 mortgage on a new home has an annual interest rate of 9.5%.

   a. Find the final balance for several different monthly payments. What is the minimum number of points needed to find the equation of the least-squares line?

   b. Find the least-squares line that fits this data.

   c. Use the equation of the line to find the payment that gives a balance of near zero after 20 yr.

8. Look back at the definition of deviation in Chapter 3. Compare this measure of error to the residual. How do they relate to each other? How are they different?

9. Another measure of error is the mean absolute residual. This is the mean of the absolute values of all the residuals. Determine this value for the model in the activity. Describe how you could use this value to determine if the line is a good fit.

10. This data gives the average daily maximum temperatures in April for various cities in North America, and the corresponding latitudes in degrees and minutes north.

Place	Lat.	Temp
Acapulco, Mex.	16°51'	87
Bakersfield, CA	35°26'	73
Caribou, ME	46°52'	50
Charleston, SC	32°54'	74
Chicago, IL	41°59'	55
Dallas, TX	32°54'	75
Denver, CO	39°46'	54
Duluth, MN	46°50'	52
Great Falls, MT	47°29'	56
Juneau, AK	58°18'	39
Kansas City, MO	39°19'	59
Los Angeles, CA	33°56'	69
Mexico City, Mex.	19°25'	78
Miami, FL	25°49'	81
New Orleans, LA	29°59'	77
New York, NY	40°47'	60
Ottawa, Ont.	46°26'	51
Phoenix, AZ	33°26'	83
Quebec, Que.	46°48'	45
Salt Lake City, UT	40°47'	58
San Francisco, CA	37°37'	65
Seattle, WA	47°27'	56
Vancouver, BC.	49°18'	58
Washington, DC	38°51'	64

a. Find the equation of the least-squares line. (Note: You will need to convert the latitudes to decimal degrees; for example,
$35°26' = 35\frac{26}{60} \approx 35.43°$.)

b. What is an appropriate domain for this model?

c. Which cities appear not to follow the pattern? Give a reason for each of these cases.

d. Choose two cities not on the list, and find the latitude for each. Use your model to predict the average daily maximum temperature in April for each city. Compare your result with the official average April temperature for the city. (An almanac is usually a good source for this information.)

11. The table below shows the percentage of women in the United States labor force.

Year	1950	1960	1970	1980	1990
Percent	29.6	33.4	38.1	42.5	45.3

a. Find the least-squares line for this data. (Use 1900 as the reference year.)

b. What is the real-world meaning of the slope? Of the y-intercept?

c. According to your model, what percent of the labor force is currently made up of women? Check with an almanac to see how accurate your prediction is.

12. Consider again the role of the graphing calculator in this course. In this chapter, have you discovered new advantages, or disadvantages, of using the graphing calculator? If so, what are they? Has your perspective or your feelings changed towards the use of the graphing calculator? Be clear and explain your response.

Section 4.7: Coefficient of Correlation

Two students, Woody and Forrest, collected data on tree diameters and heights. They plotted the data on graph paper. Woody put the diameters on the x-axis and the heights on the y-axis. Forrest squared the diameters and plotted them on the x-axis, and the heights on the y-axis. Each found a best-fit line for his data. Their graphs are shown below:

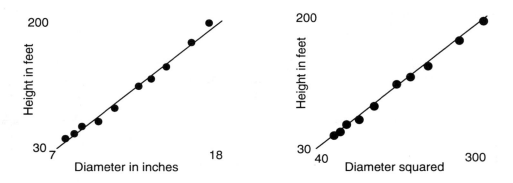

Which student found the better relationship? How good is the fit for each line? Each student believes he has found the best-fit line for his data. But is a line the appropriate model? Is there a linear relationship between Woody's original data, or is it a better relationship if you look at Forrest's data using the squares of the diameters?

One answer is to give the sum of the residuals, but you have seen that even a very poor fit can have a zero sum. You can give the range of the residuals, but this is misleading in data sets that have one or two outliers falling much farther from the line than the rest of the data. A measure that is sometimes used is the mean absolute value of the residuals. (See **APPENDIX 4F**.) There are many other measures. The most commonly used measure is called the **correlation coefficient**, denoted by the letter r (probably by the same person who chose the letter m for slope).

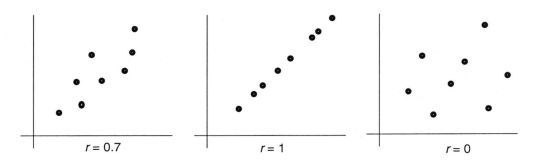

Values of r range from -1 to 1. A value of zero shows absolutely no linear correlation between the values of x and y. A value of ±1 shows a perfect correlation between x and y, meaning that the data pairs fall exactly on a line. The sign of r will be the same as the sign of the slope of the best-fit line. This means that a correlation coefficient of 0.94 for one data set and of -0.94 for another are equally accurate. For Woody's data, the correlation coefficient is 0.992. That's pretty good. For Forrest's data the correlation coefficient is 0.999. That's even better. So, for the trees measured, the relationship between the squares of the diameters and the heights is more linear.

The formal definition of r is too complex for this course, so we will use a simpler, more workable definition based on the square of the correlation coefficient.

> The value of r^2 is a percent measure of the data points that fall within a narrow linear band.

This means that if $r = 0.5$, then $r^2 = 0.25$, and 25% of the points fall within a narrow band. If $r = 0.7$, then $r^2 = 0.49$, and 49% of the points fall with a narrow band. Therefore, a coefficient of 0.7 is almost twice as good as a coefficient of 0.5 would be. Terms like "very close" and "narrow band" are not very precise, but they do allow you to use the values of r for purposes of comparison. The value of r gives you information about the data itself, not about any specific equation. It is calculated at the same time as the least-squares equation, but is not specifically tied to that equation. To determine how well a specific equation fits, look at the residuals, distribution, their relative sizes, and their sum.

Example 1: In a recent election, eight candidates ran for class president. Two "scores" were recorded for each candidate. The first was the candidate's combined SAT score. The second was the candidate's popularity, measured by the number of students who considered the candidate a friend, in a random poll of 100 students. The third column shows the number of votes that each candidate received. Which of these two measures seems to have a greater influence on the number of votes received?

Name	SAT	Popularity	Votes
Ajene	1210	65	60
Benny	1450	40	26
Caron	1380	58	47
Doug	1580	21	40
Erica	940	61	29
Fuyu	1320	51	71
Gert	1470	78	104
Hector	1320	47	52

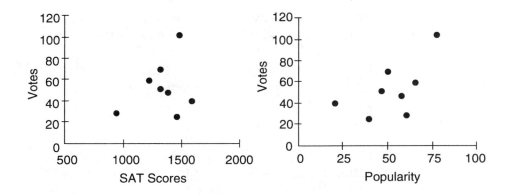

Solution: The (*SAT score, votes*) data pairs have an *r*-value of 0.25. The (*friends, votes*) data pairs have an *r*-value of 0.61. Of the two factors, friendliness has more vote-getting potential than smarts. Further investigation shows that $r^2 = 0.06$ in case one, or that only 6% of the points fall in a linear band. For this group of eight people, this is less than one person. In other words, there is no linear relationship for (*SAT scores, votes*). In the case of (*popularity, votes*), $r^2 = 0.38$. There is a very weak (38%) linear relationship between these two variables. So you must conclude that voting depends on some factor (or combination of factors) other than those presented here.

Example 2: The table at the right shows the normal monthly temperatures for New York City. Is there a correlation between the month and the temperature?

Month	Temperature
January	32
February	33
March	41
April	53
May	62
June	71
July	77
August	75
September	68
October	58
November	47
December	36

Solution: It seems easy to say "Yes, look at the way the numbers rise and fall." But this is neither precise nor conclusive. If you number the months consecutively you can name 12 ordered pairs to analyze: (1, 32), (2, 33), (3, 41), (4, 53), (5, 62), . . . , (12, 36). For this set of data, (*month, temp*), $r = 0.31$, and $r^2 = 0.10$. There is hardly any correlation at all. The meaning of linear correlation is that as the values of the domain increase, then the values of the range *must react in direct response* to that change, either always increasing or always decreasing. But, in this example, going from February to March has the opposite effect of going from August to September. While there is probably a relationship of some kind between the month and the temperature, it is not linear.

Example 3: This table shows the average height (in centimeters) of United States children from ages 7 to 15. How linear is this data?

Age	7	8	9	10	11	12	13	14	15
Height (cm)	119.3	127.0	132.0	137.1	142.2	147.3	152.4	157.5	162.2

Source:*1990 Physicians Handbook.*

Solution: The least-square model is *height* = 84.3 + 5.235(*age*). The coefficient of correlation is 0.99864796, or, to three digits, $r = 0.999$. This is a highly accurate model having an $r^2 = 0.997$. The data is very linear through the domain given. Do you suspect it will be linear much outside this domain? Explain why, or why not.

Analyzing Cereals Activity

The following table lists some information written on cereal boxes.

a. Compare the categories to find which have the strongest linear relationships.

b. Which of the characteristics of the cereals are most related? Can you explain the reason for any of these relationships?

c. Write a paragraph describing the relationships you discover. Include any nonrelationships that you find surprising.

Percent of Recommended Daily Allowance

	Thiamine	Riboflavin	Iron	Phosphorus	Magnesium
Spoon size Shredded Wheat	4	0	4	10	8
100% Bran	25	25	45	30	30
Shredded Wheat 'n' Bran	4	0	8	10	10
Grape-Nuts	25	25	45	6	6
Banana Nut Crunch	25	25	10	8	6
Golden Crisp	25	25	10	4	4
Post Raisin Bran	35	35	35	15	15
Marshmallow Alpha-Bits	25	25	15	6	4
Fruity Pebbles	25	25	10	0	0
Honey-Comb	25	25	15	2	2
Total	100	100	100	20	6
Fiber One	25	25	25	15	15
Trix	25	25	25	2	2
Cocoa Puffs	25	25	25	4	0
Special K	35	35	25	0	4
Corn Flakes	25	25	10	0	0
Frosted Flakes	25	25	10	0	0
Corn Pops	25	25	10	0	0
Product 19	100	100	100	4	2
Fruit Loops	25	25	25	2	2
Rice Krispies	25	25	10	4	2
Life	30	30	45	0	0
Cheerios	25	25	45	10	10

Problem Set 4.7

1. What is the slope of the line that passes through the point (4, 7), and is parallel to the line $y = 12(x - 5) + 21$?

2. Find the equation of the line passing through (4, 0) and (6, −3).

3. Find the point on the line $y = 16.8x + 405$ where x is equal to −19.5.

4. This table shows the percent of the African-American population that dropped out of high school in the years from 1970 through 1990.

Year	1970	1975	1980	1985	1987	1988	1989	1990
Percent	22.2	18.5	16.0	13.8	12.7	12.0	11.4	11.2

   a. What is the least-squares model for this data?

   b. What is the coefficient of correlation for this model?

   c. Using complete sentences, explain what this correlation coefficient tells you about the model.

   d. Use the model to predict what the percentage was in 1972.

   e. How accurate do you think your prediction is? (On a scale of 1 to 10 with 10 being *very* accurate.)

5. This data lists the number of bound volumes, the annual circulation, and the annual cost of operations for randomly selected public libraries. Each of the numbers in the table is in thousands.

City	Volumes	Circulation	Cost
Atlanta, GA	1600	2183	9453
Baton Rouge, LA	493	1641	2631
Boston, MA	4916	1454	11500
Buffalo, NY	3426	6228	12344
Columbus, OH	1353	4320	11500
Dallas, TX	1777	3874	14847
Denver, CO	1178	2570	11398
Detroit, MI	2446	1441	14690
Kansas City, MO	1346	875	5091
Memphis, TN	1535	2500	8726
Oakland, CA	779	1633	5869
Philadelphia, PA	3038	5205	22379
Portland, OR	1179	3237	5526
St. Paul, MN	657	1942	4640

   a. How strongly is each measure, volumes and circulation, tied to cost of operation?

   b. Which of the two seems to have the stronger correlation to cost?

   c. Explain your reasoning using complete sentences.

6. This table shows the number of seats on various types of airplanes, the planes' cruising speeds, and their operating costs per hour.

   a. How strongly is each measure, seats and speed, related to operating cost?

   b. Which of the two seems to have the stronger correlation to cost?

   c. Explain your reasoning using complete sentences.

Plane	Seats	Speed	Cost
B747–400	403	534	7098
B747–100	399	520	5905
L–1011–100/200	293	495	4072
DC–10–10	282	488	4056
A300–600	266	474	3917
DC–10–30	265	522	4595
B767–300	224	489	3384
B757–200	188	458	2293
B767–200	187	483	2956
A320–100/200	149	441	1868
B727–200	148	430	2263
B737–400	145	400	1743
MD–80	142	419	1842
B737–300	131	415	1768
DC–9–50	122	387	1640
B727–100	117	429	2220
B737–100/200	112	387	1735
DC–9–30	102	381	1658
F–100	99	361	1445
DC–9–10	77	361	1439

7. What is the coefficient of correlation for the data from the Relating Body Lengths Activity? How does that affect the conclusions you made?

8. Consider the data below showing (*number of students, number of faculty*) at selected colleges and universities. (Be sure to save this data in your calculator. You will need it in the next section.)

   a. Find an equation that relates the number of students to the number of faculty, and another equation that relates faculty to students.

   b. Describe the correlation in this data. Use complete sentences and discuss *r* and r^2.

College	Number of students	Number of faculty	College	Number of students	Number of faculty
Agnes Scott College	600	66	Penn State	37,269	1,986
Alfred University	2,593	175	Princeton University	6,140	800
Bennington College	613	78	Rhode Island Schl of Design	1,916	275
Boston University	28,557	2,707	Rhodes College	1,346	149
Bowling Green State U	17,882	845	St. John's College	1,998	156
Brandeis University	3,689	496	St. Olaf College	3,121	382
Brown University	7,612	548	Spelman College	2,075	116
Bryn Mawr College	1,849	137	Stanford University	13,224	1,315
California College of Arts	1,119	167	Stockton State College	5,297	243
Carleton College	1,885	151	Swarthmore College	1,333	179
College of William & Mary	7,372	716	Syracuse University	16,821	1,050
Cornell University	18,088	1,597	Tufts University	7,868	589
DePaul University	24,80	218	Tuskegee University	3,371	254
DePauw University	14,699	734	University of Central Florida	18,094	754
Drake University	6,618	256	University of Cincinnati	26,475	1,457
Duquesne University	6,370	479	University of Colorado	10,090	624
Eastman School of Music	1,232	122	University of Delaware	11,090	693
Florida State University	23,883	1,434	University of Hawaii at Manoa	19,836	1,249
Gallaudet University	2,031	300	University of Houston	30,372	2,025
Hampshire College	1,232	112	University of Iowa	29,230	1,600
Howard University	10,538	1,195	University of Massachusetts	25,216	1,412
Illinois Wesleyan University	1,750	157	U niversity of Miami	11,397	1,934
Lehigh University	6,569	487	University of Michigan	35,220	3,619
Maryland Institute C. of Art	1,285	112	University of Minnesota	38,172	2,836
Miami U. of Ohio	16,044	840	University of Nevada	15,000	521
Michigan State University	42,695	3,990	University of South Florida	30,003	1,422
Mills College	1,141	74	University of Tulsa	4,431	400
Morehouse College	3,150	150	University of Utah	23,626	924
Mt. Holyoke College	1,947	203	University of Virginia	17,198	1,804
New England Conservatory	781	191	Webster University	9,049	353
New Mexico State University	15,788	651	Wesleyan University	2,938	346
New York University	31,690	5,428	Western Michigan University	24,861	1,223
Northwestern University	11,337	729	Wheaton College	2,445	236
Oakland University	12,254	617	Yale University	10,998	718

9. Consider the sample of the schools from the above list that have less than 2000 students.

   a. Find an equation that relates the number of students to the number of faculty, and another equation that relates faculty to students.

   b. Describe the correlation in this data. Use complete sentences and discuss r and r^2.

10. What ideas or topics were introduced in this chapter that you feel you do not yet understand or see the purpose of? Give examples.

Section 4.8: Accuracy

"Nine out of ten dentists recommend . . .", "Prices expected to rise 4% over the next year. . .", "Health care costs to double in the next 10 years. . ."

Many numerical claims such as these appear in news releases or in advertisements. Use of data or statistics can inform *or* mislead you. The purpose of this section is to help you understand the accuracy of predictions. Concentrate on the concepts of this section rather than the mathematics. Your answers should be based both on mathematics and on a common-sense understanding of the situation.

The accuracy of any model used to study a phenomenon or make a prediction is largely dependent on two factors. The first is the accuracy of the data that was used to create the model. For example, if all of your data were temperatures rounded to the nearest degree, then it would be misleading and unscientific to use a model to predict temperatures to the tenth of a degree. Proper use of significant digits is a major concern in scientific applications.

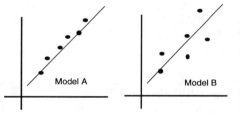

The second factor is how well or accurately the equation fits the data. Consider two sets of data gathered with very similar accuracy. From each data set a model is derived. In Model A, the coefficient of correlation (*r*) is 0.995, and in Model B, the *r*-value is 0.647. You can certainly use model A for predictions with much greater accuracy than Model B.

A low *r*-value does not always mean disaster. You may look at the residuals and see a case such as that shown at the right. If the three points far below the line can be traced to measurements made by one person, or with one piece of equipment, then you may have reason to disregard them. The accuracy of your model will then be much higher.

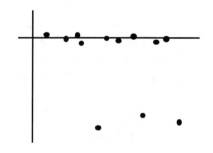

Is it important for you to give the accuracy of a model? In routine usage of a model, a little less accuracy will not hurt. However, if it is a medical model involving lives, or a financial model that is critical to the existence of a company and its employees, accuracy can be very important. For example, if a mathematical model predicts a patient can undergo radiation for 10.785 min before there is damage to healthy cells, then the doctor may decide to give a 10-min treatment. But if it is known that there is a 2.5-min error factor in the model, then the treatment might be shortened to as little as 8 min, to be safe.

There are several ways to estimate the accuracy of a model. One way is to look at the range of the residuals: their maximum and minimum values. A second way to estimate the accuracy is to consider the average size of the residuals. In the following examples, you will examine both of these methods.

Example 1: Consider the data collected from the U. S. Bureau of the Census showing the number of one-parent families headed by a male, from 1965 through 1990.

Year	'65	'70	'75	'80	'85	'90
Households (in thousands)	1,168	1,228	1,485	1,733	2,228	2,884

The least-squares regression, using 1900 as the base year is $y = 67.589x - 3450.448$ and $r = 0.9558141192$. Predict the number of one-parent families in 1972 that were headed by a male.

Solution: Using 72 for x in the regression equation gives a value of 1,415,929.52 families. Because it is difficult to picture what 0.52 of a family would look like, you can give the answer as 1,415,930 families. However, because your data doesn't include this much accuracy, you should round to 1,416,000. The square of the correlation coefficient is 0.914 or about 91%. The residuals range between −224,000 and +251,000 families. The "residual range" gives a range of 1,192,000 to 1,667,000 families. Your best answer to this problem may be 1,400,000 ± 200,000 families.

Year	'65	'70	'75	'80	'85	'90
Households	1,168	1,228	1,485	1,733	2,228	2,884
Residual	225	−53	−134	−224	−67	251

The range of the residuals in the last problem was a useful guide. The actual residuals are 225, −53, −134, −224, −67, 251. Three of the six residuals are greater than two hundred. What if you have a case where one residual is +200 units and the remaining points are within ±30 units of the best-fit line? Would you be compelled to think that any prediction you make is, at best, within 200 units of the line? You would likely find that you have a higher r^2 value for this case, so you could justify a more accurate result.

Another technique is to use the mean (average) absolute value of the residuals as a measure of accuracy for your prediction. (This is similar to using the mean deviation in Chapter 3). In Example 1, this mean absolute value is 159. So your answer might be 1,416,000 ± 159,000. (See **APPENDIX F**.) There are many possible answers, depending on the method used for determining the accuracy. Being able to justify your answer is the important thing.

Example 2: The contamination of Lake Michigan trout by DDT dropped steadily between 1970 and 1984. This data represents the mean concentration of DDT found in lake trout caught and tested by the EPA Great Lakes National Program Office for the years from 1970 to 1984.

Year	1970	1971	1972	1973	1974	1975	1976
mg/Kg	19.1	13.4	11.5	10.1	8.3	7.5	5.5

Year	1977	1978	1979	1980	1981	1982	1984
mg/Kg	6.0	4.7	6.9	4.9	3.1	3.0	2.7

Use the least-squares line to estimate when the fish would show no concentration of the DDT. (Use a reference year of 1900.)

Solution: The equation of the least-squares line is $y = 81.3 - 0.962x$, where y is the concentration in milligrams of DDT per kilogram of fish, and x is the years since 1900. Setting y equal to zero, you find x equals 84.5, which indicates the year 1985. The residuals for the points are 5.2, 0.42, −0.52, −0.96, −1.8, −1.6, −2.7, −1.2, −1.5, 1.6, 0.58, −0.26, 5.99, and 2.22. Taking the absolute values of these and averaging them gives the mean absolute residual of 1.5 mg/Kg. If you think of a band of this width along both sides of your best-fit line, you see that the boundaries of your range stem from 1983 to 1986. This can be found by setting y equal to zero in the two boundary equations $y = 81.3 - 0.962x \pm 1.5$.

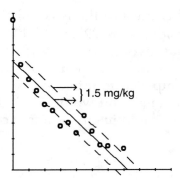

If you study the residual plot you might conclude that a line might not be the best model for this data, as there seems to be a pattern to the residuals.

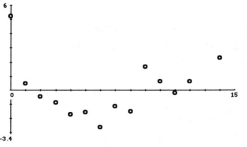

It is risky to try to extrapolate or forecast far into the future with any model. In the last example, the model predicts a negative concentration of DDT if you try to use it too far into the future. Weather predictions may be very accurate for one or two days into the future, but few people would rely on predictions made six months in advance. The accuracy of any prediction drops off quickly as you move into uncharted data. In Example 2, you could show this on the graph by flaring away from the best-fit line as you pass the final data point. The bands on both sides of the data show greater inaccuracy as you use the model to extrapolate further and further from your data.

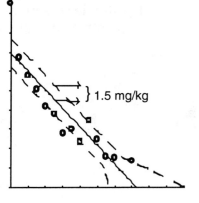

Problem Set 4.8

1. Examine the three scatter plots below.

    a. Which is the plot with the least linear correlation? Why?

    b. Which is the plot with the most linear correlation? Why?

    c. Which (if any) plots show negative correlation? How can you tell?

2. Copy the following table into your homework.

x	4	7	11	12.9	16	18.5
y	22	47	74	87	111	128
$y_1(x)$						
residual						
residual^2						

    a. Find the least-squares line (y_1), and complete the table.

    b. What is the range of the residuals?

    c. Find the sum of the absolute values of the residuals.

    d. Find the mean absolute residual.

    e. Find the sum of the squares of the residuals.

    f. Use the information calculated to analyze just how good y_1 is as a best-fit line.

3. Give an example (different from those given in the text) of when it would be of concern if a person overstated the accuracy of a prediction based on a mathematical model.

4. The data below was collected from students doing "The Wave."

Number of students	3	5	6	10	12	16	20	24
Time (seconds)	1.5	2.3	2.7	2.5	4.2	5.8	7.1	7.8

    a. Find the least-squares line for this data.

    b. Using your model, predict the time for 13 people.

    c. In a complete sentence, explain the accuracy of your prediction using the mean absolute residual.

5. You are given a model $y = 12.5 + 4.17x$, using values of x between 11 and 28, with a coefficient of correlation $r = 0.940$. The residuals range from -18.5 to $+15.8$, with a mean absolute residual of 11.2.

    a. What would you predict for y when $x = 19$?

    b. What accuracy can you give for your prediction? Describe how you might change this reported accuracy depending on what the model represented.

6. Return to the data in Problem 8, Section 4.7.

    a. Determine the mean absolute deviation for the residuals.

    b. List the schools that have residuals greater than one mean absolute deviation from the mean. What do these schools have in common?

    c. Which schools have residuals greater than two mean absolute deviations from the mean? What do these schools have in common?

    d. Explain why you think the schools in each of these lists lie so far from the model.

7. The table below gives the weights of transmitters used in some animal studies in the 1960s.

    a. Using the average of the weight range for each animal, find a relationship between the animal weights and the transmitter weights.

    b. Use your model to predict the proper weight of a transmitter for tracking *Alopex lagopus*, whose weight range is from 10,000 to 25,000 grams.

    c. Describe the accuracy of this prediction. Explain how you determined this.

    d. How might you improve this measure of accuracy using the same data?

Study	Species	Weight of animal (g)	Weight of transmitter package (g)
Rawson & Hartline (1964)	*Peromyscus sp.* (Deer Mouse)	10–35	2.6
Beal (1967)	*Sciurus carolinensis,* (Gray Squirrel)	340–680	21
	S. niger (Fox Squirrel)	545–1,360	21
Cochran et al. (1965)	*Sylvilagus floridanus* (Cottontail Rabbit)	900–1,800	32
Mech et al. (1965)	*Lepus americanus* (Snowshoe Hare)	900–1,800	50
Merriam (1963, 1966)	*Marmota monax* (Woodchuck)	2,300–4,500	45
Moore & Kluth (1966)	*Dasypus novemcinctus* (Nine Banded Armadillo)	3,400	40
Cochran et al. (1965)	*Vulpes fulva* (Red Fox)	4,500–6,800	130
Cochran et al. (1965)	*Taxidea taxus*	5,900–11,300	140

	(Badger)		
Mech et al. (1965)	*Procyon lotor*	5,400–15,900	115
	(Raccoon)		
Tester et al. (1964)	*Odocoileus virginianus*	34,000–91,000	180
	(White Tailed Deer)		
Cochran et al. (1965)	*Odocoileus virginianus*	34,000–91,000	300
	(White Tailed Deer)		
Craighead & Craighead (1965)	*Ursus arctos*	147,000–385,000	906
	(Polar Bear)		

Section 4.9: Chapter Review

Problem Set 4.9

1. Find the slope of the line containing the points (16, 1300) and (−22, 3250).

2. What is the slope of the line $y = -5.0247 + 23.45x$?

3. Find the point on the line $y = 16.8x + 405$, where y is equal to 740.

The following is a table of health indicators for some non-Western countries. Use this data when working the problems that follow.

Country	Life expectancy	Daily calorie supply	Infant mortality	Health services (%)	Safe water (%)	Sanitation (%)
Algeria	66	2,866	61	90	70	60
Angola	46	1,807	125	30	34	18
Benin	51	2,305	110	30	54	42
Botswana	68	2,375	35	89	60	42
Cambodia	51	2,166	116	53	37	15
Central African Republic	47	2,036	105	30	12	21
China	71	2,639	38	90	83	97
Egypt	62	3,336	57	99	88	51
Ethiopia	49	1,667	168	46	28	16
Ghana	55	2,248	81	60	54	42
Guinea	44	2,132	133	40	64	24
Indonesia	60	2,750	72	80	51	44
Iran	65	3,181	65	87	61	51
Iraq	64	2,887	58	99	91	70
Jordan	70	2,634	47	97	99	76
Kenya	59	2,163	66	77	50	43
Kuwait	75	3,195	14	100	100	98
Liberia	55	2,382	131	39	54	15
Libya	63	3,324	68	100	93	95
Madagascar	51	2,158	113	65	20	5
Malaysia	71	2,774	14	90	72	94
Mongolia	64	2,479	60	100	79	73
Mozambique	47	1,680	147	39	24	24
Niger	46	2,308	123	30	55	10
Nigeria	52	2,312	84	72	50	15
Papua New Guinea	56	2,403	54	97	32	56
Philippines	65	2,375	40	75	82	69
Rwanda	46	1,971	110	80	66	58
Saudi Arabia	69	2,874	31	98	93	82
Senegal	48	2,369	80	40	47	54

Singapore	75	3,198	6	100	100	96
Somalia	49	1,906	127	27	60	17
Sri Lanka	72	2,277	18	90	71	60
Sudan	52	1,974	99	60	45	70
Tanzania	51	2,206	115	80	51	66
Thailand	69	2,316	26	70	76	74
Togo	54	2,214	85	60	59	21
Zaire	52	1,991	91	40	33	25
Zambia	48	2,077	108	74	48	43
Zimbabwe	60	2,299	47	83	36	42

Source: pp. 379–380 *The Universal Almanac 1994–1995.*

Section 4.1

4. Determine good windows for viewing points given by each data pair.

   a. *(daily calorie supply, life expectancy)*

   b. *(availability of health services, infant mortality)*

   c. *(safe water, sanitation)*

Section 4.2

5. Refer to the *(daily calorie supply, life expectancy)* data. What is the slope of the line connecting the points associated with Rwanda and Kuwait?

6. Find the equation of the line using the points from Problem 5.

7. Graph the *(daily calorie supply, life expectancy)* data points and the line from Problem 6 on your calculator. Experiment by changing the *y*-intercept and/or the slope until you find an equation that appears to be a better fit for the data.

Section 4.3

8. What is the domain for the line in Problem 7? What are the units of the domain?

9. What are the units of the slope for the equation you found in Problem 7?

10. Give a real-world meaning for the slope and the *y*-intercept for the line in Problem 7.

11. Use your equation from Problem 7 to predict the daily calorie supply for a country whose people have a life expectancy of 57 years.

12. What life expectancy would you predict for a country whose average daily calorie value is 2012?

Section 4.4

13. What is the median of the life expectancy values?

14. What are the three points you would use to find the equation of the median-median line for the (*safe water, life expectancy*) data?

15. What is the slope of the median-median line, based on the three points you named in Problem 14?

16. What is the equation of the median-median line?

Section 4.5

17. Draw a graph of the residuals on your calculator. What does this graph tell you about your model?

18. What is the residual for the point representing Ethiopia? Explain how you calculated this number.

19. Which point most poorly fits the median-median line, from Problem 16?

Section 4.6

20. Find the least-squares line for the (*health services, infant mortality*) data.

21. Write a sentence explaining the real-world meaning of the slope.

22. Find the median-median line for the data in Problem 20. Compare this equation to the one for the least-squares line. Which line seems to be the best fit for the data?

23. What infant mortality rate would each of the models predict for a health service rate of 55%?

Section 4.7

24. What is the coefficient of correlation for the least-squares line in Problem 20? Explain the significance of this value.

25. Sort the data in ascending order according to the residuals for the least-squares line. Delete the first three data points and the last three data points. Find the least-squares line and the coefficient of correlation for this altered set of data points. Describe how removing these points changes the equation of the least-squares line and the coefficient of correlation.

Section 4.8

26. How would you describe the accuracy of your solution to Problem 23?

27. Describe at least three conclusions you can make based on your analysis in Problems 4–26.

Section 4.10: Projects

Project 4.1: Least-Squares Formulas

Where do the numbers come from in a least-squares analysis? Given n points of data, $\sum\limits_{i=1}^{n} x_i$ is equal to the sum of all the x-values in the data. Likewise, $\sum\limits_{i=1}^{n} y_i$ is equal to the sum of the y-values from 1 to n. The sum of the squares of the x-values is $\sum\limits_{i=1}^{n} x_i^2$, and $\sum\limits_{i=1}^{n} x_i y_i$ is the sum of the products of the x- and y-values.

Year	1965	1970	1975	1979	1980	1981	1982
Households (in thousands)	1,181	1,239	1,499	1,655	1,733	1,933	1,986

For each pair of data points, find the values in the table. Use 1900 as the reference year. Sum the values in each column. Use these sums to evaluate each formula given below.

n	x	y	x^2	y^2	xy
1	.	.	.	.	.
2	.	.	.	.	.
.	.	.	.	.	.
sum					

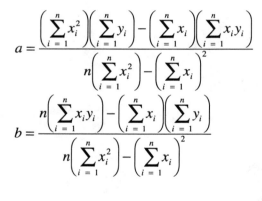

$$a = \frac{\left(\sum\limits_{i=1}^{n} x_i^2\right)\left(\sum\limits_{i=1}^{n} y_i\right) - \left(\sum\limits_{i=1}^{n} x_i\right)\left(\sum\limits_{i=1}^{n} x_i y_i\right)}{n\left(\sum\limits_{i=1}^{n} x_i^2\right) - \left(\sum\limits_{i=1}^{n} x_i\right)^2}$$

$$b = \frac{n\left(\sum\limits_{i=1}^{n} x_i y_i\right) - \left(\sum\limits_{i=1}^{n} x_i\right)\left(\sum\limits_{i=1}^{n} y_i\right)}{n\left(\sum\limits_{i=1}^{n} x_i^2\right) - \left(\sum\limits_{i=1}^{n} x_i\right)^2}$$

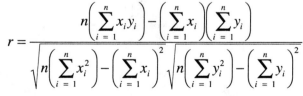

$$r = \frac{n\left(\sum\limits_{i=1}^{n} x_i y_i\right) - \left(\sum\limits_{i=1}^{n} x_i\right)\left(\sum\limits_{i=1}^{n} y_i\right)}{\sqrt{n\left(\sum\limits_{i=1}^{n} x_i^2\right) - \left(\sum\limits_{i=1}^{n} x_i\right)^2}\sqrt{n\left(\sum\limits_{i=1}^{n} y_i^2\right) - \left(\sum\limits_{i=1}^{n} y_i\right)^2}}$$

Enter the data in your calculator and verify the values for a, (the y-intercept), b, (the slope), and r, (the correlation coefficient), by using the built-in least-squares regression.

Project 4.2: Linear Extrapolation

Look through magazines and newspapers to find a case when someone has used a linear mathematical model to project into the future. (This is usually identifiable by a graph in which the rightmost portion is drawn with a dashed line.) Study the data and determine your best guess at the method used by the author to find the line. Offer other models with the same data and give projections using those models. What is your best guess at the accuracy of the forecast? Give your reasons for this measure of accuracy. If it is an old article, try to find data to determine if the model remains nearly accurate today.

Project 4.3: Talkin' Trash Project

The amount of trash that this country produces is staggering. And with the growing population, we have a growing problem! It is estimated that 190 million tons of trash were placed in United States landfills during the year 1993. Even as you read this, landfills are eating up more and more space. There are already over 9,000 of them in the United States; more than 80% of them will have to be closed within the next 20 years. It is becoming more difficult to locate new sites; people don't want them in their communities because they leak, stink, and pollute!

Year	Waste (million tons/year)	Population (millions)
1960	87	179
1965	104	190
1970	121	203
1975	136	214
1980	150	227
1985	166	238
1990	182	249

How much trash do you think you and your family generate each day? Does your family recycle and try not to waste? Is recycling our only solution? What are some alternatives to landfills and recycling? As you complete this project, keep your own habits of trash disposal in mind.

Describe how you find or select your models, and provide real-world meanings for all equation values. Use complete sentences as you write up your results. Try to discover more information about this problem.

Find best-fit models for (*year, waste*) and (*year, population*). Select a domain and range to view all the data and graphs. Predict the population and the amount of waste that you might expect in the years 1995 and 2000. Use your graphs and equations to help you decide if the amount of waste is increasing because of the increase in population, or if there more to this situation. Justify your answer.

Calculate a new column of data which contains pounds per person per day. Explain how you calculated these values. Analyze and sketch a graph of this data. Predict the number of pounds of garbage per person per year, for the years 1995 and 2000. Do some research to find out if this result typical of other countries.

Investigate the total amount of trash from your household for some convenient time period. Calculate the pounds per person per day from your household. Compare your result to the data provided in the table.

Project 4.4: Counting Forever

How long would it take to count to one million? Some numbers require more time to say; some numbers have one digit, some have two digits, and so on. Collect data by recording the time required to say different numbers. Prepare a table showing the number of digits and the time it takes to say the number. Explain the procedure you used to collect this data. Describe the approach you used to determine how long it will take to count to one million; include graphs, data, and equations. Extend the problem by predicting the time it would take to count to one billion, one trillion, and to the federal debt amount.

Chapter Five

FUNCTIONS

Contents

Section 5.1: Interpreting Graphs 188

A picture is worth a thousand words

Section 5.2: Connections with Sequences 193

Old stuff–new notation

Section 5.3: The Linear Family 199

Line up for this!

Section 5.4: The Parabola Family 203

What goes up must come down

Section 5.5: The Square Root Family 208

Every family has its roots

Section 5.6: The Absolute Value Family 212

A positive attitude

Section 5.7: Stretching a Curve 215

Is this better than stretching a point?

Section 5.8: A Summary 220

Putting it all together

Section 5.9: Compositions of Functions 225

If Beethoven were a mathematician

Section 5.10: Chapter Review 230

Assessing yourself

Section 5.11: Projects 232

Taking it one step further

Section 5.1: Interpreting Graphs

Students at Central High School have been complaining that the soft drink machine is empty too often. Student council members Rita and Noah have decided to study this problem. First, they recorded information and made a graph showing the number of cans in the soda machine at various times during a typical school day. Their graph gives them a lot of information about the use of the soda machine.

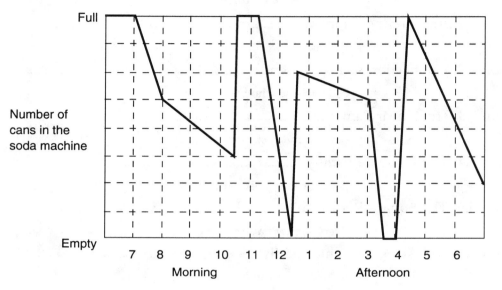

The school cafeteria doesn't open until 7 a.m., so no one can use the machine before that time. Rita and Noah figured out from the graph that Jake, who maintains the machine, fills it to capacity just before the first lunch period, then quickly recharges it before the last lunch period is complete. (A quick recharge fills the machine to 75% capacity.) Jake told them that it takes him about five minutes to do a quick recharge and ten minutes to completely fill the machine. Although it was difficult for Rita and Noah to provide a minute-by-minute analysis from the graph, the overall picture was very useful, and they could observe definite tendencies. Each horizontal segment indicates a time interval when the vending area is closed, when the machine is empty, or when no one is drinking soda. Rita and Noah reported to the student council that the machines are filled overnight, again at 10:30 a.m., and again just after school lets out. The greatest consumption is pictured by the steep, declining slopes during the lunch periods and when school lets out. By studying the graph, the student council was able to determine whether or not a change in the refill schedule was needed. What do you think their recommendation was?

Although Rita and Noah were interested in solving a problem related to soda consumption, they could also have used the graph to answer many other questions about Central High School. When do students arrive at school?

What time do classes begin? When is lunch? When do classes let out for the day?

There is a dynamic relationship between a graph and a real-world situation. In this section, you will investigate this relationship. A picture can be worth a thousand words *if you can interpret the picture*.

Example 1: What is the real-world meaning of this graph picturing the relationship between the number of people getting haircuts, and the amount charged for each haircut?

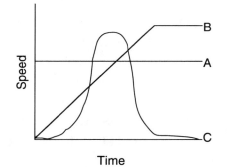

Cost of a haircut

Solution: The number of haircuts depends on what is charged for each haircut. As the price increases, the number of haircuts decreases linearly. The slope indicates the number of haircuts lost for each dollar increase. The x-intercept represents the haircut cost that is too expensive for everyone. The y-intercept indicates the number of haircuts when they are free. Why isn't the y-intercept bigger? Do you think this should be a straight-line graph? Why or why not?

Example 2: Which of these graphs pictures a student's walking speed from the time she realizes she might be tardy for class until she arrives at class?

Solution: Graph B is probably the best answer.

Graph A isn't a good answer, because it is unlikely that anyone can instantly get up to speed and maintain that exact speed.

Graph C indicates she knows she will be late and has given up trying to beat the clock. Notice, however, that her speed isn't zero.

Invent a Story Activity

Part 1: The graph at the right tells a story. It could be a story about a lake, a bathtub, or whatever your imagination can create. Spend some time with your group discussing all the information contained in the graph. Write a story that conveys all of this information.

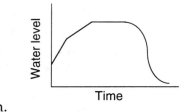

Part 2: Sketch a graph that reflects all the information given in the story below.

"It was a dark and stormy night. The old bucket stood empty in the yard before the torrents of rain came. As day broke on the horizon, the rain subsided. The bucket stood quietly through the morning until Old Dog Trey arrived as thirsty as a dog. The sun shone brightly through the afternoon when Billy, the kid next door, arrived. He noticed two plugs in the side of the bucket. One of them was about a quarter of the way up, and the second one was near the bottom. As fast as you could blink an eye, he pulled out the plugs and ran away as fast as he could."

Problem Set 5.1

1. Birdie Parr's brother, Hawkeye, describes himself as an inconsistent golfer. His concentration often wanders from the mechanics of golf to the mathematics involved in his game. His scorecard frequently contains mathematical doodles and graphs.

   a. What is a real-world meaning for this graph found on one of his recent scorecards?

   b. What units might he be using?

   c. Describe a realistic domain and range for this graph.

   d. Does this graph show how far the ball traveled? Explain.

2. Make up a story to go with this graph.

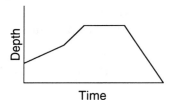

3. Trace on your paper the section of a roller coaster that is pictured below.

   a. Sketch a graph of the roller-coaster car's speed over this portion of the track. The graph should compare the speeds at each of the points A through K. No numbers are needed on your graph.

   b. At which lettered point is the roller-coaster car moving the fastest?

   c. At which lettered point is the roller-coaster car moving the slowest?

   d. Name two points where the speeds are about the same.

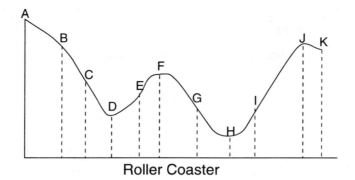

Roller Coaster

Sketch what you think is a reasonable graph for each relationship described in Problems 4–20. If one variable is clearly dependent on the other, put it on the vertical axis. Put the independent variable on the horizontal axis. Label the units. Decide whether each graph should be continuous or not. The graph doesn't need to be detailed, but *do justify* the shape you have chosen by writing one or two complete sentences.

4. The amount of money you have in an account that is compounded annually, over a period of several years.

5. The same amount of money you started with in Problem 4, hidden in your mattress over this time period.

6. The distance it takes to stop a car that has been moving at a constant speed.

7. The height of a baseball after it leaves the bat.

8. The temperature of a hot drink sitting on your desk.

9. The temperature of an iced drink sitting on your desk.

10. Your height above the ground as you ride a Ferris wheel.

11. The money you earn during a week, compared to the number of hours you worked during the week.

12. The speed of a falling acorn, after it is dropped by a squirrel from the top of an oak tree.

13. Your height over your entire life span.

14. Your speed as you cycle up a hill and down the other side.

15. Your distance from Detroit during a flight from Detroit to Newark, if your plane is directed to circle Newark in a holding pattern.

16. The daily maximum temperature over a period of time.

17. The amount of postage charged for different weights of letters.

18. Adult shoe sizes as related to the adult's foot length.

19. The intensity of light available for reading, and your distance from the reading lamp.

20. The altitude of a hot dog wrapper after it is released by your little brother from the top row in the football stadium.

21. Describe a functional relationship of your own and draw a graph to go with it.

Section 5.2: Connections with Sequences

Distance from Home Activity

Each group member should draw a graph that will picture his or her distance from home from 7 a.m. to 9 p.m. today. Then compare and discuss your graphs. Does each graph indicate: When the person left home? How far home is from school? When and what is the greatest distance from home? What times during the day the person is not traveling? When the person is traveling the fastest? When the person gets home?

Distance from home

7 9 11 1 3 5 7 9
Time of day

Frequently, you are given information or data that can be pictured as a **discrete** graph, which is made up of distinct points. Suppose the *mileage* on your family car's short-trip odometer reads as shown in the table.

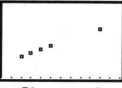

Discrete graph

Time (in minutes)	2	3	4	5		10
Mileage	104.4	105.1	105.8	106.5	. . .	110

Many things—like growth, changes in speed, or distance from home—really happen in a continuous way. Graphs of these relationships are not made up of separate distinct points, but should be smooth lines or curves. The line pictured at the right shows a distance in miles for every possible time from zero minutes through 10 minutes.

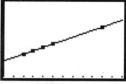

Continuous graph

What was the odometer reading before the car started moving? What was the average speed during the trip to school? What is the equation of the line pictured? How do you put a continuous graph on a sequence or set of discrete points? This section will help you answer questions like these.

Up to now in this book, sequences and their terms have been identified with subscripts, as in this sequence: $u_1, u_2, u_3, \ldots, u_n$. You will make a simple notation change in the next example. The term u_1 will be identified as $u(1)$, u_2 will be identified as $u(2)$, and so on. This means that the sixth term of the sequence in Graph A will be called $u(6) = 25$ instead of $u_6 = 25$. This transition will help prepare you for the function notation introduced in this section.

Example 1: Write an explicit formula for each sequence graph.

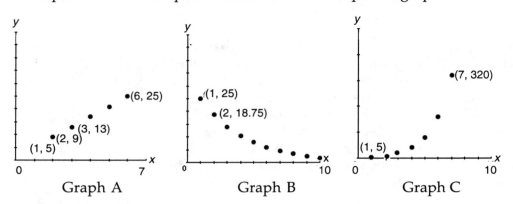

Graph A   Graph B   Graph C

Solution: Graph A represents an arithmetic sequence, {5, 9, 13, . . . },
because the points are linear. The term $u(1)$ equals 5, and the slope
between any two points is $\dfrac{y_2 - y_1}{x_2 - x_1} = 4$.

The sequence point that precedes the first pictured point is (0, 1),
which means that $u(0) = 1$. The point (0, 1) is also the vertical
intercept. Therefore, the explicit formula is $u(n) = 4n + 1$.

The next two graphs represent geometric sequences. An explicit
formula for a geometric sequence is given by $u(n) = u(0) \cdot r^n$.
In Graph B, you know that $r < 1$, because the sequence decreases.
In Graph C, you know that $r > 1$, because the sequence is increasing.

In Graph B, the common ratio is $\dfrac{u(2)}{u(1)} = \dfrac{18.75}{25} = \dfrac{3}{4}$. To find $u(0)$ you
must back up one term from $u(1)$. Because $u(0)$ times $\dfrac{3}{4}$ will be 25,
you can divide 25 by $\dfrac{3}{4}$ to get $u(0) = \dfrac{100}{3}$. A specific explicit formula
for this graph is $u(n) = \dfrac{100}{3} \cdot \left(\dfrac{3}{4}\right)^n$. You should confirm this by using
the formula to find $u(2)$.

In Graph C, $u(1) = 5$ and $u(7) = 320$. Therefore, $5r^6 = 320$ or $r^6 = 64$.
This means $r = 2$. The vertical intercept is 2.5 and the explicit
formula is $u(n) = 2.5 \cdot 2^n$. Confirm this by using the formula to find
$u(7)$.

Sequence formulas generate discrete points because you can only substitute nonnegative integers for n. You have used u_n or $u(n)$ notation for sequences. If you wish to show what would happen for other possible values of the independent variable, like 2.3 or −1.9, then the graphs will need to show that the points are connected. A change in the variable from n to x indicates that you are using real numbers in the expression. For these nondiscrete functions, the notation involves x instead of n, and you generally write equations in the form $y = $ *some expression in* x.

> Example 2: Write an equation in the form $y = $ *some expression in* x, which contains the points pictured in each of the following graphs, and draw smooth unbroken (*continuous*) curves that indicate x can be any real number. Use the graphing calculator to plot the given points on the screen and then draw graphs that contain the points.

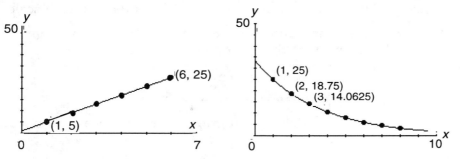

> Solution: Equations for the continuous graphs are $y = 4x + 1$ and $y = \dfrac{100}{3} \cdot \left(\dfrac{3}{4}\right)^x$. Trace the graphs to locate values of y at other real-number choices of x.

In a sequence $(1, u(1))$, $(2, u(2))$, $(3, u(3))$, . . . , the value of $u(n)$ is a **function** of n because exactly one value is produced for any choice of n. Another way of expressing this is that there is a single output for each input.

The equation $y = 4x + 1$ contains the sequence points and an infinite number of other points. The variable y is a function of x. The function $f(4)$, read as "f of 4," means the y-value, or the height of the graph, when $x = 4$. Because this function is continuous, it also makes sense to consider numbers other than positive integers, like $f(4.5)$. The value of y when $x = 4.5$ will be $4(4.5) + 1$, or 19. If y is a function of x, then $f(x)$ is the function value of y at that choice of x. This means $y = f(x)$. For this reason, functions like $y = 4x + 1$ are frequently written $f(x) = 4x + 1$. This signals that you are considering a function, and it gives you a convenient notation for evaluating the function at particular choices of x, like 4.5.

A **function** $y = f(x)$ is a description relating the variables x and y to each other. For each specified value of x, the description allows you to define a single value of y.

This a fairly simple definition of a very important concept in mathematics. One of the first definitions of "function" was given by the Swiss mathematician Leonhard Euler in 1755. He said:

> If some quantities so depend on other quantities that if the latter are changed the former undergo change, then the former quantities are called functions of the latter. This denomination is of broadest nature and comprises every method by means of which one quantity could be determined by others. If, therefore, x denotes a variable quantity, then all quantities which depend on x in any way or are determined by it are called functions of x.

Which definition do you prefer?

Temperature Activity

Find a relationship between the Fahrenheit and Celsius temperature scales.

a. Collect data by taking temperatures, in °F and °C, in several different environments. Be certain that the thermometer stays in the medium long enough to stabilize the temperature before you record the value.

°C	°F	location of reading

b. Plot all data on an appropriately-scaled graph. Use Celsius as the independent variable.

c. Find the line of best fit using the method of your choice. Explain why you selected that method.

d. Write your equation as $F(c)$.

e. Convert this equation to a function that finds Celsius in terms of Fahrenheit, $C(f)$.

f. Predict the temperature in °C for 95°F. Plot this point on your graph.

g. Predict the temperature in °F for −5°C. Plot this point on your graph.

h. What is the possible error in part e and part f? Explain how you found this error.

i. Give a real-world meaning for the y-intercept of your graph.

j. Give a real-world meaning for the slope of your graph.

k. Find a temperature where both scales give the same reading.

Problem Set 5.2

1. Find the coordinates for each unlabeled point pictured in Graph A, Graph B, and Graph C of Example 1.

In Problems 2–4, complete the following steps.

   a. plot the first three discrete points of the sequence,

   b. write the explicit equation of the associated continuous function, using $f(x)$ notation, and

   c. draw its graph through the points. (The domain should include all numbers that make sense.)

2. $u(n) = n^2$ 3. $u(n) = \sqrt{n}$ 4. $u(n) = \begin{cases} 4 & \text{if } n = 1 \\ 1.3 \cdot u(n-1) & \text{if } n > 1 \end{cases}$

5. Complete 5a through 5d for the sequence in Problem 4.

   a. Mark the point $(4, f(4))$ on your graph and describe, in complete sentences, its location relative to the point $(0, 0)$.

   b. What are the coordinates of the point $(7.25, f(7.25))$?

   c. What is the height of the point determined by $f(6.5)$?

   d. Draw a segment on your graph that represents $f(6.5)$.

6. Suppose $f(x) = \dfrac{-3}{5}x + 25$.

   a. Draw a graph of this function.

   b. Identify the point $(7, f(7))$ by marking it on your graph.

   c. What is $f(7)$?

   d. Draw a segment on your graph that identifies $f(7)$.

   e. Find the value of x when $f(x) = 27.4$. Mark this point on your graph.

7. Frequently, wild economic behavior occurs in a country experiencing a dramatic change in philosophy or government. The fallout of this behavior might be in the form of inflation. A 10% annual inflation rate means that at the end of a year, it will cost $110 for goods or services that cost $100 at the beginning of the year. A 1992 report indicated that the inflation rate in Russia was 3% per week.

   a. Given the above data about the economy in Russia, write an explicit equation and draw a continuous graph that illustrates the inflationary growth of $100.

   b. What will the height of the graph be after 10.5 weeks?

   c. What will the height of the graph be after one year?

   d. What is the real-world meaning of the last answer?

   e. When will the inflationary value reach $295?

8. Dr. Bella Donna has prescribed a new drug for her patient, Ben Zine. Suppose he starts by taking a pill containing 200 mg of the drug. Assume that his body eliminates 10% of the drug daily.

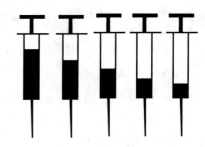

   a. Write an explicit equation and draw a continuous graph that illustrates this situation.

   b. How much of the drug remains in Ben's body after 4 days? After 10.5 days?

   c. What are the heights of each point named in 8b?

   d. When will his drug level reach 5 mg?

   e. When will the drug be totally eliminated from Ben's body?

9. Sketch a graph showing the oven temperature after you turn off an oven that has been on for an hour.

Section 5.3. The Linear Family

Linear functions were introduced as extensions of arithmetic sequences. You have considered both the median-median line and the least-squares line as you modeled data.

> A function is **linear** if it can be put in either of the forms
>
> $$y = mx + b \text{ or } y = m(x - x_1) + y_1$$
>
> where m is the **slope** of the line, b is the **y-intercept**,
>
> and (x_1, y_1) is a **point** on the line.

What do you remember about the slope of a horizontal line? What makes one line steeper than another? How do the slopes compare if two lines are parallel? What can you say about the slopes of two lines that are perpendicular?

Example 1: The equation $4x - 2y = 16$ describes a linear relation, but it can't be entered directly into your calculator without correctly solving for y (putting the equation in $y=$ form). What is $y=$ form for this example?

Solution:

$$4x - 2y = 16$$

$-2y = -4x + 16$	Add $-4x$.
$y = (-4x + 16)/-2$	Divide by -2.
$y = 2x - 8$	An alternate form.

Special Slopes Activity

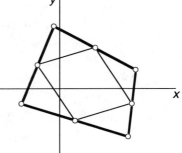

Part 1: Each member of the group should choose any four points with integer coordinates and plot them on a piece of graph paper. Connect the points to form a quadrilateral. Locate and label the midpoints of each side. Connect these midpoints in order. What shape appears to have been created? Which sides, if any, seem to be parallel? Calculate the slope of a pair of parallel sides. What can you conclude about the slopes of parallel lines? What kind of figure did you create? Compare your drawing to other drawings in your group.

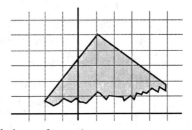

Part 2: Each member of the group should take the right-angled corner of a piece of paper and place it on top of a piece of graph paper. Line it up so that the corner is at a point with integer coordinates, and the sides pass through other integer points. Trace along the edges of the paper to form two perpendicular lines. Calculate the slope of each line. Is there a relationship between the slopes? Compare your slopes with those of the others in your group. What can you conclude about the slopes of perpendicular lines?

Problem Set 5.3

1. Example 1 in this section shows algebraically that $4x - 2y = 16$ and $y = 2x - 8$ are equivalent equations.

   a. Name an x-value and a y-value that make $4x - 2y = 16$ a true statement.

   b. Show that the same values make $y = 2x - 8$ a true statement.

   c. Find another pair (x, y) and show that it works in both forms of the equation.

   d. Explain what it means to say that two equations are equivalent.

2. Graph the equation $2.8x + 5.1y = 22$. Identify the slope, the y-intercept, and the x-intercept of the line.

3. a. Write the equation of the line shown at the right. Check your equation by graphing the line on your calculator and using the trace function.

   b. Write the equation and graph the function that is two units above, and parallel to, the pictured line.

   (graph showing points (-5.2, 3.18) and (1.4, -4.4))

4. Graph each function in this problem on the same set of coordinate axes. (Be certain that your calculator graphing window accurately pictures perpendicular lines.)

   a. Suppose function f is $3x + 2y + 12 = 0$. Rewrite it in $y=$ form and graph it.

   b. Write the equation for a line that is perpendicular to f at its y-intercept. Suppose this is function g. (Hint: Perpendicular lines have slopes that multiply to -1.)

   c. Write the equation for a line that is perpendicular to f at its x-intercept. Suppose this third line is function h.

   d. Write the equation for a fourth line that is perpendicular to g at its x-intercept.

   e. What is the geometric figure outlined by the four lines?

5. When graphing equations, it is often convenient to use a graphing window such that the pixel coordinates are "friendly" values. This means that when you trace a graph, you will get integer values for x. **APPENDIX 5A** explains how to get a friendly window on your calculator, and how to automatically set your window to these values.

   a. Determine a window setting where the origin is at the center of the screen, and the distance between pixels is 0.1.

   b. Determine a window setting where the origin is at the lower left corner of the screen, and the distance between pixels is 0.1.

6. Write an equation for each line pictured below. (In each case, the grid spacing is one unit.) For more practice, see **APPENDIX 5B**.

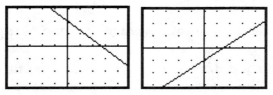

7. When *y varies directly with x*, you can write a special linear function, $y = kx$. The constant of variation, k, is just another name for slope, and the graph passes through the origin. Draw several different-sized squares on graph paper. For each square, measure the length of the side and the length of the diagonal. Collect data from other students until you have at least twelve data points.

   a. Plot the points (*side length, diagonal length*) and find the equation of a line of best fit. Remember that the point (0, 0) is also on your line.

   b. Your equation is of the form $d = ks$, where d is the length of the diagonal and s is the length of the side. This is a direct variation. What is your constant of variation, k, for $d = ks$?

   c. If a square has side length 6.4 cm, what is the length of its diagonal?

   d. What is the side length of a square with diagonal $14\sqrt{6}$?

8. The Internal Revenue Service has approved Ten-Year Linear Depreciation as one method for determining the value of business property. This means the value declines to zero over a ten-year period.

   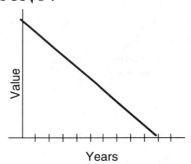

   Suppose a piece of equipment costs $12,500 originally and is depreciated over a ten-year period.

   a. What is the *y*-intercept? Give a real-world meaning for this value.

   b. What is the *x*-intercept? Give a real-world meaning for this value.

   c. What is the slope? What is the real-world meaning of the slope?

   d. Write an explicit equation that describes the value of the equipment during the ten-year period.

   e. When is the equipment worth $6500?

9. Suppose that your basketball team's scores in the first four games of the season were 86 points, 73 points, 76 points, and 90 points.

   a. What will your team's scoring average be if the next game total is 79 points?

   b. Write a function and draw a graph that compares the next-game score and the average score.

   c. What score will give a five-game average of 84 points?

10. Mr. and Mrs. De La Cruz want to buy a new house, and must finance $60,000 at 9.6% on the unpaid balance.

   a. Make several guesses for a monthly payment to pay off the loan in 25 years.

   b. Plot the points determined by your guesses (*monthly payment* versus *balance after 25 years*).

   c. Find a line of best fit for the points.

   d. What is the *y*-intercept? What is the real-world meaning of the *y*-intercept?

   e. What is the *x*-intercept? What is the real-world meaning of the *x*-intercept?

   f. What is the slope? What is the real-world meaning of the slope?

11. Use the data and the equation from Problem 8 to determine the average value of the equipment over the ten-year period. To figure this out, determine the starting value, the value each year, and the final value. Then average these numbers.

Section 5.4: The Parabola Family

What would this graph look like if a teacher decides to add five points to each of the numerical scores pictured in this histogram? Do teachers do that?

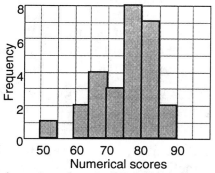

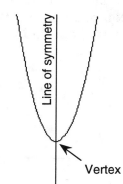

What change or transformation will move the triangle on the left to its position on the right? Did you do transformations like this in your geometry class?

Transformations are a natural feature of the real world, including the world of art. Music is often transposed from one key to another. Melodies are often shifted by a certain interval within a composition. Can you find other examples of transformations?

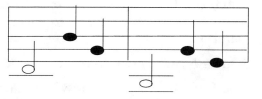

This section will deal entirely with alterations to the equation and graph of the function pictured at the right. The **parabola** $y = x^2$ is a simple building-block function. One variation of this function models the height of a projectile from the ground as a function of time. Another variation gives the area of a square as a function of the length of a side.

> Example: If you are given a stick that is 100 cm in length, is there a way you can break it so that the pieces form a rectangle with the largest possible area?

> Solution: Make a table of values $(x, y) = (side\ length,\ area)$ that can represent this situation. Invent several possible side lengths and then compute the associated areas.

Length (x)	5	10	15	20	25	30	35	40	45
Width	45	40	35	30	25	20	15	10	5
Area (y)	225	400	525	600	625	600	525	400	225

The graph of (*side length, area*) is a parabola that is upside-down and translated from its usual position. Do you see that the **vertex** is at the highest point, and pictures a side length of 25 cm and the greatest area of 625 cm²? What geometric shape has maximum area in this case?

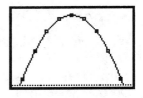

Set your "friendly" graphing window so that both Δx and Δy are 0.2. Enter this y-symmetric graph on your calculator as $y = x^2$. Some of the points not shown on the screen include $(-3, 9)$, $(3, 9)$, $(-4, 16)$, $(4, 16)$, and in general, (x, x^2).

All parabolas are related to this simple parent function: $y = x^2$ with **vertex** at $(0, 0)$. The major focus of this section will be for you to (a) slide or translate this graph to a new position, (b) write the equation of a parabola based on its shape and the position of its vertex, and (c) predict the graph of a parabola given its equation. Locating the vertex and connecting it to an equation is your key to success with parabolas.

Make My Graph Activity

The function $y = x^2$ is shown on each graph below. Experiment by changing this equation to find out how you can slide the parabola up and down. Use a combination of calculator guess-and-check, logic, and common sense. Try to learn from your mistakes. When you have succeeded, write the equation that worked.

a.

b.

c.

d.

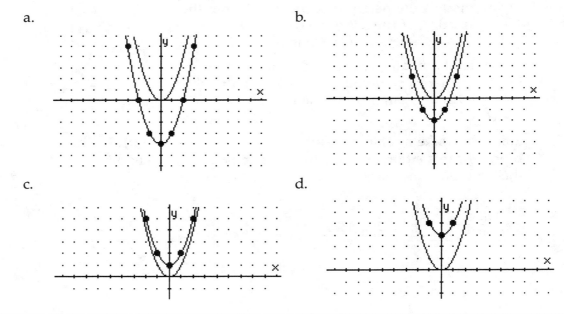

Problem Set 5.4

1. Use your calculator to find the equation for each parabola. Each one is congruent to $y = x^2$.

a.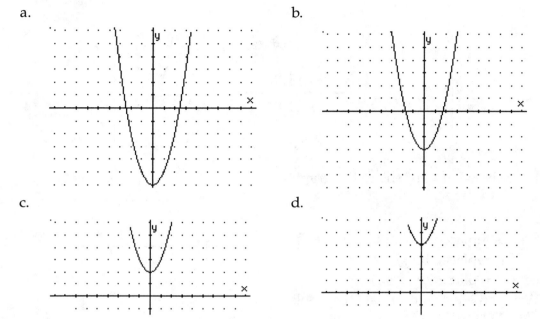

b.

c.

d.

2. In each part of this problem, the parent function $f(x) = x^2$ is slid or translated vertically (up or down). Each parabola is congruent to the parent function, but has been moved to a different position.

a. Write the equation and draw the graph of a parabola that is congruent to $f(x) = x^2$ with the given translation.

    i.   six units down from $f(x)$ ii. two units up from $f(x)$

b. Write equations in $y=$ form and describe the location of each parabola relative to $f(x)$.

    i. $f(x) - 5$ ii. $f(x) + 4$

c. In general, $y = x^2 + c$ means the same thing as $f(x) + c$ when $f(x) = x^2$. Describe the location of $f(x) + c$.

3. Now that you have discovered how to move the parabola up and down, experiment to find out how to move it from side to side. Write the equation you used for each shifted parabola.

   a.   b.   c.

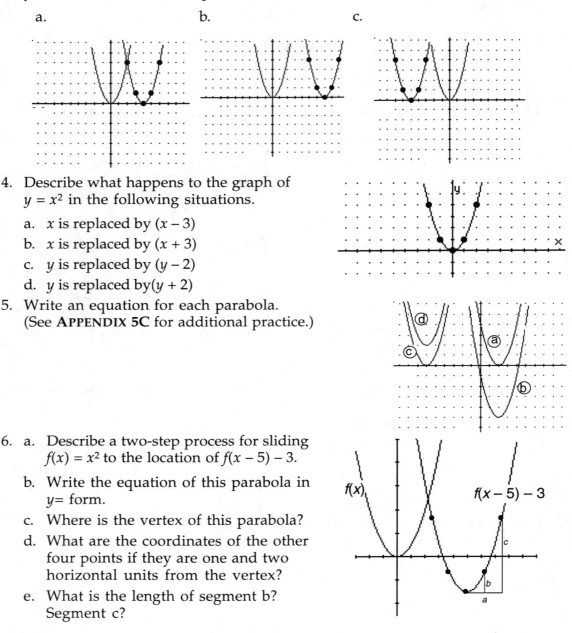

4. Describe what happens to the graph of $y = x^2$ in the following situations.

   a. x is replaced by $(x - 3)$
   b. x is replaced by $(x + 3)$
   c. y is replaced by $(y - 2)$
   d. y is replaced by $(y + 2)$

5. Write an equation for each parabola.
   (See **APPENDIX 5C** for additional practice.)

6. a. Describe a two-step process for sliding $f(x) = x^2$ to the location of $f(x - 5) - 3$.

   b. Write the equation of this parabola in $y=$ form.

   c. Where is the vertex of this parabola?

   d. What are the coordinates of the other four points if they are one and two horizontal units from the vertex?

   e. What is the length of segment b? Segment c?

7. Write the equation and graph each parabola. (Each parabola is still congruent to $y = x^2$, just a little upset.)

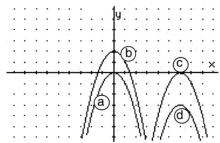

8. Write the equation of a graph that is congruent to $y = -1(x + 3)^2 + 4$, but shifted five units right and two units down.

9. The **graphing form** of the equation of a parabola is often written as $y = \pm 1(x - h)^2 + k$. Based on your work in the previous problems, explain the effect of ± 1, h, and k on the graph of the parent function. Be as explicit as possible.

10. Write an equation of the form $y = \pm 1(x - h)^2 + k$ that provides the table values for the (*length, area*) example in this section. Graph your equation to check your answer.

11. Make a table of values that compares the number of teams in a league and the number of games required for each team to play every other team twice, (once at home and once away).

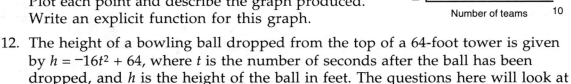

Number of teams	1	2	3	. . .	10
Number of games	0	2	6		

Plot each point and describe the graph produced. Write an explicit function for this graph.

12. The height of a bowling ball dropped from the top of a 64-foot tower is given by $h = -16t^2 + 64$, where t is the number of seconds after the ball has been dropped, and h is the height of the ball in feet. The questions here will look at the average height of the ball during the first two seconds.

    a. Make a table showing the time and the height of the ball when it is dropped, when it hits the ground, and every 1/2 second in between. Then average these heights.

    b. Find the average height by using the heights every 1/4 sec.

    c. Find the average height by using the heights every 1/10 sec.

    d. Explain the differences in your answers to 12a, b, and c. Which best answers the question, "What is the average height?" Why?

Section 5.5: The Square Root Family

The square root graph is another parent function that can be used to illustrate transformations.

Both the domain and range of $f(x) = \sqrt{x}$ are real numbers that are zero or greater. If you trace the graph, there are no function values for y unless x is at least 0. Trace to show that $\sqrt{3}$ is about 1.732 and that $\sqrt{8}$ is about 2.828. Describe how you would use the graph to find $\sqrt{31}$. What happens when you try to trace for values of $x < 0$? What is $\sqrt{-4}$?

Pendulum Experiment

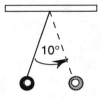

For this activity, you will need some string and an object to use as a weight. Tie the weight at one end of a length of string.
Firmly hold or tie the other end of the string to something, so that the weight hangs freely. Measure the length from the center of the weight to the point where the string is held. Then carefully extend and release the weight so that the weight swings back and forth in a short 10° arc. Time ten complete swings; forward and back is one swing. Find the period by dividing by ten. The period of your pendulum is the time for one complete swing (back and forth). Complete a table of values relating period and string length. Use a variety of short, medium, and long string lengths. Save this data for one of the problems.

Length (in cm)						
Period						

Example: An object falls to the ground because of the influence of gravity. If an object is dropped from a height of 1000 meters, the height of the object at any given time (in seconds) is given by the function $h(t) = -4.9t^2 + 1000$. How long does it take for the object to reach the ground?

Solution: You are finding the time until the height will be 0.

$0 = -4.9t^2 + 1000$	Set the height = 0.
$4.9t^2 = 1000$	Add $4.9t^2$ to both sides.
$t^2 = \dfrac{1000}{4.9}$	Divide both sides by 4.9.
$t = \sqrt{\dfrac{1000}{4.9}} \approx 14.3$ seconds	Take the square root of both sides.

Certainly the falling time depends on the starting height. How long will it be until an object reaches the ground, if it is dropped from 800 meters? From 650 meters? From d meters? This is just one of many functional relationships involving the square root function.

Problem Set 5.5

1. Write the equation for each transformed graph. The parent function is
   $y = \sqrt{x}$. Verify each answer by graphing it on your calculator.

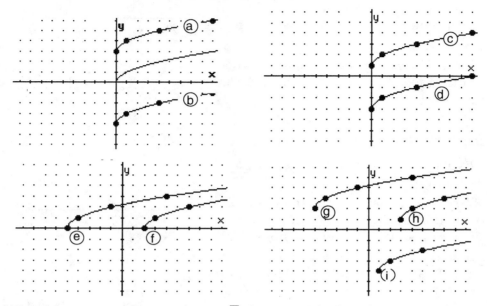

2. a. What happens to the graph $y = \sqrt{x}$ if x is replaced with $(x - 3)$?
      With $(x + 3)$?

   b. What happens to the graph $y = \sqrt{x}$ if y is replaced with $(y - 2)$?
      With $(y + 2)$?

3. Write an equation for each graph.

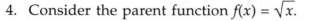

4. Consider the parent function $f(x) = \sqrt{x}$.

   a. Name three pairs of integer coordinates that are on the graph of
      $f(x + 4) - 2$.

   b. Write $f(x + 4) - 2$ in $y=$ form and graph it.

   c. Write $-f(x - 2) + 3$ in $y=$ form and graph it.

5. a. Graph this parabola on your calculator. (Hint: You will need to graph two functions.)

   b. Combine the two functions in 5a and write the equation in condensed form, $y = \pm \sqrt{x}$.

   c. What is the resulting equation when both sides of the equation from 5b are squared?

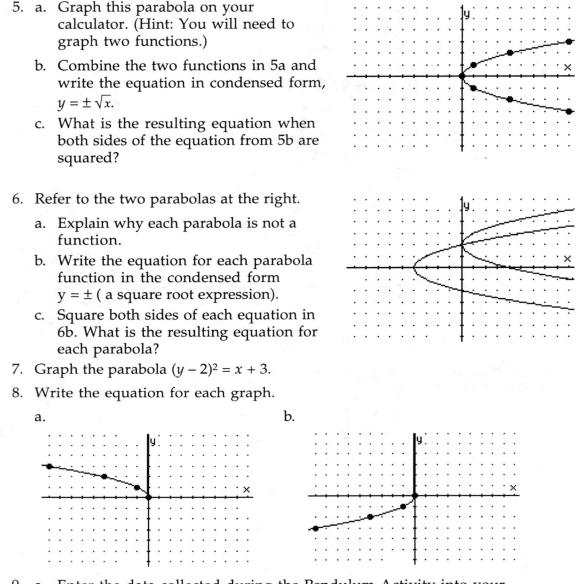

6. Refer to the two parabolas at the right.

   a. Explain why each parabola is not a function.

   b. Write the equation for each parabola function in the condensed form $y = \pm$ (a square root expression).

   c. Square both sides of each equation in 6b. What is the resulting equation for each parabola?

7. Graph the parabola $(y - 2)^2 = x + 3$.

8. Write the equation for each graph.

   a.   b.

9. a. Enter the data collected during the Pendulum Activity into your calculator.

   b. Plot the data, and write an equation that best fits the data. Graph the residuals.

   c. Use your model to predict the period for a 10-meter pendulum length.

   d. Find the length for a clock pendulum that has a period of one second.

10. The table provides information about the (*distance, velocity*) relationship for an object dropped near earth's surface. Velocity is in feet per second, and the distance the object has fallen is measured in feet. Use guess-and-check to write a square root function that provides a good fit for the data.

Distance	0	2.5	5	10	15	20	25
Velocity	0	12.65	17.89	25.30	30.98	35.78	40.00

Section 5.6: The Absolute Value Family

Hao and Dayita ride the subway to school each day. They live on the same east-west subway route. Hao lives 7.4 miles west of the school, and Dayita lives 5.2 miles east of the school. This information is shown on the number line below.

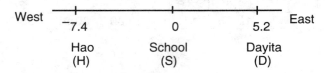

The distance from Hao's stop to school, HS, is 7.4 units. The distance from Hao's stop to Dayita's stop, HD, is 12.6 units. When you talk about distance, you usually don't mention direction, unless you're interested in the directed distance. A distance will be either positive or zero.

This is exactly what the **absolute value** function does. It makes numbers positive or zero. The job is easy when the number is zero or a positive number, and not difficult when the number is negative. The mathematical notation for the absolute value of -3, or the distance from -3 to the origin, is $|-3|$. What is $|-3|$?

What is $|5.2 - {}^{-}7.4|$, the distance from D to H? What is $|13.4|$?

The absolute value function was first described by the French mathematician Augustin-Louis Cauchy in the 1820s. The symbol used today for absolute value was introduced by the German mathematician Karl Weierstrass in 1841.

When you determined the absolute deviation, or the distance from a data point to the mean, you were using the absolute value function. You also used this function when finding the mean absolute value of the residuals.

In this section you will learn about the graph of $y = |x|$ as another example of a function that can be transformed. The parent function $y = |x|$ is shown at the right. Graph this equation on your calculator. In the problems, you will find equations of the form $y = a|x - h| + k$. What you have learned about moving other graphs will work with this function as well.

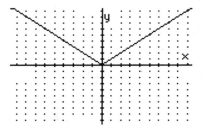

Problem Set 5.6

In Problems 1–6, write the equation of each graph. Be sure to check each equation by graphing it on your calculator.

1.

2.

3.

4.

5.

6.

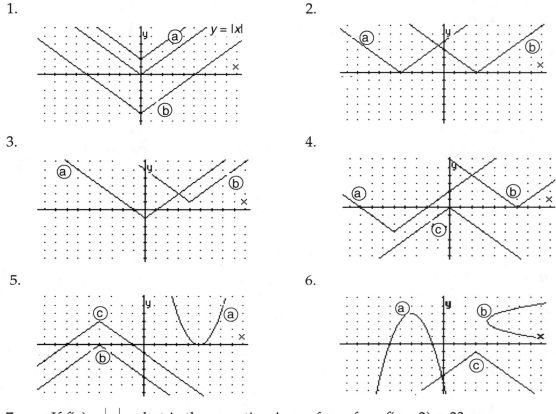

7. a. If $f(x) = |x|$, what is the equation in $y=$ form for $-f(x-2) + 3$?

   b. Describe the transformations needed to move $f(x)$ into this position.

8. a. What is the graphic result when x is replaced by $(x-5)$ in an equation?

   b. What is the graphic result when x is replaced by $-x$ in an equation?

   c. What is the graphic result when y is replaced by $(y-3)$ in an equation?

   d. What is the graphic result when y is replaced by $-y$ in an equation?

9. At the right is an illustration of how to solve the equation $|x - 4| = 3$ graphically. The equations $y_1 = |x - 4|$ and $y_2 = 3$ were graphed on the same coordinate axis.

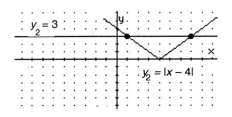

What is the x-coordinate of each point of intersection? What x-values are solutions of the equation $|x - 4| = 3$?

10. Solve the equation $|x + 3| = 5$ using the method shown in Problem 9. Sketch the graph in your homework, and indicate where the solutions are on the graph.

11. Graph two equations that show the x-value(s) when $-(x + 3)^2 + 5 = |x - 1| - 4$. Sketch a graph in your homework and indicate where the solutions are on your graph. Trace and zoom to find these values to the nearest 0.1.

12. Sketch $y = x$, $y = -x$, and $y = |x|$ on graph paper on the same axes. Use a different color pen or pencil for each equation. Study the three graphs, especially where they overlap, and write a definition of $|x|$ in terms of x and $-x$.

13. Each year the local school district schedules a math and science fair. A panel of judges rates each exhibit. The ratings for the top twenty exhibits are shown in the table.

Exhibit	1	2	3	4	5	6	7	8	9	10	11	12	13	14	15	16	17	18	19	20
Rating	68	71	73	77	79	79	81	83	83	84	85	86	88	89	89	90	92	92	92	94

The judges decide that the top rating should be 100, so they add 6 points to each rating score.

a. What was the mean and mean absolute deviation of the ratings before raising them? After raising them? What do you notice about the change in the mean? The mean absolute deviation?

b. Plot the original ratings on a graph, using the exhibit number as the x-coordinate.

c. Plot the raised ratings on the same graph. Describe how the alteration of the ratings affected the graph.

14. You can use a single receiver to find the distance to a homing transmitter by measuring the strength of the signal, but you cannot determine the direction from which the signal is emanating. The following distances were measured when driving east along a straight road. Find a model that closely fits the data. Where do you think the homing transmitter might be located?

Miles traveled	0	4	8	12	16	20	24	28	32	36
Distance to object	18.4	14.4	10.5	6.6	3.0	2.6	6.0	9.9	13.8	17.8

Section 5.7: Stretching a Curve

You have explored several functions and moved them around the plane. You know that a horizontal translation occurs when x is replaced by $(x - h)$, and a vertical translation occurs when y is replaced by $(y - k)$. You have flipped or reflected graphs over the y-axis and x-axis by replacing x with (^-x), and y with (^-y), respectively. In each case, however, the final image was the same size and shape (or congruent to) the original graph.

You can also distort a graph so that the image isn't congruent to the original graph. One of the easiest ways to do this is to stretch the y-values, or the x-values, or both. In Section 5.5 you stretched the graph of $y = \sqrt{x}$ to fit the (*distance, velocity*) relationship for an object dropped near earth's surface. Using guess-and-check, you were able to show that $v = 8\sqrt{d}$ provides a good fit of the data.

Distance	0	2.5	5	10	15	20	25
Velocity	0	12.65	17.89	25.30	30.98	35.78	40.00

The graph that shows distortions most clearly is the circle. Suppose P is a point on a unit circle with center at the origin. A **unit circle** has a radius of one unit.

You can derive the equation of a circle based on this diagram using the Pythagorean theorem. The equation is $x^2 + y^2 = 1$, because the legs of the right triangle are of lengths x and y and the length of the hypotenuse is one unit.

> $x^2 + y^2 = 1$ is the equation of a **unit circle** with center (0,0).

What is the domain and range of this circle? If a value, like 0.5, is substituted for x, what are the output values of y? Is the graph a function? Why or why not?

In order to draw the graph of a circle on your calculator, you will need to solve the above equation for y. When you do this you will get two equations, $y = +\sqrt{1 - x^2}$ and $y = ^-\sqrt{1 - x^2}$. By graphing both of these equations, you will be able to draw the complete circle. Be sure to use an appropriate window so that the circle will look like a circle and not an ellipse.

Problem Set 5.7

When possible, verify your work by graphing each equation on your calculator. Be sure to use a "friendly" graphing window.

1. The equation $y = \sqrt{(1 - x^2)}$ is the equation for the top half of the unit circle with center at (0, 0) shown on the left. Alter this equation to graph the figure on the right below. What is the equation of the semicircle after it has been stretched vertically?

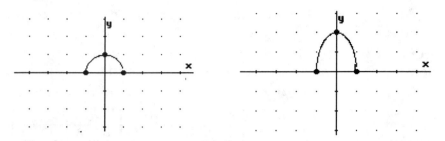

2. Write the equation of each graph. The graph should be a **stretched** or **compressed** version of $y = \sqrt{(1 - x^2)}$.

   a.   b.

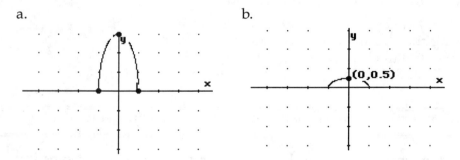

3. Consider the function $f(x) = \sqrt{(1 - x^2)}$, and graph each of the following.

   a. $-f(x)$
   b. $-2f(x)$
   c. $2f(x) - 3$

4. Write an equation in $y=$ form for each graph.

   a.   b.

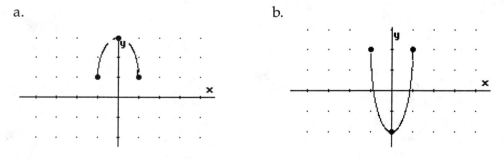

Preliminary Edition

5. Suppose the top half of the unit circle with center (0, 0) is named $f(x)$.

   a. Write the equation of each graph in terms of $f(x)$.

   b. Write the $y=$ form of each graph.

6. Write an equation in $y =$ form for each graph.

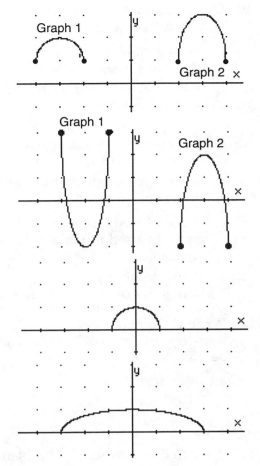

7. Write an equation, and graph each distortion of the unit semicircle.

   a. Replace y by $(y - 2)$.
   b. Replace x by $(x + 3)$.

   c. Replace y by $\frac{y}{2}$.

   d. Replace x by $\frac{x}{2}$.

8. a. Write the equation of this distorted semicircle. The x-coordinate of each point has been stretched by a factor of three.

   b. What term did you use to replace x in the parent equation?

   c. If $f(x)$ was the original semicircle, then what is this new function in $f(x)$ notation?

9. In this figure, each point of the semicircle has been stretched vertically by a factor of two, and horizontally by a factor of three.

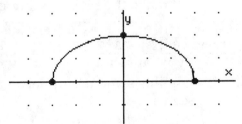

   a. What is the equation of this set of points?

   b. What is the equation of the reflection image over the x-axis?

10. Given the semicircle pictured, write the equation that generates each distortion.

   a. Each y-value is half as big as the original y-value.

   b. Each x-value is half as big as the original x-value.

   c. Each y-value is half as big as the original y-value, and each x-value is twice as big as the original x-value.

11. a. Write two equations that can be used to graph this relation.

   b. Write one equation in "$y = \pm$" form that could be used to replace the two equations in 11a.

   c. Write another equation by squaring both sides of the equation in 11b.

12. Write the equation of this transformed semicircle as indicated below.

   a. In $y=$ form

   b. In $f(x)$ form

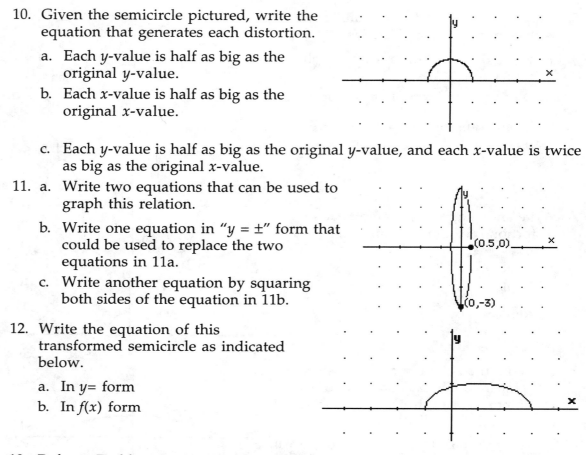

13. Refer to Problem Set 5.6, Problem 13. After the judges raised the rating scores by adding the same number to each score, one of the judges suggested that perhaps they should have *multiplied* the original scores by a factor that would make the highest score equal 100. They decided to try this method.

Exhibit	1	2	3	4	5	6	7	8	9	10	11	12	13	14	15	16	17	18	19	20
Rating	68	71	73	77	79	79	81	83	83	84	85	86	88	89	89	90	92	92	92	94

   a. By what factor should they multiply the highest score, 94, to get 100?

   b. Use this same multiplier to alter all of the scores, and record the altered scores.

   c. What is the mean and mean absolute deviation of the original scores? The altered scores?

   d. Plot the original and altered scores on the same graph. Describe what happened to the scores visually. How does this explain what happened to the mean and mean absolute deviation?

   e. Which method do you think the judges should use? Explain your reasoning.

14. What is the average value of the function $y = \sqrt{1 - x^2}$ in the interval between $x = {}^-1$ and $x = 1$?

    a. Find the value of the function at $^-1$, $^-0.5$, 0, 0.5, and 1. Then average these values.

    b. Find the value of the function at $^-1$, $^-0.8$, $^-0.6$, . . . , 0.8, and 1. Then average these values.

    c. Repeat this process once more using more closely-spaced x-values.

    d. Compare the answers from 14a, b, and c. If you continue to do this with more and more closely-spaced x-values, what would you expect to get for an average value? You can use a program that will compute the average value of a function. (See **APPENDIX 5D**.)

15. You probably used your graphing calculator quite a bit in this chapter to explore several families of graphs. Some people might think it isn't necessary to study these families, because graphing calculators are available. What do you think? Support your opinion with clear statements and examples.

Section 5.8: A Summary

In this chapter, you have studied a variety of graphs. You have learned how to recognize a graph and match it with its basic or parent equation.

Function Name	Parent Function
line	$y = mx + b$
square root	$y = \sqrt{x}$
absolute value	$y = |x|$
parabola	$y = x^2$
semicircle	$y = \sqrt{(1 - x^2)}$

A **function** is a relationship between two variables such that there is exactly one value of the dependent variable (y) for each value of the independent variable (x). You see functions as graphs, equations, two-variable data, or verbal descriptions. Function equations can be defined recursively or explicitly. The data might be in the form of points (x, y) or tables of information. But in each instance where y is **function** of x, exactly one output value is paired with each input value. The graph on the left below displays this quality. If you draw a vertical line at any x-value, it will not intersect the graph at more than one point. This is called the **vertical line test** to determine if a graph is a function.

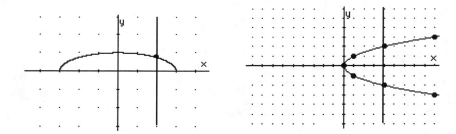

The graph on the right above doesn't qualify as a function because it is possible to find an instance where there is more than one output value for an input value. This is pictured with the vertical line intersecting the graph in more than one point. The graph fails the vertical line test. The graph still qualifies as a relation, however. Every graph is a **relation** or correspondence between a dependent variable and an independent variable.

The **domain of a function** is the set of allowable input values for the independent variable, while the **range of a function** is the set of resulting output values. The domain of the graph below is all real numbers and the range is real numbers greater than or equal to $^-1$.

Preliminary Edition

The notation $f(x)$ has been used to identify a relation as a function. It offers an easy and standard way of (1) identifying points, and (2) indicating transformations. For example, the graph of $y = 2(x + 3)^2 - 1$ is a function and the equation can be written in function form like this: $f(x) = 2(x + 3)^2 - 1$. The graph is a parabola with **vertex** at $(-3, -1)$ and a **line of symmetry** at $x = -3$. The graph is congruent to $y = 2x^2$ (a stretched version of $y = x^2$). $f(-2)$ is the y-coordinate when x is -2. So $f(-2) = 1$.

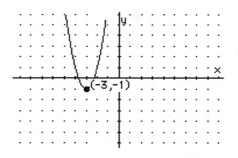

Translations, reflections, stretches or compressions of graphs, and combinations of these, all qualify as transformations. Translations and reflections produce images that remain congruent to the original image (pre-image). However, with stretches and compressions (like the vertical distortion caused by $af(x)$) the original graph and the new graph are *not* congruent.

In many of the following problems, you will combine translations and stretches or compressions. At times the order won't make any difference. You will always be correct, however, if you perform any stretches *before* you translate points vertically.

Problem Set 5.8

1. Suppose the function pictured is $f(x)$.

   a. $f(3) = ?$
   b. $f(-2) = ?$
   c. When is $f(x) = 0$?
   d. When is $f(x) = 2$?
   e. What is the range, R_f, of f?
   f. What is the domain, D_f, of f?

2. Using the graph in Problem 1 as function f, carefully sketch a separate graph of each transformation.

   a. $f(x) - 3$ b. $f(x - 3)$ c. $-f(x)$

   d. $2f(x) - 3$ e. $f(-x)$ f. $f(\frac{x}{2})$

3. Use what you know about translations and stretches to write an equation for each graph. Then check your answer by graphing each equation on your calculator.

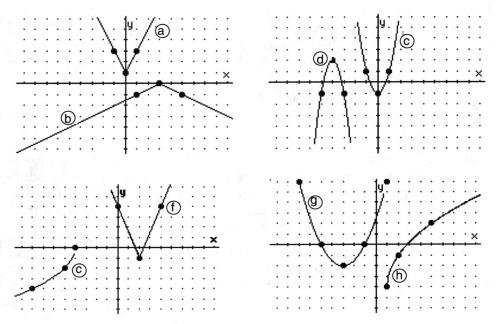

4. Respond to each of the following with a selection from {all, some, none}. If your choice is some or none, then draw an instance where the graph isn't a function.

   a. Circles are functions.

   b. Parabolas are functions.

   c. Lines are functions.

5. Suppose $f(x) = x^2$. Name a sequence of transformations, in a correct order, that will change $f(x)$ into:

   a. $y = 2x^2 - 3$ b. $y = (x - 4)^2 - 2$

   c. $y = {}^-(x + 3)^2 + 1$ d. $y = 0.5(x - 2)^2 - 3$

6. Rewrite each equation without parentheses, and graph the parabola (using both forms, to check your work).

   a. $y = 2(x - 4)^2 + 1$

   b. $y = {}^-(x + 3)^2 + 2$

   c. $y = 0.5(x - 2)^2 - 3$

7. In previous problems you found the average value of a function. The value of a function at any point can be thought of as the height of the graph above the x-axis. Therefore, the average value can be considered as the average height of the graph. Draw the graph of $y = {}^-(x - 3)^2 + 4$ for $x = 1$ to $x = 5$. (**See APPENDIX 5D.**)

   a. Calculate the average value of the function over this interval. Evaluate the function at each endpoint, and every 0.2 units in between. Average these values.

   b. Calculate the average value again using values of x every 0.1 unit.

   c. What do you think the average value would be if you used extremely closely-spaced x-values? Support your answer.

   d. Draw a rectangle using the interval on the x-axis as the base, and the average height of the function as the height of the rectangle. What is the area of this rectangle?

   e. How do you think this compares with the area enclosed by the curve? Explain.

8. Describe a procedure to find the area indicated in the graph at the right.

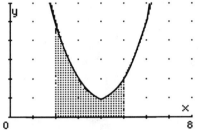

9. The Canz4U Container Corporation receives 450 drums of plastic packing pellets every 30 days. The inventory function (drums on hand as a function of days) is $I(d) = 450 - \frac{d^2}{2}$. Find the average daily inventory. If the cost of keeping one drum is two cents per day, find the average daily holding cost.

10. Solve each equation for y, and draw the graph.

   a. $2x - 3y = {}^-12$

   b. $^-2(x + 1.5) + 3(y - 2) - 3 = 0$

   c. $\frac{y}{2} = (x - 3)^2 - 2$

   d. $^-y + \frac{(x - 3)^2}{2} = 1$

11. Suppose f is a linear function. What is its equation if $f(2) = 6$ and $f(^-3) = {}^-4$?

12. The distances needed to stop a car (on dry pavement in a minimum length of time) from various speeds are shown in the table below. Reaction time is considered to be 0.75 seconds.

Speed (miles per hour)	10	20	30	40	50	60	70
Stopping distance (feet)	19	42	73	116	173	248	343

a. Construct a scatter plot for this data.

b. Use guess-and-check to find the equation of a parabola that "best" fits the points; graph it.

c. Find the residual sum for this equation.

d. Predict the stopping distance from 56.5 mi/hr.

e. How fast are you traveling if you need a stopping distance of 385 feet?

13. You have studied several families of functions (parabolas, square roots, absolute value, semicircles) and transformations of these functions. Discuss the similarities and differences among the families and their transformations.

Section 5.9: Compositions of Functions

Many times, you will encounter two functions that are related, and you may need both functions in order to answer a question or analyze a problem. Figure A shows the radius of a spreading oil slick, from a leaking offshore well, growing as a function of time, $r = f(t)$. Figure B shows the area of the circular oil slick as a function of its radius, $a = g(r)$. Time is measured in hours, the radius is measured in kilometers, and the area is measured in square kilometers.

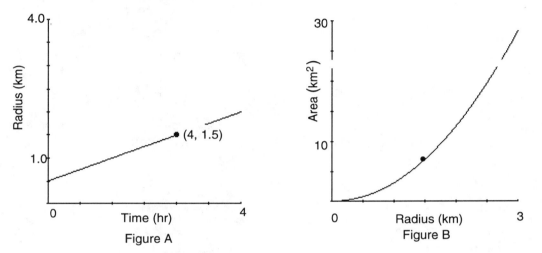

Figure A

Figure B

Example 1: The graphs can be used to find the area of the oil slick after 4 hours. From Figure A, you find the radius is 1.5 km when $t = 4$ hr. From Figure B, you find that a radius of 1.5 km indicates an area of approximately 7 km².

In the example above, two different functions, represented by their graphs, helped you find the solution. You actually used the output from one function as an input in the other function. This is an example of the composition of two functions to form a new functional relation between area and time, area = $g(f(t))$. Notice that $f(t)$ is the output from Figure A and the input in Figure B.

The symbol $g(f(x))$, read "g of f of x," is a **composition** of the two functions f and g. The composition $g(f(x))$ gives the final outcome when an x-value is substituted into the inner function f, and its value $f(x)$ is then substituted into the outer function g.

You have actually been composing functions when you transformed graphs using two or more steps. The function $3f(x) - 1$ is obtained by first stretching a function $f(x)$ by a factor of 3 to get a new image, and then subtracting 1 from these new y-values to slide the graph down 1 unit. Remember to perform stretches before you do any vertical translations.

Example 2: Consider the line pictured on the left below as an inner function, perhaps $f(x) = \frac{3x}{4} - 3$. Suppose g is the absolute value function. Then $g(f(x))$ will be absolute value of the inner linear function $f(x)$. What will $g(f(x))$ look like?

Solution: The solution is the composition graph on the right.

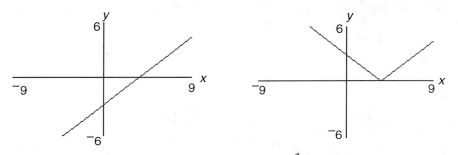

Example 3: Suppose $g(x) = 3x - 7$ and $f(x) = \frac{1}{x}$. Determine the value for each function composition.

a. $f(g(4))$ b. $f(g(x))$ c. $D_{f(g(x))}$ d. $g(f(4))$

Solution:

a. First, $g(4) = 3(4) - 7 = 5$. Then, $f(5) = \frac{1}{5}$.

b. By definition, $g(x) = 3x - 7$. Therefore, $f(3x - 7) = \frac{1}{3x - 7}$.

c. The domain required will be all real numbers except $\frac{7}{3}$ (because you cannot allow the denominator of $\frac{1}{3x - 7}$ to be zero).

d. First, $f(4) = \frac{1}{4}$. Therefore, $g\left(\frac{1}{4}\right) = 3\left(\frac{1}{4}\right) - 7 = ^-6\frac{1}{4}$.

One way to visualize what is happening when you do a composition of functions is to use a three-part graphing procedure. Graph 1 shows $g(x) = -0.5(x - .5)^2 + 8$, Graph 2 shows the line $y = x$, and Graph 3 shows $f(x) = 4(x - 3)^2$.

- Choose an x-value. In this example, an x-value of 2 has been chosen.

- Evaluate $g(2)$ by drawing a vertical line from the x-axis to the function on Graph 1.

- Then draw a horizontal line from that point to the line $y = x$ on Graph 2. The point where this line intersects the graph has x- and y-coordinates that are the same.

- Now draw a vertical line from this point to intersect the graph of the parabola in Graph 3. This is the same as evaluating f for the y-value of the original function.

- Draw a horizontal line from the intersection point to the y-axis.

- The y-value is $f(g(2))$ or 1.

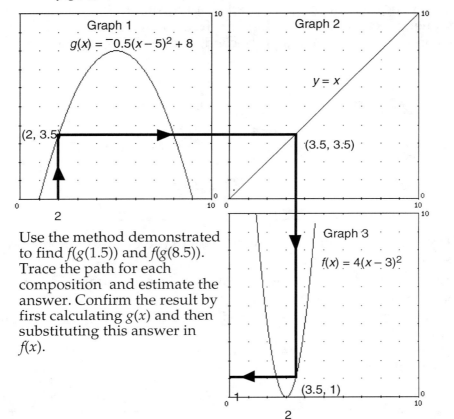

Graph 1

$g(x) = {}^-0.5(x - 5)^2 + 8$

$(2, 3.5)$

2

Graph 2

$y = x$

$(3.5, 3.5)$

Graph 3

$f(x) = 4(x - 3)^2$

$(3.5, 1)$

2

Use the method demonstrated to find $f(g(1.5))$ and $f(g(8.5))$. Trace the path for each composition and estimate the answer. Confirm the result by first calculating $g(x)$ and then substituting this answer in $f(x)$.

This procedure can be shortened by placing each graph on the same axis. The path then becomes: from the x-axis to $g(x)$ to the line ($y = x$) to $f(x)$ to the y-axis. The order is very important. A modification of this allows you to graphically show $f(f(x))$. In the following activity, you will explore this process for a specific function.

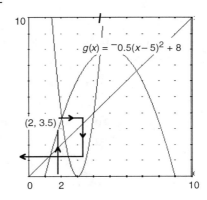

$g(x) = {}^-0.5(x - 5)^2 + 8$

$(2, 3.5)$

$f(f(f(f(...f(x)...))))$ Activity

You will need a worksheet with graphs of $y = ax(1 - x)$ for various values of a. Begin each graph with an x-value of 0.3. Then use a graphical method similar to the one described above to find $f(f(f(f(...f(x)...))))$. Carefully draw each graph. Repeat the graphical steps enough times to be able to predict what is going to happen. Did everyone in the group draw the same types of graphs? Describe what happened in each case.

Problem Set 5.9

1. Figure A shows a swimmer's speed as a function of time. Figure B shows the swimmer's oxygen consumption as a function of her speed. Time is measured in seconds, speed in meters per second, and oxygen consumption in liters per minute.

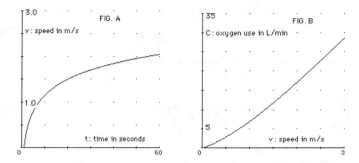

a. Use the graphs to find the swimmer's oxygen consumption after 20 seconds of swimming.

b. Sketch the graphs on your homework paper and draw segments on both graphs that verify your thinking.

c. How many seconds have elapsed if the swimmer's oxygen consumption is 15 L/min?

2. a. Write the equation in $y=$ form for the graph pictured at the right.

   b. Invent two functions f and g so that the figure is the graph of $f(g(x))$.

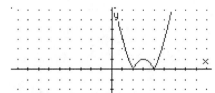

3. A, B, and C are thermometers with different linear scales. When A reads 12 and 36, B reads 13 and 29, respectively. When B reads 20 and 32, C reads 57 and 84, respectively.

a. Sketch a separate graph for each function. Label the axes.
b. If A reads 12, what does C read?
c. Write a function with B depending on A.
d. Write a function with C depending on B.
e. Write a function with C depending on A.

4. Draw a separate graph for each function.

   a. $h(x) = \sqrt{g(x)}$

   b. $h(x) = |g(x)|$

   c. $h(x) = g(x)^2$

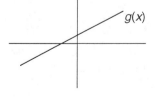

5. Suppose $g = \{(1, 2), (-2, 4), (5, 5), (6, -2)\}$ and $f = \{(0, -2), (4, 1), (3, 5), (5, 0)\}$.

   a. Find $g(f(4))$ b. Find $f(g(-2))$

6. Suppose $g = \{(1, 2), (-2, 4), (5, 5), (6, -2)\}$ and $f = \{(2, 1), (4, -2), (5, 5), (-2, 6)\}$.

   a. Find $g(f(2))$

   b. Find $f(g(6))$

   c. Select any number from the domain of either g or f and find its composite value by using the two functions. Describe what is happening.

7. The two graphs pictured below are $f(x) = 2x - 1$ and $g(x) = \frac{1}{2}x + \frac{1}{2}$. Begin by sketching the graph accurately into your homework. Solve each problem both graphically and numerically.

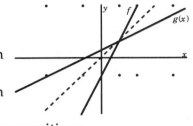

   a. Start with $x = 2$, and find $g(f(2))$.

   b. Start with $x = -1$, and find $f(g(-1))$.

   c. Pick your own starting value of x in the domain of f, and find $g(f(x))$.

   d. Pick your own starting value of x in the domain of g, and find $f(g(x))$.

   e. Carefully describe what is happening in these compositions.

8. Suppose $f(x) = -x^2 + 2x + 3$ and $g(x) = (x - 2)^2$. Find each value below both graphically and algebraically.

   a. $f(g(3))$ b. $f(g(2))$ c. $g(f(0.5))$ d. $g(f(1))$

9. Your calculator can create graphical compositions like those in the activity. See **APPENDIX 5F** for specific instructions. Use your calculator to verify your conclusions from the activity. Determine the value that each of the functions appears to approach in the long run as you continue the process.

10. Aaron and Davis are both studying the graph shown at the right. They need to write the equation that will produce this graph.

   "This is impossible!" Aaron exclaimed. "How are we supposed to know if the parent is a parabola or a semicircle? If we don't know the parent of this function, there is no way to write the equation."

   "Don't panic yet," Davis replied. "I am sure we can determine its parent function if we study the graph carefully."

   Who is correct? Explain completely and, if possible, write the equation of the graph.

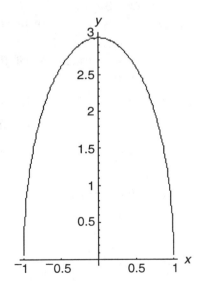

Section 5.10: Chapter Review

Problem Set 5.10

1. Sketch a graph that shows the relationship between the number of pops per second and the time since you plugged in the popcorn popper. Describe in words what your graph is showing.

2. If $f(x) = -2x + 7$, $g(x) = x^2 - 2$, and $h(x) = (x + 1)^2$, find each value.

   a. $f(g(3)) =$　　　　　　b. $g(h(-2)) =$　　　　　　c. $h(f(-1)) =$
   d. $f(g(x)) =$　　　　　　e. $h(f(x)) =$　　　　　　f. $g(f(x)) =$

3. For each function pictured below, draw the indicated transformation.

   a. $f(x) - 3$　　　　　　　　　　　　　b. $f(x - 3)$

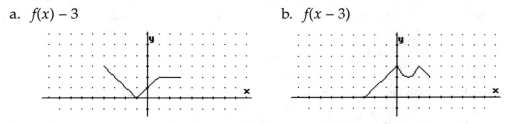

4. Describe the correct order for performing a combination of transformations on a function $f(x)$ in order to draw each of the following graphs.

   a. $f(x + 2) - 3$　　　　b. $-f\left(\frac{x}{2}\right) + 1$　　　　c. $2f\left(\frac{x - 1}{0.5}\right) + 3$

5. Solve for y.

   a. $2x - 3y = 6$　　　　b. $(y + 1)^2 - 3 = x$　　　　c. $\sqrt{1 - y^2} + 2 = x$

6. The graph of $y = f(x)$ is given. Draw each requested transformation, or combination of transformations, of this function on a separate axis.

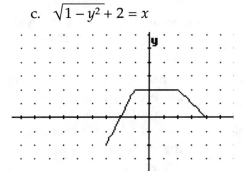

   a. $f(x) - 2$　　　　　　b. $f(x - 2) + 1$

   c. $-f(x)$　　　　　　　d. $2f(x + 1) - 3$

   e. $f(-x) + 1$　　　　　f. $f\left(\frac{x}{2}\right) - 2$

   g. $-f(x - 3) + 1$　　　h. $-2f\left(\frac{x - 1}{1.5}\right) - 2$

7. For each graph, name the parent function and write an equation.

a.

b.

c.

d.

e.

f.

g.

h.

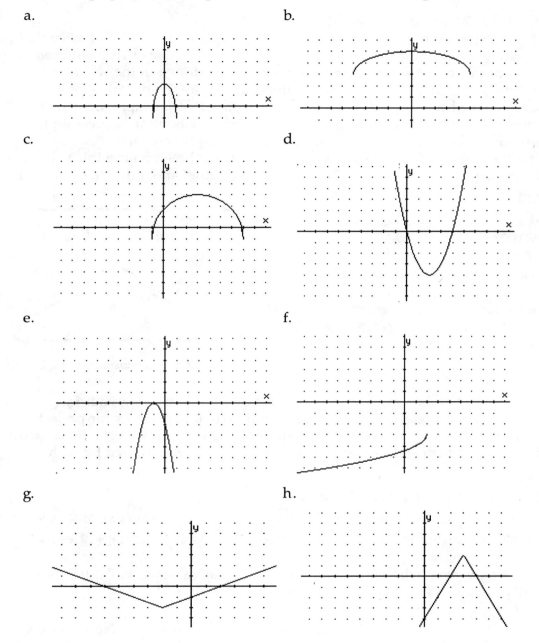

Section 5.11: Projects

Project 5.1: Make a Face at Me

Write a program that will draw a face on the graphics screen of your calculator. Your face graphs should incorporate all five of the functions that have been covered in this chapter. The example below is a car drawn in the window $0 \le x \le 9.4$ and $0 \le y \le 6.2$ on a T-82 graphics calculator. The domains for some functions have been limited or restricted by using Boolean expressions that specify x-values over which to graph that function. A Boolean expression is interpreted to be true or false. If you divide by an expression like $(x \ge 3)$ the graph of the function will "disappear" when x is less than three because this value will make the expression false $(= 0)$. Because the calculator cannot divide by zero, it will ignore that part of the graph.

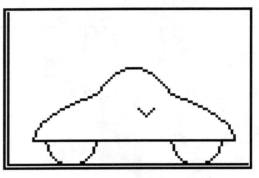

```
Prgm6:CAR
:ClrDraw
:DrawF  1/(X≥1)(X≤9)
:DrawF  (1.2⌈(X-1)+1)/(X≤3.5)
:DrawF  (1.2⌈-(X-9)+1/(X≥6.5)
:DrawF  (-.5(X-5)²+4)/(X≥3.5)(X≤6.5)
:DrawF  -⌈(1-(X-2.5)²)+1
:DrawF  -⌈(1-(X-7.5)²)+1
:DrawF  (abs (X-5.5)+2)/(X≥5.2)(X≤5.8)
```

Include at least one example of all five functions when drawing your face. Use translations, stretches, and vertical and horizontal flips. In your project report, explain each line of program code in terms of the transformations made on the parent function, and also which part of the face was created by each equation.

Project 5.2: Even and Odd Functions

Graph each of the functions $y = x^2$, $y = \sqrt{4 - x^2}$, and $y = |x|$. Describe any symmetry appearing in these graphs. These functions are examples of **even functions**.

A function f is even when $f(-x) = f(x)$ for all defined values of x. Explain how this definition relates to the symmetry you see in the graphs.

Graph these examples of **odd functions**; $y = x^3$, $y = \dfrac{1}{x}$, and $y = \sqrt[3]{x}$. Now rotate your calculator $180°$. Each graph should look the same as it looked before the rotation. This property is called symmetry with respect to the origin. Odd functions are defined as those functions f where $-f(x) = f(-x)$ for all defined values of x. Explain how this definition relates to the symmetry you see in the graphs.

Give an example of a function which is neither even nor odd. Graph your example and explain why you think it qualifies.

When functions are combined, the symmetry may change. Use functions from the examples given for odd and even functions above to investigate what happens when even and odd functions are combined. Is the result even, odd, or neither? Record your results in the table below.

	$f(g(x))$	$g(f(x))$	$f(x) + g(x)$	$f(x)g(x)$	$\dfrac{f(x)}{g(x)}$
$f(x)$ even, $g(x)$ even					
$f(x)$ even, $g(x)$ odd					
$f(x)$ odd, $g(x)$ odd					

Choose three entries from the table and prove your result. A sample proof is given below.

Prove: If $f(x)$ is even and $g(x)$ is odd, $f(g(x))$ is even.

If $g(x)$ is odd, then $g(-x) = -g(x)$. This means $f(g(-x)) = f(-g(x))$.

If $f(x)$ is even, then $f(-g(x)) = f(g(x))$.

Therefore, $f(g(-x)) = f(g(x))$ and $f(g(x))$ is even.

Project 5.3: Melting Ice

Algebra student Mel Ting carefully crafted a device from a wire coat hanger and a rubber band. He placed this device on a scale and attached an ice cube to the rubber band. He then carefully read the mass every 10 minutes for 100 minutes, when the ice cube dropped off the rubber band. Because melting occurs on the surface of the ice, he was sure the relationship would be quadratic, because the surface area is measured in square centimeters. The data he collected is in the table below. Time is recorded in minutes and mass is recorded in grams.

Time	0	10	20	30	40	50	60	70	80	90	100
Mass	52.4	51.9	50.8	49.4	47.9	46.4	45	43.3	42.1	40.6	39.2

Much to his dismay, he discovered the data was quite linear. Plot the data and draw the least-squares line. (Be sure to label the scale and units in each graph you create in this project.) Upon reflection, he recalled that he had forgotten to subtract the mass of the hanger and the rubber band, which was 34.3 grams. Subtract this from the original y-values and plot the points with the new y-values on the same graph. Find the equation that fits this new data.

Then Mel decided that, because little significant melting happened in the first 10 minutes, he would subtract 10 from each of the x-values. Graph the data and the equation for this set of data. Things still weren't working out as he thought they should, so he converted ounces to grams by dividing each y-value by 28.35. Afterwards he repeated his analysis. Add this graph and equation to your report. Still not happy, he decided to convert the time to seconds so he multiplied all the x-values by 60. He thought again about the coat hanger and wondered if he should subtract its weight first and then change to ounces, or change to ounces and then subtract the weight. Try these two to determine which is correct. Even after all this, he was not content, so he thought he would check the mass of the melted water. He made all the y-values negative and added the mass of the original cube.

Write a summary of what Mel, and you, learned at each step of this analysis. Explain how each step relates to the transformation of functions.

Project 5.4: The Greatest Integer Function

In this chapter you have studied in detail five parent functions and several generic unknown functions. You have shifted, flipped, and stretched functions. In this project you will look at a quite different, but important, parent function known as the greatest integer function. Its full name is the "Greatest Integer Less Than or Equal To Function." The symbol $[\![x]\!]$ is used for this function, but most computers and calculators use int(x) instead (like they do with abs(x) for absolute value). Change the calculator mode to disconnected or dot graphs to study this function, because the function is not always smooth and it jumps at times. (See **APPENDIX 5G** for specific notes on your calculator.)

Your task is to explain what the function does, to describe its graph with both words and pictures, and to give a detailed account of how this function behaves with shifts, flips, and stretches (both vertical and horizontal). Use graphs, equations, and complete sentences to describe each of the above. Look at both the overall nature of the function, and at what happens at specific x-values, such as 2.5, 4.7, −3.1, 5, −4, and so on.

Chapter Six

PARAMETRIC EQUATIONS AND TRIGONOMETRY

Contents

Section 6.1: Graphing Parametric Equations.. 236

Where and when

Section 6.2: Parametric to Nonparametric.. 244

Changing things around

Section 6.3: Right Triangle Trigonometry... 248

Reading the sines

Section 6.4: Geometric Shapes.. 256

Skipping around a circle

Section 6.5: Wind and River Problems... 261

Going against the flow

Section 6.6: Using Trigonometry to Set a Course....................................... 268

Working the angles

Section 6.7: Chapter Review... 275

Assessing yourself

Section 6.8: Projects.. 278

Taking it one step further

Section 6.1: Graphing Parametric Equations

As you walk around school each day, you probably cross paths with many of your friends. But does this necessarily mean that you meet them each time? Look at the map, or drawing, below. It shows the paths that Noah and Rita traveled during a recent school day. You can see that their paths crossed several times during the day. What other information do you need to have in order to know whether they actually did bump into each other?

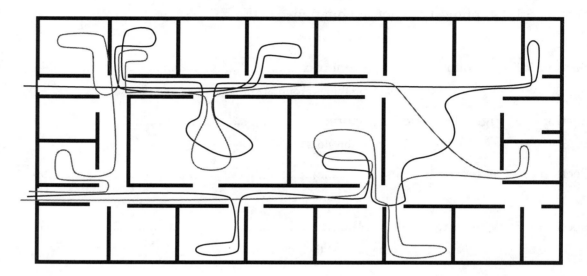

Without knowing the time they were at each of the intersections, you can't determine if they actually met. The same sort of time-related intersection situation arises often in the real world.

In your previous work with graphs and functions, you dealt with relationships between two variables, such as x and y. The graphs below are representations of x- and y-values that are related by the equation $y = x^2$. The graph on the right shows some additional restrictions that you will soon learn how to control.

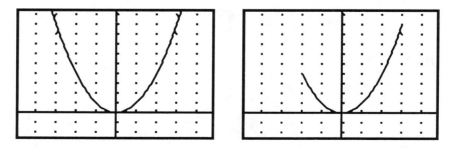

Preliminary Edition

In this chapter, you will also investigate some other interesting graphs and geometric figures. Two variables are often not enough to easily describe graphs like these.

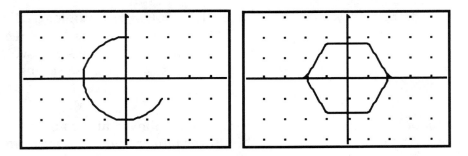

You can use **parametric equations** to separately describe the x- and y-coordinates of a point. In a parametric equation, the x- and y-variables are each written as a function of a third variable, t, called the **parameter**. Now you will be able to control which points are plotted, and when they will be plotted. In the next example, the variable t represents time. You will see how t controls the x- and y-values.

Example 1: Two tankers leave Corpus Christi at the same time, traveling 900 mi east toward St. Petersburg. Tanker A moves at 18 mi/hr and Tanker B moves at 22 mi/hr. Establish a coordinate system and use your calculator to simulate the motion involved in this situation.

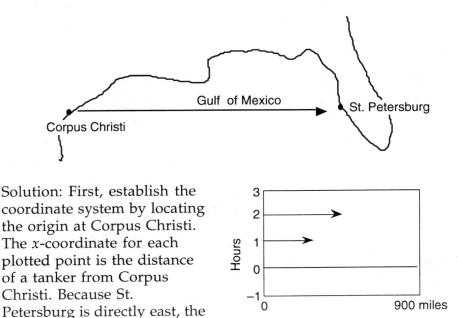

Solution: First, establish the coordinate system by locating the origin at Corpus Christi. The x-coordinate for each plotted point is the distance of a tanker from Corpus Christi. Because St. Petersburg is directly east, the y-coordinate for each path will remain constant.

The graphing window (see **APPENDIX 6A**) should accommodate the time, the distance traveled (x-coordinate), and the path (y-coordinate) on which each tanker travels. For this problem, use these window settings: [0, 50, 0.5, 0, 900, 100, −1, 3, 1]. The first three settings in this window have to do with the variable t. As you work through this example, try to figure out what each of these settings means.

You should assume that each of the tankers moves at a constant speed. At 18 mi/hr, after 2 hr, the slower tanker will be 36 mi from Corpus Christi. After 3 hr, it will be 54 mi out; after 10 hr, it will be 180 mi out; and after t hr, it will be $18t$ mi out, or $x = 18t$. (Enter this equation into x_{1t}.) This equation provides the distance traveled and locates the position of Tanker A at any given time. You can see that the x-value is dependent on the time or t-value. Position the starting point of Tanker A 1 mi north of Corpus Christi by setting $y_{1t} = 1$, so that you can avoid the x-axis and see the tanker moving. These two equations ($x_{1t} =$ and $y_{1t} =$) are examples of a pair of parametric equations. The t-values selected will determine which (x, y) points are plotted.

The motion and position of the second tanker can be simulated with $x_{2t} = 22t$ and $y_{2t} = 2$. What real-world meaning can you give to $22t$, and what reason supports using $y_{2t} = 2$?

Simulating Motion Activity

Trace the path of the appropriate tanker to help you answer each question.

a. How long does it take the faster tanker to reach St. Petersburg?

b. Where is the slower tanker when the faster tanker reaches its destination?

c. When, during the trip, is the faster tanker exactly 82 mi in front of the slower tanker?

d. During what part of the trip are the tankers less than 60 mi apart?

Work with your group to extend this list of questions. Then provide explanations and solutions to all of your questions. Be sure to include a list of your assumptions. Share your results and explanations with another group.

Parametric equations allow you to simulate motion, and to picture related paths when the location of the points is dependent on time. A parametric representation lets you see the dynamic nature of the motion. You can even adjust the plotting speed by changing the Tstep value. However, the parameter t doesn't always have to represent time. It can be a number just like x and y. Sometimes you may want to control which x- and/or y-values are plotted. You can do this by defining a range for the t-values.

Example 2: Graph the curve described by the parametric equations $x = t + 2$ and $y = t^2$ for $0 \le t \le 4$ on graph paper.

t	x	y
0	2	0
1	3	1
2	4	4
3	5	9
4	6	16

Solution: The problem states that you may only use values of t between 0 and 4. Use the given equations to calculate the x- and y-values that correspond to each value of t. Next, graph the points. Graph the point with the lowest value of t first. Then graph the rest of the points as t increases, connecting each point to the previous one as you graph them. Add arrows to indicate the direction of increasing values of t. When you look at the graph on paper, you can only see the x- and y-coordinates. Values of t are used to determine x and y, but they do not appear in the actual plot of the graph. Verify the graph on your calculator.

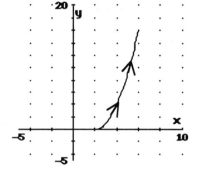

Exploring Parametrics Activity

Set your graphing window so that $-14 \le x \le 14$ and $-10 \le y \le 10$. Use the interval $0 \le t \le 4$ for the values of t with a Tstep of 0.1. The objective of this activity is to explore equations of the form

$$x = x_0 + at \quad \text{and} \quad y = y_0 + bt$$

a. Organize an investigation of these equations by choosing a set of values for a, b, x_0, and y_0. Choose values for x_0 and y_0 from $\{-3, -2, -1, 0, 1, 2, 3\}$ and values for a and b from $\{-1, 0, 1\}$. Then change the value of only one of these variables (for example, the variable a) several times to see what effect the changes have on the graph. Repeat this with each of the other variables. Observe at least six graphs for each of the variables. Be sure to trace the graphs and look at the values for x and y.

Make conjectures that describe the effects of changing the values. Describe similarities and differences in the graphs. Calculate the slope of each line, and indicate at least one endpoint. Make a connection between the slope and the values of a and b.

b. Change the interval for t to $-4 \le t \le 0$, and graph some of the same equations again. Are your earlier conjectures still true? What is the same and what has changed?

c. Describe what happens if you don't restrict the values of x_0 and y_0 to those suggested. Describe what happens if you don't restrict the values of t.

d. It is possible to write two sets of parametric equations that graph perpendicular segments. What is the relationship between the equations?

Example 3: Find values of t that generate the graph described by the parametric equations $x = t - 1$, $y = \frac{1}{2}t + 2$ shown in the window at the right.

Solution: Substitute an x- or y-value into the appropriate equation and solve for t.

$$-5 = t - 1 \quad \text{or} \quad 0 = \frac{1}{2}t + 2$$

t	x	y
	-5	0
	-3	1
	-1	2
	1	3
	3	4

Either substitution will give you $t = -4$ when $(x, y) = (-5, 0)$. Complete the table for each of the other pairs of x and y.

To find the t-value that gives the point at the left edge of the screen, solve the equation $x = t - 1$ by substituting the Xmin value (-9.4) for x. You will find that when $x = -9.4$, $t = -8.4$. Use the Xmax to find the t-value at the other edge of the screen. You will find that $t = 10.4$ when $x = 9.4$. These t-values, or a range that includes them, can be used as Tmin and Tmax to generate a graph like the one shown. In this example, part of the screen on the right-hand side was not used because the y-coordinates of the points were outside the range. If you don't want to graph that part of the line, you will need to reduce the range of t-values. Because the graph reaches the Ymax value before it reaches the Xmax value, set $\frac{1}{2}t + 2 = 6.2$ (Ymax) and solve for t. Use this t-value as your new Tmax.

Problem Set 6.1

1. Graph each pair of parametric equations. Be careful to account for any restrictions on t that are included. Indicate (with arrows) the direction of increasing t-values along the graph. If an interval for t isn't listed, then find one that shows all of the graph that fits in a window with $-10 \le x \le 10$ and $-6 \le y \le 6$.

    a. $x = 3t - 1, y = 2t + 1$

    b. $x = t + 1, y = t^2$

    c. $x = t^2, y = t + 3, -2 \le t \le 1$

    d. $x = t - 1, y = \sqrt{4 - t^2}, -2 \le t \le 2$

2. In the last chapter, you learned how to transform functions. You can do these same transformations with parametric equations. Parametric transformations are probably easier and may seem more natural to you. Use a t-interval equal to your x-interval, and a Tstep of 0.1 when drawing each graph.

    a. Graph $x = t, y = t^2$.

    b. Graph $x = t + 2, y = t^2$. How does this compare to the graph in 2a?

    c. Graph $x = t, y = t^2 - 3$. How does this compare to the graph in 2a?

    d. Predict what the graph of $x = t + 5, y = t^2 + 2$ will look like compared to the graph in 2a. Graph the equations to verify your conjecture.

    e. Predict what the graph of $x = t + a, y = t^2 + b$ will look like compared to the graph in 2a. Graph the equations to verify your conjecture.

3. a. Graph $x = t, y = |t|$.

    b. Graph $x = t - 1, y = |t| + 2$. How does this graph compare to the graph in 3a?

    c. Write a pair of parametric equations that will move the graph in 3a four units left and three units down.

    d. Graph $x = 2t, y = |t|$. How does this graph compare to the graph in 3a?

    e. Graph $x = t, y = 3|t|$. How does this graph compare to the graph in 3a?

    f. Describe how the numbers 2, 3, and 4 in the equations $x = t + 2$ and $y = 3|t| - 4$ change the graph in 3a.

4. Write parametric equations of the form $x = f(t)$, $y = g(t)$ for each graph. (Hint: You can always invent a parametric equivalent of a function by setting $x = t$ and changing y to a function of t by substituting t for x in the $y=$ equation.)

a.

b.

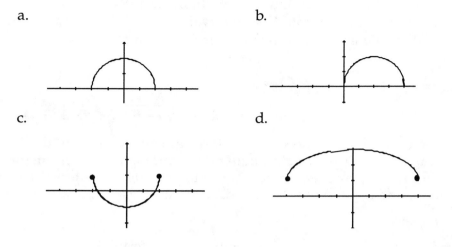

c.

d.

5. The graph of the parametric equations $x = f(t)$ and $y = g(t)$ is pictured at the right.

a. Sketch a graph of $x = f(t)$ and $y = {}^-g(t)$ on paper. Describe the transformation that you have just completed.

b. Sketch a graph of $x = {}^-f(t)$ and $y = g(t)$ on paper. Describe the transformation that you have just completed.

6. At the right is a graph of a pair of parametric equations $x = f(t)$ and $y = g(t)$. Write the parametric equations for each graph below in terms of $f(t)$ and $g(t)$.

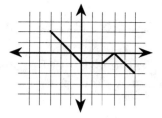

a.

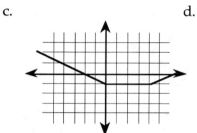

b.

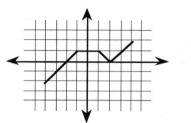

c.

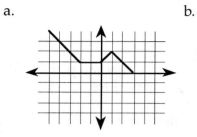

d.

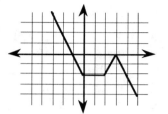

Section 6.2: Parametric to Nonparametric

In the last set of problems, you learned that you can always find a parametric equivalent of a function by setting $x = t$ and making y a function of t instead of a function of x. This means $y = x^2$ can be graphed in parametric form using $x = t$ and $y = t^2$.

If you know the parametric equations of a graph, you can write an equation *eliminating the parameter*. In other words, you can change the equation so that it no longer contains t, by solving either the x- or the y-equation for t and substituting the result into the other equation. Generally, you start by choosing the equation in which it is easier to solve for t. Do this with the equations in Example 2 from the last section.

$x = t + 2$ and $y = t^2$ Given equations.

$t = x - 2$ Solve the x -equation for t.

$y = (x - 2)^2$ Substitute for t in the y-equation

The graph of the function $y = (x - 2)^2$ gives a parabola with vertex at $(2, 0)$. (See **APPENDIX 6B**.) Notice that in this case you get the entire parabola, whereas the parametric form gives only a portion of the parabola because of the domain restrictions that were placed on t.

Example 1: Graph the curve described by the parametric equations $x = t^2 - 4$ and $y = \frac{t}{2}$, for $-9.4 \le t \le 9.4$. Then eliminate t from the equations and graph the result.

Solution: Plot the points, connecting them as t increases. Verify this graph on your calculator. Notice the graph is not a function, even though both x and y are functions of t.

Eliminate the parameter, and solve for y.

$x = t^2 - 4, y = \dfrac{t}{2}$ Given equations.

$t = 2y$ Solve the y equation for t.

$x = (2y)^2 - 4$ Substitute into the x equation.

$x = 4y^2 - 4$ Expand.

$4y^2 = x + 4$ Add 4 to both sides.

$y^2 = \dfrac{x + 4}{4}$ Divide both sides by 4.

$y = \pm \sqrt{\dfrac{x + 4}{4}}$ Take the square root of both sides.

You can also solve the original x-equation for t and substitute into the y-equation.

$x = t^2 - 4, y = \dfrac{t}{2}$ Given equations.

$t^2 = x + 4$ Add 4 to both sides.

$t = \pm \sqrt{x + 4}$ Take the square root of both sides.

$y = \dfrac{\pm \sqrt{x + 4}}{2}$ Substitute into the x-equation.

Notice that both methods give the same equation.

You might recognize this as the equation of a "sideways" parabola similar to those you studied in the previous chapter. Check the result by graphing to show that the graphs of $y = \pm \sqrt{\dfrac{x + 4}{4}}$ and $x = t^2 - 4, y = \dfrac{t}{2}$ are the same.

Problem Set 6.2

1. Eliminate the parameter in each pair of equations and solve the resulting equation for y. Graph this new relation in a window with $-9.4 \le x \le 9.4$ and $-6.2 \le y \le 6.2$. Verify that the graph of the new equation is the same (except for restrictions forced on t) as the graph of the parametric equation.

     a. $x = t + 1, y = t^2$ b. $x = 3t - 1, y = 2t + 1$

     c. $x = t^2, y = t + 3, -2 \le t \le 1$ d. $x = t - 1, y = \sqrt{4 - t^2}, -2 \le t \le 2$

2. Write a nonparametric equation that is equivalent to each pair of parametric equations.

    a. $x = 2t - 3, y = t + 2$ b. $x = t^2, y = t + 1$

    c. $x = \frac{1}{2}t + 1, y = \frac{t-2}{3}$ d. $x = t - 3, y = 2(t - 1)^2$

3. a. Graph $x = t + 5$ and $y = 2t - 1$.

    b. Write parametric equations that produce a graph with coordinates that are the reverse of the coordinates graphed in 3a. For example, if (6, 1) is a point on the original graph, then (1, 6) should be a point on the new graph. Use a "friendly" graphing window.

    c. Describe the relationship between the two graphs.

4. Set the graphing window to $^-9.4 \leq x \leq 9.4$ and $^-6.2 \leq y \leq 6.2$. Find the smallest interval for t that provides the same graph for the parametric equations $x = t + 2$ and $y = t^2$ and the nonparametric form, $y = (x - 2)^2$.

5. The slides and stretches in the problems in Section 6.1 are transformations. Graph $x(t) = t + 2$ and $y(t) = \sqrt{1 - t^2}$. Then graph the parametric functions below. Test your conclusions by experimenting with other parametric functions, and use them to support your answers, or to come to a new conclusion.

    a. Graph $x = x(t), y = ^-y(t)$ and identify any transformations of the original equations.

    b. Graph $x = ^-x(t), y = y(t)$ and identify any transformations of the original equations.

    c. Graph $x = ^-x(t), y = ^-y(t)$ and identify any transformations of the original equations.

6. Write parametric equations for two perpendicular lines that intersect at the point (3, 2). One of the lines should have a slope of $^-0.5$.

7. Tanker A moves at 18 mi/hr and Tanker B moves at 22 mi/hr. St. Petersburg is 900 mi east of Corpus Christi. Simulate the tanker movements, if Tanker A leaves Corpus Christi at noon and Tanker B leaves at 5 p.m.

   a. Write the equations you used to simulate the motion.

   b. Name the window you used to graph the equations in 7a.

   c. When and where does Tanker B overtake Tanker A?

   d. Simulate the tanker movements if both tankers leave at noon, but Tanker A leaves from Corpus Christi, Tanker B leaves from St. Petersburg, and the two ships are heading toward each other. Record your equations and determine the time interval during which they are within 50 mi of each other.

Section 6.3: Right-Triangle Trigonometry

Panama City is 750 mi from Corpus Christi on a heading, or bearing, of 73°. How can you simulate the movement of Tanker A from Corpus Christi to Panama City? As pictured below, a heading of 73° refers to the 73° angle measured clockwise from north. Now you have to model a motion that isn't strictly left-to-right or up-and-down.

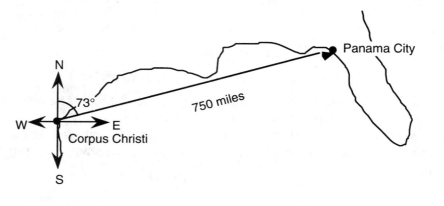

Parametric equations are especially useful for modeling motion that is at an angle to the horizontal. In these situations, you will be working with right triangles (which include the acute angle between the horizontal axis and the line of motion) using **trigonometric ratios**.

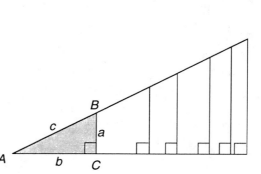

Do you see where the 17° comes from?

Trigonometric Ratios Activity

Each group member should choose a different angle between 0° and 90°. Carefully draw six overlapping right triangles with the base leg of each triangle on the same horizontal line. (See the diagram at the right.) For each triangle, measure the lengths of a, b, and c, to the nearest 0.1 cm. Each person should make a table like the one below, but with six empty rows. In the table, record the lengths of a, b, and c, where a is the height, b is the base, and c is the hypotenuse. Compute each ratio, $\dfrac{a}{b}, \dfrac{a}{c}$, and $\dfrac{b}{c}$, to the nearest hundredth. Do this for all six triangles.

Make sure your calculator is set in *degree* mode. Find the values of sin A, cos A, and tan A, rounding each to the nearest 0.01. Each group member should share his results with other group members. Look for relationships between the calculator ratios and the sin, cos, and tan columns. Carefully describe any relationships you think might be true.

Measure of angle A _____

a	b	c	$\dfrac{a}{c}$	$\dfrac{b}{c}$	$\dfrac{a}{b}$	sin A	cos A	tan A

Did you discover that the ratios of the lengths of any two pairs of corresponding sides of your similar right triangles are equal?

In the similar right triangles pictured at the right, the ratio of the length of the shorter leg to the length of the longer leg is always 0.75, and the ratios of the lengths 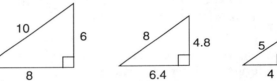 of other pairs of corresponding sides are also equal. In right triangles, there are special names for each of these ratios.

> The **sine** of an acute angle in a right triangle is defined to be the ratio of the length of the opposite leg to the length of the hypotenuse.
>
> The **cosine** of an acute angle in a right triangle is the ratio of the length of the adjacent leg to the length of the hypotenuse.
>
> The **tangent** of an acute angle in a right triangle is the ratio of the length of the opposite leg to the length of the adjacent leg.

In triangle ABC, the sine, cosine, and tangent are defined as follows:

$$\text{sine } A = \frac{a}{c}$$

$$\text{cosine } A = \frac{b}{c}$$

$$\text{tangent } A = \frac{a}{b}$$

If, instead, you refer to angle B, then the ratios are

$$\text{sine } B = \frac{b}{c} \qquad\qquad \text{cosine } B = \frac{a}{c} \qquad\qquad \text{tangent } B = \frac{b}{a}.$$

The Indian mathematician and astronomer Arybhata introduced the concept of sine in his best-known work, the *Aryabhatiya*, written around A.D. 499 when he was twenty-three years old. The astronomer Varahamihira (c. 505–587) gave a detailed exposition of trigonometry that included a number of relations between the sine and cosine functions.

You can use the sine and the other trigonometric ratios to find the unknown side lengths of a right triangle when you know the measure of one acute angle and the length of one of the other sides.

Example 1: Find the length of the indicated side in each triangle.

a.

b.

Solution:

a. The sides involved with respect to angle A are the two legs. Therefore, you will use the tangent ratio. (You can't use sine or cosine, because the hypotenuse isn't involved.)

$$\tan 42° = \tfrac{a}{20}$$

$$a = 20 \tan 42°$$

$$a \approx 18.008$$

(If you don't get this answer, check to see if your calculator is in *degree* mode.)

b. The sides involved with respect to angle A are the adjacent leg and the hypotenuse. Therefore, you will use the cosine ratio.

$$\cos 38° = \tfrac{52}{b}$$

$$b \cos 38° = 52$$

$$b = \frac{52}{\cos 38°}$$

$$b \approx 65.689$$

Example 2: Find the measure of angle A.

Solution:

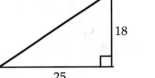

a. The sides involved with respect to angle A are the two legs. Therefore, you will use the tangent ratio; $\tan A = \tfrac{18}{25}$. You know the lengths of the sides but not the angle measures, so $A = \tan^{-1}\left(\dfrac{18}{25}\right) \approx 35.75°$. The −1 in this case indicates that you are using the **inverse tangent function**. This is a function that tells you the angle when you know the tangent ratio. Inverse trigonometric functions are written $\sin^{-1} x$, $\cos^{-1} x$, and $\tan^{-1} x$. Although the −1 looks like an exponent, it isn't. It doesn't mean $\dfrac{1}{\tan x}$. The equation $A = \tan^{-1}\left(\dfrac{18}{25}\right)$ means A is the angle that has a tangent ratio of $\dfrac{18}{25}$.

Finding the Height of a Tree Activity

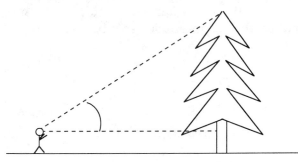

Assign a task to each member of the group. The four tasks are the walker, the hugger, the VAMD operator, and the recorder. Your group will need a length of string, a meter stick, and a VAMD (Vertical Angle Measuring Device).

a. Determine the length of the walker's step by having the walker pace off a given marked distance, then calculating the average.

b. Choose a tree to measure.

c. The VAMD operator locates the point where she needs to stand in order to sight the top of the tree.

d. The walker paces off the distance between the tree and the spot where the VAMD operator is standing.

e. The VAMD operator measures the angle between the horizontal and the top of the tree, with the recorder's assistance.

f. Meanwhile the hugger measures the circumference of the tree using the string and the meter stick.

g. The recorder records the measurements provided by the hugger, the walker, and the VAMD operator.

Repeat this for at least six trees of the same species. Be sure to measure the circumference at the same height on each tree. When you have the data, organize it in a table. Calculate the height and diameter of each tree and add this information to your table. Show in detail an example of each of the two calculations. Plot the heights and diameters, and find the best-fit line for this data.

Distance	Angle	Circumference	Height	Diameter

Problem Set 6.3

1. Find the length of the indicated side of each triangle.

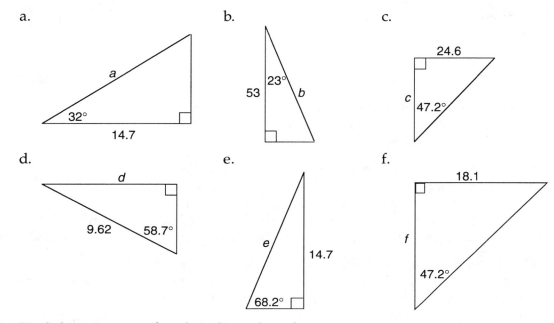

a.

b.

c.

d.

e.

f.

2. Find the measure of each indicated angle.

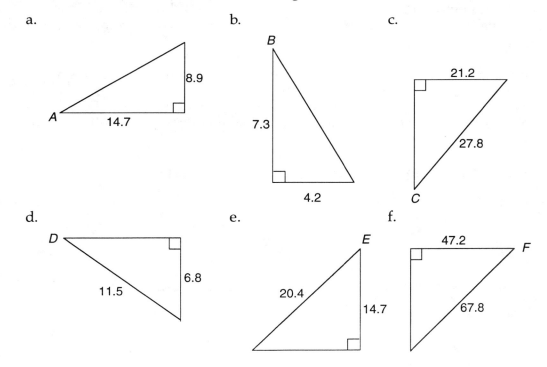

a.

b.

c.

d.

e.

f.

3. Two ants leave the nest. One walks east 28.5 cm and the other walks south 60.3 cm.

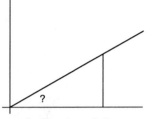

a. After the ants get where they're going, what is the heading of the line of sight from the southern ant to the eastern ant?

b. How far apart are the ants?

4. a. Graph the parametric equations $x = t \cos 39°$ and $y = t \sin 39°$. Use a graphing window with $0 \le x \le 10$ and $0 \le y \le 6.5$. Describe the graph.

b. In order to determine the angle between this line and the x-axis, trace to a point on the line and find the coordinates. Make a triangle by drawing a line from the point to the x-axis. Label the lengths of the legs of the triangle. What is the angle between the line and the x-axis?

5. Graph the parametric equations $x = t \cos 45°$ and $y = t \sin 45°$. Use a graphing window with $0 \le x \le 10$, $0 \le y \le 6.5$, and $0 \le t \le 10$. Describe the graph and name the angle between the graph and the x-axis. What is the relationship between this angle and the parametric equations?

6. What parametric equations could you use to graph a line that makes a 57° angle with the x-axis? Find an interval for t that gives a complete graph in the window with $-4.7 \le x \le 4.7$ and $-3.1 \le y \le 3.1$.

7. What parametric equations could you use to graph a line that makes a 29° angle with the x-axis?

8. Write parametric equations, involving the tangent ratio, that will graph a line that makes a 29° angle with the x-axis.

9. Write parametric equations for each graph and indicate the t-interval that you used.

a.   b.

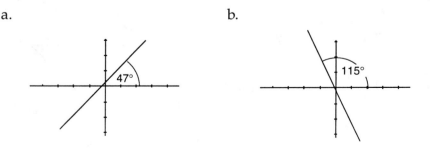

10. Suppose a tanker is moving at 10 mi/hr on a bearing of 60°.

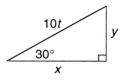

a. Use the right triangle pictured to write equations for x and y, in terms of t, that simulate the motion.

b. What t-values are required to picture 100 mi of tanker motion?

c. What is the real-world meaning of the numerical values and variables you used in your equations?

d. What is the real-world meaning of the graph produced with these equations?

11. Simulate the movement of Tanker A at 18 mi/hr from Corpus Christi to Panama City. Panama City is 750 mi from Corpus Christi on a heading of 73°. Make a sketch of the tanker's motion, showing the coordinate axes you used.

a. How long does the tanker take to get to Panama City?

b. How far east and how far north is Panama City from Corpus Christi?

12. a. Simulate the movement of Tanker B at 22 mi/hr from St. Petersburg to New Orleans on a heading of 285°. The distance between the two ports is 510 mi. Make a sketch of the tanker's motion, showing the coordinate axes you used.

b. How long does it take to get to New Orleans?

c. How far west and how far north is New Orleans from St. Petersburg?

d. Suppose Tanker A in Problem 11 leaves at the same time as Tanker B. Describe where the ships' paths intersect.

Section 6.4: Geometric Shapes

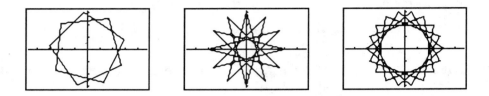

The *t*-value in parametric equations can also represent an angle. When it does, you can write equations that create a wide variety of different geometric shapes. The mathematical ideas that you'll use to create these shapes are based on the equation of a circle and some trigonometric definitions.

A **circle** is the set of all the points in a plane that are the same distance from a given point called the **center**. This distance is called the **radius**. When you graph a circle, it is apparent that it is not a function. To graph a complete circle on your calculator, you will have to write two separate function equations: one for the top half of the circle, and one for the bottom half. This task becomes much simpler with parametric equations. With parametric equations, you can draw some very interesting geometric shapes based on a circle.

In a circle with radius r and t degrees at the central angle A, $\sin t = \dfrac{y}{r}$ and $\cos t = \dfrac{x}{r}$. Solve these equations for x and y to get the **parametric equations for a circle**: $x = r \cos t$ and $y = r \sin t$.

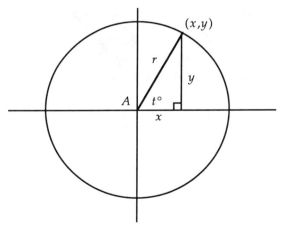

Example 1: Use parametric equations to draw the graph of a circle of radius 3 centered at $(0, 0)$.

Solution: The parametric equations for a circle of radius 3 centered at $(0, 0)$ are $x = 3 \cos t$ and $y = 3 \sin t$. The variable t represents the central angle of the circle. What does the 3 represent in the equations? Be sure your calculator is in parametric mode, and set the graphing window at $[0, 360, 15, -4.7, 4.7, 1, -3.1, 3.1, 1]$. (The first three numbers in the window setting don't actually affect the window size, but they will affect how the graph itself appears.) What would you do to graph a circle of radius 2? Of radius 1? What happens if you use a Tstep of $120°$?

Drawing Polygons Activity

a. Use the equations $x = 3 \cos t$ and $y = 3 \sin t$. Experiment with the parameter t (both interval and increment) to draw from point to point on the circumference of the circle. Can you make a square? A hexagon? An octagon? A triangle? What would it take to make a square with its sides parallel to the axes? How can you rotate a polygon shape about the origin? Be sure you can graph each shape shown below. Try to find more than one way to draw each figure. Write a paragraph summarizing your discoveries.

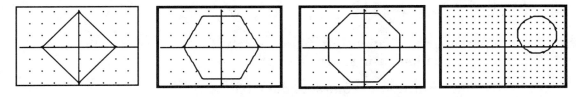

b. Translate the circle $x = 3 \cos t$ and $y = 3 \sin t$ so that it is centered at (5, 2). Reflect this graph over the y-axis, the x-axis, the line $y = x$, and the line $x = -1$. Describe the method you used for each of these reflections.

c. Graph the equations $x = 3 \cos t$ and $y = 3 \sin t$, but this time set the calculator to plot a point every 125°. You will also need to increase Tmax, so that $0° \le t \le 3600°$, or 10 times around the circle, to get a good picture. Try setting Tstep to other values, such as 100°, 150°, and 185°. You may also want to change the upper limit on t to get a better picture. Explain what happens in each case.

If you look at a special right triangle with a 1-unit hypotenuse, the definitions for sine and cosine give you the equations $\sin A = y$ and $\cos A = x$. Applying the Pythagorean theorem yields the equation $x^2 + y^2 = 1$. If you substitute the trigonometric ratios for x and y, you'll get $(\cos A)^2 + (\sin A)^2 = 1$. This equation will be true for any angle A. You can use your calculator to verify that it's true for $A = 47°$.

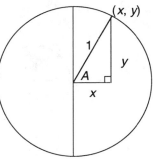

$$\cos 47° \approx 0.6820, (\cos 47°)^2 \approx 0.4651$$

$$\sin 47° \approx 0.7313, (\sin 47°)^2 \approx 0.5349$$

$$(\cos 47°)^2 + (\sin 47°)^2 \approx 0.4651 + 0.5349 = 1$$

Try substituting other angle values for A, and convince yourself that the equation will always work.

Problem Set 6.4

1. Write parametric equations for each figure. Indicate the range used for t, and the increment.

   a.   b.   c.   d.

   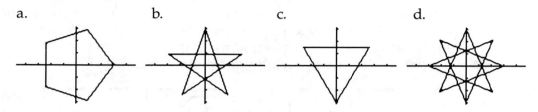

2. a. Write parametric equations for a circle of radius 1, centered at the origin. Graph the equations using a Tstep of 15°.

   b. Use the trace function to complete the table.

Angle A	0°	30°	45°	60°	90°	120°	135°
cos A							
sin A							

   c. Write an alternative definition for cos A that uses the following words: coordinate, unit circle, perimeter, central angle.

   d. Write an alternative definition for sin A that uses the following words: coordinate, unit circle, perimeter, central angle.

3. Experiment with your calculator to find parametric equations for each circle. Each one has a 2-unit radius and has been translated from the origin.

   a.   b.   c.

   d.   e.

   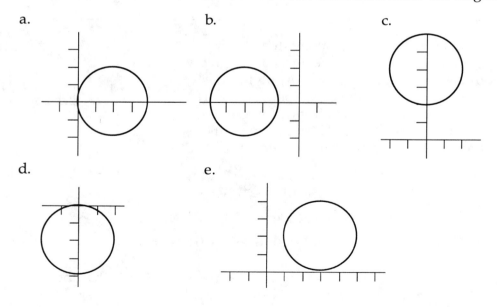

4. Complete the following steps to eliminate the parameter t in the equations $x = 3 \cos t$ and $y = 3 \sin t$.

   a. Divide both sides of each equation by 3 to isolate the t parts of the expressions. This means one equation will be solved for $\cos t$ and the other will be solved for $\sin t$.

   b. Square both sides of each equation.

   c. Add the equations together. Make sure the terms involving t are on one side of the final equation, and the terms involving x and y are on the other.

   d. Because $(\sin t)^2 + (\cos t)^2 = 1$ for any angle, use this to simplify the t side of the equation.

   e. Multiply your final equation by 9 to eliminate the fractions.

   f. The standard form of the equation of a circle in nonparametric form, when the center is at the origin, is $x^2 + y^2 = r^2$, where r is the radius. What is the value for r in your equation?

5. Use your equations from Problem 3e, and complete each step to eliminate the parameter t.

   a. Isolate the t part of each equation as in Problem 4a.

   b. Square both sides of each equation, and add them together.

   c. Use the fact that $(\sin t)^2 + (\cos t)^2 = 1$ to simplify the t side of the equation.

   d. Multiply by the appropriate number to eliminate any fractions.

   e. The standard nonparametric form of the equation of a circle that is not centered at the origin, is $(x - h)^2 + (y - k)^2 = r^2$. The center is at (h, k) and the radius is r. What are the values for h, k and r in your equation?

   f. Graph this new equation to see if it matches the parametric graph. You will have to solve it for y first.

6. Experiment to find parametric equations for each figure. The center of each figure is at the origin.

   a.   b.   c.

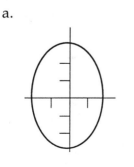 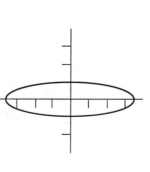 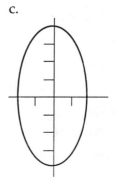

7. The figures in Problem 6 are called ellipses. They can be thought of as having two different radii: a horizontal radius and a vertical radius. Write the equations of the ellipses described below.

 a. Horizontal radius = 4, vertical radius = 3, center (0, 0)

 b. Horizontal radius = 3, vertical radius = 2, center (4, 0)

 c. Horizontal radius = 2.5, vertical radius = 1.5, center (0, 2)

 d. Horizontal radius = 2, vertical radius = 3.5, center (1, 3)

8. Follow steps a through c, as in Problem 5, to eliminate the parameter t from the equations you wrote in Problems 7a and 7c.

 d. The standard nonparametric form of the equation of an ellipse is $\dfrac{(x-h)^2}{a^2} + \dfrac{(y-k)^2}{b^2} = 1$. The center is at (h, k), and a and b represent half the length of each axis. Find the center of the ellipse, and the length of each axis.

9. Write parametric equations and give values for Tmin, Tmax, and Tstep that will result in each graph or shape.

 a.   b.

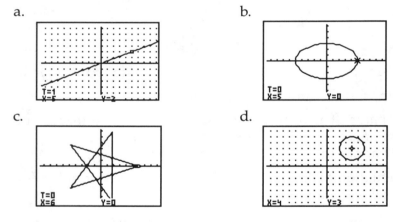

 c.   d.

10. a. Write parametric equations that accomplish the following transformations.

 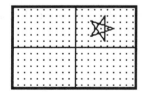

  i. Create the shape in the figure to the right.

  ii. Reflect the shape over the x-axis.

  iii. Reflect the shape over the y-axis.

  iv. Rotate the shape 180° about the origin.

 b. Name the values of Tmin, Tmax, and Tstep that you used for each pair of equations in 10a.

 c. Describe a second way to rotate the shape.

Section 6.5: Wind and River Problems

Modeling Motion Activity

Place a piece of paper lengthwise in front of you. Lightly hold a twelve-inch ruler so that you will be able to draw a straight line across the paper toward yourself. Another person will hold the end of the paper and slowly pull it under the ruler as you draw the line.

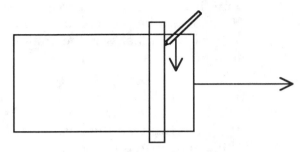

Is your line parallel to one of the sides of the paper? Is it diagonal on the paper? How does the position of your line change when the paper is pulled at a faster rate? At a slower rate? What could you do to make the line more perpendicular to the direction of the paper's motion? What will happen if your partner pulls the paper at a steadily increasing rate?

The activity above simulates what happens when you try to swim across a river with a strong current. The current sweeps you downstream, and when you reach the other side you will not be directly across from the point where you began. This movement is also similar to what happens to an airplane or a bird when the wind blows at them from the side.

Consider three toy cars on a large piece of plywood that is moving to the right across the floor at a rate of 60 cm/sec. Each car is moving 40 cm/sec in the direction indicated. After 1 sec, car A is 100 cm to the right of its original position. It is at the 200 cm mark after 2 seconds and at the 300 cm mark after 3 sec. During the same time intervals, car B is located 20 cm, 40 cm, 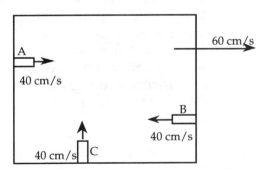 and 60 cm to the right of its original position. The velocities of car A and car B relative to the floor are 100 cm/sec and 20 cm/sec, respectively.

The motion of car C is more complicated. After 1 sec, it is 60 cm to the right and 40 cm above its original position. After 2 sec, it is 120 cm to the right and 80 cm above its original position. Using the Pythagorean theorem, you can determine that the car is moving at $\sqrt{(60^2 + 40^2)} \approx 72.1$ cm/sec relative to the floor.

Example 1: Pat Dulbote heads her boat directly across the Mississippi River, which is 2 mi wide in this stretch. Her  ancient motor can move the boat at a speed of 4 mi/hr on water where there is no current. However, the river current flows at 3 mi/hr. How far downstream is she by the time she gets across? How far did her boat actually travel? What was the actual velocity of her boat? What was the angle of the actual path, relative to a trip straight across the river?

Solution: The first step is to establish a coordinate system. Assume that Pat starts at $(0, 0)$ and heads in the positive x-direction. The distance an object travels is given by the equation $d = rt$, where r is the rate of speed and t is time. If there were no current, the distance Pat's boat would travel would be $x = 4t$, where t is measured in hours. Assume that the current flows toward the positive y-direction. The equation representing the water current would be $y = 3t$. The combined effect of these two equations will represent the distance she actually travels.

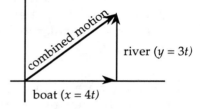

To choose an appropriate window to graph this situation, you need to be sure to include the starting point of the boat and to adjust the x- and y-values so you can see where the boat is going. In this case, a window which shows the upper right quadrant of the coordinate plane is appropriate. Because neither the boat nor the current travels very fast, the window does not need to be very big in either direction. Graph $x = 4t$ and $y = 3t$ on your calculator using these window settings: [0, 0.5, 0.01, 0, 2, 1, −1, 2, 1]. Trace to find the point when $x = 2$ at the other side of the river. The corresponding y-coordinate is 1.5. This means that the boat traveled 1.5 mi downstream during the time it took it to move 2 mi across the river. The t-value of this point is 0.5, so it took 1/2 hr to make the trip.

To determine the actual distance traveled by the boat, look at the triangle formed with the horizontal. Use the Pythagorean theorem to determine this distance.

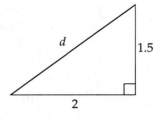

$$2^2 + 1.5^2 = d^2$$

$$4 + 2.25 = d^2$$

$$d^2 = 6.25$$

$$d = \sqrt{6.25} = 2.5$$

Therefore, Pat traveled 2.5 mi as she crossed the river.

Because *distance = rate • time*, and you know she traveled 2.5 mi in 0.5 hr, her rate can be determined using substitution.

$$2.5 = rate • 0.5 \qquad \text{or } rate = 5 \text{ mi/hr}$$

Several different methods could be used to find the angle of motion. Trace to any point (x, y) on the actual path. Then find the inverse tangent ($\tan^{-1}$) of the ratio $\dfrac{y}{x}$. (Why does this work?) The angle of motion is about 36.9°.

An airplane is affected by the wind in the same way a boat is affected by the current. The following situation illustrates what happens when a pilot does not compensate for this wind effect.

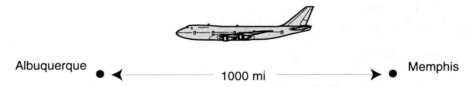

Example 2: A pilot heads a plane due west from Memphis, Tennessee, toward Albuquerque, New Mexico. The cities are 1000 mi apart, and the pilot sets the plane's controls to fly at 250 mi/hr. However, there is a constant 20 mi/hr wind blowing from the north. Where does the plane end up?

Solution: Set up a coordinate system with Memphis at the origin. The plane's motion can be described by the equation $x = -250t$. (Why is this negative?) The wind's force can be described by $y = -20t$. (Why is this negative?) Choose an appropriate graphing window and watch the result of the combined motions.

Tracing this graph will show that after 4 hr, the plane has traveled the necessary 1000 mi west, but it is 80 mi south of Albuquerque, somewhere in the White Sands Missile Range!

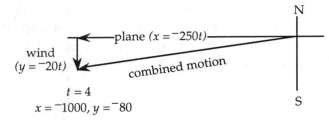

The Pythagorean theorem indicates that the plane has actually traveled $\sqrt{1000^2 + 80^2}$, or about 1003 mi in 4 hr; this is a rate of 250.8 mi/hr.

The actual angle of motion between the plane's path and due west is $\tan^{-1}\left(\frac{80}{1000}\right)$ or about 4.6°.

Problem Set 6.5

1. Convert each angle of the motion in Example 1 and Example 2 to a compass heading.

2. Pa Pye heads his boat directly across the 1.5-mi-wide Whett River to his friend Ollie Voyl's house. His boat can go 6 mi/hr and the river flows at 2 mi/hr.

   a. Write the equation that describes the effect of the river current.

   b. Write the equation that describes the boat's contribution to the motion.

   c. Graph these equations.

   d. How far downstream does Pa land?

   e. How far has his boat traveled?

3. A pilot wants to fly from Toledo to Chicago, which lies 280 mi directly west. Her plane can fly at 120 mi/hr. She ignores the wind and heads directly west. However, there is a 25 mi/hr wind blowing from the south.

a. Write the equation that describes the effect of the wind.

b. Write the equation that describes the plane's contribution to the motion.

c. Graph these equations.

d. How far off course is the plane when it has traveled 280 mi west?

e. How far has the plane actually traveled?

f. How fast did she actually travel?

4. Fred Rosewell is trying to row his boat across the Amazon. He points his boat directly across the river, which is 4 mi wide. There is a 5-mi/hr current. When he reaches the opposite shore, Fred finds that he has landed at a point 2 mi downstream.

a. Write the equation that describes the effect of the river current.

b. If Fred rows at 3 mi/hr, what equation will describe his contribution to the motion?

c. Graph these equations and then change Fred's speed (using guess-and-check) until he reaches the correct point 2 mi downstream on the opposite shore.

d. How far did Fred actually travel?

e. How long did it take him?

f. What was Fred's actual speed?

g. As the boat travels down the river, what angle does it make with the river bank?

5. A plane takes off from Orlando, Florida, heading 975 mi due north toward Cleveland, Ohio. The plane flies at 250 mi/hr. There is a 25-mi/hr wind blowing from the west.

a. Where is the plane after it has traveled 975 mi north?

b. How far did the plane actually travel?

c. How fast did the plane actually travel?

d. At what angle did the plane actually fly?

Problems 6–9 deal with the motion of a falling object. The height of the object is affected by the force of gravity. An equation for the height is $y = -16t^2 + s_o$. Here t is the time (measured in seconds) and s_o is the initial height of the object (measured in feet.) The 16 is related to the *acceleration* of the object caused by the force of gravity.

6. A ball is rolled off the end of a table with a horizontal velocity of 1.5 ft/sec. The table is 2.75 ft high.

a. If there were no gravity, what equation would describe the x-direction motion of the ball?

b. Gravity will affect the vertical motion of the ball. Use the equation given above, with the appropriate value for the initial height, to model the vertical motion of the ball.

c. Enter these two equations in your calculator and graph them.

d. How far from the table does the ball hit the floor? Give your answer to the nearest hundredth of a foot.

e. How long does it take for the ball to hit the floor? Give your answer to the nearest hundredth of a second.

7. A ball is rolled off a 3-ft high table and lands at a point 1.8 ft away from the table.

   a. How long did it take for the ball to hit the floor? Give your answer to the nearest hundredth of a second.

   b. How fast was the ball traveling when it left the table? Give your answer to the nearest hundredth of a second. (Hint: You can find this answer by guess-and-check, or by using the answer from 7a.)

8. A wildlife biologist sees a deer standing 400 ft away. Her gun is loaded with tranquilizer darts that leave her gun traveling at 650 ft/sec. The biologist is holding the gun level, at a height of 5.5 ft above the ground.

   a. Record the equations you used to model this motion.

   b. Does she hit the deer? If not, by how much did she miss?

   c. Use guess-and-check to determine how high the biologist would have to hold the gun to hit the deer at a height somewhere between 3 ft and 4.5 ft above the ground. (The gun is held level with the ground.)

   d. How far does the dart travel before it drops 1 ft in height? Does the original height make a difference? Does the original velocity of the dart make a difference? Explain.

9. A golf ball rolls off the top step of a flight of 14 stairs, with a horizontal velocity of 5 ft/sec. The stairs are each 8 in high and 8 in wide. On which step does the ball first bounce? (To solve this problem, you may want to convert everything to inches, including the gravity constant of −16 in the vertical-component equation for the motion.)

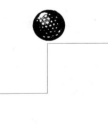

10. You have studied parametric equations in several different contexts. Explain some advantages and disadvantages of using parametric equations. Include examples if appropriate.

11. Create your own problem that is related to something you have studied so far in this chapter. Write out the complete solution to your problem and explain why you think it is a good problem. (Note: Please make sure that it is a problem or question, and not just an explanation or description.)

Section 6.6: Using Trigonometry to Set a Course

In Section 6.5, you solved problems in which a plane or a boat was moving in a direction perpendicular to a wind or a current. Planes and boats actually travel at a variety of angles with respect to the wind and water flow. These situations can also be modeled with trigonometric ratios, and by breaking a motion into vertical and horizontal components.

> Example 1: An object is moving at a speed of 10 units/sec, at an angle of 30° to the x-axis. What are the horizontal and vertical components of this motion?

> Solution: Make a triangle with an angle of 30°. The hypotenuse represents the path of the object and its length represents the distance traveled by the object; label it $10t$. Do you see why?
> Now you can use trigonometry to calculate the lengths of the legs of the triangle, which are the horizontal and vertical components of the motion.

$$\sin 30° = \frac{y}{10t} \qquad \cos 30° = \frac{x}{10t}$$

$$y = 10t \sin 30° \qquad x = 10t \cos 30°$$

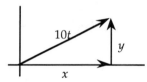

Check to see that these equations will provide the motion required. In general, the horizontal component is $x = v_0 t \cos A$, where v_0 is the initial velocity, A is the angle, and the vertical component is $y = v_0 t \sin A$.

> Example 2: A pilot heads from Memphis, Tennessee, toward Albuquerque, New Mexico. The cities are 1000 mi apart; Memphis is due east of Albuquerque. The plane flies at 250 mi/hr, and there is a constant 20 mi/hr wind blowing from the north. What angle and heading should the pilot set so that he actually lands in Albuquerque and is not blown off course?

> Solution: Set up a coordinate system with Memphis at the origin, and sketch the plane's path slightly to the north. The plane's distance along the hypotenuse can be described by $250t$.
> The horizontal component is $x = -250t \cos A$, where A is the tiny angle toward the north that the pilot must set. (The negative sign directs the motion to the west.)

The wind's force can be described by $y = {}^-20t$ because it is blowing south. The vertical component of the plane's course, $y = 250t \sin A$, must exactly match the force of the wind (add up to zero) if the pilot hopes to land in Albuquerque.

$250t \sin A + {}^-20t = 0$

or $20t = 250t \sin A$

$20 = 250 \sin A$.

So A is about $4.59°$.

wind at 20 mi/hr

Turn off the axes on your calculator and graph $x = {}^-250t \cos 4.59°$ and $y = 250t \sin 4.59° - 20t$ to see the plane move directly west. Be sure to use an appropriate graphing window.

The pilot would actually set his instruments at a heading of $270° + 4.59°$ or $274.59°$.

Example 3: A plane is headed from Memphis to Albuquerque, which is 1000 mi due west. The plane flies at 250 mi/hr. On this trip the pilot encounters a 20 mi/hr wind blowing in from the northwest. Where will the plane end up if the pilot does not compensate for the wind?

Solution: You will begin by setting up the same type of coordinate system as before. Because the plane is headed directly west, you use the equation, $x = {}^-250t$ to model the plane's contribution to the motion. Because the wind is blowing at an angle, it will affect both the east-west and north-south directions of motion. You must break the force of the wind into these two components. A picture such as the one below is helpful.

The problem now is to find the lengths of the two legs of the triangle.

To find the vertical (southward) leg use the sine ratio.

$\sin 45° = \frac{-y}{20t}$ $\qquad\qquad y = -20t \sin 45° \approx -14.14t$

To find the horizontal (eastward) leg use the cosine ratio or the Pythagorean theorem.

$\cos 45° = \frac{x}{20t}$ $\qquad\qquad x = 20t \cos 45° \approx 14.14t$

Notice that the signs of these equations are determined by the directions of the arrows in the diagram.

Both the plane's motion and the wind contribute to the actual path of the plane, so you add the x-contributions together and the y-contributions together to form the final equations:

$$x = -250t + 20t \cos 45° \text{ and } y = -20t \sin 45°$$

You may also use the decimal forms of these equations, $x = -250t + 14.14t$, or $x = -235.86t$, and $y = -14.14t$, but you will lose some accuracy in your calculations.

After graphing these equations and tracing, you find that it takes the plane about 4.24 hr to fly 1000 mi west, and it is then about 60 mi south of Albuquerque, somewhere in the middle of nowhere.

Example 4: What angle adjustment should the pilot in Example 3 make in the flight so that he will land in Albuquerque?

Solution: For the plane to actually fly straight west, it must head a bit north. It must have a vertical component to its motion that will exactly counteract the vertical effect of the wind. The vertical component of the plane's motion will be $y = 250t \sin A$, where A is that unknown little angle to the north. The wind's contribution will remain $y = -20t \sin 45°$. For the plane to fly directly west, these must add up to 0.

$250t \sin A + {}^-20t \sin 45° = 0$

$250t \sin A = 20t \sin 45°$ Add $20t \sin 45°$ to both sides.

$\sin A = \dfrac{20}{250} \sin 45°$ Divide by $250t$.

$A = \sin^{-1} \left(\dfrac{20}{250} \sin 45° \right) \approx 3.24°$ Take the inverse sine.

At this angle, the plane will fly directly west. To model the motion on the calculator, you must also use this angle to modify the *x*-equation.

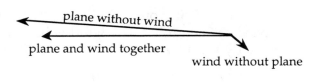

plane without wind

plane and wind together

wind without plane

$$x = -250t \cos 3.24° + 20t \cos 45°,$$

$$y = 250t \sin 3.24° + -20t \sin 45°$$

Enter these two equations and graph. (Turn off the axes or you may see nothing happening, because the graph is being drawn on top of the *x*-axis.) A trace of the graph will show that after 4.28 hr, the plane has traveled the 1000 mi west, and is only about a tenth of a mile north of its destination. (This slight error could be reduced by using a more accurate measure for the angle.) Therefore, the pilot must set an instrument heading of 270° + 3.25°, or 273.25°.

Problem Set 6.6

1. Beau Terr wants to travel directly across the Wyde River, which is 2 mi wide in this stretch. His boat can move at a speed of 4 mi/hr. The river current flows at 3 mi/hr. At what angle upstream should he aim the boat so that he ends up going straight across?

    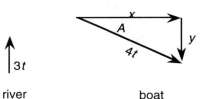

    river   boat

    a. Write an equation for the vertical component of the boat's motion.

    b. Write an equation for the vertical component of the river's motion.

    c. Equate these components and solve for *A*.

    d. Write equations for the horizontal components of motion.

    e. Model the motion on your calculator, and verify that Beau will travel directly across the river. Record your equations.

2. A plane is flying on a heading of 310° at a speed of 320 mi/hr. The wind is blowing directly from the east at a speed of 32 mi/hr.

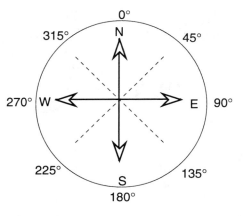

a. Make a drawing to indicate the plane's motion.

b. Write equations that model the plane's motion without the wind.

c. Make a drawing to indicate the wind's motion.

d. Write equations that model the wind's motion.

e. What are the resulting equations that model the motion of the plane with the wind?

f. Where is the plane after 5 hr?

3. a. Use guess-and-check to find the angle adjustment the pilot must make in Problem 2 so that the plane is not blown off course during this flight. (Hint: What are the x- and y-coordinates of the plane in Problem 2 if it isn't blown off course? Use this point as a target on your screen.)

b. Write the final equations that combine both the plane's and the wind's contributions to the flight.

c. Test your equations by graphing and tracing.

4. A plane is flying on a heading of 250° at a speed of 220 mi/hr. The wind is blowing 40 mi/hr toward a heading of 160°. Where is the plane after 5 hr?

a. Make separate diagrams for the plane and the wind. Find the angle each path makes with the x-axis.

b. Write equations for the horizontal and vertical components for the wind and the plane.

c. Write combined equations for x and y, and graph them.

d. Where is the plane after 5 hr?

e. How far has it traveled from its starting point?

f. At what heading did it actually travel?

5. a. Describe how you can find the angle adjustment the pilot must make in Problem 4 so that the plane is not blown off course during the flight.

   b. Write the final equations you used that combine both the plane's and the wind's motion contributions for the flight.

   c. Test your equations by graphing and tracing.

6. Superman takes off from Metropolis to fly to Central City, which is 800 mi directly west; he flies at a leisurely rate of 75 mi/hr. The wind is blowing toward a heading of 300° at a speed of 32 mi/hr. Follow the steps below to find the correct heading that he should set, and the length of time it will take him to reach Central City.

   a. Write an equation showing the relationship between the vertical components of the wind and Superman's flying speed. Solve this for the angle at which Superman must fly to arrive in Central City. Convert this to a heading.

   b. Write an equation showing the relationship between the horizontal components of the wind and Superman's flying speed, and the 800 mi he needs to travel.

   c. How long does it take him to fly to Central City?

7. A bird is starting its annual migration from northern Michigan to Florida. It takes off on a heading of 165°. The bird flies at an average speed of 10 mi/hr. On the day it takes off, there is a 8 mi/hr breeze blowing toward a heading of 100°.

   a. Make a diagram showing the effect of the wind. Label the horizontal and vertical components.

   b. Make a diagram showing the bird's contribution to the motion. Write equations for the horizontal and vertical components.

   c. Write the combined equations for the motion and graph the equations. Where is the bird after 8 hr of travel?

   d. At what heading has the bird actually traveled?

   e. How do birds actually stay on course during migration? Investigate this and write a paragraph summarizing the theories.

8. A new plane is proposed that will fly from New York to Tokyo in 3 hr.

   a. If the distance for such a flight is about 12,000 mi, how fast will the plane have to go?

   b. Suppose this plane flies on a heading of 270° (straight west) and there is a 30-mi/hr wind blowing toward the south. How far off course will the plane be after traveling 12,000 mi?

   c. At what heading should the plane fly to correct this? How practical is this? Explain your answer.

9. Is there a problem in this section that you are having difficulty solving? If so, write out the problem and as much of the solution as you can. Then, clearly explain what is keeping you from solving the problem. Be as specific as you can.

Section 6.7: Chapter Review

Problem Set 6.7

1. a. Make a (*time, distance*) graph that represents motion at 20 m/sec for 5 sec and then at 30 m/sec for 8 sec.

    b. What does the (*time, speed*) graph of this motion look like?

2. Use the parametric equations $x = -3t + 1$ and $y = \frac{2}{t+1}$ to answer each question.

    a. Find the x- and y-coordinates of the points that correspond to the values of $t = 3$, $t = 0$, and $t = -3$.

    b. Find the y-value that is paired with $x = -7$.

    c. Find the x-value that is paired with $y = 4$.

    d. Sketch the curve for $-3 \le t \le 3$, showing the direction of movement. Trace the graph and explain what happens when $t = -1$.

3. Do the following for each set of parametric equations below.

    i.   Graph them.

    ii. Eliminate the parameter and solve for y.

    iii. Graph the resulting nonparametric equation and describe how it compares with the original graph.

    a. $x = 2t - 5, y = t + 1$ b. $x = t^2 + 1, y = t - 2, -2 \le t \le 6$

    c. $x = \frac{t+1}{2}, y = t^2, -4 \le t \le 3$ d. $x = \sqrt{t+2}, y = t - 3$

4. Write parametric equations that will transform each curve from Problems 3a and 3c as stated below.

    i.   Reflect the curve across the y-axis.

    ii. Reflect the curve across the x-axis.

    iii. Slide the curve 3 units up.

    iv. Slide the curve 4 units left and 2 units down.

5. Solve to find the angle or side indicated in each triangle.

a. 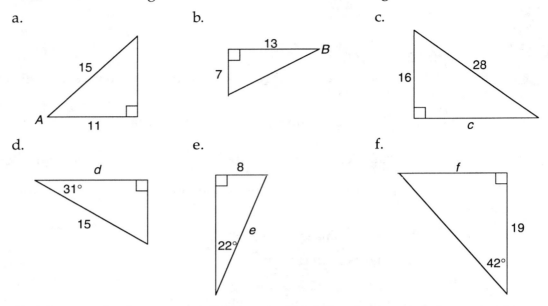 b. c.

d. e. f.

6. Sketch a graph of $x = t \cos 28°$, $y = t \sin 28°$. What is the angle between the graph and the x-axis?

7. A diver runs off a 10-m platform with an initial horizontal velocity of 4 m/sec. The edge of the platform is directly above a point 1.5 m from the pool's edge. Where will she hit the water? (Use $h = -4.9t^2 + s_0$ for the vertical-component equation.)

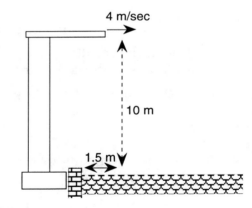

8. Jemima Puddle Duck paddles 2.4 ft/sec aiming directly for the other bank of a 47-ft wide river. When she lands, she finds herself 28 ft downstream from the point across from where she started. What is the speed of the current?

9. Wildlife biologist T. R. Zan sees a monkey in a tree that is 94 ft away from him. He is also in a tree, at the same height as the monkey. The muzzle velocity of his tranquilizer gun is 150 ft/sec. If he holds his gun horizontally when he fires, will he hit the monkey? (Locate the monkey by entering his coordinates as a pair of parametric equations.)

10. If T. R. Zan knows that the monkey will drop from the branch the moment the gun is fired, describe what will happen.

11. A pilot wishes to fly his plane to a destination 700 mi away at a bearing of 105° from north. The cruising speed of the plane is 500 mi/hr, and the wind is blowing between 20 mi/hr and 30  mi/hr toward a bearing of 30°. At what angle should he steer the plane to compensate for the wind? With the variation in the wind, what is the widest margin of error by which the pilot could miss the airport?

12. If you had to choose a favorite problem from this unit, what would it be? Why?

Section 6.8: Projects

Project 6.1: Spirograph™

A Spirograph is a children's drawing toy. A pen is placed in a hole in a wheel that rolls outside or inside a second circle, or along a straight bar. The resulting graphic is a pattern of loops and curves. You might be able to locate one of these toys and experiment with it.

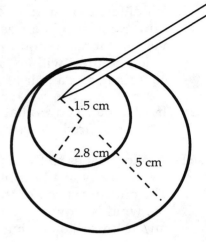

The pattern pictured can be described parametrically by using data from the wheels. In this example, a wheel of radius 2.8 cm moves inside a wheel of radius 5.0 cm. The pen is placed in a hole 1.5 cm from the center of the 2.8 cm wheel. The equations are

$$x(t) = (5 - 2.8) \cos t + 1.5 \cos (5/2.8)t$$

$$y(t) = (5 - 2.8) \sin t + 1.5 \sin (5/2.8)t$$

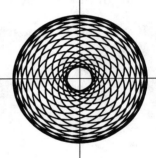

Experiment with your calculator to find a window and a range for t that produces the complete picture. Then change one or more of the values in the example above. Find a new window and t-range and investigate the graphic result. Repeat this process until you can determine the value relationships for any wheels.

How would you change the equation if the small wheel was outside the large wheel? Do the relationships you discovered still hold for wheels outside of wheels? In a paragraph, explain how someone can determine all window values for a given problem (drawing).

Project 6.2: Boolean Expressions

Boolean expressions are mathematical statements that are true or false; they are often used by computer programmers. *True* has a value of one and *false* has a value of zero. (Telling the truth is better than lying.) If you type 4 = 7 on your calculator, it will give you zero. If you enter 4 = 4, it will give you 1. Try this now.

If you enter $x > 3$ in your calculator and it gives you 1, you know that the current value stored in x is greater than 3. Try graphing the function $y = (x > 3)$.
The graph will look like the one on the left if you are in *connected* mode. It you are in *dot* mode, it will look like the one on the right. Be sure you can explain what is happening.

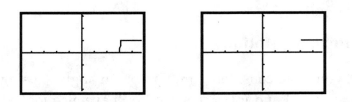

You can use Boolean expressions when you simulate motion that changes at a particular time. For example, Trodd Myles walks at 3 mi/hr at a bearing of 210° for 2 hr 30 min, then turns and walks due east for 1 hr 45 min.

$$x(t) = -3t \cos 60 \cdot (t \le 2.5) + (-7.5\cos 60 + 3(t - 2.5) \cos 0) \cdot (t > 2.5)(t \le 4.25)$$

$$y(t) = -3t \sin 60 \cdot (t \le 2.5) + (-7.5 \sin 60 + 3(t - 2.5) \sin 0) \cdot (t > 2.5)(t \le 4.25)$$

Write a paragraph detailing the meaning of each of the parts and numbers in the equations above. Then find the third leg of the journey to return back to the starting point and adjust the equations to show the complete trip.

Project 6.3: Viewing Angle

When classrooms are arranged, one thing that should be considered is how well all students will be able to see the chalkboard. Those students who sit toward the center of the room will have no difficulty. However, those who sit on the sides, along the walls, will have a more limited view. Consider the classroom design below. Determine the angle of view for the students in the each of the desks shown.

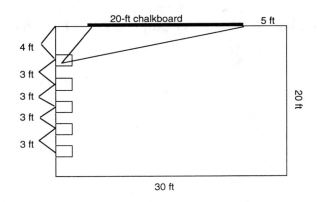

Which seat will have the best view of the chalkboard? Show all of your calculations and justify your conclusions.

For the desks in your classroom, determine an arrangement that you believe will provide all students with the best view possible. Present your plan, along with its justification, to your teacher.

Project 6.4: Projectile Motion

In this chapter, you have considered motion on an angle A using the parametric equations $x(t) = vt \cos A$ and $y(t) = vt \sin A$ You have also looked at motion affected by gravity, using the equations $x(t) = vt + x_0$ and $y(t) = -at^2 + y_0$. In this project, you will combine these two ideas to consider motion at an angle relative to the ground that is affected by gravity. Explain in detail with words, equations, graphs, and diagrams how you would solve the following problem.

Great Gonzo, the human cannonball, is fired out of a cannon at a speed of 40 ft/sec. The cannon is tilted at an angle of 60°. A 10-ft diameter net is hung 10 ft above the floor, at a distance of 30 ft from the cannon. Does Gonzo land in the net?

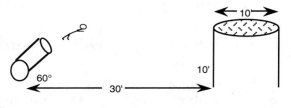

Project 6.5: Baseball Pitcher

Model the path of a ball thrown by a major-league baseball pitcher. The speed of the ball will depend on the type of pitch, as well as on how hard it is thrown. For example, a fastball might be released at 98.5 mi/hr, while a forkball change-up pitch might be released at 80 mi/hr. Suppose the pitches are thrown parallel to the ground directly across home plate. In your model, be sure to consider the height of the pitcher's mound, and at what height the ball will be released. Determine the speed of the strike pitches. Determine how long it takes for these pitches to reach the plate. Justify all assumptions you have made.

Chapter Seven

EXPONENTIAL AND LOGARITHMIC FUNCTIONS

Contents

Section 7.1: The Exponential Function 282
           Remembering geometric sequences

Section 7.2: Rational Exponents and Roots 289
           Examining your roots

Section 7.3: Properties of Exponents 294
           The bottom line is

Section 7.4: Building Inverses of Functions 303
           Can I exchange this?

Section 7.5: Equations with Rational Exponents 311
           Putting the properties to good use

Section 7.6: The Logarithmic Function 317
           The opposite of raising to a power

Section 7.7: Properties of Logarithms 324
           When addition is multiplication

Section 7.8: Applications of Logarithms 330
           Making quick work of some old problems

Section 7.9: Curve Straightening and More Data Analysis 337
           Getting your ducks in a row

Section 7.10: Chapter Review 345
           Assessing yourself

Section 7.11: Projects 347
           Taking it one step further

Section 7.1: The Exponential Function

Every two seconds, nine babies are born and three people die. The net increase of three people each second results in a growth in world population of 10,600 per hour, 254,000 per day, 1.8 million per week, 7.7 million per month, and 93 million per year. It is estimated that by the year 2000, annual population growth will increase to 94 million; by 2020 it will be 98 million. Social scientists who study population often use exponential functions to model the growth.

In previous chapters, you found that geometric sequences of the form $u_n = u_0 r^n$ are used to model discrete **growth** of money, trees, populations, and a variety of other natural phenomena. In this section, you will focus on situations of *continuous* growth. Growth (or its opposite, **decay**) often occurs exponentially and continuously. The continuous exponential function form, $f(x) = ab^x$, follows naturally from the explicit geometric sequence model. In general, **exponential functions** are functions with a variable in the exponent.

> Example 1: In 1989, the population of India was 835 million people. The annual growth rate was about 1.9%. Use this information to predict future populations of the world's second most populous country.
>
> Solution:
>
> a. You have frequently found discrete or yearly totals using recursive routines:
>
>   835   Enter
>
>   *Ans*(1 + 0.019)   and press Enter repeatedly
>
> b. The explicit formula $y = 835(1 + 0.019)^x$ provides the same results when x represents the number of years since 1989. For 1991, use an x-value of (1991 − 1989) or 2. This function implies that the growth is continuous. Populations actually grow discretely, because there are no fractional people. However, because the numbers here are so large, and you are measuring in millions of people, the discrete graph is nearly continuous, so you can use a continuous function to model the growth.
>
> This model predicted $y = f(2) = 835(1.019)^2 = 867$ million people in 1991. What value of x gives the population in 1995?

If you assume a constant growth rate, you can see that millions more people will soon be living in India. (Look at the table that follows.) The population graph also suggests a little of the curvature that you will soon recognize as a characteristic of exponential relations. Enter the data in your calculator and make a scatter plot that looks like the one below.

Year	India
1989	835
1991	867
1992	883.5
1993	900.3
1994	917.4
1995	934.8
1996	952.6
1997	970.7
1998	989.1
1999	1007.9
2000	1027.1
2001	1046.6
2002	1066.5
2009	1216.7
2114	1336.7
2018	1441.2

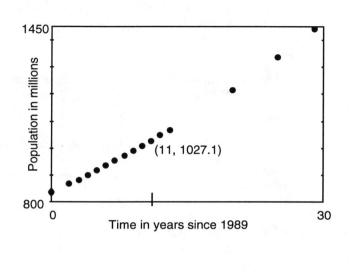

The population of India is constantly growing. If you assume that the growth rate will remain constant, then from 1989 to 2018 the graph will show a continuous population growth from 835 to 1441.2 million people.

For example, when $x = 4.6$ years, $y = 835(1.019)^{4.6} = 910.5$ million people. A smooth curve drawn through the indicated table values is a better graphic representation of the increasing population of India from 1989 to 2018 than a discrete graph showing only points.

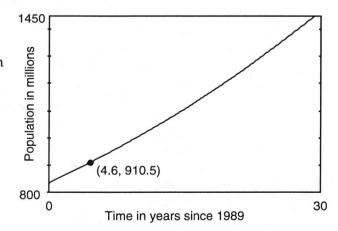

Example 2: Most automobiles depreciate as they get older. Suppose that every year a $14,000 auto loses one-fifth of its value.

a. What is the value of this automobile after two and one-half years?

b. Approximately when is this automobile worth $7,000 (half of its initial value)?

Solution:

a. The recursive solution to this problem only furnishes automobile values after 1 year, 2 years, 3 years, and so on.

14000   Enter

Ans(1 − 0.2)   press Enter repeatedly to get the values.

Original investment	After 1 yr	After 2 yr	After 2.5 yr	After 3 yr	After 4 yr
$14,000	$11,200	$8,960		$7,168	$5,734.40

Looking at the table you can see that if $2 \leq year \leq 3$, then $8,960 \geq auto\ value \geq 7,168$. You can verify the table entries using the explicit formula $y = 14000(1 − 0.2)^x$.

$$y = 14000(1 − 0.2)^2 = \$8,960$$

$$y = 14000(1 − 0.2)^3 = \$7,168$$

You can also assign noninteger values, like 2.5, to x.

$$y = 14000(1 − 0.2)^{2.5} = \$8014.07$$

b. Experimenting with exponents between 3 and 4 can produce a value as close to $7,000 as you want. The value of $14000(0.8)^{3.10628372}$ is very close. This means that after 3.10628372 years (about 3 years and 39 days), the value of the auto is half of its original value. This is the **half life** of the value of the

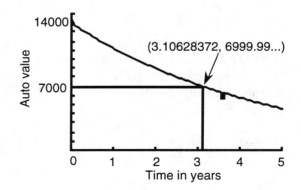

automobile, or the amount of time needed for the value to decrease to half of the original amount.

When the **base**, b, of the exponential function $y = ab^x$ is less than one ($b < 1$), the value of the function decreases (or decays) as the value of x increases. Decay is a way of describing growth in reverse. In the example of declining auto values described by $y = 14000(0.8)^x$, the base (0.8) was less than one.

Radioactive Squares Activity

Radioactive decay occurs when an unstable atom is bombarded with energy, and the atom breaks apart into a different form. Energy bombardment can strike any atom at random. If it strikes a stable atom, then no change occurs. In this activity, you will simulate what happens when a sample of 900 radioactive (unstable) atoms are randomly bombarded with energy. The sample is represented by 900 (uncolored) small squares, in a 30-by-30 configuration. You will color each "atom" as it decays to a more stable form. Your group will need a sheet of acetate and a 30-by-30 grid of small squares, numbered horizontally and vertically from 0 to 29. (See the drawing at the right.)

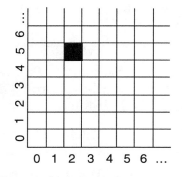

One group member should lay the clear acetate over the grid and carefully outline the area. Be sure to mark the "top" on your acetate. Another member should enter the program or routine found in **APPENDIX 7A** into a calculator. As the calculator gives the coordinates of a square, such as (2, 5), color that square (if it is not already colored), and continue until your group has generated 50 pairs of coordinates. If the square represented by a pair of coordinates has already been colored, you still count that pair as one of the 50 pairs.

When each group has finished collecting data and coloring squares, take turns placing each acetate on an overhead projector. Count how many squares have not been colored as each group lays its acetate on top of the previous one, and record this data in a chart like the one below.

Group		1	2	3	4	. . .
Number of points generated	0	50	100	150	200	. . .
Number of points not colored	900					

a. What does an uncolored square represent?

b. What does a colored square represent?

c. Find a geometric sequence that models the recorded data.

d. Find a continuous function that models the data.

e. What is the approximate half-life of this simulated radioactive decay?

Example 3: Radioactivity is measured in units called *rads*. A sample of phosphorous-33 is found to give off 480 rads initially. The half-life of phosphorous-33 is 25 days.

a. What continuous function represents the radioactivity measure of this sample?

b. What is the radioactivity measure after 225 days?

Solution:

a. A half-life of 25 days means that during each 25-day period the radiation is decreased by half. This leaves *Ans* $(1 - 0.5)$ after every 25-day period. A function that models this behavior is $f(x) = 480(1 - 0.5)^x$, where x is the number of 25-day periods, 480 is the initial value, and 0.5 is the rate of decay every 25 days.

b. During 225 days you have nine 25-day periods. Use your calculator to show that $f(9) = 0.9375$ rads.

Problem Set 7.1

1. In 1991, the population of the People's Republic of China was 1.151 billion (or 1151 million), with a growth rate of 1.5% annually.

   a. Write an explicit equation that models this growth.

   b. Complete the table for the years indicated.

   c. Use the population growth equations for India and China to predict the year (and population) when the populations of the two countries will be about equal.

Year	China
1991	
1992	
1993	
1994	
1995	
1996	
1997	
1998	
1999	
2000	

   d. What assumptions allow you to make this prediction? How much confidence do you place in the prediction? Why?

2. A lad by the name of Jack Fum made a shrewd trade of an undernourished bovine for a start in a new experimental crop, *leguman magicous*. With the help of his mother he planted the bean just outside his kitchen window. It immediately sprouted 2.56 cm above the ground. Contrary to popular legend, it did not reach its full height in one night. Being a student of mathematics and the sciences, Jack kept a careful log of the growth of the sprout. On the first day at 8:00 a.m., 24 hours after planting, he found the plant to be 6.4 cm tall. At 8:00 a.m. on the second day, the growing bean sprout was 16.0 cm in height. At 8:00 a.m. on the third day, he recorded 40.0 cm. At the same time on the fourth day, he found it to be 1 m (100 cm) tall.

Time in days	Initially	After 1 day	After 2 days	After 3 days	After 4 days
Height	2.56 cm	6.4 cm	16.0 cm	40.0 cm	1 m or (100 cm)

   a. Write an explicit formula for this pattern. If the pattern were to continue, what would be the heights on the fifth and sixth days?

   b. Jack's younger brothers Phee and Fy measured the plant at 8:00 p.m. on the third day, and found it to be about 63.25 cm tall. Show how this value can be found mathematically. You may need to experiment with your calculator.

   c. Find the height that his youngest brother Foe tried to measure at 12:00 noon on the sixth day.

   d. Experiment with the equation to find the day and time (to the nearest hour) when the stalk reached its final height of one kilometer (1000 m or 100,000 cm).

3. Use your calculator to find each number. (Express answers to four decimal places unless the answer is a whole number.)

   a. 7^2 b. $7^{2.25}$ c. $7^{2.5}$ d. $7^{2.75}$ e. 7^3

   f. Find the difference between 3b and 3a, between 3c and 3b, between 3d and 3c, and between 3e and 3d. What do these differences tell you?

   g. Find the ratios of the results of 3b to 3a, 3c to 3b, 3d to 3c, and 3e to 3d. What do these values tell you?

   h. What observation can you make about decimal powers?

4. Given that $f(x)$ is an exponential function and that $f(4) = 1229$ and $f(5) = 3442$, give your best guess for the value of $f(4.5)$. Justify your answer.

5. In Example 3, you are given the function $f(x) = 480(0.5)^x$, where x is the number of 25-day periods and $f(x)$ is the number of rads.

    a. Find $f(3)$ and provide a real-world meaning for it.

    b. Find $f(3.2)$ and provide a real-world meaning for it.

    c. Find $f(0)$ and provide a real-world meaning for it.

    d. Find $f(-1)$ and provide a real-world meaning for it.

    e. For what value of x does $f(x)$ equal 240? What does this mean?

    f. How many rads will be measured after 110 days? (Hint: Find the x-value first.)

6. Five thousand dollars is invested in an account that pavs interest at a rate of 6.5% compounded annually.

    a. Name the function that furnishes the account balance after x years.

    b. Find $f(5)$.   c. What is the real-world meaning of $f(5)$?

    d. Find $f\left(4\dfrac{1}{3}\right)$.   e. What is the real-world meaning of $f\left(4\dfrac{1}{3}\right)$?

    f. Find $f(0)$ and give its real-world meaning.

    g. What is the value of the account after 7 yr 9 mo? If the account is closed at this time, do you expect the bank would pay this amount?

7. Ice is added to a glass of water. If not stirred, the water at the bottom cools according to the formula $g(x) = 23(0.94)^x$, where x is the number of minutes since the ice was added, and g is the temperature in Celsius.

    a. What is the real-world meaning of 0.94? (Hint: 0.94 can be written as $(1 - 0.06)$.)

    b. What is the initial temperature of the water?

    c. Find $g(7.4)$ and give its real-world meaning.

    d. Find the temperature after 5 min 45 sec.

    e. Find x to make $g(x) = 10$. What is the real-world meaning of your answer?

    f. Find how long (to the nearest hundredth of a minute) until the water has cooled to 5°C.

Section 7.2: Rational Exponents and Roots

Noninteger values of x are meaningful and useful. In the last section, you used noninteger x-values in the model $f(x) = 14000(0.8)^x$ to predict declining values of an automobile. You used fractional x-values to represent parts of a day in $f(x) = 2.56(2.5)^x$ to find beanstalk heights. Now you are ready to discover important connections and properties involving fractional exponents.

Fractional Exponents Activity

a. Use your calculator to set up a list of pairs $(x, x^{0.5})$. (See **APPENDIX 7B**.) As you view the list, there are a few pairs that should help you discover another relationship between x and $x^{0.5}$. (Note: The values of $x^{0.5}$ have been rounded.)

x	... 21	22	23	24	25	26	27 ...
$x^{0.5}$	4.5826	4.6904	4.7958	4.899	5	5.099	5.1962

b. Set your grapher to a "friendly" window, with factor 2, and graph $y_1 = x^{0.5}$. Does this graph look familiar? What is another equation of this function? Enter this equation in y_2 and verify that the equation gives the same value at each x as the original equation.

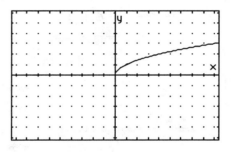

c. The list suggests that when 25 is raised to the one-half power, you get 5. What other operation on 25 gives you 5? Check a few more pairs in your list to verify this relationship.

d. Write a true statement about raising a number to the one-half power. Include an example with your statement.

e. Use your calculator to calculate values for $f(x) = 25^x$ in a table like this.

x	$\dfrac{1}{2}$	$\dfrac{2}{2}$	$\dfrac{3}{2}$	$\dfrac{4}{2}$	$\dfrac{5}{2}$ ...	... $\dfrac{11}{2}$
25^x	5	25	125		3125	

f. Values in row two in the table above are also powers of 5. In particular, because 125 is 5^3, $25^{3/2}$ is $(25^{1/2})^3$. Explain why $25^{3/2} = \left(\sqrt{25}\right)^3$.

g. Write an equation involving a root that is equivalent to $y = x^{3/2}$.

Complete the table and sketch a graph of each equation.

x	$y_1 = x^{3/2}$	$y_2 =$
5	11.18	
8		
10		
11	36.483	

h. Name an equation that produces the same graph as $y = x^{5/3}$ over the domain of $x \geq 0$. Write a statement, using the word "root," which defines $27^{n/3}$. Use your grapher to confirm your statement. Explain why the domain was restricted.

Other roots, such as the fifth root $\sqrt[5]{\ }$, the sixth root $\sqrt[6]{\ }$, and so on, can be written using fractional exponents like $\frac{1}{5}$ and $\frac{1}{6}$. For fractional exponents with numerators other than one, the numerator is interpreted as the power to which to raise the root. In general, fractional exponents are defined as follows:

Definition of Fractional Exponents

$$a^{m/n} = \left(\sqrt[n]{a}\right)^m \text{ or } \sqrt[n]{a^m} \text{ for } a \geq 0.$$

Example 1: What does $9^{5/2}$ mean?

Solution: $9^{5/2}$ means the square root of 9 raised to the fifth power, or $\left(\sqrt{9}\right)^5 = 3^5 = 243$. Therefore, $9^{5/2} = 243$. The definition also indicates that $9^{5/2} = \sqrt{9^5}$. Evaluate $\sqrt{59049}$ to verify that it is also 243.

The square root of 9 raised to the fifth power, $\sqrt{9^5}$, can also be written $9^{1/2}$ raised to the fifth power, or $(9^{1/2})^5$. This means $9^{5/2} = (9^{1/2})^5$. Therefore, an alternative definition of fractional exponents, which doesn't involve radicals (or roots), is $a^{m/n} = (a^{1/n})^m = (a^m)^{(1/n)}$. Verify these results with your calculator.

Example 2: Rewrite each expression using the radical (root) definitions. Use your calculator to evaluate each expression. Be sure to enclose fractional exponents in parenthesis.

a. $64^{2/3}$
b. $4096^{3/4}$
c. $\left(\dfrac{9}{49}\right)^{3/2}$

Solution: Convert the expressions to radical or root form and evaluate.

a. $64^{2/3} = \left(\sqrt[3]{64}\right)^2 = 4^2 = 16.$

Or,

$64^{2/3} = \left(\sqrt[3]{64^2}\right) = \sqrt[3]{4096} = 16.$

Therefore, $64^{2/3} = 16.$

b. $4096^{3/4} = \left(\sqrt[4]{4096}\right)^3 = 8^3 = 512.$

Or $4096^{3/4} = \sqrt[4]{4096^3} = \sqrt[4]{68719476736} = 512.$

Therefore, $4096^{3/4} = 512.$ (See **APPENDIX 7C.**)

c. $\left(\dfrac{9}{49}\right)^{3/2} = \left(\sqrt{\dfrac{9}{49}}\right)^3 = \left(\dfrac{3}{7}\right)^3 = \dfrac{27}{343}.$

Or $\left(\dfrac{9}{49}\right)^{3/2} = \sqrt{\left(\dfrac{9}{49}\right)^3} = \sqrt{\dfrac{729}{117649}} = \dfrac{27}{343}.$

Therefore, $\left(\dfrac{9}{49}\right)^{3/2} = \dfrac{27}{343}.$

Example 3: Solve the following equation for x: $4^x = 8$.

Solution: Enter the left side of the equation in y_1 and the right side of the equation in y_2. Graph the functions in a "friendly" window with a factor of one. Trace along the curve to locate the point of intersection. The coordinates are (1.5, 8). Therefore, $x = \dfrac{3}{2}$ is the solution to the equation.

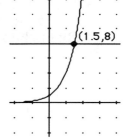

Example 4: Solve the equation $2 \cdot 125^x = 50$.

Solution: The equation is equivalent to $125^x = 25$. Do you see why? What will you enter as y_1 and y_2? Trace to locate the point where the curves intersect. In this case, you will not be able to locate the exact intersection without zooming in (either graphically or with a table). (See **APPENDIX 7D.**) Zoom in on this point until you are satisfied that the

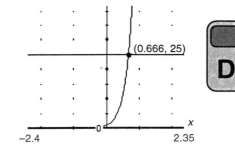

x-coordinate is 0.666 . . . . Therefore, $x = \dfrac{2}{3}$ is the solution to the equation.

Problem Set 7.2

1. Write a complete sentence that relates each expression to a power of a root. Then find the numerical value in two different ways.

   a. $49^{5/2}$

   b. $16^{3/4}$

   c. $64^{5/3}$

   d. $32^{2/5}$

2. From ages one to seven, Hannah's weight (in kg), was equal to her height (in cm) to the 2/3 power.

   a. At one year of age, Hannah was 64 cm tall. What was her weight?

   b. She was 125 cm tall at age seven. What was her weight?

   c. At age four, she weighed 20.25 kg. What was her height?

3. Convert each radical expression to exponent form:

   a. $\sqrt[4]{x}$

   b. $\sqrt[5]{x^3}$

   c. $\left(\sqrt[3]{x}\right)^7$

   d. $\sqrt[5]{x^4}$

4. Evaluate each of these expressions on your calculator.

   a. $\left(\sqrt[3]{8}\right)^7$

   b. $\sqrt[5]{243^4}$

   c. $\sqrt[3]{25^6}$

   d. $\left(9^5\right)^{3/10}$

5. a. Lieutenant Bolombo found a cryptic message containing a clue about where the money was hidden. After consulting his high school algebra book, he knew where to look. The clue was

   $$\sqrt[\frac{1}{2}]{cin} \; a \; \sqrt[\frac{1}{2}]{t} \, i$$

   Find the location and explain how you knew.

   b. Invent a cryptic message of your own like the clue that Lieutenant Bolombo found.

6. Rewrite each exponential expression in radical (root) form:

   a. $x^{2/3}$

   b. $x^{2.75}$

7. Solve each equation for x:

   a. $9^x = 27$

   b. $32^x = 128$

Preliminary Edition

8. One dollar is invested at 4% annual interest, compounded once each year.

   a. Write a recursive formula for the balance.

   b. Write an explicit formula for the balance after x years.

   c. Find when the account will reach $50.

9. Explain how you would instruct your calculator to graph $y = \sqrt[5]{x}$.

10. Consider the equation $y = 4000\left(1 + \dfrac{0.072}{12}\right)^x$, where x represents the number of months since 1900. Explain the real-world meaning of each number in parts a–f below.

   a. 4000

   b. 0.072

   c. $\dfrac{0.072}{12}$

   d. $x = 1$

   e. $x = 0$

   f. $x = {}^-1$

   g. Find the value of x when $y = 8000$.

11. Graph the parametric equations $x(t) = t^4$ and $y(t) = t^3$ for $t \geq 0$. Find a function, $f(x)$, that gives the same graph.

Section 7.3: Properties of Exponents

Often you will need to rewrite a mathematical expression in a different form. Changing from fractional exponent form to an equivalent radical form is one example. If you get an answer such as $\sqrt[5]{x^3}$, and find a different-looking expression in the answer section, you need to be able to recognize whether the two answers are equivalent forms. Many equivalent expressions might be listed as the answer, including $x^{3/5}$ or $\sqrt[10]{x^6}$, when $x \geq 0$. In this section, you will use the calculator to discover, and verify, other ways to write an exponential expression.

In the chessboard problem, the inventor asked for one grain of wheat on the first square of the chessboard, two grains on the second, four grains on the third, and so on, with each square containing twice the number of grains as its predecessor.

The third square contained $2 \cdot 2 = 2^2$ grains, the fourth square contained $2 \cdot 2 \cdot 2 = 2^3$ grains, and so on, and the last square contained $2 \cdot 2 \cdot 2 \ldots \cdot 2 = 2^{63}$ grains. Exponents are used to indicate repeated multiplication of a base.

> Example 1:
>
> a. What does $2^3 \cdot 2^4$ mean?
>
> b. Name another pair of factors that provide an equivalent product.
>
> Solution:
>
> a. By definition, $2^3 \cdot 2^4$ means $(2 \cdot 2 \cdot 2) \cdot (2 \cdot 2 \cdot 2 \cdot 2)$.
>
> b. The exponential expression 2^7 can be written as $(2 \cdot 2 \cdot 2 \cdot 2 \cdot 2 \cdot 2 \cdot 2)$, which is the same as $(2 \cdot 2) \cdot (2 \cdot 2 \cdot 2 \cdot 2 \cdot 2)$, or $2^2 \cdot 2^5$. This is just one of many possibilities.

Name two different combinations of exponents that make each equation correct.

i. $2^m \cdot 2^n = 2^{50}$ 　　　　ii. $3^c \cdot 3^d = 3^{63}$ 　　　　iii. $a^x \cdot a^y = a^{17}$

Test $a^m \cdot a^n = a^{(m+n)}$ for enough different values of m, n, and a ($a > 0$) to convince yourself that the following property is true.

$$\boxed{\begin{array}{c} \textbf{Multiplication Property of Exponents} \\ a^m \bullet a^n = a^{(m+n)} \text{ for all } a > 0 \end{array}}$$

Another property of exponents helps you rewrite expressions such as $(x^3)^2$. The definition of exponents means you can write $(x^3)^2$ as $x^3 \bullet x^3$ and the Multiplication Property gives you $x^{3+3} = x^6$. Therefore, $(x^3)^2 = x^6$.

$$\boxed{\begin{array}{c} \textbf{Nested Power Property of Exponents} \\[6pt] (a^n)^m = a^{(mn)} \text{ for all } a>0 \end{array}}$$

Example 2: Use the Nested Power Property to rewrite each expression as a power of a smaller positive base.

a. 8^x

b. 16^x

c. $\left(\dfrac{49}{9}\right)^{3/2}$

Solution:

a. Because $2^3 = 8$, $8^x = \left(2^3\right)^x = 2^{3x}$

b. $16^x = \left(2^4\right)^x = 2^{4x}$

c. $\left(\dfrac{49}{9}\right)^{3/2} = \left(\dfrac{7}{3}\right)^{2 \bullet 3/2} = \left(\dfrac{7}{3}\right)^3$

What graphs could you examine to verify that $\left(2^3\right)^x = 2^{3x}$?

Ratios and Exponents Activity

In this activity, you will explore how some ratio expressions can be written as exponential expressions. You will also learn about another property of exponents.

a. Express each ratio using exponents.

i. Each square on the chessboard contains twice as many grains of wheat as the previous square. Write an exponential expression representing the ratio of the number of grains on the last square of the chessboard to the number of grains on the tenth square.

ii. A one-dollar investment grows at a rate of 8% annually. Write an exponential expression representing the ratio of the investment's value after twenty years to its value after six years.

iii.	A ball, with a rebound ratio of 0.65, is dropped from a height of 300 cm. Write an exponential expression representing the ratio of the height of the second bounce to that of the fifth bounce.

iv.	A bacteria population grows according to the model $y = 25 \cdot 2^x$, where x is the number of hours that have elapsed. Write an exponential expression representing the ratio of the population at fifteen hours to the population at seven hours.

b.	Find at least six combinations of exponents m and n, so that $\dfrac{2^{20}}{2^n} = 2^m$.

c.	Write an equivalent equation in exponential form that represents this relationship:

$$\frac{(4)(4)(4)(4)(4)}{(4)(4)} = \frac{(4)(4)(4)\cancel{(4)}\cancel{(4)}}{\cancel{(4)}\cancel{(4)}}$$

d.	If possible, rewrite each expression using a single exponent. If any of these are not possible, explain why.

i.	$\dfrac{8^5}{8^2}$
ii.	$\dfrac{x^{5.5}}{x^3}$
iii.	$\dfrac{240 \cdot (0.94)^{15}}{240 \cdot (0.94)^5}$
iv.	$\dfrac{x^3 + x^7}{x^2}$

e.	Use your calculator to test $\dfrac{a^m}{a^n} = a^{(m-n)}$ for several different values of m, n and a, $(a > 0)$.

In the previous activity, you investigated the division property of exponents. This property can be generalized as follows:

Division Property of Exponents

$$\frac{a^m}{a^n} = a^{(m-n)} \text{ for } a > 0$$

Negative Exponents Activity

In this activity, you will explore the concept of a negative exponent and see how it can be related to real-world applications.

a. Earlier in the chapter, you used a model for the population growth in India from the year 1989, which was $f(x) = 835(1.019)^x$. You can use a negative exponent to compute the population for a year prior to 1989. Find the function values, and provide a real-world meaning for each answer:

   i. $f(^-3)$ ii. $f(^-2)$ iii. $f(^-1)$

b. Rewrite $\dfrac{x^3}{x^5}$ as $\dfrac{xxx}{xxxxx}$, and divide out common factors. Using the Division Property of Exponents, how can you express this answer? Carefully describe why $x^{-2} = \dfrac{1}{x^2}$.

c. Give an example, similar to the one in part b, that shows that $x^{-1} = \dfrac{1}{x^1}$.

d. For each equation, write another equivalent equation. Verify that your new equation is equivalent to the original one by graphing.

   i. $y = x^{-3}$ ii. $y = \dfrac{1}{2^x}$ iii. $y = 10.5(1 + 0.035)^{-4x}$

e. Rewrite each complex fraction as a simple fraction:

   i. $\dfrac{1}{\frac{2}{3}}$ ii. $\dfrac{1}{\frac{3}{2}}$ iii. $\dfrac{1}{\left(\frac{2}{3}\right)^2}$ iv. $\dfrac{1}{\frac{a}{b}}$

f. The ball with a rebound factor of 0.65 is dropped from a height of 300 cm. Find the ratio of the height of the fifth bounce to that of the second bounce.

g. Use your calculator to verify that $a^{-n} = \dfrac{1}{a^n}$ for $a > 0$ and that $\left(\dfrac{a}{b}\right)^{-n} = \left(\dfrac{b}{a}\right)^{n}$ for $a, b > 0$. (Use several different values of a and b.)

h. What x-value in the function $f(x) = 835(1.019)^x$ gives the original population? Carefully show or describe how you found this x-value.

i. Write a reason for each step in this logical argument.

$$x^3 \cdot x^{-3} = x^0$$

$$x^3 \cdot x^{-3} = x^3 \cdot \left(\frac{1}{x^3}\right)$$

$$x^3 \cdot \left(\frac{1}{x^3}\right) = 1$$

Therefore, $x^0 = 1$

j. A solution manual will not list $\frac{2^5}{2^5}$ as an answer. Use the Division Property of Exponents to rewrite $\frac{2^5}{2^5}$ as $\frac{2 \cdot 2 \cdot 2 \cdot 2 \cdot 2}{2 \cdot 2 \cdot 2 \cdot 2 \cdot 2}$ and divide out common factors. What do you get? What conclusion can you state about 2^0?

In the above activity, you investigated two more exponent properties. The general form of these properties is summarized below.

Definition of Negative Exponents
$a^{-n} = \dfrac{1}{a^n}$ for $a > 0$ or $\left(\dfrac{a}{b}\right)^{-n} = \left(\dfrac{b}{a}\right)^n$ for $a, b > 0$

Definition of Zero Exponent
$a^0 = 1$ for $a > 0$

Example 3: Rewrite $\left(\dfrac{9}{49}\right)^{-3/2}$ without an exponent.

Solution:

$$\left(\frac{9}{49}\right)^{-3/2} = \left(\frac{49}{9}\right)^{3/2}$$ Definition of negative exponents.

$$= \left(\sqrt{\frac{49}{9}}\right)^3$$ Definition of fractional exponents.

$$= \left(\frac{7}{3}\right)^3$$ Take the square root.

$$= \frac{343}{27}$$ Cube the number.

This example shows another property of exponents, the Power of a Product Property, which is generalized below.

Power of a Product Property
$(ab)^n = a^n b^n$ for all a and $b > 0$

Be careful that you don't apply this property to powers of binomials. In other words,

$$(a + b)^n \neq a^n + b^n \text{ (except when } n = 1.)$$

This is a common error made by many students. What expression is equivalent to $(a + b)^2$?

Example 4: Rewrite $0.94^x \cdot 0.5^x$ using the Power of a Product Property.

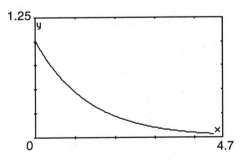

Solution: $0.94^x \cdot 0.5^x = (0.94 \cdot 0.5)^x$

Verify the result by graphing $y_1 = (0.94)^x \cdot (0.5)^x$ and $y_2 = (0.94 \cdot 0.5)^x$.

Example 5: Solve $4^x = \frac{1}{16}$ without graphing.

Solution: If you can write both sides of the equation with exponents of the same base, you can solve this problem by inspection.

$$4^x = \frac{1}{16}$$ Given.

$$4^x = \frac{1}{4^2}$$ Because $4^2 = 16$.

$$4^x = 4^{-2}$$ Definition of negative exponents.

$$x = {}^-2$$ By inspection.

Problem Set 7.3

1. Rewrite each expression in fractional form without using exponents or radicals. Then verify that the new expression is equivalent to the original one by evaluating each expression on your calculator.

   a. 3^{-3} b. $25^{-1/2}$ c. $-36^{3/2}$ d. $({}^-12)^{-2}$

   e. $\left(\frac{3}{4}\right)^{-2}$ f. $\left(\frac{2}{7}\right)^{-1}$ g. $-\left(\frac{8}{27}\right)^{-1/3}$ h. $\left(\frac{4}{9}\right)^{-5/2}\left(\frac{2}{3}\right)^{5}$

2. Find an alternate way to write each expression.

   a. $(2x)^{-3}$ b. $2x^{-3}$ c. $x^{(1/2)}x^{(2/3)}$ d. $(4x)^{(-1/2)}(8x^3)^{(2/3)}$

3. Mr. Higgins told his wife, the math professor, that he would make her breakfast. She handed him this message.

   > I want $\dfrac{(Eas)^{-1}(ter)^{0}\ Egg}{y}$

   What should Mr. Higgins fix his wife for breakfast?

4. Indicate whether each equation is true or false. If it is false, explain why.

   a. $3^5 \cdot 4^2 = 12^7$ b. $100(1.06)^x = (106)^x$ c. $\sqrt{a^2 + b^2} = a + b$

   d. $\dfrac{a + b}{a} = b$ e. $\sqrt[4]{16x^{20}} = 2x^5$ f. $\dfrac{6.6 \cdot 10^{12}}{8.8 \cdot 10^{-4}} = 7.5 \cdot 10^{15}$

5. Solve each equation by using the exponent properties.

   a. $3^x = \frac{1}{9}$ b. $\left(\frac{5}{3}\right)^x = \left(\frac{27}{125}\right)$ c. $\left(\frac{2}{3}\right)^x = 243$ d. $5 \cdot 3^x = 5$

6. Graph the following equations on the same screen: $y_1 = 1.5^x$, $y_2 = 2^x$, $y_3 = 3^x$, $y_4 = 4^x$. Then sketch each graph on paper. How do the graphs compare? What points (if any) do they have in common? Predict what the graph of $y = 6^x$ will look like. Verify your prediction using your calculator.

7. Graph the following equations on the same screen: $y_1 = 0.2^x$, $y_2 = 0.3^x$, $y_3 = 0.5^x$, $y_4 = 0.8^x$. Then sketch each graph on paper. How do the graphs compare? What points (if any) do they have in common? Predict what the graph of $y = 0.1^x$ will look like. Verify your prediction using your calculator.

8. Refer to the graphs and equations in Problems 6 and 7. What do all of the equations in Problem 6 have in common? What do all of the equations in Problem 7 have in common? Guess the function that produces each graph shown below.

a.   b.

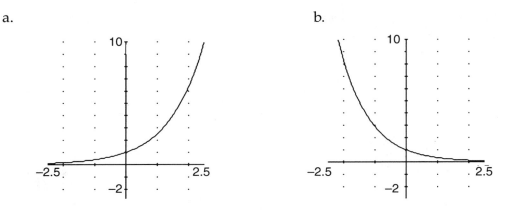

9. Some functions can be classified as increasing or decreasing functions. The first graph in Problem 8 is an example of an increasing function. The second graph is an example of a decreasing function. A function is an **increasing function** if and only if for each $x_1 > x_2$, $f(x_1) \geq f(x_2)$. This means that as the x-values increase, the y-values also increase.

   a. Which of the functions in Problems 6 and 7 are increasing?

   b. Write a definition for a decreasing function that is similar to the definition of the increasing function.

10. a. Describe and compare the graphs if x is replaced with ^-x in the equation $y = ab^x$. What is another way to write this equation?

   b. Describe and compare the graphs if y is replaced with ^-y in the equation $y = ab^x$.

   c. Describe and compare the graphs if x is replaced with $(x - 2)$ in the equation $y = ab^x$.

11. Indicate whether each statement is true or false. Justify each answer.

  a. A negative number raised to a negative power is always positive.

  b. When a number larger than one is raised to a positive power that is less than one, the number becomes larger.

  c. A positive number raised to the zero power is equal to zero.

  d. If $a < b$, and a and b are both positive, then $a^n < b^n$ for any number n.

Section 7.4: Building Inverses of Functions

Rita and Noah were both making a graph for a project in their science class. They were both using the same data, but their graphs looked different. "I know my graph is right!" exclaims Rita, "I've checked and rechecked it. Yours must be wrong, Noah." Noah disagrees, "I've entered this data in my calculator, and I made sure I entered the correct numbers." The graphs look like the ones below. Can you explain what's happening?

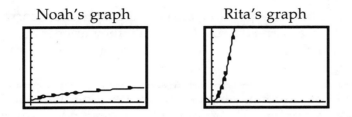

Noah's graph   Rita's graph

Sometimes it makes sense for either one of two related variables to be used as the independent variable. This occurred, for example, when you studied the $(°C, °F)$ and $(°F, °C)$ temperature relationships. Two related but different-looking functions can be used to model this temperature relationship.

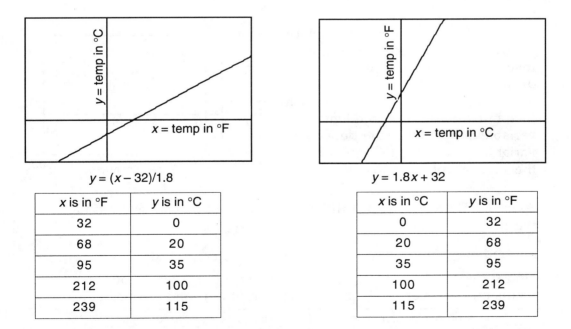

$$y = (x - 32)/1.8$$

x is in °F	y is in °C
32	0
68	20
95	35
212	100
239	115

$$y = 1.8x + 32$$

x is in °C	y is in °F
0	32
20	68
35	95
100	212
115	239

Convince yourself that the table values are correct. Do you recognize both the freezing and boiling temperatures for water? Try other values for F° and C° that are not already listed in the tables, to see if the coordinates are always reversed.

In this figure, both temperature graphs are drawn in the same graphing window ($^-50 \leq x \leq 150$, $^-50 \leq y \leq 150$). The graphing window was "squared up," and the graph of $y = x$ was added. (See **APPENDIX 7E**.)

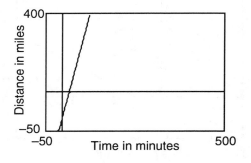

The two temperature functions $y = 1.8x + 32$ and $y = \frac{(x - 32)}{1.8}$ are inverses of each other. This means that every point (a, b) on one graph has a corresponding point (b, a) on the other. In a correctly-sized window, they appear as reflection images of each other over the line $y = x$. This will happen for any pair of inverse relations.

> The **inverse** of a relation is obtained by exchanging the x- and y-coordinates of all points. The graph of an inverse relation will be a reflection of the original relation over the line $y = x$.

In this section, you will learn how to find the inverse of a function or relation, and you will learn about some other important connections between relations and their inverses.

Example 1: At the right is a graph of $y = 6.34x - 140$, which models the relationship between time and distance for continental United States flights. There is no reason why *time* must be the independent variable and *distance* the dependent variable. Find a model representing the inverse relation (*distance, time*).

Solution: There are at least three methods that you can use to find the inverse relation.

Method 1:

Find some points on the graph of $y = 6.34x - 140$. Then name some points on the inverse relation by switching the x- and y-coordinates.

Points on original function		Points on inverse function	
Time in minutes	Distance in miles	Distance in miles	Time in minutes
50	177	177	50
80	367.2	367.2	80
100	494	494	100
150	811	811	150

These new points are also linear (check this). Choose two points and find the equation of the line that represents the inverse relation.

$$y = \frac{(150 - 50)}{(811 - 177)} (x - 177) + 50, \text{ or}$$

$$y = \frac{100}{634} x + \frac{14000}{634}.$$

Method 2:

To find the equation of the inverse, you must find the equation that will *undo* what the original equation does. In the original function, x is multiplied by 6.34, and then 140 is subtracted from this value. Therefore, to find the inverse relation, you need to do the opposite operations in reverse order. Thus, you would add 140 to x and divide by 6.34. One form for the inverse relation will be $y = \frac{(x + 140)}{6.34}$. Check to see that this is equivalent to the inverse relation found using the first method.

Method 3:

Switch the x- and y-variables in the original equation, and solve for y.

$y = 6.34x - 140$	Original equation.
$x = 6.34y - 140$	Inverse equation.
$y = \frac{(x + 140)}{6.34}.$	Inverse equation solved for y.

What is the real-world meaning of the slope, x-intercept, and y-intercept of this inverse function?

Example 2:

a. Find and graph the inverse of the parametric equations $x = t + 2$ and $y = t^2$.

b. Write the nonparametric equations of the function and its inverse.

Solution:

a. You can easily find the inverse relations for parametric equations by switching the x- and y-variables in the equations. (See the equations and graphs below.) If possible, set your grapher so that both graphs are drawn simultaneously. Trace both curves and examine the corresponding coordinates.

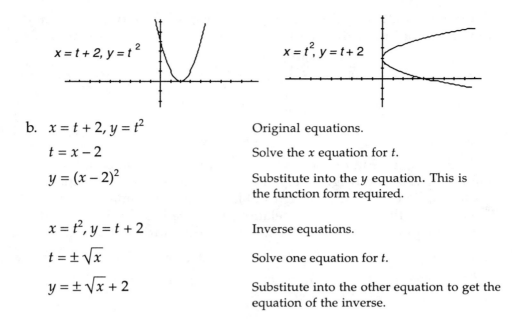

$x = t + 2, y = t^2$

$x = t^2, y = t + 2$

b. $x = t + 2, y = t^2$ Original equations.

    $t = x - 2$ Solve the x equation for t.

    $y = (x - 2)^2$ Substitute into the y equation. This is the function form required.

    $x = t^2, y = t + 2$ Inverse equations.

    $t = \pm \sqrt{x}$ Solve one equation for t.

    $y = \pm \sqrt{x} + 2$ Substitute into the other equation to get the equation of the inverse.

Notice that in this case the inverse of the original function is not a function. Do you see why? Check the nonparametric graphs to make certain you have correctly represented the same points. (See **APPENDIX 7F.**) When the original function, written as $f(x)$, has an inverse that is a function, you write the inverse as $f^{-1}(x)$. For example, the temperature functions could be written as $f(x) = 1.8x + 32$ and $f^{-1}(x) = \frac{(x - 32)}{1.8}$. The next activity considers the composition of inverse functions, $f^{-1}(f(x))$ and $f(f^{-1}(x))$.

Compositions of Inverse Functions Activity

In this activity, you will explore what happens when you form a new function that is a composition of a function and its inverse.

a. Set your graphing window at $-50 \le x \le 150$, $-50 \le y \le 150$, and then square up the window.

b. Enter $f(x) = 1.8x + 32$ as y_1 and its inverse $f^{-1}(x) = \dfrac{(x - 32)}{1.8}$ as y_2. Choose five different values for x and determine values for $f(x)$, $f^{-1}(x)$, and $f^{-1}(f(x))$, either from a table or by evaluating the functions. (See **APPENDIX 7G.**) Use values from this list as your x-values: today's temperature, the coldest day during the last month, the warmest day during the last month, the coldest day since school started, the warmest day since school started, the temperature at which you feel the most comfortable, the coldest day you have ever experienced, the hottest day you have ever experienced. (If you're not sure about one of these temperatures, you can use an estimate.) Carefully describe the relationship between each x and $f^{-1}(f(x))$.

c. Describe what the graph of $f^{-1}(f(x))$ will look like by looking at the values you have generated. What function can you enter into your grapher that generates this graph?

d. What will you do differently to find values for $f(f^{-1}(x))$? Describe a graph of $f(f^{-1}(x))$ by looking at these values. What function can you enter into your grapher that generates this graph?

e. Enter a new function, $y_1 = x^3$. What inverse relation should you enter into y_2? Investigate by trying enough values so that you can describe what $f(f^{-1}(x))$ and $f^{-1}(f(x))$ will look like.

Problem Set 7.4

1. Find the inverse of each pair of parametric equations. Graph the original pair of equations and the inverse equations on the same set of axes.

   a. $x = 2t - 3$, $y = t + 2$ b. $x = t^2$, $y = t + 1$

   c. $x = \dfrac{1}{2}t + 1$, $y = \dfrac{t - 2}{3}$ d. $x = t - 3$, $y = 2(t - 1)^2$

   e. Describe the relationship between the graph of the original parametric equations and the graph of the inverse equations.

   f. How do you graph the line $y = x$ in parametric mode?

2. Which graph below is the inverse of the graph at the right? Explain how you know.

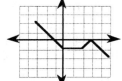

a.   b.

c.   d.   e.

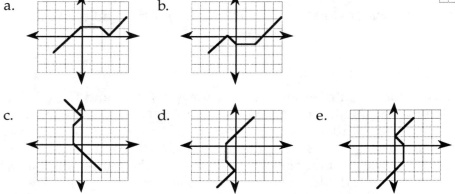

3. a. Eliminate the parameter from $x = t + 5$, $y = 2t - 1$ by solving the x-equation for t and substituting into the y-equation.

   b. Find parametric equations for the inverse relation of the equations given in 3a.

   c. Eliminate the parameter in the inverse by solving the y-equation for t and substituting into the x-equation.

   d. Compare the nonparametric equations for the original relation and those for the inverse. Describe any similarities and differences between the original relation and its inverse.

4. a. Eliminate the parameter from $x = t^2 + 2$, $y = t + 3$ by solving the y-equation for t and substituting into the x-equation.

   b. Write parametric equations for the inverse of the relation in 4a.

   c. Eliminate the parameter in the inverse by solving the x-equation for t and substituting into the y-equation.

   d. Compare the nonparametric equations for the original relation and the inverse. Describe any similarities and differences between the original relation and its inverse.

5. Find a range of t-values for t so that both $x = t - 1$, $y = (t - 3)^2$ and its inverse are functions.

6. Find a range of t-values for t so that both $x = t^2 + 2$, $y = \dfrac{t - 3}{4}$ and its inverse are functions.

7. a. Use your knowledge of transformations to write parametric equations for $y = (x + 1)^2 - 2$.

   b. Write parametric equations for the inverse of the function in 7a.

   c. Eliminate the parameter and solve the resulting equation for y. It doesn't matter whether you start with the x-equation or with the y-equation.

   d. Write the original and inverse equations in nonparametric form.

8. Write each function using $f(x)$ notation and find its inverse. If the inverse is a function, write it using $f^{-1}(x)$ notation.

   a. $y = 2x - 3$ b. $3x + 2y = 4$ c. $x^2 + 2y = 3$

9. For each function find:
   i. $f^{-1}(x)$,   ii. $f(f^{-1}(15.75))$,   iii. $f^{-1}(f(15.75))$ iv. $f(f^{-1}(x))$ and $f^{-1}(f(x))$.

   a. $f(x) = 6.34x - 140$ b. $f(x) = 1.8x + 32$

10. The data in the table describes the relationship between altitude and air temperature.

feet	meters	°F	°C
1,000	300	56	13
5,000	1,500	41	5
10,000	3,000	23	−5
15,000	4,500	5	−15
20,000	6,000	−15	−26
30,000	9,000	−47	−44
36,087	10,826	−69	−56

   a. Write a best-fit equation for $f(x)$ that describes the relationship (*altitude in meters, temperature in °C*). Use at least three decimal places in your answers.

   b. Use your results from 10a to write the equation for $f^{-1}(x)$.

   c. Write a best-fit equation for $g(x)$, describing (*altitude in feet, temperature in °F*).

   d. Use the results of 10c to write the equation for $g^{-1}(x)$.

   e. What would the temperature in °F be at the summit of Mt. McKinley, which is 6194 m high?

   f. Write a composition of functions that will provide the answer for 10e. (Choose your functions from this problem and from the activity.)

11. Gabriel Fahrenheit (1686–1736) worked as a glassblower in Holland. He invented the Fahrenheit scale of temperature, which used as its reference points the melting temperature of a mixture of ice and salt, and the temperature of the human body. Anders Celsius (1701–1744) was a Swedish astronomer. His thermometric scale used the freezing and boiling temperatures of water as reference points, where freezing corresponded to 100° and boiling to 0°. His colleagues at the Uppsala observatory reversed his scale five years later, giving us the current version.

    a. Celsius's original scale had freezing corresponding to 100° and boiling to 0°. Write a formula that converts a temperature given by today's Celsius scale into the scale that Celsius invented.

    b. Explain how you would convert a temperature given in degrees Fahrenheit into a temperature on the scale Celsius invented.

12. Rewrite the expression $125^{2/3}$ as many different ways as you can.

13. This is the paper Anisha turned in for a recent quiz in her math class.

    Name: <u>Anisha</u>   Score

    1. Rewrite x^{-1}.

       Ans: $\dfrac{1}{x}$

    2. What does $f^{-1}(x)$ mean?

       Ans: $\dfrac{1}{f(x)}$

    3. Rewrite $9^{-1/5}$.

       Ans: $\dfrac{1}{9^5}$

    4. $0^0 = ?$

       Ans: 0

    If it is a four-point quiz, what is Anisha's score? For each problem that Anisha got incorrect, give her the correct answer and explain to her what she did wrong, so that next time she will get it right!

Section 7.5: Equations with Rational Exponents

Rita has $500 that she would like to invest, because her economics teacher has convinced her that if she starts saving money now, she will have a sizable "nest egg" when she gets older. She has been investigating several options. One investment advisor told her that if she puts her money into a Save-a-Lot Account, her investment will double in eight years. She would like to be able to figure out whether this is a good deal. Fortunately, in her math class, she is learning about solving these kinds of equations.

r	$(1 + r)^8$
0.08	1.8509^+
0.09	1.9925^+
0.091	2.0072^+
0.0905	1.9998^+

Frequently, exponential growth situations are described in terms of doubling time. Rita has been told that her investment of $500 compounded annually will double in eight years. What is the annual rate of interest for this account? She knows that if this is true, she will have $1000 in eight years, so she needs to find r in the equation $1000 = 500(1 + r)^8$. This is equivalent to solving $2 = (1 + r)^8$. Do you see why? Can you help Rita solve this equation?

Using substitution and experimentation, you can come as close as you want in a short time. Another way to do this would be to zoom in on the intersection of $y_1 = (1 + x)^8$ and $y_2 = 2$.

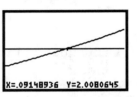

You could also use an algebraic process to solve an equation when the base is unknown, but the power or exponent is given. This process involves finding an inverse operation, or "undoing" the power applied to the base. How do you undo a power?

$2 = (1 + r)^8$ The given equation.

$2^{1/8} = ((1 + r)^8)^{1/8}$ **Power Property of Equality** (see below).

$2^{1/8} = 1 + r$ Nested Power Property of Exponents.

$2^{1/8} - 1 = r$ Subtract 1 from both sides.

This means r ≈ 0.0905077327

This means that if Rita were to put her money in this account it would earn 9% interest.

This procedure for finding inverses of a given power, or solving by "undoing" an exponent, is generalized in the property below.

Power Property of Equality

If $a = b$, and a, b are positive real numbers, then

$a^n = b^n$ for all values of n.

Example 1: Solve each equation for x.

a. $x^2 = 49$ b. $\sqrt{x} = 6$ c. $x^{5/2} = 243$

Solution:

a. You can solve this problem "by inspection." One solution is $x = 7$. A standard strategy, involving the Power Property of Equality, is to raise each side to the one-half power (or take the square root of each side). Then $\sqrt{x^2} = \sqrt{49}$ gives you the positive solution, $x = 7$.

b. Again, solve by inspection. The answer is $x = 36$. You can also get this solution by squaring both sides, $\left(\sqrt{x}\right)^2 = 6^2$.

c. Raise both sides to the power that is the reciprocal of the power on x, so that the exponent on x becomes one. $(x^{5/2})^{2/5} = 243^{2/5}$. Therefore, $x = 9$.

Each equation in Example 1 was solved by "undoing" an exponent. Graphs of $x^{5/2}$ and $x^{2/5}$ show that these functions are inverses of one another. In solving the equation in part c, you actually used a composite of the two functions, $y = \left(x^{(5/2)}\right)^{(2/5)}$, to arrive at the identity function, $y = x$. The Power Property is true for all *positive* bases. Many fractional exponents, like $\frac{1}{2}$, do not 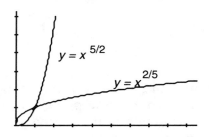 give real solutions when applied to negative numbers. Can you explain why? If you use the Power Property to solve an equation you will *only* get the positive solution. This is because you are working with functions, and there can be only one output for any input in a function. It is standard practice that if there is a choice, the positive answer is chosen.

Example 2: To predict the likelihood of snow on an overcast day, you have the following relationship with temperature, T, in degrees Fahrenheit.

$$\text{Percent chance of snow} = 100 - \frac{(T - 15)^2}{4}$$

What temperature would indicate that there is a 5% chance of snow?

Solution:

$$5 = 100 - \frac{(T-15)^2}{4}$$ Set equation equal to 5.

$$-95 = -\frac{(T-15)^2}{4}$$ Add ⁻100 to both sides.

$$380 = (T-15)^2$$ Multiply both sides by ⁻4.

$$380^{1/2} = (T-15)$$ Raise both sides to the 1/2 power.

$$19.5 \approx T - 15$$ Evaluate $380^{1/2}$.

$$34.5 \approx T$$ Add 15 to both sides.

Therefore, there is a 5% chance of snow when the temperature is 34.5°. Examine the graph of the function to see a second solution to the problem. What is it? In a later chapter you will learn some other techniques so you can find multiple solutions to equations.

Example 3:

a. Given $f(x) = 3.4\, x^{3/2} + 2$, find $f^{-1}(x)$. In other words, solve $x = 3.4\, y^{3/2} + 2$ for y.

b. Graph $f(x), f^{-1}(x), f(f^{-1}(x))$, and $f^{-1}(f(x))$.

Solution:

a. $x = 3.4\, y^{3/2} + 2$ Given equation.

$x - 2 = 3.4\, y^{3/2}$ Subtract 2 from both sides.

$\dfrac{x-2}{3.4} = y^{3/2}$ Divide both sides by 3.4.

$\left(\dfrac{x-2}{3.4}\right)^{2/3} = (y^{3/2})^{2/3}$ Raise both sides to the 2/3 power so that the exponent on y will be 1 when $x \geq 2$.

Therefore, $f^{-1}(x) = \left(\dfrac{x-2}{3.4}\right)^{2/3}$

b. Below are the graphs of $f(x), f^{-1}(x), f(f^{-1}(x))$ and $f(x), f^{-1}(x),$ $f^{-1}(f(x))$. Check them with your grapher and try to figure out why they look like they do. Why do they start at (2, 0) and (0, 2)? Why is there a difference in the graphs of the composites?

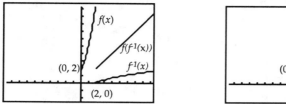

Bacterium in a Bottle Activity

There is single bacterium in a bottle at 11:00, and this type of bacteria doubles every minute. The bottle will be full of bacteria in one hour.

11:01	There is lots of room in the bottle.
11:02	There is still lots of room in the bottle.
. . .	
12:00	The bottle is full.

In your opinion, what percent of the bottle will be full when the bacteria start to feel crowded? Use the information given to calculate what time the bacteria will start to feel crowded. What percent of the one-hour time period do you think they will feel uncrowded?

In 1974, it was estimated that the total coal reserves in the United States were about $4.34 \cdot 10^{11}$ tons. Approximately $5.58 \cdot 10^8$ tons were consumed in 1975. If the consumption doubling time was fourteen years, how many tons were left in 1988? How many tons will be left in 2002?

Discuss the bacteria's predicament and compare it with a nonrenewable resource situation, such as the United States' coal reserves. Describe a problem that you think exists, and some possible solutions. Write a paragraph about this comparison, the situation, and a proposed solution.

Problem Set 7.5

1. Solve each equation for x, where x is a real number.

   a. $x^5 = 50$

   b. $\sqrt[3]{x} = 3.1$

   c. $x^2 = {}^-121$

   d. $x^{1/4} - 2 = 3$

   e. $4x^7 - 6 = {}^-2$

   f. $3(x^{2/3} + 5) = 207$

   g. $1450 = 800\left(1 + \dfrac{x}{12}\right)^{7.8}$

   h. $14.2 = 222.1 \cdot x^{3.5}$

2. Rewrite each expression without parentheses.

   a. $(27x^6)^{2/3}$

   b. $(16x^8)^{3/4}$

   c. $(36x^{-12})^{3/2}$

3. A one-millimeter-thick sheet of translucent glass has been designed to reduce the intensity of light. If six sheets are placed together, the outgoing light intensity is 50% of the incoming light intensity. What is the reduction rate of one sheet in this exponential relation?

4. The population of the earth in 1975 was about 4 billion, and was doubling every 35 yr.

   a. Write a formula describing the relationship between time and population.

   b. Use the formula to predict the population of the earth today.

   c. Look up the current population of the earth and calculate the percent error of your prediction.

5. In 1994, the cost of a gallon of milk was $2. At the 1994 rate of inflation, it will cost $4 in the year 2016. What was the rate of inflation in 1994?

6. If $f(x) = x^{2/3}$ and $x \geq 0$, sketch a graph of each function.

   a. $f(x - 4)$

   b. $f(x^2)$

   c. $f(f(x))$

   d. $f^{-1}(x - 4)$

7. a. Find the inverse of $f(x) = 2(x^{2/3} - 4)$.

   b. Give a detailed explanation of how you would use your grapher to graph $f(f^{-1}(x))$. (See **APPENDIX 7G**.)

   c. Give a detailed explanation of how you would use your grapher to graph $f(f^{-1}(x + 2))$.

8. There is a relationship between the radius of orbit and the time of one orbit for the moons of Saturn.

Moon	Radius (100,000 km)	Orbit Time (days)
1980S28	1.3767	0.602
1980S27	1.3935	0.613
1980S26	1.4170	0.629
1980S3	1.5142	0.694
1980S1	1.5147	0.695
Mimas	1.8554	0.942
Enceladus	2.3804	1.370
Tethys	2.9467	1.888
Dione	3.7742	2.737
1980S6	3.7806	2.739
Rhea	5.2710	4.518

The 28th satellite or moon, discovered in 1980, is 1980S28. Many moons were discovered in 1980 as the Voyager spacecraft passed by Saturn on its path through the solar system.

   a. Plot the relation (*radius, time*).

   b. Find a best-fit line, $y = a + bx$, and write a statement describing how well this model fits the data. Describe the tools you have used to reach this decision.

   c. Experiment with different values of a and b in $y = ax^b$ to find the best values for this model. Work with a and b one at a time, first adjusting one and then the other until you have a good fit. Write a statement describing how well this model fits the data.

9. a. Use your model from Problem 8 to find the orbit radius for Titan, which has an orbit time of 15.945 days.

   b. Find the orbit time for Phoebe, which has an orbit radius of 1,295,400 km.

10. Create your own problem, one you think would make a good assessment question, that covers the material in this chapter you have studied so far. Write out the complete solution to your problem, and explain why you believe it is a good problem. Please make sure that it is a problem or question, not just an explanation or description.

Section 7.6: The Logarithmic Function

In the last section, you learned to solve equations like $x^8 = 32$. The variable was in the base and the exponent was a number. In this section, you will investigate solving exponential equations where the variable is in the exponent. You have already solved this kind of equation by graphing, by guess-and-check using substitution, and by changing both sides of an equation to expressions with a common base.

Example 1: Solve each equation by finding a common base.

a. $49^x = 7$ b. $125^x = \sqrt{5}$ c. $1000^x = 0.0001$

Solutions:

a. $(7^2)^x = 7^1$ b. $(5^3)^x = 5^{1/2}$ c. $(10^3)^x = 10^{-4}$

$\quad 7^{2x} = 7^1$ $\quad\quad 5^{3x} = 5^{1/2}$ $\quad\quad 10^{3x} = 10^{-4}$

$\quad 2x = 1$ $\quad\quad\quad 3x = \dfrac{1}{2}$ $\quad\quad\quad 3x = {}^-4$

$\quad x = \dfrac{1}{2}$ $\quad\quad\quad x = \dfrac{1}{6}$ $\quad\quad\quad x = \dfrac{-4}{3}$

You could have solved each equation in Example 1 by graphing. In fact, you can find the solution by graphing when you can't easily find a common base.

The graph of $y = 3^x$ shows that y must be positive. This means, for example, that there is no solution for $3^x = {}^-9$, because the curve doesn't intersect $y = {}^-9$. The graph of $y = 3^x$ never goes below zero; it approaches zero (from above) as the x-values approach negative infinity. This means that $y = 0$ is an **asymptote** of the equation, or a boundary that the curve approaches. But, if y is any positive number, you can solve by zooming in on the point of intersection between the

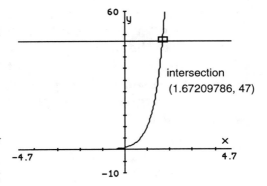

function and the horizontal line representing a particular y-value. You can solve the equation $3^x = 47$ by graphing $y = 3^x$ and $y = 47$. This means 47 can be written as a power of 3, even if the exponent is a bit nasty. What is it?

Example 2: Solve $10^x = 47$.

Solution: The graph indicates that $x \approx 1.67209786$. Again, this means that 47 can be written as a power of 10.

By substitution, $10^x \approx 10^{1.67209786}$.

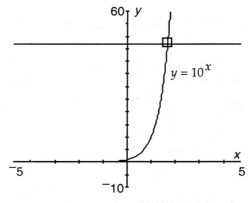

intersection (1.67209786, 47)

The number 47 isn't special. No matter what positive number replaces 47, you can solve for x. But what if you want to solve the equation $10^x = 47$ without graphing? You'll need an approach, involving inverses, that will "undo" the variable as an exponent. This inverse process will provide an x-value when you have to solve equations like $3^x = 30$, $10^x = 47$, or $6^x = 280$. This means the inverse will give the power (exponent) you can put on a given base to get 30, or 47, or 280. Like all inverses, its graph will be a reflection image of the original function over the line $y = x$, and coordinates of its points will be the reverse of points of the function.

Look at the exponential function $y = 4^x$. A table of values for the inverse can be written by simply exchanging the x- and y-values of the original function. See if you can make sense of these values. An input of 1 into the inverse gives a value of 0, because $1 = 4^0$. When you input 16, you get 2, because $16 = 4^2$. In general, the inverse should give *the exponent that you would put on 4 to get x.*

$y = 4^x$		The inverse function, $x = 4^y$	
x	y	x	y
$^-1$	$\frac{1}{4}$	$\frac{1}{4}$	$^-1$
0	1	1	0
1	4	4	1
2	16	16	2
x	4^x	4^x	x

The inverse of the exponential function $y = 4^x$ is called the **logarithm function**. The expression $\log_4 x$ is read "log base 4 of x." The functions $y = 4^x$ and $y = \log_4 x$ are inverses of each other.

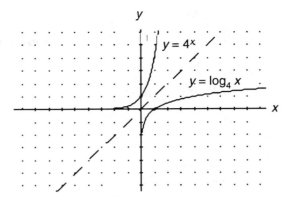

You also know that you can name the inverse relation by switching variables in $y = 4^x$ to get $x = 4^y$. This means $y = \log_4 x$ is equivalent to $x = 4^y$. Stop now and make certain you understand this before going on.

Definition of Logarithm

Given $a = b^x$ and $a, b > 0$

then $\log_b a = x$

The $\log_b a$ provides the value for x, which is the **exponent** in the defining equation. The logarithm function is an *exponent producing* function.

Example 2 (Again): Solve $10^x = 47$.

Solution:

$x = \log_{10} 47$ Using the definition of logs; "the log base 10 of 47" is the exponent you can place on 10 to get 47.

$x \approx 1.672097858$ Use the log key on your calculator to get this answer.

Ten is the **common base** for logarithms. This means log 47 is understood to be in base 10. The calculator answer for the log of 47 is not an exact answer. The value is actually an **irrational** number—a nonrepeating, nonterminating decimal. You can check the answers by raising 10 to the Ans power, 10^{Ans}. Try working this example on your calculator now.

Example 3: Solve $4^x = 128$.

Solution: The calculator doesn't have a *base four* logarithm function built into it, so you will have to convert each side of the equation to a power with a base of ten.

$$4^x = 128$$

$$10^? = 4 \qquad \text{The exponent you put on 10 to get 4 is } \log 4 \approx 0.60206.$$

$$10^? = 128 \qquad \text{The exponent you put on 10 to get 128 is } \log 128 \approx 2.10721.$$

$$\left(10^{0.60206}\right)^x = 10^{2.10721} \qquad \text{Substitute } 10^{0.60206} \approx 4; \ 10^{2.10721} \approx 128.$$

$$10^{0.60206x} = 10^{2.10721} \qquad \text{Nested Power Property.}$$

$$0.60206x = 2.10721 \qquad \text{Common Base Property.}$$

$$x = \frac{2.10721}{0.60206} = 3.5 \qquad \text{Check: } 4^{3.5} = 128.$$

This technique always works. Forming a composite of two inverse functions should produce an output value that is the same as the input. By definition, the equation $10^x = 4$ is equivalent to $x = \log 4$. Substitution from the second equation into the first equation gives you another look at the definition.

$$10^{\log 4} = 4$$

Check this with your calculator. Is $10^{\log n} = n$ an identity? What two equations can you graph to check this? Is it true for every n? If so, you can use this substitution to help solve equations similar to this example.

Example 4: $500 is invested at 8.5% compounded annually. Find how long it will take until the fund grows to $800.

Solution: Let x represent the number of years the investment is held.

$$500(1 + 0.085)^x = 800 \qquad \text{Growth formula for compounding interest.}$$

$$(1.085)^x = 1.6 \qquad \text{Multiply both sides by } 1/500.$$

At this point you could write $x = \log_{1.085} 1.6$, but you don't know base 1.085 logarithms. So you must change to base 10.

$$\left(10^{\log 1.085}\right)^x = 10^{\log 1.6} \qquad \begin{array}{l}\text{Substitute for 1.085 and 1.6 using the logarithm} \\ \text{identity } (10^{\log n} = n).\end{array}$$

$$10^{x \log 1.085} = 10^{\log 1.6} \qquad \text{Nested Power Property.}$$

$$x \log 1.085 = \log 1.6 \qquad \text{Common Base Property.}$$

$$x = \frac{\log 1.6}{\log 1.085} \qquad \text{Notice that this would be equal to } \log_{1.085} 1.6.$$

$$x \approx \frac{0.2041199827}{0.03542973818} \approx 5.76126139$$

Therefore, it takes about 6 years for the fund to grow to $800.

Example 5: Solve $\log_6 280 = x$

Solution:

$$6^x = 280 \qquad \text{Definition of logarithm.}$$

You could write this as $x = \log_6 280$, but you don't have base 6 logarithms. So you must change your base to 10.

$$\left(10^{\log 6}\right)^x = 10^{\log 280} \qquad \text{Substitute for 6 and 280 using the logarithm identity.}$$

$$10^{x \log 6} = 10^{\log 280} \qquad \text{Nested Power Property.}$$

$$x \log 6 = \log 280 \qquad \text{Common Base Property.}$$

$$x = \frac{\log 280}{\log 6} \approx 3.14483596 \quad \text{This is the same as } \log_6 280.$$

Check this by calculating $6^{3.14483596}$.
It should be very nearly 280.

Problem Set 7.6

1. Rewrite each logarithm in exponential form using the definition of log.

    a. $\log 1000 = x$ b. $\log_5 625 = x$ c. $\log_7 \sqrt{7} = x$

    d. $\log_8 2 = x$ e. $\log_5 \frac{1}{25} = x$ f. $\log_6 1 = x$

2. Use your results from Problem 1 and solve each equation by changing each side of the answer to an expression with a common base of ten.

3. For each compound inequality, find the nearest integers A and B.

    a. $A < \log 1250 < B$ b. $A < \log 125 < B$ c. $A < \log 12.5 < B$

    d. $A < \log 1.25 < B$ e. $A < \log 0.125 < B$ f. $A < \log 0.0125 < B$

4. Graph each equation. Write a sentence explaining how it compares to either $y = 10^x$ or $y = \log x$.

    a. $y = \log(x + 2)$ b. $y = 3 \log(x)$ c. $y = -\log(x) - 2$

    d. $y = 10^{(x + 2)}$ e. $y = 3(10^x)$ f. $y = -(10^x) - 2$

5. The function $g(x) = 23(0.94)^x$ gives the Celsius temperature x minutes after a large quantity of ice has been added to a bowl of water. When will the water reach 5.0°C?

6. The United States public debt, in billions of dollars, has been estimated with the model $y = 0.051517(1.1306727)^x$. The exponent represents years since 1900.

   a. According to the model, when did the debt pass one trillion (1000 billion) dollars?

   b. According to the model, what is the annual rate of growth?

   c. What is the doubling time for this growth model?

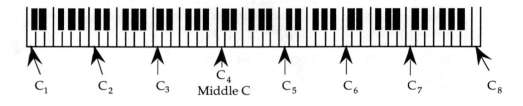

C_1 C_2 C_3 C_4 Middle C C_5 C_6 C_7 C_8

7. The relative frequencies of the C-notes on a grand piano (C_1, C_2, C_3, C_4, C_5, C_6, C_7, and C_8) are pictured on the right. These consecutive notes are one octave apart, which means the frequency will double from one C-note to the next.

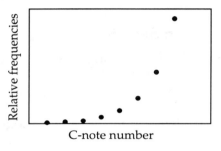

   a. If the frequency of middle C (C_4) is 261.6 cycles per second, and the frequency of C_5 is 523.2 cycles per second, find the frequencies of the other C-notes.

   b. Even though this is a discrete function, you can model it using a continuous explicit function. Write a function that can be used to generate these notes.

   c. Sketch the general shape of a grand piano and describe how its shape is related to the curve pictured.

8. Carbon-14 is an isotope of carbon that is formed when radiation from the sun strikes ordinary carbon dioxide in the atmosphere. Plants, such as trees, which get their CO_2 from the air, contain small amounts of carbon-14. No more carbon-14 is formed once a tree is cut down, and the amount that is present begins to decay slowly. The half-life of the carbon-14 isotope is 5750 years. That means, if there is 100% at time zero, then there is 50% at time 5750.

   a. Find the equation that models the percent of carbon-14 in a sample.

   b. A piece of wood, supposedly from Noah's Ark, is found to contain 48.37% of its original carbon-14. According to this, approximately when was the great flood? What assumptions are you making, and why is this answer approximate?

9. Crystal has been looking at old radio dials, and she noticed that the numbers are not evenly spaced. She hypothesizes that there is an exponential relationship involved. The display on her digital radio is out. She turned on the radio at 88.7 FM. After six "clicks" of the tuning knob, she was listening to 92.9 FM.

   a. Write the equation of a general exponential function using a and b.

   b. Name two points that the function must fit. (Use zero clicks for 88.7.)

   c. Write the general form of the equation using the first point, and find a value for a.

   d. Write the general form of the equation using the second point, and solve to find a value for b.

   e. Use the equation you have found to find how many "clicks" she should turn to get from 88.7 FM to 106.3 FM.

10. Find a problem in one of the first six sections of this chapter that you cannot solve. Write out the problem and as much of the solution as you can. Then, clearly explain what is keeping you from solving the problem. Be as specific and clear as you can.

Section 7.7: Properties of Logarithms

You found out in the last section that your calculator can only calculate with base ten logarithms. (Actually, it can also use what is called the natural base, e, which you will investigate in one of the projects.) So what do you do if you have to evaluate an expression like $\log_5 12$, or solve an equation like $y = \log_8 15$? Do you always have to express these logs in term of a base ten logarithm? Or is there another way to approach these problems?

Log Function Activity

This activity will help you to better understand the relationship between a base, an exponent and a logarithm. It will also help you to learn how you can solve an equation with a base other than ten.

a. Complete the table for the function $x = 4^y$.

x									
y	-2	-1.5	-1	-0.5	0	0.5	1	1.5	2

b. Enter this data in your calculator, set the appropriate window, and graph the data. Experiment to find the best value of a to make the equation $y = a \log x$ fit the data.

c. Repeat steps a and b for the equations $x = 7^y$, $x = 10^y$ and $x = 0.2^y$. Enter your results in a table like the one below.

Base	4	7	10	0.2
a				
Log of the base				

d. What is the relationship between the base and the value of a? (Hint: Look at reciprocals.)

e. Use the relationship you discovered in part d to help find y such that $4^y = 8$.

f. Use the relationship you discovered in part d to help find y such that $5^y = 10$.

Look back at Example 5 in the last section. In that example you solved the equation $\log_6 280 = x$ and found that $x = \dfrac{\log 280}{\log 6}$. Therefore, $\log_6 280 = \dfrac{\log 280}{\log 6}$. This is an example of what is called the Logarithm Change of Base Property; this property provides a shortcut for solving an exponential equation when the base is some number other than ten.

Logarithm Change of Base Property
$$\log_b x = \frac{\log x}{\log b} \qquad \text{for } b, x > 0$$

Does this statement agree with your conclusion in the Log Function Activity?

Example 6: Use the Change of Base Property to solve $5^x = 47$.

Solution:

$\log_5 47 = x$ 　　　　　　　　Rewrite in logarithm form.

$x = \dfrac{\log 47}{\log 5}$ 　　　　　　　Change of Base Property.

$x \approx 2.39223121$ 　　　　　　Check this answer.

If a logarithm is an exponent, then there must be other properties for logarithms similar to the ones for exponents. The problems in this section require the use of a special logarithmic ruler, which you will construct in the activity. You must work carefully and accurately, so that you can use your ruler to discover more properties of logarithms.

Making a Log Ruler Activity

To construct your logarithmic ruler, you will need a piece of graph paper and a strip of card stock. Everyone in the class should use the same kind of graph paper. Draw two lines down the center of your strip of card stock. (See the dotted lines in the diagram.) Then make a mark every ten units along one of the long edges of your graph paper. Label these marks 0, 1, 2, 3, and so on.

Use your calculator to find log 5 (≈ 0.693). Find the approximate location of 0.693 units on the graph paper, and draw a line across the width of your card stock ruler. Label this line "5" at both ends. Use your calculator to find log 10 (=1). Find the location of 1 unit on the graph paper and draw another line on your card stock ruler. Label this line "10." Continue drawing lines on your ruler for all the integers between 1 and 10. Then draw lines for the logs of all the multiples of 10. Next draw lines for the logs of the multiples of 100. Do the same thing for the logs of the multiples of 1000, 10,000, and so on.

Where is zero on your ruler? Why is it difficult to mark the logs of 0.1, 0.01, 0.001, and so on, on your ruler? Where is −1? What is the largest number on your ruler? Note that the distance from 1 to 10 is the same as the distance from 10 to 100. The ruler has no fixed unit length. Can you locate 0.1?

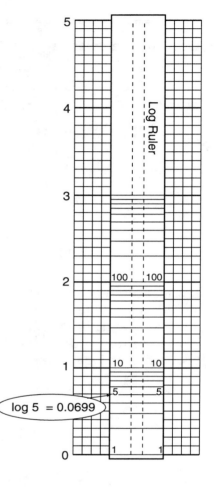

log 5 = 0.0699

Cut your ruler in half between the dotted lines. Now you have two log rulers, which you will use to learn about some other properties of logarithms in the Problem Set.

You could use two *ordinary* rulers to find the sum for an addition problem, like 4 + 3 = 7, by sliding one of the rulers along the other ruler as shown in the diagram at the right. Experiment with a few addition and subtraction problems to make sure

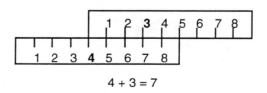

4 + 3 = 7

that you understand the process. Is it possible to model multiplication when using ordinary rulers? Can you model 2 • 4? How? How about 3.5 • 4.7?

Problem Set 7.7

1. Use two logarithmic rulers to perform each addition. Look for patterns. Keep a record of both the problem and its answer.

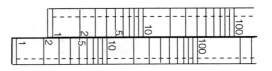

    a. log 2 + log 5   b. log 2 + log 50

    c. log 30 + log 30   d. log 40 + log 5

    e. Describe any patterns that you see.

    f. Use your calculator to confirm the calculations for 1a–1d.

    g. Complete the statement, "log a + log b = ."

        This is called the **Logarithm Product Property**.

    h. Explain why this property works. (Hint: Where else do you add when multiplying?)

2. Use two logarithmic rulers to perform each subtraction. Look for patterns. Keep a record of both the problem and its answer.

    a. log 30 – log 6   b. log 200 – log 10

    c. log 600 – log 20   d. log 600 – log 15

    e. Describe any patterns you see.

    f. Use your calculator to confirm the calculations for 2a–2d.

    g. Complete the statement, "log a – log b = ."

        This is called the **Logarithm Quotient Property**.

    h. Explain why this property works. (Hint: Where else do you subtract when dividing?)

3. Place your log ruler on graph paper to answer these questions. (Be sure to use the same kind of graph paper that you used to construct your log ruler.)

    a. Use your log ruler to find each value.

          i. log 2   ii. log 2^3, or log 8

    b. Compare the two values. Describe any relationship you see.

    c. Use your log ruler to find each value.

          i. log 50   ii. log 50^2, or log 2500

    d. Compare the two values. Describe any relationship you see.

    e. Use your calculator to confirm the calculations for 3a–3d.

f. Complete the statement, "log a^b = ."

This is called the **Logarithm Power Property**.

g. Is this relationship true for exponents that are not positive integers? Investigate this with your calculator.

h. How would you write log $\sqrt{a}$ in terms of log a?

4. Determine whether each equation is true or false. If false, rewrite one side of the equation to make it true.

a. log 3 + log 7 = log 21   b. log 5 + log 3 = log 8

c. log 16 = 4 log 2   d. log 5 − log 2 = log 2.5

e. log 9 − log 3 = log 6   f. log $\sqrt{7}$ = log $\frac{7}{2}$

g. log 35 = 5 log 7   h. log $\frac{1}{4}$ = −log 4

i. $\frac{\log 3}{\log 4}$ = log $\frac{3}{4}$ j. log 64 = 1.5 log 16

5. Rewrite the three properties of logarithms which you discovered in this section, in your own words.

6. Draw the graph of a function whose inverse is not a function. Carefully describe what must be true about the graph of a function if its inverse is not a function.

7. The table contains consecutive notes of an octave from one C-note to the next C-note. (C# is called C-sharp.) This *well-tempered scale*, complete with semitones, is an exponential sequence of frequencies such that the frequency (in cycles per second) of a C-note is double that of the previous C-note.

a. Find a function that will generate the semitone frequencies.

b. Fill in the missing table values.

	Note	Frequency
Do	C	261.6
	C#	
Re	D	
	D#	
Mi	E	
Fa	F	
	F#	
Sol	G	
	G#	
La	A	
	A#	
Ti	B	
Do	C	523.2

8. Evaluate this expression:
$\log_4 9 \cdot \log_9 12 \cdot \log_{12} 16$. (Hint: This might be easier if you don't use a calculator.)

9. If $\log_n 2 = x$, $\log_n 3 = y$, and $\log_n 5 = z$, write each expression in terms of x, y, and z.

    a. $\log_n 6$ b. $\log_n 2.5$ c. $\log_n 125$ d. $\log_n 100$

10. Evaluate each expression using the Change of Base Property.

    a. $\log_2 16$ b. $\log_5 8$ c. $\log_8 5$ d. $\log_3 15$

11. Graph each pair of curves on the same axis. For each pair, graph $f(f^{-1}(x))$ and $f^{-1}(f(x))$. (See **APPENDIX 7H** for help.) You will need the Change of Base Property for 11b and 11c.

    a. $f(x) = 10^x$ b. $f(x) = 2^x$ c. $f(x) = 0.5^x$

        $f^{-1}(x) = \log x$ $f^{-1}(x) = \log_2 x$ $f^{-1}(x) = \log_{0.5} x$

    d. Identify the domains of $f(f^{-1}(x))$ and $f^{-1}(f(x))$? Why are the domains different?

12. Determine whether each statement is *true* or *false*. Feel free to experiment with graphs of logs of other bases.

    a. The log curve is a function.

    b. The log curve has a horizontal asymptote.

    c. The log curve has a vertical asymptote.

    d. The log curve, regardless of base, contains the point (1, 0).

    e. The log curve has no symmetry.

    f. Log curves of different bases look like vertical stretches (or flips) of the $\log_{10} x$ graph.

13. List as many methods as you can to solve the equation $4^x = 15$. Explain each method completely. Which method do you prefer? Why? Justify your preference.

Section 7.8: Applications of Logarithms

In this section you will explore how logarithms are used to solve a wide variety of problems. You can use logarithms to rewrite and solve problems involving exponential and power functions that relate to the natural world, as well as financial situations. You will be better able to make decisions about investing money, borrowing money, disposing of nuclear and toxic waste, interpreting chemical reaction rates, and managing natural resources if you have a good understanding of these functions and problem solving techniques.

The table below summarizes the properties of exponents and logarithms that you have studied to this point in the chapter. Before you go on, be sure that you understand how to apply each of these properties.

Properties of Exponents and Logarithms		
$(a^m)(a^n) = a^{(m+n)}$	$\Leftrightarrow$	$\log_a xy = \log_a x + \log_a y$
$\left(\dfrac{a^m}{a^n}\right) = a^{(m-n)}$	$\Leftrightarrow$	$\log_a \dfrac{x}{y} = \log_a x - \log_a y$
$(a^m)^n = a^{mn}$	$\Leftrightarrow$	$\log_a x^n = n \log_a x$
$a^{m/n} = \sqrt[n]{a^m}$		$\log_a x = \dfrac{\log_b x}{\log_b a}$
$(ab)^m = a^m b^m$		Given $x = a^m$, then $\log_a x = m$
$a^{-n} = \dfrac{1}{a^n}$		$\left(\dfrac{a}{b}\right)^{-n} = \left(\dfrac{b}{a}\right)^n$

Example 1: More than 800,000 earthquakes are registered by seismographs each year. Most quakes are not noticed by anyone. Millions of dollars of damage was caused by a magnitude 7.1 earthquake, centered near the San Francisco Bay area, in October 1989. In September 1985, a magnitude 8.1 earthquake, which left many people homeless, was recorded in Mexico City. Earthquakes occur without any warning, although scientists hope that by studying the earth's movements they will someday be able to predict earthquakes. A seismograph is an instrument that measures an earthquake's intensity, using what is called the Richter scale.

The Richter number is defined as $R = \log\left(\dfrac{I}{I_0}\right)$, where I is the intensity of the quake's vibrations, and I_0 is the minimum detectable intensity of an earthquake. Compare the intensities of the two earthquakes mentioned above.

Solution: $7.1 = \log\left(\frac{I}{I_0}\right)$ implies $\frac{I}{I_0} = 10^{7.1}$ or $I = I_0 \cdot 10^{7.1}$ (intensity at San Francisco). Likewise, $8.1 = \log\left(\frac{I}{I_0}\right)$ means $I = I_0 \cdot 10^{8.1}$ (intensity at Mexico City).

The ratio of the intensities is $\frac{I_o \cdot 10^{8.1}}{I_o \cdot 10^{7.1}} = 10$. Therefore, the 1985 Mexico City vibrations were ten times as intense as those during the 1989 San Francisco earthquake.

Other natural phenomena whose measurements vary greatly in magnitude (like sound intensity, star brightness, and chemical acidity), are measured using a **logarithmic scale** like the Richter scale. Logarithmic scales are used because the log graph increases slowly. A common log, (base 10), scale means that a measure of 8.1 is *10 times* as great as a measure of 7.1, and 1000 times larger than a measure of 5.1.

$$10^{8.1} = 125{,}892{,}541 \qquad 10^{7.1} = 12{,}589{,}254.1 \qquad 10^{5.1} = 125{,}892.5541$$

What does this mean about an earthquake with magnitude 5.1? How does it compare in intensity to the Mexico City quake?

Acid concentrations and star brightness normally have small values (values less than one) when measured in common units. Logarithms of these small values are negative. Instead of expressing these measures as negative numbers, it is standard practice to define them as the *opposites* of the logs of the common units. This might be a little confusing at first. Keep in mind that a star of magnitude 2 is *brighter* than a star of magnitude 3, and a pH of 2.10 is *more* concentrated than a pH of 3.70.

Example 2: How does the concentration of a nitric acid solution with a pH of 2.10 compare to a nitric acid solution with a pH of 3.70?

Solution: The pH of a solution is measured as the negative logarithm of the hydrogen ion concentration, $^-\log [H^+]$. The concentration of the acids are:

$$-\log a = 2.10 \text{ and } -\log b = 3.70$$

$$a = 10^{-2.1} \text{ and } b = 10^{-3.7}$$

The ratio of a to b is $\qquad \frac{a}{b} = \frac{10^{-2.1}}{10^{-3.7}} \approx 39.8.$

The first acid is about 40 times as concentrated as the second.

Example 3: A "learning curve" describes the rate at which a task can be learned. Suppose the equation $t = -144 \log (1 - \frac{N}{90})$ predicts the time t (number of short daily sessions) it will take to achieve a goal of N words per minute on a word processor.

a. Using this equation, how long should it take someone to learn to type 40 words per minute on a word processor?

b. Interpret the shape of the graph as related to learning time.

Solution:

a. Substitute $N = 40$ in the equation $t = -144 \log (1 - \frac{N}{90})$ to get $t \approx 37$ short sessions.

b. Many interpretations are possible. It takes much longer to improve your typing speed as you reach higher levels. What limit is involved?

Example 4: The "rate" of a chemical reaction is the speed at which the reaction progresses toward completion. It is dependent on some power of the concentration of one or more of the reactants. The rate at which iron dissolves is dependent on the concentration of acid according to the following formula:

$$R = k [H^+]^p$$

The rate R is in grams per hour, k is a constant that depends on the temperature of the solution, and $[H^+]$ is the Normal concentration (abbreviated N) of the acid. The following data was collected from solutions at a temperature of 25°C.

	Concentration	Rate
Solution 1	0.20 N	0.56 g/hr
Solution 2	0.60 N	15.12 g/hr

What is the rate if the concentration of acid is 0.80N?

Solution: Substitute the data in $R = k [H^+]^p$ to get

$$0.56 = k(0.20)^p \text{ and } 15.12 = k(0.60)^p$$

From the first equation, $k = \dfrac{0.56}{0.20^{p}}$, which can be substituted into the second equation to get

$$15.12 = \frac{0.56}{0.20^{p}} (0.60)^{p}$$

$$15.12 = 0.56 \left(\frac{0.60}{0.20}\right)^{p} \qquad \text{Power of a Product Property.}$$

$$\frac{15.12}{0.56} = 3.0^{p} \qquad \text{Multiply by } \tfrac{1}{0.56}.$$

$$27 = 3.0^{p} \qquad \text{Arithmetic.}$$

$$p = \log_{3} 27 \qquad \text{Definition of logarithm.}$$

$$p = 3$$

Therefore, the value of the constant is $k = \dfrac{0.56}{0.20^{3}} = 70.0$ and the rate is $R = k\,[\text{H}^{+}]^{p} = 70.0\,(0.80)^{3} = 35.84$ g/hr. So, at a concentration of 0.80N, the rate is 35.84 g/hr.

Hot Water Activity

In this activity, you will find a relationship between the cooling time of hot water and the temperature of the water as it cools. Heat the water and container together. (If you don't, wait two or three minutes after the hot water is poured into your container before collecting data). Measure the room temperature, and make a note of it.

a. Before collecting any data, draw a sketch of what you would expect the graph of (*time, temperature*) to look like as the water cools. Label the axes and mark the scale on your graph.

b. Suspend a thermometer in the water away from the sides and bottom of the container. Collect data by measuring the temperature as the water cools. Do this at one-minute intervals for a while, and then at longer time intervals as the water cools. Record the time and temperature for each measurement. Collect data for as long as possible (at least a half hour.)

Time	°C	°F

c. Plot (*time, temperature*) data on an appropriately-scaled graph.

You will find a model for this data later on in the unit.

Problem Set 7.8

1. Suppose $3000 is invested at 6.75% annual interest compounded monthly. How long will it take to triple your money?

2. a. Solve this equation for x: $12.85 = 4.2^x$.

   b. Explain how and why this equation can be solved by *taking the log* of both sides.

3. Solve each equation by taking the base ten logarithm of each side. Store your answer and use the stored value to check.

   a. $800 = 10^x$

   b. $2048 = 2^x$

   c. $16 = 0.5^x$

   d. $478 = 18.5(10^x)$

   e. $155 = 24.0(1.89^x)$

   f. $0.0047 = 19.1(0.21^x)$

4. Many formulas in biology involve rational exponents. One such formula, $A = 0.061(W^{0.425})(h^{0.725})$, relates the surface area of a human being (in square meters) to their weight (in pounds) and their height (in feet).

   a. If someone weighs 120 pounds and is 5 feet 6 inches tall, what is that person's surface area?

   b. If someone has 1.82 square meters of surface area and is 5 feet 8 inches tall, what is that person's weight?

   c. Describe a method you could use to actually measure the surface area of a person, to verify this formula.

5. The length of time that milk (and many other perishable substances) will stay fresh varies with the storage temperature. Suppose that milk will keep for 192 hours in a refrigerator at 0°C. Milk that is left out in the kitchen at 22°C will keep for only 42 hours.

   a. Assume that this is an exponential relationship, and write an equation that expresses the number of hours, h, that milk will keep in terms of the temperature, T.

   b. Use your equation to predict how long milk will keep at 30°C and at 16°C.

   c. If a container of milk kept for 147 hours, what was the temperature?

   d. Using all of these data points, graph the relationship between hours and temperature.

   e. What is a realistic domain for this relationship? Why?

6. The intensity of sound, D, measured in decibels (dB) is given by

$$D = 10 \log \left(\frac{I}{10^{-16}} \right)$$

where I is the power of the sound in watts per square centimeter (W/cm²) and 10^{-16} W/cm² is the power of sound just below the threshold of hearing.

a. Find the number of decibels of a 10^{-13} W/cm² whisper.

b. Find the number of decibels in a normal conversation of $3.16 \cdot 10^{-10}$ W/cm².

c. Find the number of W/cm² of the orchestra section seated in front of the brass, measured at 107 dB.

d. How many times more powerful is a sound of 47 dB than a sound of 42 dB?

7. The altitude of a plane is calculated by measuring atmospheric pressure. This pressure is exponentially related to the height above the earth's surface. At ground level, the pressure is 14.7 psi (pounds per square inch). At a height of 2 mi, the pressure is reduced to 9.46 psi.

a. Use the first fact to find the coefficient of the exponential equation.

b. Use the second piece of information to find the base of the exponential function.

c. What is the pressure at a height of 12,000 ft (1 mi = 5280 ft)?

d. What is the altitude of an airplane if the atmospheric pressure is 3.65 psi?

8. The half-life of carbon-14, which is used in dating archaeological finds, is 5750 years.

a. Assume that 100% of the carbon-14 is present at a time of 0 yr, and 50% is present at a time of 5750 yr. Write the equation that expresses the percent of carbon-14 remaining as a function of the time. (This should be the same equation you found in Problem 8, Section 7.6.)

b. Some bone pieces, with 25% of their carbon-14 remaining, were found in Colorado. What is the probable age of the bones?

c. A piece of the Ark of the Covenant found by Indiana Jones contained 62.45% of its carbon-14. When does this indicate the Ark was constructed?

d. Coal is formed from trees that lived about 100 million years ago. Could carbon-14 dating be used to determine the age of a lump of coal? Explain your answer.

9. Carbon-11 decays at a rate of 3.5% per minute. Assume that 100% is present at time 0 min.

    a. What percent remains after 1 min?

    b. Write the equation that expresses the percent of carbon-11 remaining as a function of time.

    c. What is the half-life of carbon-11?

    d. Explain why carbon-11 is not used for dating archaeological finds.

10. a. Find the average current cost (the last column) for the items listed in the table.

    b. What average annual inflation rate provides the growth in prices from the 1975 costs to today's cost?

    c. Write an equation and use it to complete the table of values for 1980, 1985, and 1990.

    d. Find the current prices of two goods or services that are of interest to you, and use your equation from 10c to complete the values in the table.

Item	1975 cost	1980 cost	1985 cost	1990 cost	Current cost
can of Coke	$0.25				
movie ticket	$3.00				
haircut	$5.00				
compact auto	$4,000				
Big Mac	$1.00				

Section 7.9: Curve Straightening and More Data Analysis

Tables of data, graphs, sums of residuals, residual plots, correlation coefficients, and experimentation are useful tools in the search for a good model to explain data. You know how to find and use median-median and least-squares linear models of best-fit lines. However, a line is not a good model for some data.

The pendulum activity in Chapter 5 provides data that is not linear. Many students have tried to model the data they collected in this activity with a straight line. A linear model often seems like a good model if there is not much variation in the string lengths. In order to see the curvature, you will need to use a wider variety of string lengths for your pendulum.

Experimental results from one group of students are listed in this table. Below is a scatter plot of data, and an equation that the students found by guess-and-check to model their data.

Length (cm)	100	85	75	30	15	5	43	60	89	140	180	195
Period (sec)	2.0	1.9	1.8	1.4	0.9	0.6	1.4	1.6	2.0	2.4	2.6	2.9

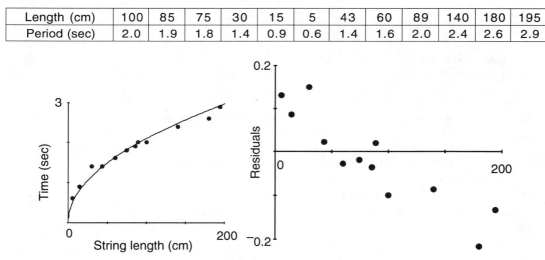

The graph of their equation, $y = 0.21\sqrt{x}$, looks like a pretty good fit. The residual plot shows that the curve should be higher for smaller values of x and lower for higher values of x. The residual sum is $^-0.2074$ and the sum of the squared residuals is 0.1322. (You will be asked to come up with a better model in the problems.) This is what data analysis is all about: trying to find a better model.

By doing the activities and working the examples that follow, you will learn how to find nonlinear models for data. These methods take advantage of everything you have learned about lines. In other words, the strategy is to linearize data, which means you will alter or transform the data to fit a line. You will accomplish this by choosing from possible combinations of (x, y), $(x, \log y)$, $(\log x, \log y)$, and $(\log x, y)$ to find a plot that is linear.

Linearizing Data Activity

Part 1. This is a good viewing window to see the graph for the exponential equation $y_1 = 47(1.61)^x$, over the domain $0 \le x \le 4.75$.

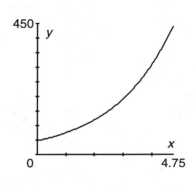

a. Find the best viewing window to see the graph of $y_2 = \log y_1$. Describe the graph of y_2.

b. Trace y_2 to find the coordinates of two different points. Store the x- and y-values for each point, keeping all the digits the calculator gives you.

c. Find a different equation for y_2 in $a + bx$ form. Do not round off the values for a and b.

d. Find a relationship between the slope of y_2 and the base of y_1. (Hint: Remember you are learning about logarithms in this chapter.)

e. Find a relationship between the y-intercept of y_2 and the coefficient, 47, of y_1.

f. Explain in your own words how the exponential curve $y_1 = ab^x$ was "linearized" (transformed into a line).

Part 2. This is a good viewing window to see the graph for the power equation $y_1 = \pi x^2$ over the domain $0 \le x \le 4.75$. (This is the equation for the area of a circle with a radius of x.) How can you linearize this curve?

a. Turn off y_1. Make a table of $(x, \log y_1)$ using the domain $0 \le x \le 4.75$. Because $\log 0$ is not defined, remove this entry from the list.

b. Find the best viewing window to see the graph of $y_2 = \log y_1$. Verify that this graph is not linear.

c. Make a table showing values of $\log x$ and $\log y$. (If you can't view this table on your calculator, then make a table like the one on the right.) Find a good viewing window and plot the graph of $(\log x, \log y)$. (See **APPENDIX 7I**.) Describe this scatter plot.

x	$y = \pi x^2$	$\log x$	$\log y$
0.5	$0.5^2\pi$		
1.0	π		
1.5	$1.5^2\pi$		
. . .	. . .		
4.5	$4.5^2\pi$		

d. Use nonrounded values of log x and log y to find a linear equation for y_2. Write this new equation for y_2 in $a + bx$ form.

e. Find a relationship between the slope of y_2 and the exponent of y_1.

f. Find a relationship between the y-intercept of y_2 and the coefficient, π, of y_1.

g. Explain, in your own words, how the power curve $y_1 = ax^b$ was linearized.

The reason you want to alter functions and data to produce a line is that it is possible to evaluate a degree of "best fit" for a line. You linearized the exponential function $y = ab^x$ by graphing $(x, \log y)$ and you linearized a power function $y = ax^b$ by graphing $(\log x, \log y)$. Here is an explanation of why this works.

$y = ab^x$ (exponential function)		$y = ax^b$ (power function)
$\log y = \log (ab^x)$	Take the log of both sides.	$\log y = \log (ax^b)$
$\log y = \log a + \log b^x$	Log Product Property.	$\log y = \log a + \log x^b$
$\log y = \log a + x \log b$	Log Power Property.	$\log y = \log a + b \log x$

A substitution of A for log a, and B for log b produces the following linear forms.

$$\log y = A + Bx \qquad \text{and} \qquad \log y = A + b \log x$$

Thus, the graphs are of the form

$$(x, \log y) \qquad \text{and} \qquad (\log x, \log y)$$

Example 1:

The table shows the number of Coho Salmon in Lake Michigan since their introduction in 1965. Find a model for this data relating (*time, number of salmon*).

Year	65	70	72	75	78	80	83	86	90
Population (in thousands)	25	45	59	83	122	151	219	315	500

Solution:

Your first guess might be that this graph has the "look" of a simple exponential curve $y = ab^x$. This is often the case when the only variable controlling the population of a species is the number of that species, food and space are ample, and no predators are present.

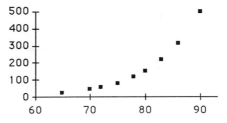

The next step is to convert this curve to a line. One way to do this is to mark the x-axis of your graph paper from 60 to 90. Then line up your log ruler with each point to find log y. Plot the points $(x, \log y)$ and find the equation of the line. Graph paper is made that is already marked off in the logarithms of numbers. It is

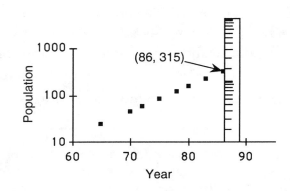

called semi-log paper and is used when trying to graph data that grows exponentially, such as a fish population or the value of an investment. In this way, a large range of y-values can be represented on a smaller sheet of paper.

A least-squares line on the new points $(x, \log y)$ gives the equation

$$y \approx {}^-1.994 + 0.0522x.$$

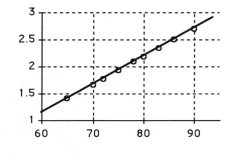

Remember that the values of the intercept and slope, A and B, are the logs of the constants in your exponential equation. You must raise 10 to the power of each of these to find the actual values. This is called finding the **antilog**.

$\log a \approx {}^-1.9943$ $\log b \approx 0.0522$

$a = 10^{-1.9943} \approx 0.0101$ $b = 10^{0.0522} \approx 1.1277$ so $y \approx 0.0101(1.1277)^x$

What is the real-world meaning of these two new values? The 1.1277, or (1 + 0.1277), means that the population is growing at a rate of 12.77% annually. The 0.0101 is the salmon population (in thousands) in 1900, your base year. However, in this problem this value has no real meaning, because salmon were not introduced into Lake Michigan until the 1960s.

Example 2: Earlier in the course you looked at the data for the relation (*radius, orbital time*) for the moons of Saturn. Now you will return to the data and find a more analytic solution to the problem.

Moon	Radius (100,000 km)	Orbit time (days)
1980S28	1.3767	0.602
1980S27	1.3935	0.613
1980S26	1.4170	0.629
1980S3	1.5142	0.694
1980S1	1.5147	0.695
Mimas	1.8554	0.942
Enceladus	2.3804	1.370
Tethys	2.9467	1.888
Dione	3.7742	2.737
1980S6	3.7806	2.739
Rhea	5.2710	4.518
Titan	12.223	15.945
Phoebe	12.954	17.395

The data

[0, 15, 5, 0, 20, 5]

The best-fit line

The residuals

[0, 15, 5, ⁻1.5, 1, 0.5]

(x, log y)

[0, 15, 5, ⁻0.5, 1.5, 0.5]

(log x, log y)

[0, 1.5, 0.5, ⁻0.5, 1.5, 0.5]

Solution: Begin by verifying that the relation isn't linear. A residual plot of (x, y) with a least-squares line should convince you. Next, verify that the graph isn't exponential. Convince yourself that a graph of $(x, \log y)$ does not linearize the data. Your next assumption might be that the data is best related by a power function, so you should plot $(\log x, \log y)$. (You could draw this graph on graph paper with x- and y-axes that are both marked in logarithmic scales. This kind of graph paper is called double log paper or log-log paper.)

$(0.13, ⁻0.2)$; $(1.1, 1.2)$ Select two points on the line.

$\dfrac{1.2 + 0.2}{1.1 - 0.13} = 1.5$ Find the slope.

$y = 1.5(x - 1.1) + 1.2$ Find the equation of the line.

$y = 1.5x - 1.65 + 1.2 = ⁻0.45 + 1.5x$ Simplify to find the intercept.

$10^{⁻0.45} \approx 0.355$ Find the anti-log of the intercept.

$y = 0.355x^{1.5}$ The final equation.

Test this equation by graphing it over the original data.

How can you decide whether to graph $(x, \log y)$ or $(\log x, \log y)$? Begin by plotting the original data using a good scale. Next, look at it and decide what needs to be done to "straighten" the data. Taking the logarithm of only the y-values will "pull" the high end of the curve down. Taking the logarithm of only the x-values will "pull" the right-most data to the left. Taking the logarithms of both x and y will do a combination of both. You may need to graph more than one possibility to find the best choice. Most of the data in these problems can be linearized by choosing from possible combinations of (x, y), $(x, \log y)$, $(\log x, \log y)$, and $(\log x, y)$.

Problem Set 7.9

1. Find a better model than $y = 0.21\sqrt{x}$ for the pendulum data listed in this section. Graph (x, y), $(x, \log y)$, $(\log x, \log y)$, and $(\log x, y)$. Which one appears to be most linear? Write an equation for this line.

2. Find an equation relating the loudness of spoken words, measured at the source, and the maximum distance another person can recognize the speech.

Loudness (in decibels)	Distance (in meters)
0.5	0.1
3.2	16.0
5.3	20.4
16.8	30.5
35.8	37.0
84.2	44.5
120.0	47.6
170.0	50.6

   a. Plot the data on your calculator and make a rough sketch on your paper.

   b. Experiment by plotting different combinations of x, y, $\log x$, and $\log y$, until you have found the graph that best linearizes the data.

   c. Find the equation of a line that fits the plot you chose in 2b.

   d. Draw the line from 2c on your graph.

   e. Use the slope and the y-intercept of the equation in 2c to find the function for the original data.

   f. Graph this curve over the original data.

3. Start with a cup of M&Ms.

   a. Put the M&Ms into a large flat empty box and mix them. Remove all M&Ms with the M showing. Record the number of M&Ms remaining in the box, mix them up, and repeat the process six or seven times.

   b. Plot the data and find a relationship between (*time, number remaining*).

   c. Count the M&Ms that have no M on either side. How will this affect your data and model? If necessary, correct your model.

4. A cup of hot water is placed in the refrigerator, and the temperature is read at the time intervals listed. You wish to find a relationship between time and temperature.

Time (in min.)	Temp (in °F)
0	159.5
5	143.3
10	125.3
15	111.8
20	102
30	88.4
40	78.5
50	70.9
65	62.3
80	55.6
95	51.3
115	46.5
135	44.3
150	42.5
180	40.7

(overnight temp 40°)

a. Plot the data using an appropriate window. Make a rough sketch of this graph in your notebook.

b. The graph of the data should resemble an exponential decay curve, except that the x-axis is not the asymptote of the curve. Sketch a horizontal asymptote on your graph of the data. If you shift the curve (the data) down 40 units, the asymptote would lie on the x-axis (approximately). Create a new set of data by subtracting 40 from each temperature. (See **APPENDIX 7I**.) Replot the new data in a new window, and make a rough sketch of this graph in your notebook.

c. Next, graph $(x, \log y)$. Reset the window, plot the new data, and make a rough sketch in your notebook.

d. Use your calculator to find the equation of the least-squares line for this data.

e. In your equation for 4d, replace y with $\log (y - 40)$, and solve for y. Use the definition of logarithm to find an equation for the original data.

f. Graph this final equation over the original data.

5. Recall that earlier in the course you considered a problem involving the radius of orbit and the time needed for one orbit of the sun. At that time you found a best-fit line, even though you may not have thought the data was exactly linear.

Planet	Radius (in 10^6 mi.)	Period (in years)
Mercury	36.0	0.24
Venus	67.2	0.62
Earth	92.9	1.00
Mars	141.5	1.88
Ceres	257.1	4.60
Jupiter	483.3	11.86
Saturn	886.0	29.46
Uranus	1781.9	84.02
Neptune	2791.6	164.78

a. Enter the data into the calculator and graph it in an appropriate window. Make a rough sketch of this graph in your homework.

b. Select a linear regression on your calculator, and record the coefficient of correlation.

c. Now select an exponential regression (See **APPENDIX 7J**), and record the coefficient of correlation. Then select a power regression, and record the coefficient of correlation. Do you agree that the power regression is the best fit?

d. Place the power regression equation in the function menu, and graph the curve over the data.

e. Graph the residual plot, and record the largest and smallest residuals.

6. Experiment with the different types of regression built into your calculator to find the function that best models your results from the Hot Water Activity conducted in Section 7.8.

a. Name the best-fit equation.

b. Name the coefficient of correlation.

c. Sketch a graph of the residuals in your homework.

7. In clear weather, the distance you can see from a window on a plane depends on the curvature of the earth and your height above the earth.

Height (in meters)	Viewing distance (in kilometers)
305	62
610	88
914	108
1,524	139
3,048	197
4,572	241
6,096	278
7,620	311
9,144	340
10,668	368
12,192	393

a. Find a best-fit equation for (*height*, *view*) using the data in this table.

b. Describe the process (step by step) that you used to find this equation.

8. When A. Quatic starts treating her pool for the season, she begins with a shock treatment of 4 gal of chlorine. Every 24 hr, 15% of the chlorine disappears. Beginning the next morning, she adds one quart ($\frac{1}{4}$ of a gallon), and she continues to do so each morning.

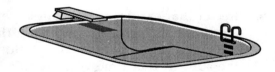

a. How much chlorine is there in the pool after one day (after she adds the first daily quart of chlorine)? After two days? After three days?

b. Use recursive notation to write a formula for this pattern.

c. Use the formula from 8b to build a table of values and sketch a graph of twenty terms.

d. Find an explicit model that fits the data.

Section 7.10: Chapter Review

Problem Set 7.10

1. Evaluate each expression without using a calculator. Then check your work with a calculator.

   a. 4^{-2}

   b. $(-3)^{-1}$

   c. $\left(\frac{1}{5}\right)^{-3}$

   d. $49^{1/2}$

   e. $64^{-1/3}$

   f. $\left(\frac{9}{16}\right)^{3/2}$

   g. -7^{0}

   h. $(3)(2)^{2}$

   i. $(0.6^{-2})^{-1/2}$

2. Rewrite each expression in another form.

   a. $\log x + \log y$

   b. $\log \frac{z}{v}$

   c. $(7x^{2.1})(0.3x^{4.7})$

   d. $\log w^{k}$

   e. $\sqrt[5]{x}$

   f. $\log_{5} t$

3. First, solve each equation by using the properties in this chapter to evaluate the expressions. Second, solve using a graphing approximation.

   a. $4.7^{x} = 28$

   b. $4.7^{x^{2}} = 2209$

   c. $\log_{x} 2.9 = 1.25$

   d. $\log_{3.1} x = 47$

   e. $7 x^{2.4} = 101$

   f. $9000 = 500(1.065)^{x}$

   g. $\log x = 3.771$

   h. $\sqrt[5]{x^{3}} = 47$

4. A new incentive plan for the Talk Alot long distance phone company varies the cost of a call according to the formula $cost = a + b \log (time)$. When calling long distance, the cost for the first minute is $0.50. The charge for 15 min is $3.44.

   a. Find the a-value of the model.

   b. Find the b-value of the model.

   c. What is the x-intercept of the graph of this model? What is the real-world meaning of the x-intercept?

   d. Use your model to predict the cost of a 30-min call.

   e. If you decide you can only afford to make a $2.00 call, how long can you talk?

5. The data are the number of AIDS cases reported by the state health departments in the United States between 1982 and 1986.

Year	# of cases
1982	434
1983	1,416
1984	3,196
1985	6,242
1986	10,620

a. Sketch a picture of the original data on graph paper, and label the axes.

b. Sketch a picture of the linearized data on graph paper.

c. Find the equation of the linearized data.

d. Use your equation to estimate the number of cases reported in 1990 and 1995, and predict the number of cases in 2000.

e. If the trend continues, when will there be 1 million cases?

f. Find the latest statistics to see if this model is still true today. If it isn't, try to explain why.

6. The federal minimum wage was increased 13 times from 1955 to 1991.

a. Find a function that models the data as pictured.

b. Use your model to predict minimum wages in the years 2000, 2010, and 2020. Include an explanation about how reasonable these predictions might be.

c. Use your model to estimate the minimum wage in 1938, when it was first established by the Fair Labor Standards Act. How does your answer compare with the actual 1938 minimum wage of $0.25?

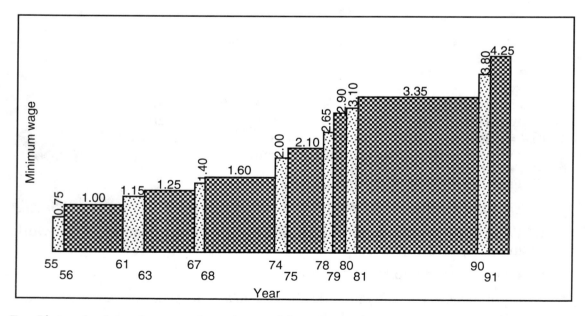

7. If you had to choose a favorite problem from this unit, which one would it be? Why?

Section 7.11: Projects

Project 7.1: Income by Gender

The median annual incomes of year-round full-time workers, ages 25 and above, are listed in this table.

a. Examine different relationships such as (*time, men*), (*time, women*), (*women, men*), (*time, men − women*), or (*time, men/women*), and so on.

b. Find best-fit models for those relationships that seem meaningful.

c. Write an article for your school newspaper in which you interpret some of your models and make predictions about what you expect to happen in the future.

Year	Men	Women
1970	9,521	5,616
1971	10,038	5,872
1972	11,148	6,331
1973	12,088	6,791
1974	12,786	7,370
1975	13,821	8,117
1976	14,732	8,728
1977	15,726	9,257
1978	16,882	10,121
1979	18,711	11,071
1980	20,297	12,156
1981	21,689	13,259
1982	22,857	14,477
1983	23,891	15,292
1984	25,497	16,169
1985	26,365	17,124
1986	27,335	17,675
1987	28,313	18,531

Project 7.2: Baseball for Bucks

The table contains average and minimum professional baseball salaries. Look in an almanac to find more recent salary information, and make some predictions about salaries ten years from now, based on mathematical models.

Year	Minimum	Average
1967	6,000	19,000
1970	12,000	29,303
1973	15,000	36,566
1976	19,000	51,501
1979	21,000	113,558
1982	33,500	241,497
1985	60,000	371,571
1988	62,500	438,729
1991	100,000	851,492

Project 7.3: Finding e

In Chapter 2, you looked at discrete models of growth; in this chapter, you extended these to continuous models. Sometimes you use a continuous model to model a function that really isn't continuous. Compounding interest is an example of when you might do this. When interest is compounded quarterly, you can model this growth with a continuous function, even though the interest is only added to your account once a quarter. So the continuous function is not really meaningful except for integer values. In reality, growth (or decay) does not happen once a year, once a month, or once a minute, but instead it occurs instantaneously and continuously. In the first part of this project, you will find the base for continuous growth. In the second part, you will compare it with the discrete models.

Part 1:   Consider $1.00 invested at 100% annual interest for one year. If the interest is compounded annually, the total will be $2.00. Write the equation that gives this value. Now find the equation for interest compounded quarterly and determine the value at the end of one year. Repeat this computation, compounding monthly, weekly, daily, hourly, by the minute, and by the second. Write an equation for 100% interest compounded x times each year for one year. What is the limit or long-run value of this investment?

Part 2:   Find e^1 on your calculator. (Usually e to a power is found above the key marked LN or ln.) In this chapter, you used a base of $(1 + 0.05)$ to indicate 5% growth. In the continuous model, you will use $e^{0.05}$ as the base. How do these two numbers compare? Compare the values of a 9% annual decay of 200 g over a 7 yr period with the two models.

$$y = 200(1 - 0.09)^7 = 103.3 \text{ g and } y = 200e^{-0.09(7)} = 106.5 \text{ g}$$

Look at the graphs of $y_1 = 200(1 - 0.09)^x$ and $y_2 = 200e^{-0.09x}$. When are these the same and when are they different? (Hint: Look at the graph of $y_2 - y_1$.)

Return to any problem involving growth or decay from this chapter, and compare the results you found before with the results using this new information. Write a paragraph explaining similarities and differences between the results.

Project 7.4: Fractal Dimensions

The graphs below show the same line. However, the spacing between the grid lines is decreased in successive views. For each of the four graphs, count the total number of squares that contain some portion of the line, no matter how small. Record this information.

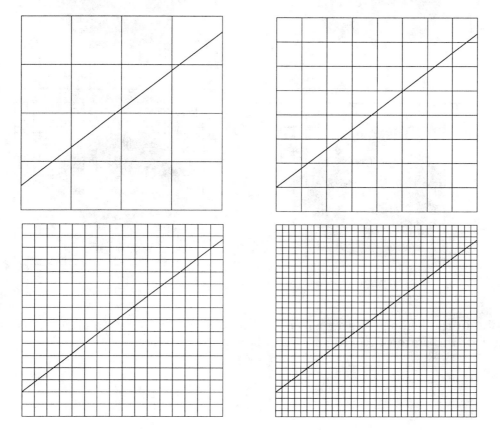

The second set of graphs show the same circle. In these graphs, count any square that contains part of the circumference of the circle, and also count any square that contains any point inside the circle. (It may be easier to count those squares that do not contain any part of the circumference or the interior of the circle, and then subtract this number from the total number of squares.) Record this information.

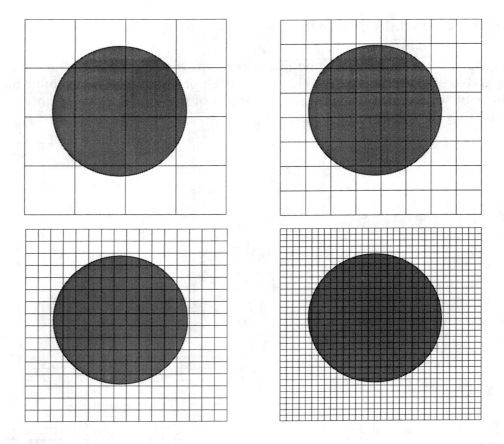

Finally, in the last set of graphs, count the squares that contain any part of the border of the state of Michigan. Record this information.

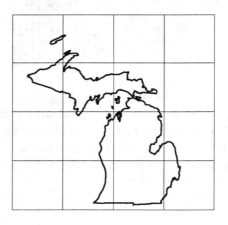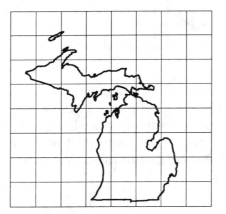

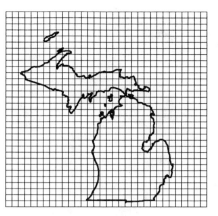

Grid	Line	Circumference of Circle	Area of Circle	Michigan
4				
8				
16				
32				

Put all of the information into a table like the one shown here. Find a power function for each set of data paired with the grid size. The power of x is called the dimension of the graph. Now it should not be surprising that the dimension of a line or the circumference of a circle is one, because these are one-dimensional objects. And likewise the dimension of a circle's area should be two. But why is the state of Michigan neither one-dimensional nor two-dimensional, but somewhere in between? Non-integer dimension values between one and two indicate the roughness or jaggedness of a boundary. A very crooked boundary, such as the seacoast of Maine, has a higher dimension than a smoother boundary, such as the west coast of Michigan. Fractal dimensions calculated for brain waves and other biological signals are being investigated as tools in medical diagnosis. Fractal dimensions of rock fractures are used to analyze the likelihood of groundwater contamination from underground storage of waste. Other applications of this concept are appearing in almost every area of science.

Select one of these two options to complete this project.

1. Find a map of your state or region. Choose a boundary of a natural feature such as a river. Overlay a series of grids on a copy of the map and calculate the fractal dimension of this feature.

2. Prepare a report of a developing application of fractal dimensions in some field of science.

Chapter Eight

DISCRETE MATH TOPICS

Contents

Section 8.1: Using Random Numbers 354

     Some of us have been using them already

Section 8.2: Random Numbers in Two Dimensions 362

     Patterns out of chaos

Section 8.3: Some Counting Techniques 366

     Didn't we do this in first grade?

Section 8.4: Waiting and Expected Value 372

     Something like standing in a lunch line?

Section 8.5: Chromatic Numbering 378

     You colored by number in first grade too!

Section 8.6: The Transition Matrix 383

     Going there in a box

Section 8.7: Matrix Operations 389

     Somebody has to operate the box

Section 8.8: Chapter Review 394

     Assessing yourself

Section 8.9: Projects 398

     Taking it one step further

Section 8.1: Using Random Numbers

"It isn't fair," complains Noah. "My car insurance rates are much higher than yours are." Feeling very smug, Rita replies, "Well, Noah, that's because insurance companies know that the chances are I'm a better driver than you, so it will cost them less to insure me." Even though insurance companies can't predict what kind of driving record you might have, they know, based on experience, the driving records for people in your age group, and they use this information to determine what your rates will be. This is just one example of how probability theory and the concept of randomness affect your life.

Many games are based on random outcomes or chance. Games of chance have existed for a long time. Paintings and excavated material from Egyptian tombs show that games with astragali were established by the time of the First Dynasty, around 3500 B.C. (An astragalus is a small bone immediately under the heel-bone, and these bones were used in dice-like games.) Later, in the Ptolemaic Dynasty (300 to 30 B.C.), games with six-sided dice seem to have become  common in Egypt. The ancient Greeks made icosahedral (twenty-sided) and other polyhedral dice. The ancient Romans were extremely enthusiastic dice players, (so enthusiastic, in fact, that laws were passed forbidding gambling except at certain seasons). Gambling casinos and lotteries continue to thrive today, in part because so many people remain more or less ignorant of the idea of randomness. Although probability theory actually began evolving in the seventeenth century as a means of determining the fairness of games, it wasn't until years later that mathematicians and scientists began to realize that probability theory affects the study of sociological and natural phenomena as well.

In this section, you will begin to learn about the concept of randomness. Randomness means that individual outcomes aren't predictable. But the long-range pattern of *many* individual outcomes often *is* predictable, even for random processes. You will probably find many of the ideas and concepts seem contrary to intuition. This is natural. As you work through this chapter and gain more experience, you will become more comfortable with these concepts.

Statisticians frequently simulate real situations and use summaries of the results to make approximate predictions about what they expect will happen. Many problems can be solved using random numbers to simulate or model a situation. When you are generating **random numbers**, each number should be equally likely to occur, and there should not be a pattern in the sequence of numbers generated. The next activity will help you to understand what is meant by a random selection.

Random Selection Activity

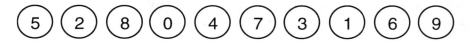

You will need ten chips (or small pieces of paper) and a container to hold them. Write a digit from 0 to 9 on each chip. Be sure to use each digit only once. Place all the chips in the container and mix them thoroughly. Remove the chips one at a time until all are selected. Record the sequence of digits in the order they are selected. After all chips have been selected, put them back into the container, and repeat this process until you have recorded 30 digits. (For example, you may have the digits 5 2 8 0 4 7 3 1 6 9 3 8 4 2 5 after emptying the container once, replacing the chips, and removing five more.)

a. Write a paragraph about this activity. Make certain that you address each of these questions in your paragraph.

- How many 7's are in *your* list of thirty digits? How many 2's? Agree or disagree with this statement and defend your position. *This list of thirty digits is random because there are equal numbers of each digit.*

- Is it ever possible for a digit to be appear twice in a row? Three (or more) times in a row? Is it ever possible to predict the next digit? Is it ever possible to name a digit that cannot be next in the list? Describe the difficulty (if any) that these questions suggest about the randomness of your list of digits.

b. Describe how you could make this selection process more random.

See **APPENDIX 8A** to select a unique random number with your calculator. The calculator is similar to other electronic computers because it produces pseudo-random numbers calculated by complex formulas. This means the random functions of some calculators can be set to produce exactly the same sequence over and over again. To see what is meant by pseudo-random, seed your calculator's random number generator with the number 1. You will probably get the same sequence of numbers as someone else with the same kind of calculator, and your sequence might be the same as the list in Example 1.

Example 1: Below is a list of twenty random numbers that were generated by a calculator. What common characteristic do all random numbers in this list share? What long-range patterns do you observe?

Solution:

.7455607728	.8559005971	.2253600617	**.469229188**
.6866902136	.0849241336	.0800630669	.6219079175
.1272157551	.2646513087	.792829631	.9489592829
.1176398942	.3445273552	.0031305767	.4990898873
.6666386115	.0598118664	.8057656643	.0963471417

Each random number is a decimal number between 0 and 1. Actually, by calculator design, all numbers generated will be in the interval $0 < x < 1$. This calculator displays ten digits, unless the last digit is 0 like the boldface number in the above list. This number is actually 0.4692291880. You can't predict what the next number will be, but you can see some long-range patterns if you make a histogram of the results.

A histogram of these twenty random numbers using a window of [0, 1, 0.1, 0, 8, 1] would look like the graph at the right. The number 0.469229188 is included in the bar between 0.4 and 0.5. What would the histogram look like if you generated many random numbers? If you combine the tallies from thousands of such experiments, what do you think the distribution will look like? Experiment with the random number generator routine in **APPENDIX 8B**.

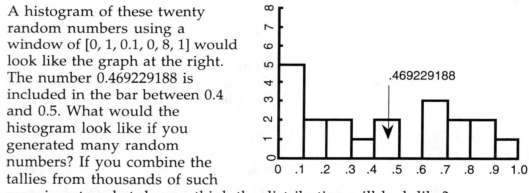

Each possibility for a random number should be equally likely. Ideally over the long run, any number should occur equally as often as any other. This means histograms should level off as the number of experiments increases.

Example 2: How can you use the calculator to simulate rolling a six-sided die with 1, 2, 3, 4, 5, and 6 as equally likely outcomes?

Solution: The *random* command can be used in different ways to model this. You could look at only the first digit. For example, 0.5246891697 would mean a 5 whereas 0.8395459099 would be ignored. You can also alter the random function so that the only random choices that appear are the numbers 1 through 6. Consider the following. Let x be the random number that is generated.

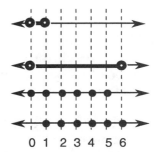

$0 < x < 1$	By calculator design.
$6 \cdot 0 < 6 \cdot x < 6 \cdot 1$	Multiply each member by 6.
$0 < 6x < 6$	Result gives numbers between 0 and 6.
$0 \le \text{Int } 6x \le 5$	The integer part, which gives just the numbers 0, 1, 2, 3, 4, and 5.
$1 \le \text{Int } 6x+1 \le 6$	Possible outcomes are 1, 2, 3, 4, 5, and 6.

0 1 2 3 4 5 6

If the random number is 0.7278813624, multiplying by 6 will give you 4.367288174, and Int(4.367288174) gives you 4. Adding 1 gives 5, which is one of the face choices on a six-sided die. See **APPENDIX 8A** for help with your calculator.

Medical Testing Activity

Hi and Pocon Driack both go to the doctor with the same symptoms. The doctor tests them for *Rarus Diseasus*. Statistics show that 20% of the people with these symptoms actually have the disease. The test the doctor uses is correct 90% of the time.

Generate random digits 0 through 9. (Use your calculator, make a spinner, draw chips from a bag, or use a random number table.)

a. Choose two digits, like 4 and 7, to represent the 20% chance of having the disease. Then choose one digit, like 9, to represent the 10% chance of the test failing.

b. Generate two numbers for each trial. The first number indicates whether or not a person has the disease. The second number indicates whether the test results are accurate or inaccurate. If you use the numbers as assigned above, a 5 followed by a 7 would mean the person *does not have the disease* and the test gave *accurate* results. A 7 followed by a 9 means the person *has the disease* and the test gave *inaccurate* results.

c. Randomly generate 100 pairs of numbers, and make a tally of your results. The first pair (5, 7) represents *doesn't have the disease, accurate*. The second pair (7, 9) represents *has the disease, inaccurate*.

Patient's condition	Test results	
	Accurate	Inaccurate
Doesn't have the disease	/	
Has the disease		/

d. A positive test result indicates that a person has the disease, while a negative test result indicates that a person doesn't have the disease. What test results, positive or negative, would be reported for each of the cells in the table in part c?

e. Hi tests positive for the disease and Pocon tests negative. What are the chances that each one has the illness? Use the results in the chart to predict the chance that Hi has the disease and the chance that Pocon has the disease.

Were you surprised by the results of the activity? People in many occupations use random numbers to test theories and make predictions. You can use tables of random numbers, or you can generate random numbers with spinners, chips, dice, shuffled decks of numbered cards, or the random function on your calculator. When you get consistent results using randomly generated values, you know that these results are meaningful. It is like using chaos to find order.

Problem Set 8.1

1. Fay Cilitator wants to collect homework from only six of her thirty students, using a random selection process. Devise a method she could use to randomly select six students. (Use chips, spinners, cards, or dice in your method.) Remember that her students will insist on fairness.

2. Suppose your job is to randomly assign one hundred members of the marching band to ride in five buses that hold forty passengers each. (The back of each bus will be used to store instruments and equipment.)

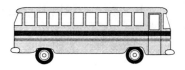

   a. Describe a method for randomizing the selection process using a die.
   b. Simulate your selection process. How many of the students are assigned to the first bus? Theoretically, how many students should be assigned to the first bus?
   c. Write a random number routine for your calculator that you can use to simulate this selection process.

d. Use your calculator random number routine from 2c to simulate the selection process. How many of the students are assigned to the first bus?

e. How does your answer to 2d compare to your answers to 2b?

3. Rank 3a, 3b and 3c as to which method will best produce a random integer between 0 and 9, inclusive. Support your reasoning with complete statements.

a. The number of heads when nine pennies are dropped.

b. The length, to the nearest inch, of a standard 9-in. pencil belonging to the next person you meet who has a pencil.

c. The last digit of the page number on your left after an open book is spun and dropped from four feet.

d. Write your own method for producing random numbers between 0 and 9.

4. Suppose you have been talked into playing one of those board games where you need to roll a 6 before you can start playing.

a. Predict the average number of turns a player should expect to wait before starting to play.

b. Describe a simulation, using random numbers, that you could use to model this problem.

c. Do the simulation ten times and record the number of turns or rolls you needed to start play in each game. (For example, the sequence of rolls 4, 3, 3, 1, 6 means you start play on the fifth turn.)

d. Find the average number of turns needed to start during these ten games.

e. Combine your results from 4d with those of three other classmates, and determine the average number of turns a player should expect to wait.

5. Suppose each box of Wheaties® contains one letter from the word CHAMPION. The letters have been equally distributed in the boxes. The grand prize is awarded when you send in all eight letters.

a. Predict the number of boxes you would expect to buy to get all eight letters.

b. Describe a method of modeling this problem with the random number table at the end of the chapter.

c. Use your method to simulate winning the grand prize. Do this five times. Record your results.

d. What is the average number of boxes you will have to buy to win the grand prize?

e. Combine your results with those of several classmates. What is the overall average number of boxes needed to win the grand prize?

6. Simulate rolling a fair die by altering the random number generator routine. (See part 2 of **APPENDIX 8B**.) This routine will simulate rolling a die many times. Then you can display the results in a histogram. Do the simulation 12 times.

a. Make a table storing the results of each simulation for your 1188 rolls. (List how many 1's, 2's, 3's , and so on.)

Trial number	1's	2's	3's	4's	5's	6's	Proportion of 3's	Cumulative proportion of 3's
1								/99 =
2								/198 =
. . .								/297 =

b. What do you think the long-range pattern should be?

c. Make a graph of the *cumulative proportion of 3's versus the number of tosses*. Plot the points (*cumulative number of tosses, cumulative proportion of 3's*). Then plot four more points as you extend the domain of the graph to 2376, 3564, and 4752 trials by *adding* the data from three classmates. Would it make any difference if you were considering 5's instead of 3's? Explain.

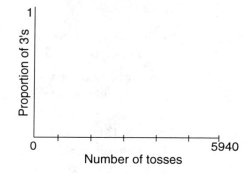

d. If you agree that the *experimental probability of rolling a 3, P(3)*, is the proportion of trials in which the 3 occurs after a very long run of trials, what is the P(3) for the die-roll experiment?

e. Ideally, what do you think P(3) should be? Explain.

7. a. Set your calculator for dot mode graphing. (See **APPENDIX 8C**.) What are the range and possible outcomes of the *y*-values generated by each equation?

   i. $y = 6$ Rand $- 2$ \qquad\qquad ii. $y =$ Int 3 Rand $+ 1$

b. Write a calculator routine using random numbers to generate graphs similar to those shown below.

   i. \qquad\qquad\qquad ii. \qquad\qquad\qquad iii.

8.   In many countries of the world, parents have traditionally depended on a son to help them out in their old age. Suppose an overcrowded country permits couples to have children until they have exactly one son.

   a.   Devise and describe a simulation for this problem. Use your simulation to determine the long-run average number of children in a family.

   b.   What is the long-run average number of girls in a family?

Section 8.2: Random Numbers in Two Dimensions

Maria can reach 1 m from her position at the corner of a table that measures 1 m by 1 m. Her sister Teresa teases her by dropping small candies randomly on the table. In this drawing, 12 of the 18 candies are within Maria's reach because they are inside the quarter circle pictured. (They are under the curve.) What happens if Teresa teases her with 200 candies? What happens in the long run?

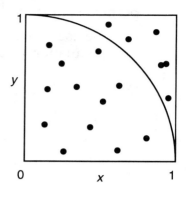

Sometimes you can model a probability situation geometrically. In this section, you will be using some ideas from geometry to calculate probabilities.

Calculator Candy Simulation Activity

Many of you probably have a sister or brother with whom you could play the candy game, but instead you will simulate this game on your calculator and keep track of the results.

a. Set a graphing window of [0, 1.5, 0, 0, 1, 0]. Enter and execute the program in **APPENDIX 8D**. Use $n = 200$ for the number of candies. The decimal answer you get is the ratio of $\dfrac{\text{number of points under the curve}}{200}$ and it will probably change every time you run the program because the candies land at random locations on the table.

It makes sense that this answer should have something to do with the area of the table and the area of the quarter circle. In other words, as the number of points increases, the ratio

$$\frac{\text{area under curve}}{\text{area of table}} \text{ should be near the ratio } \frac{\text{number of points under the curve}}{\text{total number of points}}.$$

$$\text{Or,} \frac{0.25\pi(1)^2}{1 \cdot 1} = \frac{\text{number of points under the curve}}{200}.$$

$$\text{Number of candies within reach} = 200 \cdot \frac{0.25\pi(1)^2}{1} = 157.$$

If you divide the "target" area by the total area, you can predict the ratio of those candies that land under the curve.

b. Simulate the game with 500 candies. How many of them land under the curve?

c. Theoretically, how many should land under the curve?

In the Problem Set, you will reverse the process and find unknown areas by using this same program.

Example 1: Many games use the sum of two dice to determine the next action. Suppose the first die rolled is green and the second one is white. What are the possible outcomes or sums when two dice are rolled?

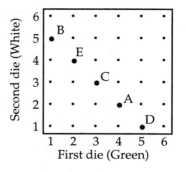

Solution: This two-dimensional graph pictures all possible outcomes when two dice are rolled. The five possible outcomes with a sum of 6 are identified. Point A, for example, represents the outcome with 4 on the first die and 2 on the second die. What does point B represent? How many different points would represent a sum of 11?

Problem Set 8.2

1. Consider rolling a green and a white die.

   a. How many different outcomes are possible for this two-dice experiment?

   b. How many different outcomes are possible in which there is a 4 on the green die? Draw a diagram to show the location of these points.

   c. How many different outcomes are possible in which there is a 2 or 3 on the white die? Describe the location of all of these points.

   d. How many different outcomes are possible in which there is an even number on the green die and a 5 on the white die?

2. Draw a graph on a grid like the one in Example 1 modeling the two-dice sums, and write equations in terms of x and y for each event.

   a. The dice sum to 9.

   b. The dice sum to 6.

   c. The dice have a difference of 1.

   d. Green + white = 6 and green − white = 2.

   e. Green + white ≤ 5.

3. Find the number of outcomes in each event, and write the fraction representing the ratio of this number to the 36 total possible outcomes.

    a. The dice sum to 9.
    b. The dice sum to 6.
    c. The dice have a difference of 1.
    d. Green + white = 6 and green – white = 2.
    e. Green + white ≤ 5.

4. At the right is a graph showing the results of a simulation after many trials.

    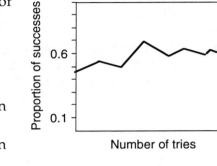

    a. Interpret the meaning of this graph.
    b. What is the long-range probability of success for this simulation?
    c. What would it mean if this proportion graph tended toward 1?
    d. What would it mean if this proportion graph tended toward 0?
    e. What is the range of values possible for numbers representing probabilities?

5. a. What is the total area of the square?

    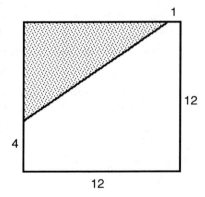

    b. What is the area of the shaded region?
    c. Over the long run, what portion of random points will land in the shaded area if both the x- and y-coordinates are determined by 0 < Rand < 12?
    d. What is the probability that any given random point will land in the shaded area?
    e. What is the probability that any given random point will not land in the shaded area?
    f. What is the probability that any given random point will land on another specific random point? On a specific line?

6. This is the square root curve for all x between 0 and 10.

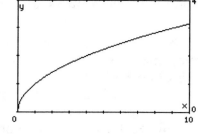

  a. Use the average value of the function to find the area under the curve. (Hint: Return to the chapter on functions.)

  b. What is the area of the rectangle?

  c. What part of the rectangle should be under the curve?

  d. Use the program in **APPENDIX 8E** to approximate the area under the curve.

  e. Compare your answers to 6a, c, and d.

7. Suppose x is a random number between 0 and 8, and y is a random number between 0 and 8. (The variables x and y are not necessarily integers.)

  a. Write a symbolic statement showing the event that the *sum of x and y* ≤ 6.

  b. Draw a two-dimensional picture of all possible outcomes and shade the event *sum of x and y* ≤ 6.

  c. Use a picture to determine the probability that the *sum of x and y* ≤ 6.

8. You and your best friend agree to meet between 3:00 and 4:00 this afternoon in the computer room. The first one to arrive will wait 10 min for the other and then leave. Arrival times are random within the hour.

  a. Draw a two-dimensional picture of all possible outcomes and shade the event that you will meet.

  b. What is the probability that the two of you will meet?

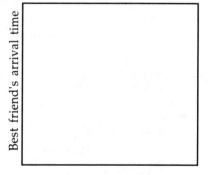

Your arrival time

9. Suppose your mom and dad have a joint checking account with a total of $400, and you have talked with both of them about the need for cash. Tomorrow, unknown to each other, they each write a check for a random amount less than $400. Find the probability for each event.

  a. More than $80 remains in the account.

  b. The account is overdrawn.

  c. The account is overdrawn, but by less than $100.

Section 8.3: Some Counting Techniques

When the outcome of an event cannot be completely determined in advance, you use probability to describe the likelihood that the event will occur. Until now you have defined probability by looking at long-range results of simulations. Probabilities that are based on trials and observations are called **experimental probabilities**. Sometimes, however, it's possible to determine the **theoretical probability** of an event by counting the number of successes and comparing this number to the total number of trials. But in order to do this you need to be able to count these trials. In this section, you will develop some strategies for counting without actually counting. You will also develop strategies to calculate the different ways particular outcomes of random selections can occur.

If $P(E)$ represents the probability of an event, then

$$P(E) = \frac{\text{the number of different ways an event can occur}}{\text{the total number of possible outcomes}}$$

Example 1: These are the results of a student survey regarding an important issue in the school.

Reaction	9th grade	10th grade	11th grade	12th grade	Totals
In favor	65	55	79	56	255
Not sure	25	34	17	13	89
Opposed	58	42	88	91	279
Totals	148	131	184	160	623

a. What is the probability that a student is a senior?
b. What is the probability that a student is opposed to the issue?
c. What is the probability that a senior is opposed to the issue?
d. What is the probability that a student is not sure about the issue?
e. What is the probability that a student favoring the issue will be in the ninth grade?

Solution:

a. $\dfrac{\text{number of seniors}}{\text{number of students}} = \dfrac{160}{623} \approx 0.257$

b. $\dfrac{\text{number of students opposed}}{\text{number of students}} = \dfrac{279}{623} \approx 0.448$

c. $\dfrac{\text{number of seniors opposed}}{\text{number of seniors}} = \dfrac{91}{160} \approx 0.569$

d. $\dfrac{\text{number of students not sure}}{\text{number of students}} = \dfrac{89}{623} \approx 0.143$

e. $\dfrac{\text{number of ninth grade students in favor}}{\text{number of students in favor}} = \dfrac{65}{255} \approx 0.255$

Example 2: Suppose a red chip, a green chip, and a blue chip are in a bag. One chip at a time is drawn and recorded, and *not* placed back in the bag. How many different arrangements (**permutations**) are possible for the final outcome?

Solution: A tree diagram will help you keep track of all the possible outcomes. If you follow the top branch, the result is RGB, which means red, then green, and then blue have been selected. The six different branches give you all six possible permutations:

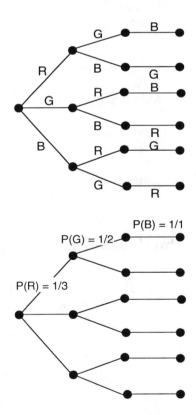

RGB	RBG	GRB
GBR	BRG	BGR

Because each branch is equally likely, the probability of any branch occurring is $\frac{1}{6}$. This means the top branch (RGB) will occur $\frac{1}{6}$ of the time. Notice the three probabilities listed on the top branch. What is the meaning of $P(R) = \frac{1}{3}$, $P(G) = \frac{1}{2}$, and $P(B) = \frac{1}{1}$? Find a connection between these individual probabilities and the probability of the entire branch.

Loops Activity

This activity works best with a group of four students. You will need three strings, each 24-in. long. One group member needs to be the holder, and the other three group members are takers.

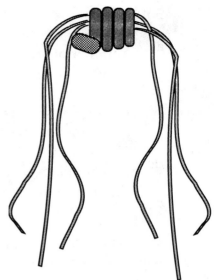

a. The holder holds the three pieces of string in the middle so that the other group members can't see which ends are from the same string.

b. Each of the other group members should grasp in his left hand an end of a string coming from the left side of the holder's hand and in his right hand an end of the string coming from the right side of the holder's hand.

c. Count the number of loops formed after you untangle the arrangement as much as you can (without letting go of the ends of the strings).

d. Repeat steps a–c several times. Each time count the number of loops that have formed.

e. Make a guess at the probabilities for each outcome.

f. Find a method to calculate the probabilities associated with each possible outcome.

g. Compare your calculated probabilities with those from other groups.

Problem Set 8.3

1. A recipe calls for four ingredients: flour, baking powder, shortening, and milk (F, B, S, M), but there are no directions as to the order in which they should be combined.

    a. How many different arrangements are there?
    b. What is the probability that milk is first?
    c. What is the probability that flour is first and shortening is second?
    d. What is the probability that the order is FBSM?
    e. What is the probability that the order isn't FBSM?
    f. What is the probability that flour and milk are next to each other?

2. Draw a tree diagram that pictures all possible equally-likely outcomes if a coin is flipped as specified.

    a. Twice   b. Three times   c. Four times

3. How many different equally-likely outcomes are possible if a coin is flipped as specified.

    a. Twice   b. Three times   c. Four times

    d. Five times   e. Ten times   f. n times

4. Three students are auditioning for different parts in a play. Each student has a 50% chance of success. Use the tree at the right to answer 4a and 4b.

    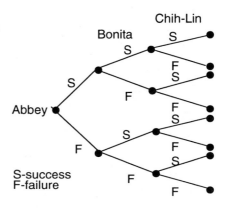

    a. Find the probability that all three students will be successful.

    b. Find the probability that exactly two students will be successful.

    c. If you know that exactly two have been successful, but not which pair, what is the probability that Chih-Lin was successful?

5. You are totally unprepared for a true/false quiz and you decide to randomly guess on each problem without reading the problem. There are four questions. Make a tree diagram and use it to find the probabilities in 5a–5e.

    a. P(none correct)

    b. P(just one correct)

    c. P(exactly two correct)

    d. P(exactly three correct)

    e. P(all four correct)

    f. What should be the sum of the five probabilities in 5a–5e?

    g. If a passing grade means at least three correct, what is your probability of passing the quiz?

6. Use the histogram pictured at the right for 6a–6d.

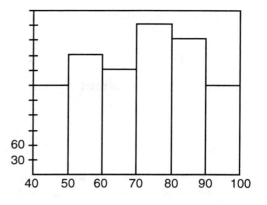

a. Find the frequency of the group scoring from 80 to 90.

b. Find the sum of all the frequencies.

c. Find P(a score between 80 and 90).

d. Find P(a score is not between 80 and 90).

7. The registered voters represented in the table below have been interviewed and rated. Assume this sample represents the voting public. Find each probability.

a. P(A randomly chosen voter will be over 45 and liberal.)

b. P(A randomly chosen voter will be conservative.)

c. P(A randomly chosen voter will be conservative if under 30.)

d. P(A randomly chosen voter will be under 30 if conservative.)

	Liberal	Conservative	Totals
Age under 30	210	145	
Age 30–45	235	220	
Age over 45	280	410	
Totals			

8. The proportion of phones manufactured at each of three sites M1, M2, and M3 are 0.2, 0.35, and 0.45 respectively. The diagram also shows some of the proportions of defective (D) and good (G) phones. The top branch indicates that 0.2, or 20%, of the phones are manufactured at plant M1. The proportion of these phones that are defective is 0.05, or 5%. Therefore, 0.95, or 95%, of these phones are good. The probability that a randomly selected phone is both from site M1 and defective is (0.20)(0.05) = 0.01 or 1%.

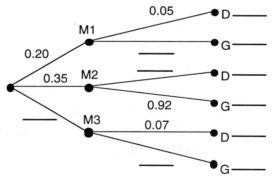

a. Draw the diagram and fill in the blanks.

b. Find P(a site M2 phone is defective).

c. Find P(a randomly chosen phone is defective).

d. Find P(a phone is manufactured at site M2 if you already know it is defective).

9. The Detroit Pistons and Chicago Bulls are tied and time has run out in the game. However, Ali Oop of the Pistons is at the free-throw line with two shots. He is an 83% free-throw shooter. Make a tree diagram and use it to find each probability.

    a. P(overtime)
    b. P(no overtime and Pistons win)
    c. P(no overtime and Pistons win by 2 points)

10. Draw a tree diagram to represent the gender of the children in a four-child family. Label the outcome at the end of each branch, for example, FMMF. (There should be 16 branches.) Locate all branches that represent a family with exactly two girls. What is the probability that there are exactly two girls in a four-child family?

11. A 6-in. cube painted on the outside is cut into 27 smaller congruent cubes. Find the probability that, if one of the smaller cubes is picked at random, it will have the specified number of pointed faces.

    a. Exactly one.
    b. Exactly two.
    c. Exactly three.
    d. No painted face.

Section 8.4: Waiting and Expected Value

"You need to roll a 6 on a standard die before you can start the game." This situation is similar to ones that occur very often in nature as well as in daily life. For many events, there are probabilities of success or failure. An event may need to be repeated more than once before a success occurs. In some cases, you may never succeed. Imagine rolling a die 10,000 times and not getting a 6. It's unlikely, but not impossible.

Imagine that you are sitting near the rapids on the bank of a rushing river. Salmon are attempting to swim upstream. They must jump out of the water to pass the rapids. While you are sitting on the bank, you observe 100 salmon attempt to pass the rapids and, of those, 35 succeed. Having no other information, you can conclude that the probability of success is 35%.

What is the probability that a salmon will make it on its second attempt? Note that this requires two conditions be met: that it fails on the first jump and that it succeeds on the second. In the diagram, you see that this probability is $(0.65)(0.35) = 0.2275$ or 22.75%. To determine the probability that the salmon makes it on the first or second jump, you would sum the probability of making it on the first jump and the probability of making it on the second jump. The sum is $0.35 + 0.2275 = 0.5775$ or about 58%.

S = 0.35
S = 0.35
F = 0.65
F = 0.65

Example 1: "Last Minute" Larry has a half-hour lunch break before his afternoon classes. He has neither studied for his vocabulary quiz nor completed his math homework. If he doesn't study his vocabulary, he will likely score only 13 out of 20 points. But if he spends the half hour studying, he could boost his score to 16 points. His math teacher randomly collects homework from 1/3 of the class each day. If the assignment is complete, he will score 10 points. Otherwise, he will get a zero. It will take Larry the entire lunch period to complete his math homework, so he must choose to do one or the other. Should he study for his vocabulary quiz or do his math homework?

Solution: If Larry studies for the vocabulary quiz, he will get the 16 points in English, but he will score nothing in math. On the other hand, if he chooses to complete the math, he will score 13 points in English, but he will have a 1/3 chance of scoring 10 points in math.

Preliminary Edition

	English points	+	Math points	=	Total points	
Study English	16	+	0	=	16 points	
Do math	13	+	0	=	13 points	or
	13	+	10	=	23 points	

To evaluate the math homework options, multiply the probability of each event times the value of the event and find the sum. The result is $(2/3)(13) + (1/3)(23) = 16.33$ points. Larry could never actually get this number of points, but it serves as an indicator that in this case time spent on math has a slightly higher value (16.33) than time spent on vocabulary (16).

Example 2: Pablo really likes purple gumballs. He approaches a nearly-empty gumball machine in which there are eight gumballs remaining and only two of them are purple. In the worst case, Pablo may have to buy seven gumballs before he gets a purple one. Assuming they come in a random order, how many should he *expect* to buy?

Solution: A simulation of this situation will give you a value for the experimental probability. You could do this with eight pennies or eight pieces of paper, but it may take quite a while to get an accurate estimate. A programmed simulation on the calculator is much faster. (See **APPENDIX 8F** for a gumball simulation program.)

You can also find the theoretical probability for this simulation. Copy the tree diagram below showing some of the probabilities of success and failure, and determine the probability of each segment.

Find the probability of each of the seven branches. Do they sum to one?

Pablo would expect to buy one gumball 25% of the time, and exactly two gumballs about 21% of the time. (Find this on your tree diagram.) That is, if there were 100 different gumball machines, each with their own eight gumballs, he would expect to get a purple gumball on the first try with 25 of the machines. He would expect it to take two gumballs on 21 of the machines, and three gumballs on 18 of them.

To find the **expected value**, give each branch a value, which is the number of gumballs he would need to purchase in order to get a purple one, and multiply this value by the probability of the branch. Then find the sum of all the branches. What is the expected value of the average number of gumballs purchased?

$$(0.25)(1) + (0.21)(2) + (0.18)(3) + \ldots = \,?$$

> The **expected value** is an average value found by multiplying the value of each event by its probability and then summing all of the products.

Pennies on a Grid Activity

Darken some of the lines on graph paper to form one-inch squares. Throw a handful of pennies on the paper. Record the number of coins that land on the paper. Also record the number of coins that do not cover any darkened line. (The example shows two such coins.) Repeat this several times to find the experimental probability of landing completely within a square.

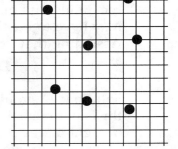

Now imagine a game where you must toss a penny on the paper until one falls within a square. Determine the average number of single pennies tossed until you would be successful (to the nearest 0.1). Write an argument to convince someone that you have found the correct value.

Problem Set 8.4

1. Sly Gamer offers to play a game with Les Mathhe. They will each roll a die. If the sum is greater than seven, Les scores five points. If the sum is less than eight, Sly scores four points.

    a. Find a friend and play the game ten times. (See **APPENDIX 8G** if you have no dice.) Record the final score.

    b. What is the experimental probability that Les will win?

    c. Draw a simple tree diagram of this situation showing the theoretical probabilities.

    d. If you consider this game from Les's point of view, his winning value is *positive five* and his losing value is *negative four*. What is the expected value of the game from his point of view?

    e. Suggest a different distribution of points that would favor neither player.

2. Dr. Will Sayphly works quite often with patients who are highly contagious. He has chosen a method of protection that research has claimed "is 98% effective when used correctly."

a. What is the probability of no failure in 10 correct uses? In 20 uses?

b. What is the expected number of uses before one failure?

c. Enter and execute the program in **APPENDIX 8H** and give the expected value after 99 failures.

d. According to your data what is the greatest number before failure and the smallest number before failure? (You may want to sort the data first.)

e. Sketch a histogram of the data and give a one- or two-sentence summary of the information in the graph.

3. Rocky Role has organized an outdoor concert. If the weather is good, Rocky will make $400,000. If the weather is bad, he will have to pay the bands and refund all the tickets. This means that he will lose $1,000,000. According to the weather report, there is a 40% chance of rain.

a. Make a tree diagram of the outcomes and label the value of each branch.

b. What is his expected value?

c. If he cancels the concert right now, he will only lose $100,000. What should he do? Write an argument to convince Rocky that you are giving him good advice.

4. Research has shown that a Blue-Footed Booby has a 47% chance of surviving from egg to adulthood. You have found a nest of four eggs.

a. What is the probability that all four will survive to adulthood?

b. What is the probability that none of the four will survive to adulthood?

c. How many birds would you expect to survive?

5. You are given the following information about the algebra enrollment in a local high school: 16% sophomore male, 24% sophomore female, 32% junior male, and 28% junior female.

    a. What is the probability that the algebra book you found under the tree belongs to a junior?

    b. If you know that a book belongs to a male, what is the probability that it belongs to a junior?

    c. If there are 100 students, how many of them are male?

    d. How many algebra students are male juniors?

    e. Do these last two pieces of information agree with your answer to 5b? Why or why not?

6. Return to the data collected in the Medical Testing Activity in Section 8.1.

    a. Based on the collected data, find the each percentage.
        i.   People who don't have the disease for whom the test is inaccurate.
        ii. People who don't have the disease for whom the test is accurate.
        iii. People who have the disease for whom the test is accurate.
        iv. People who have the disease for whom the test is inaccurate.

    b. What is the probability that the test will indicate a person has the disease?

    c. If the test indicates a person has the disease, what is the probability that this person actually has the disease?

    d. Draw a tree diagram which shows a 20% probability of having the disease, and a 10% probability of the test results being inaccurate.

    e. How do the theoretical probabilities you calculated using the tree diagram compare with experimental probabilities from your data?

7. The tree diagram shows a game played by two players.

    a. Find an *x*-value that gives nearly equal value to each player.

    b. Interpret the information in the graph and design a game that would match these probabilities. (You may use coins, dice, spinners, whatever.) Be detailed about the rules of the game and the scoring of points.

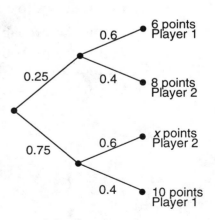

8. Create your own problem, which you think would make a good assessment question, that covers the material you have studied so far in this chapter. Write out the complete solution to your problem and explain why you believe it to be a good problem. Note: Please make sure that it is a problem or question, not just an explanation or description.

Section 8.5: Chromatic Numbering

A probability tree diagram is an application of graph theory. **Graph theory** involves diagramming a problem situation using vertices and edges. The diagram helps you find a mathematical solution. Graph theory principles can be applied to many different types of problems. It is a relatively new field of study compared to geometry or algebra. Many problems, old and new, are being solved each year using these new theorems and ideas. These problems range from sixteenth century puzzles to the design of transcontinental computer networks. In the rest of this chapter you will be introduced to a few basic techniques of graph theory.

In scientific or medical research, it is often important to classify and identify according to linked or shared attributes. The process of grouping a graph theory network is called **Chromatic Numbering**. In this section, you will find out why it has this unusual name.

Conflict Resolution Activity

Part 1: Fay Cilitator is assigning new groups in her class. She has gathered the following information:

- Art and Bao fight when they are put together.
- Carlos and Dan joke all the time and never get any work done when they are together.
- Eyota and Fadil just don't like each other.
- Greg doesn't get along with anybody in band, which includes Art, Dan, Eyota, Hisa, Isa, and Jill.
- Kono and Lusita always get A's and shouldn't be in the same group.
- Masud, Nam, Oto, and Panya are the class leaders, and no two of them should be in the same group.
- Quincy can't concentrate if he is in the same group with Lusita, Panya, or Ursala.
- Rudo, Sue, and Tai talk only about sports if any two of them are together.
- Vick and Winona just stare at each other if they are in the same group.
- Zahur doesn't like people whose first name begins with a vowel.
- Fadil, Hisa, and Quincy haven't worked together since that incident in science class last year.
- Sue and Lusita both like the same guy, so they can't work together; nor can you put either one with Dan.
- Everybody knows why Winona shouldn't work with Ursala.

Can you make four groups of six students and retain all the *dis*memberships listed above? Try this before reading further.

Below is a graph of the information. Each vertex (person) is connected with a line (called an **edge**) to any other person that he or she should *not* be grouped with. For example, you can see that Eyota (located in about the center of the graph) should not be grouped with Greg, Fadil, or Zahur. To use this diagram, you want to look at the information one piece at a time in order to make each connection. Sometimes edges will cross over each other, but this is not a problem. Don't be concerned about the beauty of your graph, and keep in mind that there can be many different correct answers.

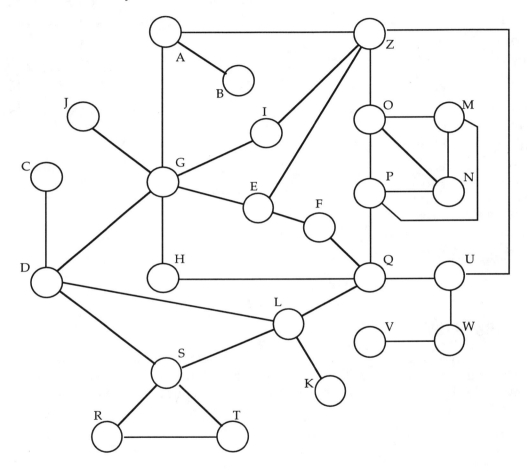

Part 2: To begin, assign a color or number to a person. It may help to start with the most complicated part of the graph first. Each point (vertex) connected to this one must have a different color. Vertices can be the same color provided they are not connected with an edge. A possible solution is on the next page, but do not look at it until you have come up with your own grouping.

There are many solutions. It is unlikely that your solution is the same as the one shown below. The objective is to find a solution that satisfies all of the restrictions.

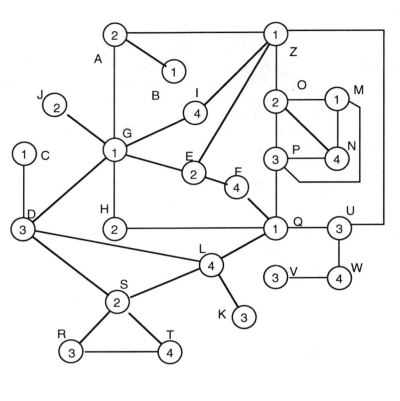

Group 1

Bao
Carlos
Greg
Masud
Quincy
Zahur

Group 2

Art
Eyota
Hisa
Jill
Sue
Oto

Group 3

Dan
Kono
Panya
Rudo
Ursala
Vick

Group 4

Isa
Fadil
Nam
Tim
Lusita
Winona

Visiting Colleges Activity

Rhoda S. Say is planning to visit some colleges while on spring break. She gathers the following flight information. What is the cheapest fare that allows Rhoda to fly from her home, visit every school, and return to her home?

	USC	Oberlin	Yale	U of M	SMU
Home	$250	$140	$128	$158	$212
SMU	$176	$130	$132	$175	
U of M	$250	$108	$112		
Yale	$315	$150			
Oberlin	$235				

Draw a graph showing the flight path and find the total cost of the trip. Explain why you are convinced there is no cheaper path.

Problem Set 8.5

1. Trace the map below on your paper. Find the smallest number of colors needed to color it. If two regions share any of the same border, they cannot be the same color. Two regions may be the same color, however, if they only meet at a corner.

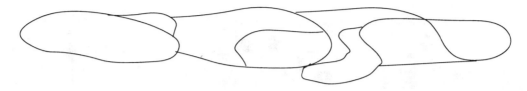

2. For 2a–2d below, design a map with 10 regions that can be colored using the same restrictions as stated in Problem 1.

   a. Use only 2 colors.
   b. Requires 3 colors.
   c. Requires 4 colors.
   d. Requires 5 colors.
   e. Do you think there is a limit to the number of colors needed to color a very complex map? Give an argument to support your reasoning.

Problems 1 and 2 are related to the Four-Color Conjecture: Not more than four colors are necessary in order to color a map of a country (divided into regions) in such a way that no two contiguous regions are of the same color. This conjecture was first investigated around 1853 when Francis Guthrie, a graduate student at University College, London, was drawing a map of England. Guthrie noticed that four colors seemed to be sufficient to distinguish the counties and wondered if there was a general theorem. Over the years, many mathematicians have devoted much effort to the Four-Color Conjecture. Out of this work has grown much of what is now known as Graph Theory. In 1976, Kenneth Appel and Wolfgang Haken, who were mathematicians at the University of Illinois, said they had a computer-generated "proof" of the conjecture. Many mathematicians do not consider this to be an adequate proof. For them the Four-Color Conjecture is still a conjecture, not a theorem.

3. The chromatic number of a graph is the fewest number of colors needed so that no connected vertices share the same color. Copy the graphs below on your paper. Find the chromatic number for each graph.

   a.

   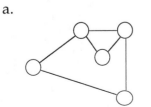

   b.

   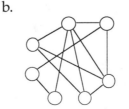

   c.

   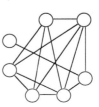

4. Design an exam schedule for spring semester. Assume the fourteen students below are representative of the entire student body. If you can avoid all conflicts within this group, the schedule will work for the entire school. What are the fewest number of time blocks needed to make an exam schedule with no conflicts? (According to this table, student 01 is currently enrolled in classes M2, E2, H2, and S1.)

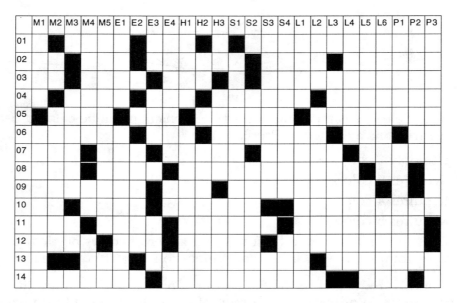

(Hint: Arrange the points on your paper as in the diagram below.)

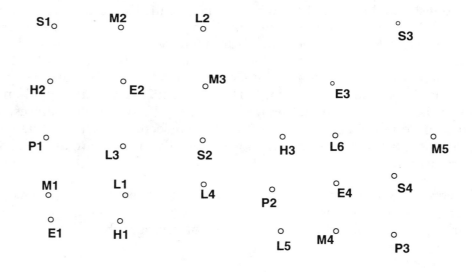

Section 8.6: The Transition Matrix

Imagine that you attend a meeting and each person there shakes hands with everyone else in the room. This situation creates a number of interesting problems and applications. You can draw a diagram of this handshake problem using a graph made up of a finite collection of edges and vertices. Because each vertex is connected by an edge to every other vertex (everyone shakes hands with everyone else), the handshake graphs are **complete graphs**. Find the chromatic number of each graph pictured at the right, and make a conjecture about the chromatic number of a complete graph.

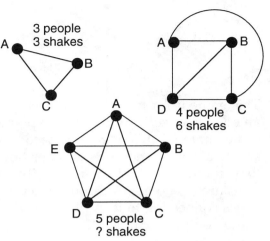

The graphs pictured above representing three people and four people are **planar**. The graph representing five people is **nonplanar** because you cannot draw all the edges without forming intersections at points other than the vertices A, B, C, D, and E. This is true even though in graph theory you may move vertices to different positions and draw a connecting edge as a curve.
To demonstrate planarity of a graph, you only need one two-dimensional picture where the edges do not intersect.

Graphs have many uses. Maps, airline systems, and transportation networks can involve working with graphs. There are also graph games like *Dot to Dot* or *Sprouts*, which you may have played.

Sprouts Activity

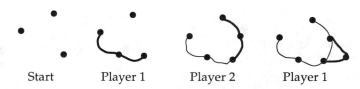

Start	Player 1	Player 2	Player 1

This game is for two players. Start by drawing three points. The first player draws an edge between any two of the points (vertices) and places another point somewhere on this edge. The second player then draws another edge between any two points and adds another point somewhere on the new edge.
Play continues in this manner with the two players alternating turns. The two rules are (1) no edges can intersect, and (2) a vertex cannot have more than three edges connecting to it. A player loses by not being able to make a play. Mark each game you play with an "F" if the first player wins or an "S" if the second player wins.

After playing several games, consider these questions:

a. Count the number of vertices in each completed game and record this number next to the game. Form a conjecture about the number of vertices and whether the first or second player wins. What is the fewest number of vertices possible in a completed game? What is the greatest number of vertices possible?

b. Is this a fair game? If not, does the advantage lie with the player who moves first or the player who moves second? Explain your reasoning.

Two vertices are **adjacent** if they are joined by an edge. For example, each vertex in Graph 1 is adjacent to every other vertex.

Graph 1   Graph 2

Graph 2 is a multigraph because it contains two vertices (V_1 and V_2) that are connected by more than one edge. As graphs get more and more complicated, it is difficult to keep track of which vertices are connected. One simple device to keep track of this information is the **adjacency matrix**.

The entry 1 in the matrix for Graph 1 means V_2 and V_3 are joined. In the matrix for Graph 2, the marked 0 means V_2 and V_3 are not joined. Given a graph, you can complete an adjacency matrix, and with an adjacency matrix you can draw a graph.

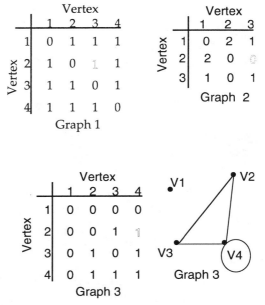

Notice the number of vertices in Graph 3 is defined by the dimensions of its matrix. This matrix has four rows and four columns, and, therefore, the graph has four vertices. Each 1 indicates an edge between the vertices and each 0 indicates no edge between the vertices. The marked 1 is in row two and column four and indicates an edge between V_2 and V_4.

Graphs and Matrices Activity

Part 1: Create a graph and an adjacency matrix that represent the following information:

A collection of converters is used to change documents from one word processor format to another. You do not have a universal translator, but rather a set of four translators. Translator 1 will convert documents to and from formats A, B, and F. Translator 2 converts between formats B and D. Translator 3 can change formats to and from D, E and F. Finally translator 4 will convert between formats C and E.

Part 2: Create a graph and a story using all the information in this adjacency matrix.

	Abe	Blake	Carl	Donna	Eula
Abe	0	1	0	0	1
Blake	1	0	1	0	0
Carl	0	1	0	1	0
Donna	0	0	1	0	1
Eula	1	0	0	1	0

All tables of information can be considered as matrices, and they can be used to hold different kinds of information. The entries in the following matrix indicate distances between Washington DC, St. Louis, Seattle, New Orleans, and Las Vegas.

	DC	SL	S	NO	LV
DC	0	862	2721	1099	2420
SL	862	0	2135	698	1620
S	2721	2135	0	2590	1180
NO	1099	698	2590	0	1732
LV	2420	1620	1180	1732	0

If you draw a map with the distances indicated, you will have the graph associated with this matrix.

Example 1: Draw a directed graph (the edges will have direction) and complete a corresponding matrix that pictures this transition: each year 10% of the California population moves to another state, and 5% of the outsiders move to California.

Solution: The edges of the directed graph indicate this transition. For instance, 0.90 of the Californians stay in the state from one year to the next.

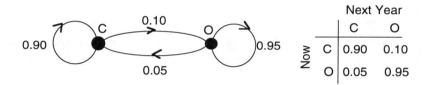

		Next Year	
		C	O
Now	C	0.90	0.10
	O	0.05	0.95

The matrix shows the same situation. The vertical identifier to the left of the matrix represents the present condition and the horizontal identifier above the matrix indicates the next condition after the transition.

Problem Set 8.6

1. Copy this map of the United States onto your paper and put vertices at the five cities named in the reading for this section. Draw the network of edges that connects the cities and has the shortest total length.

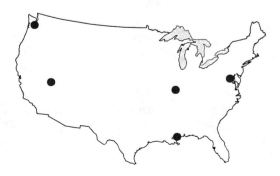

2. Draw planar versions of these solid figures, ABCD and EFGHIJKL, using the named vertices and edges.

a.

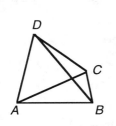

b.

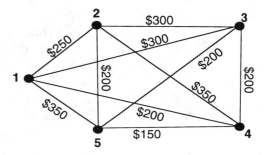

3. a. How many edges are there in the graph at the right?

   b. Create a matrix that shows the cost of one-way airline tickets between each pair of cities.

   c. How many different routes through each city start with city 1 and end with city 1? (No segment is used more than once in a route.)

   d. Which route is cheapest for a salesperson who wants to start at city 1, visit every other city, and return to where he started?

4. Suppose 20 million people live in California and 220 million live in the United States but outside of California. If the total population remains at 240 million and the year-to-year transition stays the same as in Example 1, find the number of people who live

$$\begin{bmatrix} \text{in CA} & \text{out of CA} \end{bmatrix}$$

   a. next year
   b. 2 yr from now
   c. 3 yr from now

5. Developing countries have a problem; too many people are moving to the cities. A study of a developing country shows that in a given year 10% of the rural population moves to the city, but only 1% of the urban population goes back to the country.

   a. Draw a transition graph that represents this study.

   b. Develop a transition matrix for this study.

   c. If 16 million of the country's 25 million people live in the city initially, find:

   $$\begin{bmatrix} \text{urban dwellers} & \text{rural dwellers} \end{bmatrix}$$

   i. next year   ii. in 2 yr   iii. in 3 yr

6. A mouse enters a maze at position 1 and proceeds through the maze as shown in the directed graph. At each decision point the mouse is equally likely to choose either path. Find the probability that the mouse will get to the cheese.

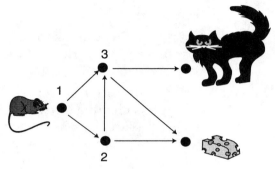

Section 8.7: Matrix Operations

You have solved this problem in previous sections using several different strategies. Now you will see how you can use matrices to solve it.

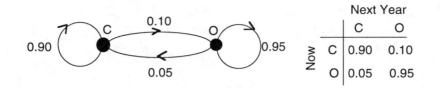

This look at the solution to the California Problem will help you to understand matrix multiplication. Assume that in the United States there are 20 million people that live in California and 220 million that live outside California. Also assume that the total population of the United States stays at 240 million and the year-to-year transition rates remain the same. Find the number of people [in CA   outside CA]

a. next year   b. two years from now   c. three years from now

$$\begin{bmatrix} 20 & 220 \end{bmatrix} \begin{bmatrix} 0.90 & 0.10 \\ 0.05 & 0.95 \end{bmatrix} = [\text{ in CA}\quad\text{outside CA }]$$

The initial matrix, $\begin{bmatrix} 20 & 220 \end{bmatrix}$, has one row and two columns and is called a 1×2 matrix ("one by two matrix"). Call this matrix with dimensions 1×2, matrix A or [A].

The transition matrix $\begin{bmatrix} 0.90 & 0.10 \\ 0.05 & 0.95 \end{bmatrix}$ has two rows and two columns and is called a 2×2 matrix. The four individual entries can be identified by their row and column numbers. For example, 0.10 is in row one and column two. If you label the transition matrix as matrix B, [B], 0.10 can be identified as entry B_{12}, indicating 0.10 is in the first row and the second column of [B]. The top row of [B] represents the transitions in the present California population and the bottom row represents the transitions in the present non-California population. See how this relates to the directed graph above.

You can define matrix multiplication by looking at how you calculate the next year's population numbers. The next year's California population will be $20 \cdot 0.90 + 220 \cdot 0.05$, or 29 million people, because 90% of the 20 million Californians stay and 5% of the 220 million non-Californians move in. You can think of this as multiplying the two entries in the row $[A] = \begin{bmatrix} 20 & 220 \end{bmatrix}$ by the two entries in the first column of [B] and adding them together. The answer, 29, is entry C_{11} in the answer matrix [C].

$$\begin{bmatrix} 20 & 220 \end{bmatrix} \begin{bmatrix} \textbf{0.90} & \textbf{0.10} \\ \textbf{0.05} & \textbf{0.95} \end{bmatrix} = \begin{bmatrix} 29 & \text{out of Calif.} \end{bmatrix}$$

Likewise, next year's population outside California will be $20 \cdot 0.10 + 220 \cdot 0.95$, or 211 million people, because 10% of the Californians move out and 95% of the non-Californians stay out. Again this is the sum of the products of the row entries in [A] with the second column entries of [B]. The answer, 211, is entry C_{12} in the answer matrix [C].

$$\begin{bmatrix} 20 & 220 \end{bmatrix} \begin{bmatrix} \textbf{0.90} & \textbf{0.10} \\ \textbf{0.05} & \textbf{0.95} \end{bmatrix} = \begin{bmatrix} 29 & 211 \end{bmatrix}$$

The equation below gives you the populations in the year following.

$$\begin{bmatrix} 29 & 211 \end{bmatrix} \begin{bmatrix} \textbf{0.90} & \textbf{0.10} \\ \textbf{0.05} & \textbf{0.95} \end{bmatrix} = \begin{bmatrix} \textbf{36.65} & \textbf{203.35} \end{bmatrix}$$

Entry C_{11} of the answer matrix is the sum of the products of the entries in row 1 of [A] and the entries in the first column of [B]. Entry C_{12} of the answer matrix is found by multiplying the entries in the first row of [A] by the entries in the second column of [B].

You can continue this process and find the populations three years from now by using the **Answer**, in another matrix multiplication.

$$\begin{bmatrix} 36.65 & 203.35 \end{bmatrix} \begin{bmatrix} \textbf{0.90} & \textbf{0.10} \\ \textbf{0.05} & \textbf{0.95} \end{bmatrix} = \begin{bmatrix} C_{11} & C_{12} \end{bmatrix}$$

> The entry C_{ij} of the answer matrix of a product of two matrices is the sum the products of the entries in row i of the first matrix with the entries in column j of the second matrix.

To find the value for entry C_{11}, you sum the products of the entries in the first row of the first matrix with the entries in the first column of the second matrix. To find the value for entry C_{12}, you sum the products of the entries in the first row of the first matrix with the entries in the second column of the second matrix.

Word to Word Activity

In this activity you will use the adjacency matrix you created in Part 1 of the Graphs and Matrices Activity. The problem was this:

A collection of converters is used to change documents from one word processor format to another. You do not have a universal translator, but rather a set of four translators that each handle some conversions. Translator 1 will convert documents to and from formats A, B, and F. Translator 2 converts between formats B and D. Translator 3 can change formats to and from D, E and F. Finally, translator 4 will convert between formats C and E.

Your matrix should look like the one in the center below. Call this transition matrix [M]. What does the 1 at position M_{24} mean? Consider an initial condition matrix that shows one document from word processor A, [1 0 0 0 0 0]. Multiply this matrix by [M] and you get the answer matrix on the right. What is the meaning of the 1 in the second column of the answer matrix?

$$[1\,0\,0\,0\,0\,0] \begin{bmatrix} 0 & 1 & 0 & 0 & 0 & 1 \\ 1 & 0 & 0 & 1 & 0 & 1 \\ 0 & 0 & 0 & 0 & 1 & 0 \\ 0 & 1 & 0 & 0 & 1 & 1 \\ 0 & 0 & 1 & 1 & 0 & 1 \\ 1 & 1 & 0 & 1 & 1 & 0 \end{bmatrix} = [0\,1\,0\,0\,0\,1]$$

Multiply the answer matrix by the same translation matrix. Repeat this process until you get a 1 in the third column of the answer matrix. What does it mean that it took three multiplications to get a 1 in column three?

Problem Set 8.7

1. Find the next year's populations in the California problem by multiplying these matrices.

$$\begin{bmatrix} 36.65 & 203.35 \end{bmatrix} \begin{bmatrix} 0.90 & 0.10 \\ 0.05 & 0.95 \end{bmatrix} = \begin{bmatrix} CA & non\text{-}CA \end{bmatrix}$$

2. Suppose the following trends continue for a few years. Of two-car families, 88% remain two-car families in the following year and 12% become one-car families in the following year. Of one-car families, 72% remain one-car families and 28% become two-car families. Presently 4800 families have one car and 4200 have two cars.

   a. Draw a transition graph of this situation.

   b. What 1×2 matrix pictures the present situation? (A_{11} should represent one-car families.)

   c. What 2×2 transition matrix can be used to solve this problem?

   d. Write a matrix equation for this transition.

   e. Find the $\begin{bmatrix} \text{one-car} & \text{two-car} \end{bmatrix}$ distribution for one year from now.

   f. Find the $\begin{bmatrix} \text{one-car} & \text{two-car} \end{bmatrix}$ distribution for two years from now.

3. Invent a story for the following equation.

$$\begin{bmatrix} 20 & 220 \end{bmatrix} + \begin{bmatrix} 2 & 11 \end{bmatrix} = \begin{bmatrix} 22 & 231 \end{bmatrix}$$

4. Find the value of each missing variable.

   a. $\begin{bmatrix} 13 & 23 \end{bmatrix} + \begin{bmatrix} -6 & 31 \end{bmatrix} = \begin{bmatrix} x & y \end{bmatrix}$

   b. $\begin{bmatrix} 0.90 & 0.10 \\ 0.05 & 0.95 \end{bmatrix} \cdot \begin{bmatrix} 0.90 & 0.10 \\ 0.05 & 0.95 \end{bmatrix} = \begin{bmatrix} C_{11} & C_{12} \\ C_{21} & C_{22} \end{bmatrix}$

   c. $\begin{bmatrix} 18 & -23 \\ 5.4 & 32.2 \end{bmatrix} + \begin{bmatrix} -2.4 & 12.2 \\ 5.3 & 10 \end{bmatrix} = \begin{bmatrix} a & b \\ c & d \end{bmatrix}$

   d. $10 \cdot \begin{bmatrix} 18 & -23 \\ 5.4 & 32.2 \end{bmatrix} = \begin{bmatrix} a & b \\ c & d \end{bmatrix}$

5. Use matrices to find each solution to the California problem. (See **APPENDIX 8I**.)

   a. The populations after one year

   b. The populations after two years

   c. The populations after three years

   d. The populations in the long run

6. Find each product.

   a. $\begin{bmatrix} 0.90 & 0.10 \\ 0.05 & 0.95 \end{bmatrix} \begin{bmatrix} 0.90 & 0.10 \\ 0.05 & 0.95 \end{bmatrix}$

   b. $\begin{bmatrix} 1 & 0 & 1 \\ 0 & 2 & 0 \\ 1 & 0 & 1 \end{bmatrix} \begin{bmatrix} 1 & 0 & -1 \\ 0 & 2 & 0 \\ -1 & 0 & 1 \end{bmatrix}$

7. A recent study compares the birth
    weights of English women and
    their daughters. The weights
    were split into three categories,
    Low (below 6 lb), Average
    (between 6 and 8 lb), and High
    (above 8 lb).

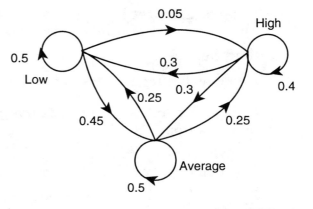

a. Complete the transition matrix using the
    information in the graph.
b. If the initial generation of women had 25%
    in the Low category, 60% in the Average
    category, and 15% in the High category,
    what was the distribution after one generation? Two generations?
    Three generations? In the long run?

	Low	Ave	High
Low			
Ave			
High			

8. Suppose a spider is in a building with
    three rooms. The spider moves from
    room to room by choosing a door at
    random. If the spider starts in Room 1
    initially, what is the probability that it will
    be in Room 1 again after four room
    changes?

9. Complete the following matrix arithmetic problems. If a problem is
    impossible, explain why.

a. $\begin{bmatrix} 1 & 2 \\ 3 & -2 \\ 0 & 1 \end{bmatrix} \begin{bmatrix} -3 & -1 & 2 \\ 5 & 2 & -1 \end{bmatrix}$

b. $\begin{bmatrix} 1 & -2 \\ 6 & 3 \end{bmatrix} + \begin{bmatrix} -3 & 7 \\ 2 & 4 \end{bmatrix}$

c. $\begin{bmatrix} 5 & -2 & 7 \end{bmatrix} \begin{bmatrix} -2 & 3 \\ -1 & 0 \\ 3 & 2 \end{bmatrix}$

d. $\begin{bmatrix} 3 & -8 & 10 & 2 \\ -1 & 2 & 3 & 4 \end{bmatrix} \begin{bmatrix} 2 & -5 & 3 & 12 \\ 8 & -4 & 0 & 2 \end{bmatrix}$

e. $\begin{bmatrix} 3 & 6 \\ -4 & 1 \end{bmatrix} - \begin{bmatrix} -1 & 7 \\ -8 & 3 \end{bmatrix}$

f. $\begin{bmatrix} 4 & 11 \\ 7 & 3 \\ 4 & 2 \end{bmatrix} + \begin{bmatrix} 3 & -2 & 7 \\ 5 & 0 & 2 \end{bmatrix}$

10. Find a problem in this chapter that you cannot solve. Write out the problem
    and as much of the solution as you can. Then, clearly explain what is
    keeping you from solving the problem. Be as specific and clear as you can.

Section 8.8: Chapter Review

Problem Set 8.8

1. Name two different ways to generate random numbers from 0 to 10.

2. Critique the following methods that might be used to generate random numbers from 1 to 12:

    a. Draw a card from a shuffled deck. The number is equal to the card number (Jacks = 11, Queens = 12, Aces = 1, Kings don't count).

    b. Call someone and ask her the number of eggs left in the last carton she bought.

    c. Roll two dice onto a table near the edge and add the spots on the dice. If one die falls off, only count the spots on the die that remains on the table. If both fall off, roll again.

3. Write a calculator command that will generate random numbers belonging to each set:

    a. $\{3, 4, 5, \ldots, 12\}$

    b. $\{-7, -6, -5, \ldots, 2\}$

    c. $-2 < x < 3$

4. a. What is the probability of a point falling in the shaded region at the right if the point is randomly plotted in the rectangle?

    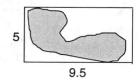

    b. One thousand points are randomly plotted in the rectangular region at the left. Suppose that 374 of the points land in the shaded portion of the region. What is your best approximation of the area of the shaded portion?

5. Suppose you roll two octahedral (eight-sided) dice.

    a. Draw a diagram that shows all possible outcomes of this experiment.

    b. Indicate on your diagram all the possible outcomes for which the sum of the dice is less than 6.

    c. What is the probability that the sum is less than 6?

    d. What is the probability that the sum is more than 6?

6. a. Draw a tree diagram representing all of the possible results when answering five questions on a true/false test.

    b. How many possible ways are there of getting three True and two False answers?

    c. Suppose you knew that the answers to the first two questions on the test were True, and you wrote these answers down. Then you randomly guessed the answers of the remaining three questions. Now what is the probability of having three True and two False answers on the test?

7. The local outlet of Frankfurter Franchise sells three types of hot dogs: plain, with chili, and with sauerkraut. The owners know that 47% of their sales are chili dogs, 36% are plain, and the rest are sauerkraut dogs. They also offer three types of buns: plain, rye, and multigrain. Sixty-two percent of their sales are plain buns, 27% are multigrain, and the rest are rye.

    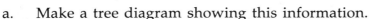

    a. Make a tree diagram showing this information.

    b. What is the probability that the next customer will order a chili dog on rye?

    c. What is the probability that the next customer will *not* order a sauerkraut dog on a plain bun?

    d. What is the probability that the next customer will order either a plain hot dog on a plain bun or a chili dog on a multigrain bun?

8. A survey was taken regarding preference for whipped cream or ice cream to be served with chocolate cake. The results tabulated by grade level are reported below.

	9th grade	10th grade	11th grade	12th grade	Total
Ice Cream	18	37	85	114	
Whipped Cream	5	18	37	58	
Total					

    a. Complete the table.

    b. What is the probability that a sophomore will prefer ice cream?

    c. What is the probability that a junior will prefer whipped cream?

    d. What is the probability that someone who prefers ice cream is a freshman?

    e. What is the probability that a student will prefer whipped cream?

9. Rita is playing a friendly game of darts with Noah. On this particular dart board she can score 20 points for a bull's-eye, and 10 points, 5 points, or 1 point for the other regions. Although Rita doesn't know exactly where her five darts will land, she has been a fairly consistent dart player over the years. She figures she hits the bull's-eye 30% of the time, the 10-point circle 40% of the time, the 5-point circle 20% of the time, and the 1-point circle 5% of the time. What is her expected score? Write a paragraph explaining how you calculated your answer.

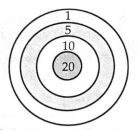

10. A Detroit car rental business has a second outlet in Chicago. It allows patrons to make local rentals or one-way rentals to the other location. Each month, one-eighth of the cars that start the month in Detroit end the month in Chicago, and one-twelfth of the cars that start the month in Chicago end it in Detroit. If at the start of operations there are 500 cars in each city, what would you expect the distribution to be four months later? After many months?

11. In Chapter 8, you explored topics in discrete math. Students in your friend's math class are not studying discrete math, yet your friend is curious about what it is. Explain to her what discrete math is and give reasons for studying it.

12. If you had to choose a favorite problem from this unit, what would it be? Why?

Random Number Table

78086	27605	80783	72059	05060	21366	84811	80730	77042	25406
36673	74153	37788	35736	83780	11566	25916	85274	27965	27549
09752	89231	06739	64351	80303	47999	15059	00677	46402	98961
58358	21124	08164	56928	95491	80511	23897	96281	19001	42952
89928	22964	26249	90286	41979	64737	99888	81369	22711	40318
49390	91663	94701	66328	08696	43795	13916	65570	73393	43882
22219	93199	21573	13645	72126	38799	89648	26301	80918	55096
28034	42119	88853	07211	56700	59113	84358	86127	94675	99511
58449	34746	64619	19171	63533	97899	84381	65023	80908	18694
10920	69975	82955	27251	43127	99059	25076	48299	71133	60036
36422	93239	76046	81114	77412	86557	19549	98473	15221	87856
78496	47197	37961	67568	14861	61077	85210	51264	49975	71785
95384	59596	05081	39968	80495	00192	94679	18307	16265	48888
37957	89199	10816	24260	52302	69592	55019	94127	71721	70673
31422	27529	95051	83157	96377	33723	52902	51302	86370	50452
07443	15346	40653	84238	24430	88834	77318	07486	33950	61598
41349	86255	92715	96654	49693	99286	83447	20215	16040	41085
12398	95111	45663	55020	57159	58010	43162	98878	73337	35571
77229	92095	44305	09285	73256	02968	31129	66588	48126	52700
61175	53014	60304	13976	96312	42442	96713	43940	92516	81421
16825	27482	97858	05642	88047	68960	52991	67703	29805	42701
84656	03089	05166	67571	25545	26603	40243	55482	38341	97781
03872	31767	23729	89523	73654	24625	78393	77172	41328	95633
40488	70426	04034	46618	55102	93408	10965	69744	80766	14889
98322	25528	43808	05935	78338	77881	90139	72375	50624	91385
13366	52764	02467	14202	74172	58770	65348	24115	44277	96735
86711	27764	86789	43800	87582	09298	17880	75507	35217	08352
53886	50358	62738	91783	71944	90221	79403	75139	09102	77826
99348	21186	42266	01531	44325	61942	13453	61917	90426	12437
49985	08787	59448	82680	52929	19077	98518	06251	58451	91140
49807	32863	69984	20102	09523	47827	08374	79849	19352	62726
46569	00365	23591	44317	55054	94835	20633	66215	46668	53587
09988	44203	43532	54538	16619	45444	11957	69184	98398	96508
32916	00567	82881	59753	54761	39404	90756	91760	18698	42852
93285	32297	27254	27198	99093	97821	46277	10439	30389	45372
03222	39951	12738	50303	25017	84207	52123	88637	19369	58289
87002	61789	96250	99337	14144	00027	53542	87030	14773	73087
68840	94259	01961	52552	91843	33855	00824	48733	81297	80411
88323	28828	64765	08244	53077	50897	91937	08871	91517	19668
55170	71962	64159	79364	53088	21536	39451	95649	65256	23950

Section 8.9: Projects

Project 8.1: Pizza Conflicts

As the social committee chairperson, you are in charge of ordering pizzas for the party. The conversation goes as follows:

Patty: "I'd like pepperoni."

Mark: "Mushrooms on mine, please."

Helena: "I only eat pizza that has ham on it."

Peter Allen: "I want pineapple, but not with pepperoni."

Mark: "Pineapple, yuk, not on my pizza!"

Gert: "I have to have green peppers."

Bryan: "I want black olives, but I'm allergic to mushrooms."

Helena: "Keep those black things off my pizza."

Sam: "Yea, same here."

Gert: "I hate them too."

Olivia: "I would like onions on mine, but no pepperoni or pineapple."

Sam: "What I really want is sausage, but not with any pineapple junk."

Helena: "Don't put ham and sausage on the same pizza."

Abby: "How about some anchovies? Hold the green peppers."

Patty: "Keep those salty things off my pizza."

Crazy Carl: "I love a pizza with crab."

Patty, Peter Allen, Gert, Bryan, Sam, and Abby in chorus: "Yuk!!"

Make a conflict matrix and a conflict graph that show the information and find the chromatic number of the graph. Explain how you made the matrix and graph. Give a real-world meaning of the chromatic number. Interpret your results in a real-world way. You will be graded on the neatness of your graph and the clarity of your explanation.

Project 8.2: Coin Toss Game

Return to the Pennies on a Grid Activity from Section 8.4.

a. Explain how to use geometric probability to calculate the theoretical probability of a penny landing within a one-inch square. Assume the "lines" are infinitely thin.

b. Extend the calculation in part a to the probability of a penny landing in square measuring a inches on a side.

c. Extend the problem again to find the probability of a coin of radius r inches landing in a square of a^2 square inches.

d. Extend the problem once more to find the probability of a coin of radius r inches landing in a square of a^2 square inches drawn with lines that are t inches thick.

e. Use your formula to design a game, played with a quarter, that has a probability of success equal to 0.1. Describe your game. Build a game board.

Project 8.3: Permutations and Combinations

In order to compute probabilities, you must first be able to count. There are three functions on your calculator that are very useful for counting things. They are the factorial (!), permutation ($_nP_r$), and combination ($_nC_r$) functions. Do some research and find out which function you should use to solve each problem. Explain how the function works and why you chose the one you did for solving the problem. Make up a problem, similar to each of the given ones, that doesn't involve letters or words.

a. How many ways are there to arrange the six letters in RANDOM? What is the probability that the letters could be randomly arranged to make DROMAN?

b. How many three-letter arrangements can you make using the letters of RANDOM? What is the probability that the letters could be randomly arranged and make ARM?

c. How many three-letter collections can you make using the letters of RANDOM? What is the probability that the letters D, N, and A could be randomly selected?

Project 8.4: Sensitive Survey

There are some questions that are difficult to survey, because the person being asked may or may not wish their answer to be publicly known. "Have you ever plagiarized on a major paper?" or "Do you believe in space aliens?" are questions that some people may be reluctant to answer. One means of collecting such information is by using random selection and coupling the question with a benign and predictable question. Consider the following scenario.

> Eric: "Excuse me Jerry, would you take part in a survey?"
>
> Jerry: "I guess so."
>
> Eric: "You will answer one of two questions, but I will not know which question you are answering. It is important to the results of this survey that you are truthful; can you do that?"
>
> Jerry: "Yes, how does this work?"
>
> Eric: "Look, I have ten cards here; six are black and four are red. You will pick one card, and if it is red, you will answer question one. If it is black, you will answer question two." (Then he hands Jerry the paper with the questions on it.)
>
> Q1: (if a red card) Does your social security number end in an even digit?
>
> Q2: (if a black card) Have you ever cheated on a test?
>
> "Answer only YES or NO. Do not tell which question you are answering."

Next, Eric mixes the cards and holds them out to Jerry. Jerry takes a card, looks again at the paper and responds YES. Then he returns the card to the deck and mixes them again. Eric simply records the YES and goes to the next person.

At the end of the survey, Eric has gathered 47 YESs and 23 NOs. Because he knows the probability of the red cards and the probability of an even social security number, he can use this to predict the distribution on his sensitive question. Here are his calculations:

Of 70 people answering the question, 42 will likely have taken black cards and 28 will likely have taken red cards. Of 28 red card takers, 14 should have answered YES and 14 should have said NO. This means that 33 of the 42 black card takers said YES and 9 said NO. This would mean that 78.6% responded YES to the sensitive question.

Part 1: Explain the logic behind Eric's calculations.

Part 2: Conduct your own sensitive question survey with your own questions and calculate your results. Write a summary describing what you did and reporting your results.

Chapter Nine

SYSTEMS OF EQUATIONS

Contents

Section 9.1: Zooming in on Systems.. 402

Getting to the root of the problem

Section 9.2: Substitution and Elimination 407

It's like search and destroy

Section 9.3: Number of Solutions 414

Do you mean quantity vs. quality?

Section 9.4: Matrix Solutions of Systems....................................... 420

Boxing in the system

Section 9.5: Linear Inequations and Systems................................. 428

It's more or less the same

Section 9.6: Linear Programming 433

Another feasibility study

Section 9.7: Applications of Linear Programming.......................... 436

Getting the most for your effort

Section 9.8: Determinants and System Classification 440

Everyone has a system

Section 9.9: Chapter Review.. 445

Assessing yourself

Section 9.10: Projects... 448

Taking it one step further

Section 9.1: Zooming in on Systems

If you are involved in student activities, you know that the number of tickets sold for a school activity, like a spaghetti dinner, helps determine the success of the event. Ticket sales income can be less than, equal to, or greater than expenses. The break-even value is pictured at the intersection of the expense function and the line $y = x$. This shows when expenses are equal to income. In this chapter, you will focus on mathematical situations and problems involving multiple equations or conditions that must be satisfied at the same time.

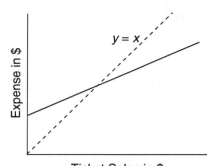

> Two or more equations that are solved or studied simultaneously are called a **system of equations**.

Example 1: Connie Soomer wants to buy a $750 trail bike. At the present time she has only $650 in a savings investment earning 5.9% annual interest compounded monthly. Because of inflation, the cost of the bike will probably increase at a rate of 0.19% per month. Will she ever have enough money saved to buy the bike? If so, when? And how much will it cost at that time?

Solution: One approach is to write two equations that represent the cost of the bike and the amount of money saved. The increasing bike cost can be modeled with $y_1 = 750(1 + 0.0019)^x$ while

$y_2 = 650\left(1 + \dfrac{0.059}{12}\right)^x$ models the growing value of Connie's account.

If you graph both equations simultaneously, the solution will be at the point of intersection.

Zooming in on this point you can see that $(47.598, 820.92)$ is a close approximation for the intersection coordinates. (See **APPENDIX 9A.**) This means that after 47.598 mo the cost of the bike and the amount saved will be about equal.

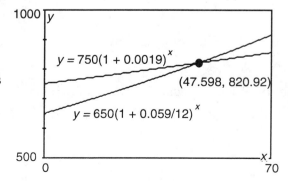

Further zooming will produce a better approximation but, because the interest is paid out monthly, the best answer to the question is actually 48 mo. At 48 mo the cost equation predicts the bike will cost $821.54 and the savings equation predicts a balance of $822.54.

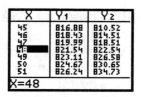

X	Y₁	Y₂
45	816.88	810.52
46	818.43	814.51
47	819.99	818.51
48	821.54	822.54
49	823.11	826.58
50	824.67	830.65
51	826.24	834.73

X=48

Example 2: Thu Pham is starting a small business and she needs to decide between long distance phone carriers. One company offers the Phrequent Phoner Plan that will cost 20¢ for the first minute and 17¢ for each minute after that. A competing company offers the Pals and Buddies Plan that costs 50¢ for the first minute and 11¢ for each additional minute. Under which circumstances is each plan the most desirable?

Solution: Because the Phrequent Phoner Plan costs less for the first minute, it is obviously better for very short calls. However, the Pals and Buddies Plan will probably be cheaper for longer calls because the cost is less for additional minutes. There should be a phone conversation length when both plans cost the same.

A cost equation modeling the PP plan is:

$Cost = 20 + 17(length\ of\ call - 1\ min)$ or $y = 20 + 17(x - 1)$

The P & B plan is:

$Cost = 50 + 11(length\ of\ call - 1\ min)$ or $y = 50 + 11(x - 1)$

In each equation, x represents the call length in minutes and y is the cost.

A graph of these equations shows the PP plan is below the P & B plan for the first part of the graph. The lines intersect at (6, 105), which means a 6 min call using either plan will cost $1.05. If Thu believes her average call will last less than 6 min, she should choose the PP plan. But if most of her calls last more than 6 min, the P & B plan is the better option.

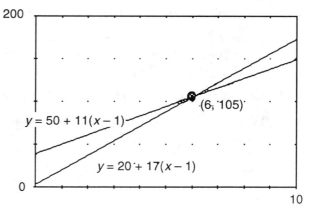

Intersecting Graphs Activity

a. Graph $y_1 = 2^x$ and $y_2 = x^2$, and locate all intersection points of the two curves. How many intersection points are there? How do you know that there aren't any more? Name a graphing window that pictures all of the intersection points. Sketch the graphs and find the coordinates of each intersection point to the nearest thousandth.

b. Sketch the graph of $y_3 = 2^x - x^2$. What does it mean when y_3 is zero? When y_3 is positive? When y_3 is negative? Find the missing table values. How do these values relate to the answers from Part a?

x			
y	0	0	0

c. How many intersection points are there for the curves $y = 3^x$ and $y = x^3$? For $y = 4^x$ and $y = x^4$? For $y = 5^x$ and $y = x^5$? Describe any patterns you have discovered. Describe what you would do if asked to find all of the intersection points of $y = 10^x$ and $y = x^{10}$.

Problem Set 9.1

1. a. Locate all points of intersection of the two curves $y_1 = x^3 - 5x^2 + 5x + 1$ and $y_2 = x^2 + 1$. Find each point's coordinates to the nearest thousandth.

   b. Describe the x-values that make $y_1 < y_2$. Describe the x-values that make $y_1 > y_2$.

2. Graph the equations $y_1 = 2.5(0.5)^x$ and $y_2 = \dfrac{4 - 2x}{1.7}$.

   a. How many points of intersection are there?

   b. Enter the equation $y_3 = y_1 - y_2$. Evaluate all three equations when $x = 1$. How does the value for y_3 compare to the values for y_1 and y_2?

   c. At any point of intersection, the y-values for a pair of intersecting equations will be equal. What does this mean about the y-value for y_3 at such a point? Where will this point appear on the graph of y_3?

   d. Graph y_3 and zoom in to find each point where it crosses the x-axis.

   e. What can you conclude about each point where y_1 and y_2 intersect?

3. Find the x-coordinate of each point of intersection of $y_1 = 2(1.02)^x$ and $y_2 = 2.5 \log x$ to the nearest thousandth.

4. The equations $y = 18 + 0.4x$ and $y = 11.2 + 0.54x$ give the lengths of two different springs as mass amounts are separately added to each.

   a. When are the springs the same length?

   b. When is one spring at least 10 cm longer than the other?

   c. Write a statement comparing the two springs.

5. Write a system of equations that has (2, 7.5) as its solution.

6. The graph at the right shows the Kangaroo Company's production costs and sales income, or revenue, for its pogo sticks. Use it to estimate the answers to the following questions:

   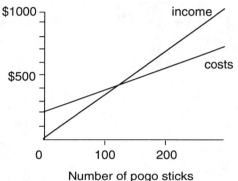

   a. If 25 pogo sticks are sold, will the company earn a profit? Describe how you would use the graph to answer this question.

   b. If the company sells 200 pogo sticks, will it earn a profit? If so, approximately how much?

   c. How many pogo sticks must the company sell to break even (income equal to costs)?

   d. What is the approximate profit if 150 pogo sticks are produced and sold?

7. Winning times for men and women in the 1500 m Olympic speedskating event are given below.

Year	1964	1968	1972	1976	1980	1984	1988	1992
Men	2:10.3	2:03.4	2:02.96	1:59.38	1:55.44	1:58.36	1:52.06	1:54.81
Women	2:22.6	2:22.4	2:20.85	2:16.58	2:10.95	2:03.42	2:00.68	2:05.87

   a. Analyze the data and predict when the winning times for men and women will be the same if the current trends continue.

   b. Show each equation you used to make this prediction.

   c. How reasonable do you think your prediction is? Explain your reasoning.

   d. The winning times in the 1994 Olympics were: Men—1:51.29 and Women—2:02.19. Do these times fit the pattern of your model? Find the residuals for the 1994 entries based on your model.

8. Suppose the long distance phone carriers in Example 2 calculate their charges so that a call of exactly 3 min will cost the same as a call of 3.25 or 3.9 min and there is no increase until the 4 min mark. Increases are calculated after each additional minute. A function that chops or truncates the decimal part of a number x is **int** x.

a. Model this interpretation of phone billings by using the int function to rewrite the cost equations in Example 2.

b. Graph the two new equations representing the Phrequent Phoner Plan and the Pals and Buddies Plan.

c. Now determine when each plan is the most desirable. Explain your reasoning.

Section 9.2: Substitution and Elimination

You and your friends have participated (or may soon participate) in some College Entrance Examination Board activities like the PSAT or SAT. Very often on CEEB exams, or other standardized tests, you must select from multiple choice answers to questions like these:

    i.   If $4x + y = 6$, then what is $(4x + y - 3)^2$?

    ii. If $4x + 3y = 14$ and $3x - 3y = 13$, what is $7x$?

When answering traditional questions like these, you need to look for creative ways of choosing the answers, or of figuring them out. Here are some possible strategies that you might consider.

    i.   You can solve by substituting 6 for $4x + y$ in the expression $(4x + y - 3)^2$. Then $(6 - 3)^2$ gives 9 as the answer. Substitution is a powerful mathematical tool that allows you to rewrite expressions and equations in different forms that are easier to use or solve.

    ii. You can solve the second question without actually knowing the x- or y-value by just adding the two equations.

$$\begin{array}{r} 4x + 3y = 14 \\ \underline{3x - 3y = 13} \\ 7x = 27 \end{array}$$

Notice that both $3y$ and ^-3y dropped out. In fact, the y-variable is eliminated when you add the two equations.

In many situations, you can use substitution and elimination to solve problems in a very efficient manner. Another advantage of these algebraic methods is that by using them you can find an exact solution, whereas by zooming you will almost always find only an approximate solution.

Example 1: The school football team scored a total of 21 touchdowns and field goals during the season, and they kicked successfully for the extra point on all but two of the touchdowns. Determine the number of touchdowns and field goals if you know the team scored a total of 129 points.

Solution: The number of touchdowns (x) plus the number of field goals (y) equals 21. The 129-point total is the sum of $6x + 3y + (x - 2)$.

Why? How many points for a touchdown? For a field goal?
Now you need to find the point (x, y) that is common to both
equations. The y-value of the first equation is equal to the y-value of
the second for some x-value. You can find this x-value by solving
for y in both situations.

$$x + y = 21 \text{ and } 6x + 3y + (x - 2) = 129$$

$$\text{or } y_1 = 21 - x \text{ and } y_2 = \frac{129 - 6x - (x - 2)}{3} \text{ or } \frac{-7x + 131}{3}.$$

Set $y_1 = y_2$;

$$21 - x = \frac{-7x + 131}{3}$$

$$63 - 3x = -7x + 131$$

$$4x = 68$$

$$x = 17$$

Then find y by substituting the x-value into either one of the
original equations:

$$y = 21 - (17) \quad \text{or} \quad \frac{-7(17) + 131}{3}$$

$$y_1 = 4 \qquad\qquad y_2 = 4$$

The point common to both functions, or the solution
to this system, is (17, 4). What do the numbers 17 and
4 represent? This method of solving a system is called
substitution because you are substituting or replacing
something, a variable or an expression, in one
equation with an equivalent expression from the other equation.
A solution to a system of equations in two variables is a pair of values
that satisfies both equations. The table function available on some
calculators is a quick method to check that $x = 17$ and $y = 4$ satisfy both of
the original equations.

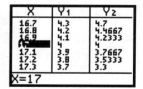

Example 2: Walter Heether must make a decision about spending
$100 to fix his old water heater. It is an older unit, and he estimates
that it costs him $125 a year to provide his home with hot water.
His other option is to buy a new $350 (including installation) gas
water heater. Because a new unit will be more efficient, he should
save 40% on the yearly operating costs. How long will it take until
the new unit pays for itself?

Solution: If Walter keeps the old electric heater, it will *cost* him $100 plus $125 operating costs for each *year* he keeps it. If he makes the switch, it will *cost* him $350 plus $125(1 − 0.40), or 350 + 125(0.60) each *year*.

<table>
<tr><td align="center">Old Heater</td><td align="center">New Heater</td></tr>
<tr><td align="center">*cost* = 100 + 125 • *number of years*</td><td align="center">*cost* = 350 + 75 • *number of years*</td></tr>
<tr><td align="center">$y = 100 + 125x$</td><td align="center">$y = 350 + 75x$</td></tr>
</table>

$$100 + 125x = 350 + 75x \qquad \text{(by substitution)}$$

$$50x = 250$$

$$x = 5$$

In 5 yr, he will have paid the same amount, $725, for either unit. If he plans to sell the house 3 yr from now, how might this affect his decision about buying the new heater?

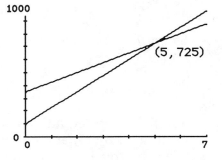

Pick A Number—Get The Point—Activity

In this activity you may discover something very surprising that happens when you multiply both sides of an equation by the same number. Work with a partner and follow the steps below.

Step 1: Graph each equation on graph paper on the same coordinate axis. Where do the lines intersect?

$$\text{Equation One: } 7x + 2y = {}^{-}3$$
$$\text{Equation Two: } 3x + 4y = 5$$

Step 2: Each partner should select a different number. Multiply both sides of Equation One by one of the numbers and both sides of the Equation Two by the other number. Add the two new equations to form Equation Three. Then graph Equation Three on the same coordinate axis as the original lines and describe the location of this new line relative to the original lines.

Step 3: Multiply the original Equation One by ⁻3 and the original Equation Two by 7. Add these two new equations to form Equation Four.
Graph Equation Four and describe the location of the line representing

Equation Four relative to the two original lines. How does Equation Four differ from the other equations?

If necessary, repeat this process with another system like $9y - 5x = 26$ and $4y - 3x = 17$ until you get the point of this activity.

Step 4: Summarize in your own words what the point of this activity is.

A standard method used to solve a system of linear equations is to combine two given linear equations to create a third new equation. Multiplying both sides of an equation by the same value does not change its solutions or its graph. For example, $2x + y = 6$ and $(-5)2x + (-5)y = (-5)6$ are the same function and have the same graph.

Example 3: Solve the system.

$$-3x + 5y = 6$$
$$2x + y = 6$$

Solution: Both equations could be multiplied by (1) and combined to form the third line in the graph. Notice that all three lines intersect in the same point.

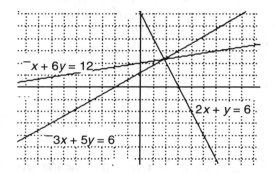

A smarter choice is to multiply the second equation by -5, and then add it to the first equation.

$-3x + 5y = 6$	Multiply both sides by 1. $\Rightarrow$	$-3x + 5y = 6$
$2x + y = 6$	Multiply both sides by -5. $\Rightarrow$	$\underline{-10x - 5y = -30}$
		$-13x = -24$

This eliminates the y-variable and gives $x = \frac{24}{13}$. Verify that this is a vertical line that intersects the graphs of the two original lines at their point of intersection. Substituting this x-value back into either of the original equations gives the y-value. Or, you can use the same process again to eliminate the x-variable:

$-3x + 5y = 6$	Multiply both sides by 2. $\Rightarrow$	$-6x + 10y = 12$
$2x + y = 6$	Multiply both sides by 3. $\Rightarrow$	$\underline{6x + 3y = 18}$
		$13y = 30$
		$y = \frac{30}{13}$

The calculator display verifies that the solution of this system is $\left(\dfrac{24}{13}, \dfrac{30}{13}\right)$. To check the solution, substitute the values in each of the original equations. The **elimination** method is useful because it produces a new equation that eliminates one of the variables. It would take a lot of effort to solve this problem using the graph-and-zoom method if you wanted to obtain the same degree of accuracy. If you had used the substitution method for this problem, you would have had to work with fractions or else maintain a lot of decimal accuracy. To solve this system, the best method to use is the elimination method.

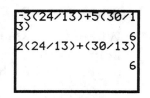

Example 4: At 2:20 Wanda Parte finds out that she can audition for a role in a new musical. The 3:00 audition is 12 miles across town. She can either take a cab, a bus, or a combination of both. A cab generally takes no more than 2 min/mi. The bus crawls along at about 5 min/mi. She must decide how to travel the 12 mi in 40 min or less on her limited income.

Solution: A cab will take 2 • 12 = 24 min, while the cheaper bus will take 5 • 12 = 60 min. Her financial situation requires a bus and cab combination.

On her paper she writes:

$$bus\ miles + cab\ miles = 12\ mi$$

$$5\ min/mi \bullet bus\ miles + 2\ min/mi \bullet cab\ miles = 40\ min$$

$b + c = 12$	Multiply both sides by −2. ⇒	$-2b - 2c = -24$
$5b + 2c = 40$	Multiply both sides by 1. ⇒	$\underline{5b + 2c = 40}$

$$3b = 16$$

$$\text{or} \qquad b = \tfrac{16}{3} \approx 5.3$$

This means she should ride the bus for 5.3 mi and take a cab for the remaining (12 − 5.3) = 6.7 mi.

Problem Set 9.2

1. Without zooming in, find an approximate solution to each system by graphing the equations. Then find the exact solution using the substitution method. List each solution as an ordered pair.

   a. $y = 3.2x + 44.61$

   $y = {}^-5.1x + 5.60$

   b. $y = \frac{2}{3}x - 3$

   $y = \frac{-5}{6}x + 7$

   c. $y = 4.7x + 25.1$

   $3.1x + 2y = 8.2$

2. Without zooming in, find approximate solutions to each system by graphing the equations. Then find the exact solutions using the substitution method. List each solution as an ordered pair.

   a.

   b.

   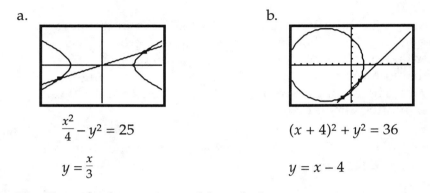

   $\dfrac{x^2}{4} - y^2 = 25$

   $y = \dfrac{x}{3}$

   $(x + 4)^2 + y^2 = 36$

   $y = x - 4$

3. Foe Tagrafer has narrowed her choice to two cameras. The first camera costs $47 and uses two alkaline AA batteries. The second camera costs $59 and uses one $4.95 lithium battery. She plans to use this camera frequently enough that she would probably replace the AA batteries six times a year at a cost of $11.50. On the other hand, the lithium battery will last the entire year.

   a. Write an equation to represent the expenses for each camera.

   b. How long will it take until the total cost of the less expensive camera is equal to the total cost of the other camera?

   c. Carefully describe three different ways to verify your solution.

4. Use the elimination method to solve for one variable. Then use substitution to find the value of the other variable. List each solution as an ordered pair.

   a. $5.2x + 3.6y = 7$

   $-5.2x + 2y = 8.2$

   b. $\frac{1}{4}x - \frac{2}{5}y = 3$

   $\frac{3}{8}x + \frac{2}{5}y = 2$

5. a. Find a good graphing window to see the intersection of $y_1 = 4.7x - 4$ and $y_2 = -1.8x + 7$. Sketch the graph and show the dimensions of your graphing window.

   b. Make $y_3 = (1.8y_1 + 4.7y_2)/6.5$ and graph all three equations in the same window.

   c. Write the equations obtained by multiplying y_1 by (1.8) and y_2 by (4.7). Do not solve.

   d. Now solve for y by adding the new equations from 5c.

   e. Explain why y_3 intersects at the solution to the problem.

6. In each system, find a multiplier for the first equation so that the sum of this new equation and the original second equation will eliminate x. Then find the y-value. Write each solution as an ordered pair.

   a. $2.1x + 3.6y = 7$
      $-6.3x + y = 8.2$

   b. $\frac{1}{4}x - \frac{4}{5}y = 7$
      $\frac{3}{4}x + \frac{2}{5}y = 2$

7. Solve each system in Problem 6 by finding a multiplier for the second equation so that the sum of this new equation and the original first equation will eliminate y. Then find the x-value. Write each solution as an ordered pair.

8. Find the ordered pair solution for each system by finding multipliers that will eliminate one of the variables from the sum of the resulting equations.

   a. $3x + 2y = 7$
      $-5x + 4y = 6$

   b. $y = x^2 - 4$
      $y = -2x^2 + 2$

9. What temperature on the Fahrenheit scale is three times the equivalent temperature on the Celsius scale?

10. Write a system of two equations that has a solution of $(-1.4, 3.6)$.

11. The two sequences below have one term that is the same. Determine which term this is and its value.

$$u_n = \begin{cases} 12 & \text{if } n = 1 \\ u_{(n-1)} + 0.3 & \text{if } n > 1 \end{cases} \qquad u_n = \begin{cases} 15 & \text{if } n = 1 \\ u_{(n-1)} + 0.2 & \text{if } n > 1 \end{cases}$$

Section 9.3: Number of Solutions

Consider a function such as $y = 4.35x - 6.78$. An infinite number of (x, y) pairs satisfy the function because every point on the line is a solution. If you consider a system of two linear equations, how many solutions might there be? What generalized statements can you make? Is every problem a unique case to be considered? What if you consider nonlinear functions or parametric functions? In many cases, you can give a range for the number of solutions if you know the types of equations in the system. But you will need specific information about the equations in order to determine the exact number of solutions.

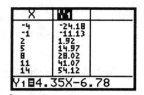

Intersecting Lines Activity

In this activity you will look at what can happen when you graph a pair of lines. You will also learn the vocabulary that is used when referring to these different possibilities.

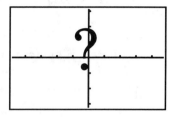

Draw two lines that *intersect in only one point*. The point of intersection is called the solution to the system.

Now draw a pair of lines that represents a system with *no solutions*. Compare your drawing with those of others around you. How can you describe a system with no solution? What relationship exists between the lines? When a system has no solutions, the equations are said to be **inconsistent**.

Next draw a pair of lines that represents a system with *more than one solution*. Compare your drawing with those of others around you. How can you describe a system with more than one solution? What relationship is there between the lines? When a system of linear equations has more than one solution, the equations are called **dependent**.

Systems of Parametric Equations Activity

Systems of parametric equations have an additional requirement that must be considered. Consider the following system of parametric equations.

$x_1 = 3t$ and $y_1 = 0$;

$x_2 = 3t$ and $y_2 = 7 - 4.9t^2$.

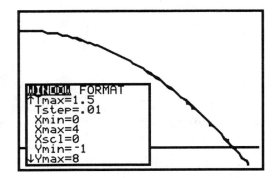

Each pair of equations models a marble rolling horizontally at 3 m/sec. One marble is rolling on the floor and the other marble rolls off a ledge that is 7 m high. The graph pictures the paths of the two marbles. The paths clearly intersect because the second marble falls to the floor when it reaches the edge of the ledge. Do the marbles hit each other? Explain your answer. Would they intersect if the ledge was 5 m high? 2 m high?

The equations describe the motion of two objects, with t indicating the time. The question of intersection means "Do the two objects actually hit each other, or do their paths merely cross?" If the marbles' paths intersect, name the (t-coordinate, x-coordinate, y-coordinate) of each point of intersection for the three heights listed.

Example 1: Solve the system of equations $x_{1t} = 3t - 4$, $y_{1t} = t + 2$ and $x_{2t} = 1.5t - 0.6$, $Y_{2t} = 4t - 4.6$

Solution: The equations appear to intersect. Use the substitution technique to check the requirement that there is a t-value that produces the same point on each line. Equate either the x-equations or the y-equations and solve for t.

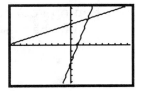

$$y_{1t} = y_{2t}$$
$$t + 2 = 4t - 4.6$$
$$6.6 = 3t$$
$$t = \frac{6.6}{3} = 2.2$$

Then substitute this t-value into both sets of x- and y-equations to find the location at that time.

$x = 3t - 4$	$y = t + 2$	$x = 1.5t - 0.6$	$y = 4t - 4.6$
$x = 3(2.2) - 4$	$y = (2.2) + 2$	$x = 1.5(2.2) - 0.6$	$y = 4(2.2) - 4.6$
$x = 2.6$	$y = 4.2$	$x = 2.7$	$y = 4.2$

When $t = 2.2$ seconds, the x-values are different, so even though the paths cross each other, the lines do not intersect.

Throughout this course you have been asked to find models that correctly interpret various situations. The solutions you find using your models should make sense. A Chapter 5 problem asked you to draw a reasonable graph that pictures the amount of money you have in an account that is compounded annually. You probably drew a graph very similar to the one pictured here, with the value of the account increasing to the larger amount at the instant the money is compounded.

The Forever Green Nursery (Chapter 1) owns 7000 white pine trees. Every year the nursery sells 12% of the remaining trees and plants 600 new trees. The recursive solution you wrote to provide the yearly totals might have been similar to

$$u_1 = 7000 \text{ and } u_n = (1 - 0.12)u_{(n-1)} + 600.$$

Did it bother you that some answers reflected fractions of trees? Can you find a better model, so that each answer shows a whole number of trees? One way to do this is to use the **int** function on your calculator. If you assume no fraction of a tree will be harvested, then a reasonable model is

n	U_n	
0	7000	
1	6760	
	6548.8	
3	6362.9	
4	6199.4	
5	6055.5	
6	5928.8	

$n=2$

$$u_n = \text{int} \left((1 - 0.12)u_{(n-1)} + 600 \right).$$

Try it.

The function, **int** x, chops or truncates the decimal part of a number.

What does the graph of $y = \text{int } x$ look like? The table values and graph of $(x, \text{int } x)$ both indicate that $y = \text{int } x$ rounds a number *down* to the next integer less than or equal to x. This is the function a company uses if

X	✖1
3.6	3
3.8	3
4	4
4.2	4
4.4	4
4.6	4
4.8	4

Y₁目int X

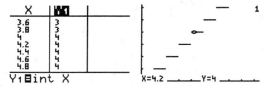

X=4.2 _____ Y=4 _____

they bill to the integer minute at or below the actual time used.

The function, $^-\text{int}\ -x$, rounds a number *up* to the next integer greater than or equal to x. If the phone company charges $0.30 a minute for a call, which function gives the cost for a call of 4 minutes and 12 seconds (or 4.2 min): $y = 0.30\ \text{int}\ x$ or $y = ^-0.30\ \text{int}\ (^-x)$? The answer is $y = ^-0.30\ \text{int}\ (^-x)$ because the phone company charges the next minute's fee.

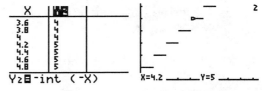

Problem Set 9.3

1. a. By graphing, find which of the following systems are inconsistent (have no solutions).

    i. $y = 0.7x + 8$
        $y = 1.1x - 7$

    ii. $y = \frac{3}{4}x - 4$
         $y = 0.75x + 3$

    iii. $4x + 6y = 9$
          $1.2x + 1.8y = 4.7$

    iv. $\frac{3}{4}x - \frac{1}{2}y = 4$
         $0.75x + 0.5y = 3$

    b. Describe the graphs of the equations in the systems that are inconsistent.

    c. Try to solve each inconsistent system either by substitution or elimination. Show your steps. Describe the outcome of these solutions.

    d. Describe how can you recognize an inconsistent linear system without graphing it.

2. For each equation, write a second linear equation that would create an inconsistent system.

    a. $y = 2x + 4$

    b. $y = \frac{^-1}{3}x - 3$

    c. $2x + 5y = 10$

    d. $x - 2y = ^-6$

3. a. Which of the following systems have multiple solutions? (These are dependent linear systems.)

    i. $y = 1.2x + 3$
       $y = 1.2x - 1$

    ii. $y = \frac{1}{4}(2x - 1)$
        $y = 0.5x - 0.25$

    iii. $4x + 6y = 9$
         $1.2x + 1.8y = 2.7$

    iv. $\frac{3}{5}x - \frac{2}{5}y = 3$
        $0.6x + 0.4y = 3$

    b. Describe the graphs of those equations that have multiple intersections.

c. Solve each dependent system by substitution or elimination. Show your steps. Describe the outcome of each solution.

d. Describe how can you recognize a dependent linear system without graphing it.

4. Write a second linear equation that would create a dependent system for each given equation.

a. $y = 2x + 4$

b. $y = \frac{-1}{3}x - 3$

c. $2x + 5y = 10$

d. $x - 2y = {}^{-}6$

5. For each system of parametric equations, determine when and where they intersect, or whether they have no solution.

a. $x = 3t + 1$ $x = 2 - 4t^2$
   $y = 8t^2 - 2$ $y = 6t - 3$

b. $x = 3t + 1$ $x = 2 - 3t$
   $y = 4t + 2$ $y = 4 - 2t$

6. A plane takes off from Detroit at noon flying 200 mi/hr on a heading of 45°. There is no wind. At the same time, a plane takes off from Cleveland, 200 mi directly east. It is flying at 180 mi/hr on a heading of 300°. Should the air traffic controllers make sure that the planes are at different altitudes, or will they be in no danger of hitting each other even if they fly at the same altitude? How close do they get to each other?

7. The data at the right was collected from a bouncing ball experiment. You should recall that the height is exponentially related to the number of the bounce, $height = a \cdot b^{bounce}$. Find the values of a and b for this function.

Bounce number	Height
3	34.3 cm
7	8.2 cm

8. The Mother Goose Company ships educational materials to day care providers. One mail service charges a flat rate of 6¢ per package plus 23¢ per ounce. Another charges $5.50 per package and $1.75 for each pound. Both mailing services bill any fraction of an unit at the rate for the next higher unit. Use the int function and find a breakdown of weights so that the Mother Goose Company uses the most cost-efficient mailer.

9. The angles of elevation to the top of a tower are 40° and 50° as shown in the picture at the right. Points A and B are 10 m apart. Write two equations involving the distance x and tower height h, and solve for the missing values.

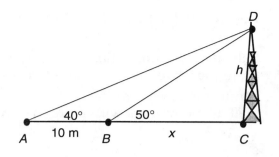

10. The table below gives the populations of San Jose and Detroit.

   a. If the current trends continue, when will the population of San Jose surpass the population of Detroit?

   b. What will the two populations be at that time?

   c. Show the equations you used to make this prediction.

Year	1950	1960	1970	1980	1990
San Jose	92,280	204,196	459,913	629,442	782,248
Detroit	1,849,568	1,670,144	1,514,063	1,203,339	1,027,974

Section 9.4: Matrix Solutions of Systems

Substitution, elimination, and graphing techniques can be extended to systems of more than two equations and two variables, but they become more involved and confusing. A process involving matrices is direct and simple for 2×2 systems, as well as for systems with more than two variables.

Consider the equation $ax = b$. To solve for x, multiply both sides of the equation by $\frac{1}{a}$, which is the **multiplicative inverse** of a. What is the multiplicative inverse of a real number? The inverse of 2.25, for example, is the number that you can multiply by 2.25 to get 1.

$$2.25a = 1$$

$$a = \frac{1}{2.25} = 0.4 \qquad (\text{check: } 2.25 \bullet 0.4 = 1)$$

In a matrix solution of a system, you must also find an inverse. Consider a 2×2 matrix $\begin{bmatrix} 2 & 1 \\ 4 & 3 \end{bmatrix}$. If an inverse matrix exists, then when you multiply the inverse by your matrix you should get the matrix equivalent of one. The matrix equivalent of one is called the multiplicative *identity* matrix. That means when you multiply any matrix by the identity matrix, the original matrix should remain unchanged.

An **identity matrix**, symbolized by [I], is one of a set of matrices that do not alter or transform the elements of any matrix [A] under multiplication.

[A] [I] = [A] *and* [I] [A] = [A]

Though the dimensions of one identity matrix may differ from another, the property holds true.

Example 1: Find an *identity matrix* for $\begin{bmatrix} 2 & 1 \\ 4 & 3 \end{bmatrix}$.

Solution: This means to find a matrix $\begin{bmatrix} a & b \\ c & d \end{bmatrix}$ that satisfies the definition of the identity matrix.

$$\begin{bmatrix} 2 & 1 \\ 4 & 3 \end{bmatrix} \begin{bmatrix} a & b \\ c & d \end{bmatrix} = \begin{bmatrix} 2 & 1 \\ 4 & 3 \end{bmatrix}$$

$$\begin{bmatrix} 2a + c & 2b + d \\ 4a + 3c & 4b + 3d \end{bmatrix} = \begin{bmatrix} 2 & 1 \\ 4 & 3 \end{bmatrix}$$

Because the two matrices are equal, you get the following systems:

$$2a + c = 2 \qquad\qquad 2b + d = 1$$
$$4a + 3c = 4 \qquad\qquad 4b + 3d = 3$$

Use either substitution or elimination to find the answers $a = 1$, $b = 0$, $c = 0$, and $d = 1$. Do this now. This means the 2×2 identity matrix is $\begin{bmatrix} 1 & 0 \\ 0 & 1 \end{bmatrix}$. There are corresponding identity matrices for matrices with greater dimensions. Will an identity matrix always be square? Why or why not?

Now that you know what the identity matrix looks like for a 2×2 matrix, you can return to the problem of finding the inverse of a matrix.

> The **inverse matrix** of [A], symbolized by $[A]^{-1}$, is the matrix that will produce an identity matrix when multiplied by [A].
>
> $$[A][A]^{-1} = [I] \ and \ [A]^{-1}[A] = [I]$$
>
> (Not every matrix has an inverse.)

Example 2: Find the inverse of $\begin{bmatrix} 2 & 1 \\ 4 & 3 \end{bmatrix}$.

Solution: Set up a matrix equation.

$$\begin{bmatrix} 2 & 1 \\ 4 & 3 \end{bmatrix} \begin{bmatrix} a & b \\ c & d \end{bmatrix} = \begin{bmatrix} 1 & 0 \\ 0 & 1 \end{bmatrix}$$

Matrix multiplication on the left side of the equation provides the following systems:

$$2a + c = 1 \qquad\qquad 2b + d = 0$$
$$4a + 3c = 0 \qquad\qquad 4b + 3d = 1$$

Using the techniques of the previous section, you find the answers $a = 1.5$, $b = -0.5$, $c = -2$, and $d = 1$. The inverse matrix is $\begin{bmatrix} 1.5 & -0.5 \\ -2 & 1 \end{bmatrix}$. Your calculator also provides the inverse of a matrix A, [A] $^{-1}$. (See **APPENDIX 9B** for specific instructions.)

Consider the system of two equations:

$$2x + 3y = 7$$
$$x + 4y = 6$$

Verify that the system can be written as the matrix equation:

$$\begin{bmatrix} 2 & 3 \\ 1 & 4 \end{bmatrix} \begin{bmatrix} x \\ y \end{bmatrix} = \begin{bmatrix} 7 \\ 6 \end{bmatrix}$$

Let the coefficient matrix be [A] so that $[A] = \begin{bmatrix} 2 & 3 \\ 1 & 4 \end{bmatrix}$. Let the variable matrix be [X] so that $[X] = \begin{bmatrix} x \\ y \end{bmatrix}$. If the constant matrix is [B], then $[B] = \begin{bmatrix} 7 \\ 6 \end{bmatrix}$, and the equation can be written as [A][X] = [B]. The calculator inverse to [A] is $[A]^{-1} = \begin{bmatrix} 0.8 & -0.6 \\ -0.2 & 0.4 \end{bmatrix}$. Multiply both sides of the equation by this inverse to produce the solution to the original system.

$\begin{bmatrix} 2 & 3 \\ 1 & 4 \end{bmatrix} \begin{bmatrix} x \\ y \end{bmatrix} = \begin{bmatrix} 7 \\ 6 \end{bmatrix}$ [A][X] = [B]   Rewrite in matrix form.

$\begin{bmatrix} 0.8 & -0.6 \\ -0.2 & 0.4 \end{bmatrix} \begin{bmatrix} 2 & 3 \\ 1 & 4 \end{bmatrix} \begin{bmatrix} x \\ y \end{bmatrix} = \begin{bmatrix} 0.8 & -0.6 \\ -0.2 & 0.4 \end{bmatrix} \begin{bmatrix} 7 \\ 6 \end{bmatrix}$ $[A]^{-1}[A][X] = [A]^{-1}[B]$ Multiply by the inverse.

$\begin{bmatrix} 1 & 0 \\ 0 & 1 \end{bmatrix} \begin{bmatrix} x \\ y \end{bmatrix} = \begin{bmatrix} 0.8 & -0.6 \\ -0.2 & 0.4 \end{bmatrix} \begin{bmatrix} 7 \\ 6 \end{bmatrix}$ $[I][X] = [A]^{-1}[B]$ The definition of inverse.

$\begin{bmatrix} x \\ y \end{bmatrix} = \begin{bmatrix} 0.8 & -0.6 \\ -0.2 & 0.4 \end{bmatrix} \begin{bmatrix} 7 \\ 6 \end{bmatrix}$ $[X] = [A]^{-1}[B]$ The definition of identity.

$\begin{bmatrix} x \\ y \end{bmatrix} = \begin{bmatrix} 2 \\ 1 \end{bmatrix}$ Multiplication.

$2(2) + 3(1) = 7$ and $(2) + 4(1) = 6$ Check the solution.

Example 3: On a recent trip to the movies, three students—Noah, Carey, and Rita—each spent some money at the concession counter. Noah bought two candy bars, a small drink, and two bags of popcorn for a total of $5.35. Carey spent $4.16 on a candy bar, two small drinks, and a bag of popcorn. Meanwhile, Rita spent $5.85 on three bags of popcorn, two small drinks, and no candy bars. If no tax was included in these totals, what was the purchase price for each item?

Solution: Let C = price of a candy bar, D = price of a small drink, and P = price of a bag of popcorn. The purchases may be represented by the following system. What is the meaning of row two?

$$\begin{bmatrix} 2C + 1D + 2P \\ 1C + 2D + 1P \\ 0C + 2D + 3P \end{bmatrix} = \begin{bmatrix} 5.35 \\ 4.16 \\ 5.85 \end{bmatrix}$$

These equations can be translated into the following matrix equation:

$$\begin{bmatrix} 2 & 1 & 2 \\ 1 & 2 & 1 \\ 0 & 2 & 3 \end{bmatrix} \begin{bmatrix} C \\ D \\ P \end{bmatrix} = \begin{bmatrix} 5.35 \\ 4.16 \\ 5.85 \end{bmatrix} \qquad \text{in the form of } [A][X] = [B]$$

Store the coefficient matrix as $[A]$ and the constant matrix as $[B]$.

The solution to the system is $[A]^{-1}[B]$, which is $\begin{bmatrix} 0.89 \\ 0.99 \\ 1.29 \end{bmatrix}$. This means that a candy bar costs 89¢, a small drink costs 99¢, and a bag of popcorn costs $1.29. Substituting these answers into the original system shows that they are correct.

$$2(0.89) + 1(0.99) + 2(1.29) = 5.35$$

$$1(0.89) + 2(0.99) + 1(1.29) = 4.16$$

$$2(.99) + 3(1.29) = 5.85$$

Another way to check the answers is to store them in the calculator and evaluate the expressions.

Checking the solutions is important!

$0.89 \rightarrow C$	
$0.99 \rightarrow D$	
$1.29 \rightarrow P$	
$2C + D + 2P$	
	5.35
$C + 2D + P$	
	4.16
$2D + 3P$	
	5.85

Example 4: Solve the following system:

$$x + \frac{1}{2}y + \frac{1}{3}z = 1$$

$$\frac{1}{2}x + \frac{1}{3}y + \frac{1}{4}z = 2$$

$$\frac{1}{3}x + \frac{1}{4}y + \frac{1}{5}z = 3$$

Solution: See **APPENDIX 9B** for help entering fractions as matrix elements. The difficulty involved in using decimal approximations is illustrated in this table. There is no problem entering the fractions $\frac{1}{2}, \frac{1}{4}$ or $\frac{1}{5}$. Because $\frac{1}{3}$ is a repeating decimal, here are results for various approximation choices of $\frac{1}{3}$.

Approximation	x	y	z
0.333	30.505	−209.990	226.697
0.33333	27.03207	−192.16442	210.15253
1/3	27	−192	210

The lesson to be learned here is that answers must be checked. If they don't work, then adjust for more accuracy in your matrix or look for another technique. If you get 4 E −13 for an answer, this is probably meant to be zero. Likewise, 3.99999992 is probably meant to be 4. The calculator introduces round-off inaccuracies when it finds the inverse matrix and during matrix multiplication. Don't expect your calculator to give you answers that are precise. Check them yourself and adjust for rounding.

Problem Set 9.4

1. Multiply each pair of matrices. If multiplication is not possible, explain why.

a. $\begin{bmatrix} 5 & 2 \\ 7 & 3 \end{bmatrix}\begin{bmatrix} 1 & -3 \\ 5 & -2 \end{bmatrix}$ b. $\begin{bmatrix} 4 & -1 \\ 3 & 6 \\ 2 & -3 \end{bmatrix}\begin{bmatrix} 2 & -5 & 0 \\ 1 & -2 & 7 \end{bmatrix}$ c. $\begin{bmatrix} 9 & -3 \end{bmatrix}\begin{bmatrix} 4 & -6 \\ 0 & -2 \\ -1 & 3 \end{bmatrix}$

2. Use matrix multiplication to expand each system. Then solve for each variable.

a. $\begin{bmatrix} 1 & 5 \\ 6 & 2 \end{bmatrix}\begin{bmatrix} a & b \\ c & d \end{bmatrix} = \begin{bmatrix} -7 & 33 \\ 14 & -26 \end{bmatrix}$ b. $\begin{bmatrix} 1 & 5 \\ 6 & 2 \end{bmatrix}\begin{bmatrix} a & b \\ c & d \end{bmatrix} = \begin{bmatrix} 1 & 0 \\ 0 & 1 \end{bmatrix}$

3. The calculator gives the second matrix as the inverse of the first. Multiply the two matrices together to verify that they are inverses.

a. $\begin{bmatrix} 5 & 2 \\ 7 & 3 \end{bmatrix}\begin{bmatrix} 3 & -2 \\ -7 & 5 \end{bmatrix}$

b. $\begin{bmatrix} 1 & 5 & 4 \\ 6 & 2 & -2 \\ 0 & 3 & 1 \end{bmatrix}\begin{bmatrix} 0.16 & 0.14 & -0.36 \\ -0.12 & 0.02 & 0.52 \\ 0.36 & -0.06 & -0.56 \end{bmatrix}$

c. In your own words, describe how you know when two matrices are inverses of each other.

4. Find the inverse of each matrix.

a. $\begin{bmatrix} 4 & 3 \\ 5 & 4 \end{bmatrix}$

b. $\begin{bmatrix} 6 & 4 & -2 \\ 3 & 1 & -1 \\ 0 & 7 & 3 \end{bmatrix}$

c. $\begin{bmatrix} 5 & 3 \\ 10 & 7 \end{bmatrix}$

d. $\begin{bmatrix} -1 & 2 & -3 \\ 2 & 3 & -1 \\ 3 & -2 & -1 \end{bmatrix}$

5. Rewrite each system as a matrix equation.

a. $5.2x + 3.6y = 7$

$-5.2x + 2y = 8.2$

b. $\frac{1}{4}x - \frac{2}{5}y = 3$

$\frac{3}{8}x + \frac{2}{5}y = 2$

6. Solve each system by multiplying by an appropriate inverse matrix. Check your solutions.

a. $8x + 3y = 41$
   $6x + 5y = 39$

b. $11x - 5y = -38$
   $9x + 2y = -25$

c. $2x + y - 2z = 1$
   $6x + 2y - 4z = 3$
   $4x - y + 3z = 5$

d. $4w + x + 2y - 3z = -16$
   $-3w + 3x - y + 4z = 20$
   $5w + 4x + 3y - z = -10$
   $-w + 2x + 5y + z = -4$

7. Write a system of equations that models each situation, and solve for the appropriate values of the variables.

a. The perimeter of a rectangle is 44 cm. Its length is 2 cm more than twice its width.

b. The perimeter of an isosceles triangle is 40 cm. The base length is 2 cm less than the length of a leg of the triangle.

c. The Fahrenheit reading on a dual thermometer is 0.4 less than three times the Celsius reading.

8. At the High Flying Amusement Park there are three kinds of rides: rides for the timid, rides for the adventurous, and rides for the thrill seekers. You can buy a book that includes the admission fee and ten tickets for each type of ride, or you can pay $5.00 for admission and then buy tickets for each of the rides individually. Noah, Rita, and Carey went to the park. They all decided not to buy the admission book and instead paid for each of the rides.
Noah rode on seven of the rides for the timid, three of the rides for the adventurous, and nine of the rides for the thrill seekers, for a cost of $19.55 for the rides only. Rita rode on nine of the rides for the timid, ten of the rides for the adventurous, and none of the rides for the thrill seekers, for a cost of $13.00 for the rides. Carey paid $24.95 for eight rides for the timid, seven rides for the adventurous, and ten rides for the thrill seekers.

a. How much did each type of ride cost?

b. What is the total cost of a 30-ride ticket book?

c. Would any of the three have been better off to have purchased a ticket book, or did they all make the right decision to pay for the admission and the rides separately?

9. The Fan C. Feate Dance Company is given two choices of how they will be paid for their next series of performances. The first option is to receive $12,500 for the series plus 5% of all ticket sales. The second option is $6,800 for the series plus 15% of ticket sales. The company will perform three consecutive nights in a hall that seats 2,200 persons. All tickets will cost $12.

a. How much will the company receive under each plan if a total of 3,500 tickets are sold for all three performances?

b. Write an equation that gives the amount the company will receive under the first plan for any number of tickets sold.

c. Write an equation that gives the amount the company will receive under the second plan for any number of tickets sold.

d. How many tickets must be sold for the second plan to be the better choice?

e. What would your advice be to the company regarding which plan to choose? Justify your choice.

10. During the last semester one-half of the students in Fay Cilitator's second-hour class worked on projects about fractals. One-fourth of the class collected and analyzed data, and the rest conducted a survey and analyzed their results. In her third-hour class, one-third worked on projects about fractals, one-half collected and analyzed data, and the rest conducted a survey and analyzed their results. In the seventh-hour class, one-fourth of the students worked on projects about fractals, one-sixth of them collected and analyzed data, and the others conducted a survey and analyzed their results. Overall, there were 18 students who completed projects on fractals, 16 students who collected and analyzed data, and 20 students who conducted surveys and analyzed their results. How many students are in each of Fay Cilitator's classes?

11. Being able to solve a system of equations is definitely not "new" math. Mahavira, the best-known Indian mathematician of the ninth century, worked this problem. See if you can solve it.

> "The mixed price of 9 citrons and 7 fragrant wood apples is 107; again the mixture price of 7 citrons and 9 fragrant wood apples is 101. O you arithmetician, tell me quickly the price of a citron and of a wood apple here, having distinctly separated those prices well."

Section 9.5: Linear Inequations and Systems

Frequently, real-world situations involve ranges of values. "Do not spend more than $10"; "Write an essay between two and five pages in length"; "Practice more than an hour each day"; "Be home before 10:00"; "The post office is open from 9:00 to noon"; "Stu Dent has to spend three hours in his room with his homework each evening." From this last statement, you don't know how much time Stu actually spent working on math, or on chemistry, or even daydreaming about Rachel. The time spent thinking about Rachel is not a concern to you, except that you cannot say that *math time + chem time* = 3 hr. The third variable changes your equation to *math time + chem time* ≤ 3 hr.

Math Time vs. Chemistry Time Activity

Graph the equation *math time + chem time* = 3 hr on your calculator. Let x represent *math time* and y represent *chem time*. Make a table of points which includes x- and y-values with a sum of less than 3, more than 3, or equal to 3

x (math time)	y (chem time)	$x + y$

hours. Fill in the third column of the table. Circle the points that fit the actual condition *math time + chem time* ≤ 3 hr. Where are these points located on the graph? Describe some points that fit the condition but do not make sense for the situation. Describe where all possible solutions to the inequation $x + y ≤ 3$ are located. Describe where all possible solutions to $x + y > 3$ are located.

When there are one or two variables, you can model the solution of an inequation as a set of ordered pairs graphed on a coordinate plane. The region is shaded to indicate the location of the solution. Frequently there are additional common-sense conditions, like no negative amounts of time. In the activity above, there were three conditions: *math time + chem time* ≤ 3 hr, *math time* ≥ 0, and *chem time* ≥ 0. Because these conditions must be satisfied simultaneously, they form a system.

> Example 1: Stu Dent spent three hours on homework last night. He spent more time working on his math than on his chemistry. Stu spent at least a half-hour on chemistry. Restate the conditions of the system algebraically in terms of x and y for *math time* and *chem time*, respectively. Then graph the inequations and all solutions on the same coordinate axis.

Solution: $x + y \leq 3$

$\qquad\qquad x > y$

$\qquad\qquad y \geq 0.5$

Convert each inequation to an equation by replacing the inequality with an equal sign. Find the points of intersection by using previously learned techniques.

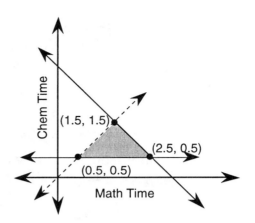

Equations	Intersections
$x + y = 3$ and $x = y$	$(1.5, 1.5)$
$x + y = 3$ and $y = 0.5$	$(2.5, 0.5)$
$x = y$ and $y = 0.5$	$(0.5, 0.5)$

Select one of the lines. Choose a sample point on either side of the line. Test the coordinates of this point in the inequation to see if it makes a true statement. If so, shade on the side of the line where the point lies. If not, shade on the other side of the line. Repeat this process for each line. The solution to the entire system is the area that represents the overlap of all the shaded regions. This region is called the **feasible region**, and every point in this region is a possible (feasible) solution to the system.

See **APPENDIX 9C** for help with graphing systems of inequations on your calculator screen. The appendix suggests that you shade the nonfeasible region. This alternative allows you to see individual points as you move the cursor within the feasible region on your calculator screen.

Example 2: Maria is planning a snack of graham crackers and blueberry yogurt. Because she is concerned with nutrition, she wants to make sure that she eats less than 700 calories and no more than 20 grams of fat with this snack. She would like to eat at least 17 grams of protein and at least 30% of the daily requirement of iron. Use this information to show the possibilities that Maria must choose from.

Solution:

	Serving	Calories	Fat	Protein	Iron
graham crackers	1 cracker	60	2 g	2 g	6 %
blueberry yogurt	4.5 oz	130	2 g	5 g	1 %

Using x as the number of crackers and y as the number of servings of yogurt, you get the following set of condition inequations.

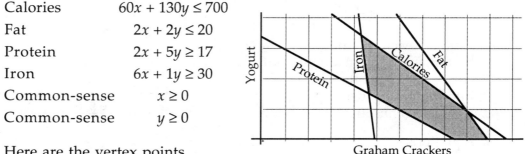

Calories	$60x + 130y \leq 700$
Fat	$2x + 2y \leq 20$
Protein	$2x + 5y \geq 17$
Iron	$6x + 1y \geq 30$
Common-sense	$x \geq 0$
Common-sense	$y \geq 0$

Graham Crackers

Here are the vertex points of the feasible region (clockwise from top left).

Calories and Iron = (4.44, 3.33)

Calories and Fat = (8.57, 1.43)

Fat and Common-Sense = (10, 0)

Common-Sense and Protein = (8.5, 0)

Protein and Iron = (4.75, 1.5)

You are not interested in every intersection of a pair of lines. In this example, the intersection of the fat inequation with the iron inequation occurs outside the feasible region, so you don't list it as a vertex point. The inequation $x \geq 0$ does not form any of the actual border of the region even though $x \geq 0$ is satisfied by all points in the feasible region. Frequently, only points in the feasible region that have integer coefficients make sense. So this is another common-sense restriction that you will have to consider. Such would be the case here if whole crackers and full yogurt servings are the only possibilities.

Problem Set 9.5

1. The graphs of $y = 2.4x + 2$ and $y = -x^2 - 2x + 6.4$ serve as the boundaries of the shaded region. What two inequations identify this region?

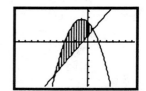

Sketch a graph of the feasible region described by each system of inequations. Label each vertex point and find its coordinates.

2. $y \leq -0.51x + 5$
    $y \leq -1.6x + 8$
    $y \geq 0.1x + 2$
    $y \geq 0$
    $x \geq 0$

3. $y \geq 1.6x - 3$
    $y \leq -(x - 2)^2 + 4$
    $y \geq 1 - x$
    $y \geq 0$
    $x \geq 0$

4. $4x + 3y \leq 12$
    $1.6x + 2y \leq 8$
    $2x + y \geq 2$
    $y \geq 0$
    $x \geq 0$

5. $y \geq |x - 1|$
    $y \leq \sqrt{9 - x^2}$
    $y \leq 2.5$
    $y \geq 0$
    $x \geq 0$

6. In Luxembourg's Lux Art Gallery, rectangular paintings must satisfy the following restrictions: $200 \leq$ area (in square inches) ≤ 300 and $66 \leq$ perimeter (in inches) ≤ 80.

    a. Write four inequations involving *length* and *width* that represent these conditions.

    b. Graph this system of inequations and identify the feasible region.

    c. Will they hang a picture that measures 12.4 in by 16.3 in? A 16 in by 17.5 in picture? A 14.3 in by 17.5 in picture?

7. Al Geebra just sold 40 of his dad's old records. He sold each classical record for $5 and each jazz record for $2. The rest of the records were worthless and he gave them away. Al knows that he sold fewer than 10 jazz records, and he collected more than $100.

    a. If he sold x classical records and gave away y records, then how can you represent the number of jazz records? (Write this as an expression involving x and y.)

    b. In terms of x, how many dollars did he receive from selling the classical records?

    c. Write the inequation to show he earned over $100.

    d. List three common-sense inequations.

    e. Graph this system of inequations.

    f. Name each vertex of the feasible region.

    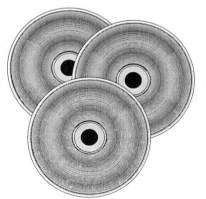

8. A parabola $y = ax^2 + bx + c$ passes through the points $(-2, -32)$, $(1, 7)$, and $(3, 63)$.

 a. Describe how you can use matrices and systems to find the values of a, b, and c in this parabola.

 b. Write the equation of this parabola.

 c. Describe how to verify that your answer is correct.

9. How many different methods do you know to solve a system of equations? What are they? Which one do you prefer? Why?

Section 9.6: Linear Programming

In the last section, you looked at an example about Maria's dietary requirements. The modeling inequations are reprinted below:

Calories	$60x + 130y \leq 700$
Fat	$2x + 2y \leq 20$
Protein	$2x + 5y \geq 17$
Iron	$6x + y \geq 30$
Common-sense	$x \geq 0$
Common-sense	$y \geq 0$

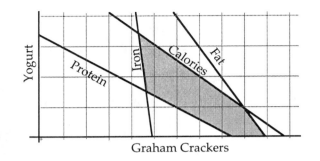

The variable x represents the number of graham crackers, and the variable y represents the number of servings of blueberry yogurt.

Suppose each cracker costs 6¢ and each serving of yogurt costs 30¢. Now you can determine the cost of her meals, with the equation $cost = 0.06x + 0.30y$.

By choosing points in the shaded area or feasible region you can list the costs of several different meal combinations. Verify the costs of the following meals that meet her dietary requirements.

$Cost = 0.06x + 0.30y$

# of crackers	Servings of yogurt	Cost of meal
5	2	0.90
7	2	1.02
7	1	0.72

What is Maria's least-expensive snack combination? Suppose you assume the only solutions that make sense are those that are whole numbers (whole crackers and whole servings of yogurt). Identify all of the integer points that are in the feasible region and list the cost for each of these.

x	y	cost	x	y	cost	x	y	cost
5	3	1.20	7	2	1.02	9	1	0.84
5	2	0.90	7	1	0.72	9	0	0.54
6	2	0.96	8	1	0.78	10	0	0.60
6	1	0.66	9	1	0.84			

From this listing you can see that the least expensive combination is to eat *nine crackers and no yogurt*. Cheap, but not very exciting.

This process of finding a feasible region, and determining the point that gives the maximum or minimum value to a specific expression, is called **linear programming**.

Nutritional Elements Activity

Choose two food items. Record information about Calories, Fat, Protein, Iron (or other appropriate ingredients) for your two food items. Either use Maria's restrictions or alter the diet constraints. Using the information and constraints your group has selected, describe and solve a problem similar to the cracker/yogurt snack combination problem in this section.

Problem Set 9.6

1. a. Carefully graph each system of inequations.

   b. Determine the coordinates of each vertex of the feasible region.

   c. Find the coordinates of each point in the region with integer coordinates. Then find the point with integer coordinates that gives the highest or lowest value for the final expression. (Do not evaluate each integer point in the feasible region. Evaluate only those that you feel may yield the desired maximum or minimum.)

   i. $3y \leq -2x + 6$
   $y \leq 6 - 4x$
   $x \geq 0, y \geq 0$
   maximize $5x + 2y$

   ii. $x + y \leq 10$
   $5x + 2y \geq 20$
   $-x + 2y \geq 0$
   minimize $x + 3y$

   iii. $3x - y \leq 12$
   $x + y \leq 15$
   $x \geq 2, y \geq 5$
   maximize $2x + y$

   iv. $x + 2y \geq 10$
   $2x + y \geq 12$
   $x - y \leq 8$
   minimize $3x + 2y$

2. Evaluate the maximum/minimum expression in Problem 1 for each vertex. What generalizations can you make about the location of the point that provides the maximum or minimum expression value?

3. a. Graph the system $x \geq 5500$, $y \geq 5000$, $y \leq 3x$, and $x + y = 40{,}000$.

   b. Name the integer point that provides the maximum value in the expression $P = 0.08x + 0.10y$. What is this maximum value of P?

4. During the nesting seasons two different bird species inhabit a region 180,000 m² in area. Mr. Chamberlin estimates this ecological region can provide 72,000 kg of food during the season. Each nesting pair of species X needs 39.6 kg of food during this time and 120 m² of area. Each nesting pair of species Y needs 69.6 kg of food and 90 m² of area. Let x be the number of pairs of species X and y be the number of pairs of species Y.

   a. Carefully describe the meaning of $x \geq 0$ and $y \geq 0$.

   b. Carefully describe the meaning of $120x + 90y \leq 180{,}000$.

   c. Carefully describe the meaning of $39.6x + 69.6y \leq 72{,}000$.

   d. Graph the inequations (constraints) listed, and identify each vertex of the feasible region.

   e. Maximize the total number of nesting pairs, N, by considering the function $N = x + y$.

5. Write three chapter-appropriate, interesting questions about the graph at right.

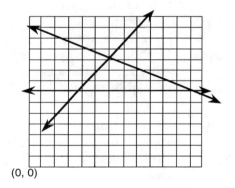

(0, 0)

Section 9.7: Applications of Linear Programming

Noah and Rita are members of the math club, and the club has the opportunity to sell popcorn at the weekly basketball games. Their job is to figure out whether the club can make money doing this. There are a number of questions they need to answer. How can they maximize profit? What are the expenses, guidelines, and restrictions involved, and what is the break-even point for the amount of popcorn sold? How many members are needed for the most efficient operation? These kinds of questions can be answered when applying linear programming techniques to a situation.

Business or industrial managers often investigate more economical ways of doing something. They must consider physical limitations, standards of quality, customer demand, availability of materials, and manufacturing expenses as restrictions or constraints. Problems that can be modeled with linear programming may involve anywhere from two variables to hundreds of variables. Computerized modeling programs that analyze up to 200 constraints and 400 variables are used regularly to help businesses choose their best plan of action. In this section, you will look at problems involving two variables because you are relying on the visual assistance of a two-dimensional graph to help you find the feasible region.

Once you have identified the variables, you must write the constraints, or inequations. You will have to find some way to organize the information. The text of the problem must be broken down, and the mathematical facts extracted. The following example shows one way to carry out this process. As you study this example, be aware that not every problem can be organized in the same way.

Example 1: The Elite Tweet Pottery Shoppe makes two kinds of birdbaths: glazed and unglazed. The unglazed birdbath requires 1/2 hr to throw on the wheel and 1 hr in the kiln. The glazed birdbath takes 1 hr on the wheel and 6 hr in the kiln. The wheel is available for at most 8 hr/day and the kiln is available for at most 20 hr/day. The pottery shop's profit on each unglazed birdbath is $10.00, while its profit on each glazed birdbath is $15.00. How many of each kind of birdbath should be produced in order to maximize profit?

Preliminary Edition

Solution: The variables in this problem are the number of each type of birdbath. The choice of x and y is arbitrary because neither is dependent on the other. Organize the information into a table.

	Number of unglazed birdbaths x	Number of glazed birdbaths y	Constraining value
Throwing hours	1/2	1	≤ 8
Firing hours	1	6	≤ 20
Profit	$10	$15	none

Once you have organized the data in a table, the inequations or constraints can be written.

Throwing hours constraint: $0.5x + y \leq 8$

Kiln hours constraint: $x + 6y \leq 20$

Common-sense constraints: $x \geq 0; y \geq 0$

The profit expression to be optimized is: $profit = 10x + 15y$

Graph all of the constraint inequations to locate the feasible region. Note that the nonfeasible region is shaded, allowing you to see more clearly and identify points contained in the feasible region. You are looking for integer solutions because you

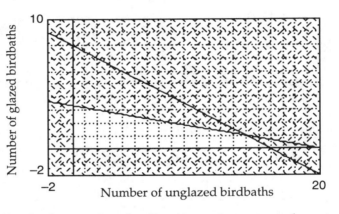

will not sell part of a birdbath. Determine the integer points at or closest to each vertex of the region, and calculate the profit for each point.

The vertices are $(0, 0)$, $(1, 3)$, $(14, 1)$, and $(16, 0)$.

Here are the profits corresponding to each vertex.

(0, 0) $10(0) + 15(0) = \$0.$

(1, 3) $10(1) + 15(3) = \$55.$

(14, 1) $10(14) + 15(1) = \$155.$

(16, 0) $10(16) + 15(0) = \$160.$

The profit for each vertex is found by putting the coordinates of the point into the profit equation: $10x + 15y = profit$. Producing no glazed birdbaths and 16 unglazed birdbaths maximizes the profit. However, if you were aware that customers are happier when given a choice of products, would you settle for $155 profit, and offer your customers a choice?

Paying for College Activity

Marti's parents are about to invest up to $40,000 to save for her college education. The stock fund has been paying 10% per year and the bond fund has been paying 8% per year. Both funds require $5000 as a minimum investment. Because of recent economic conditions and the advice of their financial advisor, they have decided that the amount invested in stocks should be no more than three times the size of their bond investment. Find the amount they should invest in each fund to maximize their investment return by carrying out the following steps.

i. Identify the variables.

ii. Translate the limitations or constraints provided into a system of inequations. A table might help organize this information.

iii. Graph the system of inequations and determine the feasible region. Find each vertex of this region. (If integer solutions are required and a vertex doesn't have integer coefficients, identify integer points near the vertex.)

iv. Write a linear function that will maximize their investment.

v. Find the answer to the question.

Problem Set 9.7

1. Xavier, Yolanda and Zeus have a small business producing handmade shawls and afghans for the Old Math Teachers Retirement Home. They spin the yarn, dye it, and weave it. A shawl requires 1 hr of spinning, 1 hr of dyeing, and 1 hr of weaving. An afghan needs 2 hr of spinning, 1 hr of dyeing, and 4 hr of weaving. They make a $16 profit per shawl and a $20 profit per afghan. Xavier does the spinning on his day off, when he can spend at most 8 hr spinning. Yolanda does the dyeing on her day off, when she can spend up to 6 hr dyeing. Zeus does all the weaving on Friday and Saturday, when he has at most 14 hr available. How many of each item should they make each week to maximize profit?

2. The International Canine Academy raises and trains Siberian sled dogs and dancing French Poodles. Breeders can supply ICA with at most 20 poodles and 15 huskies each year. Each poodle eats 2 lb of food a day and each sled dog will eat 6 lb a day. ICA food supplies are restricted to at most 100 lb of food each day. Poodles require 1000 hr of training per year, while a sled dog requires 250 hr/yr. The Academy restricts training time to no more than 10,000 hr each year. How many of each kind of dog should the ICA breed in order to maximize their profit? Find the maximum yearly ICA profit if each poodle will sell for a profit of $200 and each sled dog will sell for a profit of $80.

3. The Elite Tweet Pottery Shoppe budgets a maximum of $1000/mo for newspaper and radio advertising. The newspaper charges $50 per ad and requires at least four ads per month. The radio station charges $100/min and requires a minimum of 5 min of advertising per month. It is estimated that each newspaper ad reaches 8000 people and that each minute of radio advertising reaches 15,000 people. What combination of newspaper and radio advertising should the business use in order to reach the maximum number of people?

4. A small South American country grows coffee and cocoa for export. The country has 500,000 hectares of land available for the crops. It has contracts that require at least 100,000 hectares be devoted to coffee and at least 200,000 hectares to cocoa. Available equipment and labor limit cocoa production to 270,000 hectares. Coffee requires two workers per hectare while cocoa requires five workers per hectare. No more than 1,750,000 workers are available. Coffee provides a profit of $220 per hectare and cocoa provides a profit of $310 per hectare. How many hectares should the country devote to each crop in order to maximize profit? Find the maximum profit.

5. A small electric generating plant is making a decision involving a mixture of low-sulfur (2%) and high-sulfur (6%) oil. The final mixture must have a sulfur content of not more than 4%. At least 1200 barrels of oil are needed. Low-sulfur oil costs $18.50 per barrel and high-sulfur oil costs $14.70 per barrel. How much of each type of oil should be used to keep the cost of oil at a minimum? What is the minimum cost?

Section 9.8: Determinants and System Classification

Inconsistent systems have no solutions. Dependent systems have an infinite number of solutions. In these two special situations, the coefficient matrix will not have an inverse. If you get an error message when trying to solve a system using matrices and their inverses, you'll know that the system is either dependent or inconsistent.

If the coefficient matrix, [A], has no inverse and you ask for $[A]^{-1}$, you will get an error message on your calculator. This error message means you must then determine if the system is dependent or inconsistent. In a 2×2 system, you will have to check to see if a point selected from one equation will or will not work in the other equation. If it works, the system is dependent.

Example 1: Examine the system

$$3.2x + 2.4y = 9.6$$
$$2x + 1.5y = 6$$

Solution: $\begin{bmatrix} 3.2 & 2.4 \\ 2.0 & 1.5 \end{bmatrix} \begin{bmatrix} x \\ y \end{bmatrix} = \begin{bmatrix} 9.6 \\ 6.0 \end{bmatrix}$

$\begin{bmatrix} x \\ y \end{bmatrix} = \begin{bmatrix} 3.2 & 2.4 \\ 2.0 & 1.5 \end{bmatrix}^{-1} \begin{bmatrix} 9.6 \\ 6.0 \end{bmatrix}$ ERROR

The next step is to find a point that satisfies the first equation. If $x = 1$, then $3.2(1) + 2.4y = 9.6$, so $y = \frac{9.6 - 3.2}{2.4} = \frac{8}{3}$ and $(1, \frac{8}{3})$ is on the first line.

$(1, \frac{8}{3})$ also works in the second equation because $2(1) + 1.5(\frac{8}{3}) = 6$. Therefore the system is dependent.

An inverse matrix is found by a long process (the larger the matrix, the longer the process). In this process, small errors tend to magnify themselves. The calculator, even though it may have 12 digits of accuracy, sometimes gives an inverse to a matrix when the inverse should not exist.

The det [A], **determinant of matrix A**, is a single value or measure associated with a square matrix that you can use to determine whether a matrix has an inverse. (See **APPENDIX B**.) Use your calculator to verify that $\det \begin{bmatrix} 2 & 1 \\ 4 & 3 \end{bmatrix} = 2$.

What is the **determinant**, det [B], for B = $\begin{bmatrix} 2 & 6 \\ 3 & 5 \end{bmatrix}$?

A Matrix without an Inverse Activity

Find the inverse and determinant for each 2×2 matrix. Divide up the problems in your group, but share the results. Some matrices will not have an inverse. Determine a connection between the value of det [A] and whether there is an inverse, $[A]^{-1}$.

i. $A = \begin{bmatrix} 2 & 6 \\ 3 & 5 \end{bmatrix}$ ii. $A = \begin{bmatrix} 7 & 2 \\ 3 & 4 \end{bmatrix}$ iii. $A = \begin{bmatrix} 3 & 1 \\ 5 & 1 \end{bmatrix}$ iv. $A = \begin{bmatrix} 2 & 6 \\ 4 & 12 \end{bmatrix}$

v. $A = \begin{bmatrix} 2 & 3 \\ 1 & 4 \end{bmatrix}$ vi. $A = \begin{bmatrix} 3 & -1 \\ 4 & 2 \\ 3 & -2 \end{bmatrix}$ vii. $A = \begin{bmatrix} 8 & -3.5 \\ -2 & 1 \end{bmatrix}$ viii. $A = \begin{bmatrix} 3 & -2 \\ 5 & 5 \\ 0.6 & -0.4 \end{bmatrix}$

Find values for e and f so that the 2×2 matrix $\begin{bmatrix} 2 & 6 \\ e & f \end{bmatrix}$ doesn't have an inverse. What do you notice about the entries in the matrix? Write a hypothesis concerning 2×2 matrices that have no inverses. Test your hypothesis by completing the missing elements in the matrix $\begin{bmatrix} 8 & -3.5 \\ \_\_ & \_\_ \end{bmatrix}$ so that it has no inverse. What is the **determinant**, det [A], for $A = \begin{bmatrix} a & b \\ c & d \end{bmatrix}$?

The Japanese mathematician Seki Kowa developed the concept of determinant in 1683. This concept was implicit in the work of the German mathematician, philosopher, and diplomat Gottfried Wilhelm Leibniz in 1693. Around 1729, before Leibniz's work on determinants was published in 1850, determinants were rediscovered in Europe by the Scottish mathematician Colin Maclaurin.

Example 2: Governor Lyle Lott has made some promises to his constituents. He promised the upper class that 20% of their taxes would be spent on the environment, 11% on increasing jobs, and 31% on education. He promised the middle class that 25% of their taxes would be spent on the environment, 8% on creating new jobs, and 33% on education. He promised the poor that 5% of their tax dollars would go to the environment, 31% on increased jobs and 36% on education. Now he must raise taxes to cover the budget. He needs $18 billion for the environment, $34 billion for new jobs, and $74 billion for education. Explain to the Governor the difficulties his promises will cause him.

Solution: The Governor sets the taxes at x dollars from the upper class, y dollars from the middle class and z dollars from the poor.

$$\begin{array}{l} 0.20x + 0.25y + 0.05z = 18 \\ 0.11x + 0.08y + 0.31z = 34 \\ 0.31x + 0.33y + 0.36z = 74 \end{array} \quad \text{or} \quad \begin{bmatrix} 0.20 & 0.25 & 0.05 \\ 0.11 & 0.08 & 0.31 \\ 0.31 & 0.33 & 0.36 \end{bmatrix} \begin{bmatrix} x \\ y \\ z \end{bmatrix} = \begin{bmatrix} 18 \\ 34 \\ 74 \end{bmatrix}$$

$$\det \begin{bmatrix} 0.20 & 0.25 & 0.05 \\ 0.11 & 0.08 & 0.31 \\ 0.31 & 0.33 & 0.36 \end{bmatrix} = 0 \text{ (It may read } 4.6 \times 10^{-15} \text{ on your calculator.)}$$

This means, (1) there are an infinite number of solutions and the Governor has no problems, or (2) there are no solutions, and he again must break a promise. You need three dimensions to visualize this situation because each equation involves three variables, and a three-variable equation determines a plane. If the system is dependent, then the planes intersect in either a line or a plane. If they intersect in a plane, then all three equations must represent the same plane. If they intersect in a line, this is like three pages of an open book that all intersect in the binding.

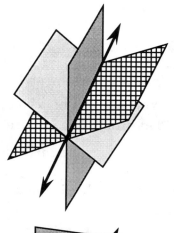

Start by assuming the planes intersect in a line (the more likely option). Replace one of the three equations with a different equation. To do this, edit the coefficient matrix so that the first row is [1 0 0]. This creates a new system that models "turning" one of the three planes in the picture. The solution to this new system will provide one point on the line. Test this point in the original first equation. If it satisfies this equation, then your system is dependent; otherwise it is inconsistent.

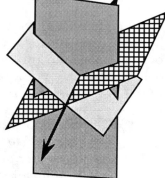

Show that the new coefficient matrix has an inverse by finding its determinant value.

$$\det \begin{bmatrix} 1 & 0 & 0 \\ 0.11 & 0.08 & 0.31 \\ 0.31 & 0.33 & 0.36 \end{bmatrix} = -0.0735$$

Find the solution point for this system:

$$\begin{bmatrix} 1 & 0 & 0 \\ 0.11 & 0.08 & 0.31 \\ 0.31 & 0.33 & 0.36 \end{bmatrix}^{-1} \begin{bmatrix} 18 \\ 34 \\ 74 \end{bmatrix} = \begin{bmatrix} 18 \\ 131.7415 \\ 69.2925 \end{bmatrix}$$

Substitute the coordinates of this point (18, 131.7415, 69.2925) into the original first equation:

$0.20(\mathbf{18}) + 0.25(\mathbf{131.7415}) + 0.05(\mathbf{69.2925}) = 40 \neq 18$

Because this point is not a solution of the original first equation, you know that the Governor lied and broke a promise.

Unfortunately, if the remaining two equations are in the same plane or parallel planes, this process will not work. If the determinant is still zero after replacing the first equation, then replace the second row of the matrix with [0 1 0], leaving only the third row intact. When you have produced a point, then test the point in both equations to find if the system is dependent (all equations work) or inconsistent (at least one equation does not work).

The ideas presented here are true for all linear systems whether they have two variables, ten variables, or more. With more than three variables the visual or geometric meaning breaks down, but the algebraic meaning remains the same. The method is not 100% foolproof and will still give false results if you end up with a column of zeros.

Problem Set 9.8

1. Use the determinant of the coefficient matrix to determine whether or not each system has a unique solution.

   a. $2x + 3y = 16$
      $5x + 7.5y = 40$

   b. $12.75x - 18.21y = 45.32$
      $3.25x + 5.12y = 9.71$

   c. $2x + y - 4z = 21$
      $7x + 5y + z = 63$
      $3x + 2y - z = 28$

   d. $7.13x - 2.14y + 11.6z = 15.2$
      $9.12x + 5.7y - 8.25z = 21.7$
      $13.7x + 7.12y + 4.41z = 18.11$

   e. $2.5x + 7.1z = 16$
      $3.1x - 2.4y = 12$
      $6y + 22.01z = 9$

   f. $5w + 4x - 3y + 2z = 1$
      $7w - 4x + 5y + z = 8$
      $3w + 2x + y - 6z = 5$
      $4w + 3x - y - 2z = 6$

2. Classify each system in Problem 1 that does not have a unique solution as inconsistent or dependent. Explain your reasoning.

3. Your social studies teacher has decided that the next test will contain 20 questions. Each question will be either true/false, fill-in-the-blank, matching, or short essay. Each true/false question will be worth 2 points, fill-in-the-blank questions will be worth 4 points each, matching questions will be 6 points each, and essays will be 10 points each. The test will total 100 points. True/false questions will be designed to take 1 minute each, fill-in-the-blank questions will take 2 minutes each, matching questions will take 5 minutes each, and essay questions will take 6 minutes each. The test should last one hour. The true/false questions will each use 4 lines of a page, the fill-in-the-blank questions will each use 3 lines, matching questions will each use 15 lines, and the essays will each use 9 lines. The test should fill two pages. There are 110 lines available. Give the teacher as much help as you can so she can plan the test.

4. a. Create your own system of three unknowns that is dependent.

   b. Create your own system of three unknowns that is inconsistent.

5. The title of this chapter is <u>Chapter Nine: Systems of Equations</u>, and although this title is appropriate, suggest another title that is more interesting yet still conveys what the chapter is about. Explain your title and justify why you think it is a good title.

6. If you had to choose a favorite problem from this unit, which one would it be? Why?

Section 9.9: Chapter Review

Problem Set 9.9

1. Locate each point of intersection of the two curves $y = -(x - 3)^2 + 5$ and $y = x^2 - 1$. Give all answers to the nearest thousandth.

2. When two lines have very similar slopes it is difficult to graphically find the point of intersection.

    a. Find the best graphing window to see the intersection of $y_1 = 3.2x - 4$ and $y_2 = 3.1x - 3$.

    b. Graph $y_3 = y_1 - y_2$. What is a good window to see the intersection of y_3 with $y = 0$ (the x-axis)?

    c. Write the equation obtained by substituting the y-value from y_1 into y_2.

    d. Solve the equation from 2c for x.

    e. Explain why this solution is the same as the x-intercept for y_3.

3. Use substitution to solve each system.

    a. $y = 6.2x + 18.4$
    $y = -2.1x + 7.40$

    b. $y = \frac{3}{4}x - 1$
    $\frac{7}{10}x + \frac{2}{5}y = 8$

4. Use elimination to solve each system.

    a. $3x + 2y = 4$
    $-3x + 5y = 3$

    b. $5x - 4y = 5$
    $2x + 10y = 2$

5. Identify each system as being dependent or inconsistent.

    a. $y = -1.5x + 7$
    $y = -3x + 14$

    b. $y = \frac{1}{4}(x - 8) + 5$
    $y = 0.25x + 3$

    c. $2x + 3y = 4$
    $1.2x + 1.8y = 2.6$

    d. $\frac{3}{5}x - \frac{2}{5}y = 3$
    $0.6x - 0.4y = -3$

6. Find the inverse, if it exists, of each matrix.

a. $\begin{bmatrix} 2 & -3 \\ 1 & -4 \end{bmatrix}$

b. $\begin{bmatrix} 5 & 2 & -2 \\ 6 & 1 & -0 \\ -2 & 5 & 3 \end{bmatrix}$

c. $\begin{bmatrix} -2 & 3 \\ 8 & -12 \end{bmatrix}$

d. $\begin{bmatrix} 5 & 2 & -3 \\ 4 & 3 & -1 \\ 7 & -2 & -1 \end{bmatrix}$

7. Solve each system using matrix multiplication.

a. $8x - 5y = 17$

$6x + 4y = 33$

b. $4w + x + 2y - 3z = -11$

$-3w + 2x - y + 4z = 20$

$5w + 4x + 6y - z = -10$

$-2w + 3x + 5y + 7z = -45$

8. Sketch a graph of the region described by each system of inequations. Find the coordinates of each vertex. Then find the point with integer coordinates that gives the maximum value for the final expression.

a. $2x + 3y \le 12$

$6x + y \le 18$

$x + 2y \ge 2$

$x \ge 0, y \ge 0$

maximize $1.65x + 5.2y$

b. $x + y \le 50$

$10x + 5y \le 440$

$40x + 60y \le 2400$

maximize $6x + 7y$

9. Heather (Walter Heether's neighbor) has an electric water heater in need of repair. The repair man says it will cost $300 to fix the unit. She could buy a new gas water heater for $500 including installation, and the new heater would save her 60% of her annual $75 operating costs. How long would it take for the new unit to pay for itself?

10. Art Easte needs a particular color that is five parts red, six parts yellow, and two parts black. Not having the pure colors at his disposal, he finds three color mixtures that he can use. The first is two parts red and four parts yellow, the second is one part red and two parts black, and the last is three parts red, one part yellow, and one part black.

   a. Write an equation that gives the correct portion of red using the three available color mixtures.

   b. Write an equation that gives the correct portion of yellow and another equation that gives the correct portion of black.

   c. Solve the system.

   d. Find an integer that can be used as a multiplier for your solutions in 10c to provide integer solution values.

   e. Explain your solutions in real-world terms.

11. In this chapter, you looked at solving systems of equations for both two and three variables. Explain the similarities and differences between the graphs of two-variable systems of equations and those of three-variable systems of equations.

12. How has your ability to do mathematics changed through the year? Do you feel you have improved? Explain.

Section 9.10: Projects

Project 9.1: Nonlinear Systems with Three Variables

You have looked at solving nonlinear systems in two variables using graphical analysis of functions. You have also looked at linear systems with three variables using matrices. Using all that you have learned, and more that you have not yet learned, find the solutions for each system. Show proof that the solutions you find satisfy the system. Then find some way to convince others that you have found all possible solutions.

a.

$$z = 9x^2 + 4y^2 - 36$$
$$z = 3x - 2y$$
$$z = 6xy + 12$$

b.

$$z = 5(1.02)^x + 7(1.05)^y$$
$$z = 40(0.97)^x + 50(0.95)^y$$
$$z = 12x + 15y$$

Project 9.2: Inverse by Hand

There are several different methods for finding the inverse of a 3×3 matrix that were used before calculators were available in the mathematics classroom. Find out about two different methods. Use one method to find the inverse of the first matrix, and use the other method to find the inverse of the second matrix. Show that your new matrix is the inverse of the original matrix by multiplying the original matrix by its inverse without using a calculator.

a.

$$\begin{bmatrix} 4 & 3 & 2 \\ 2 & 1 & 3 \\ 2 & 2 & 4 \end{bmatrix}$$

b.

$$\begin{bmatrix} {}^-1 & 4 & 3 \\ {}^-0.5 & {}^-3 & 2 \\ {}^-2 & 6 & 7 \end{bmatrix}$$

Project 9.3: Nonlinear Programming

Make a complete and accurate graph of the following system of inequations. Locate and label all vertices of the feasible region.

$$3x + 4y \leq 72$$
$$x^2 - 3y \geq 9$$
$$5x + 2y^2 \geq 50$$
$$0.5x - 10^y \leq 4$$

Graph $(x - 10)^2 + (y - 5)^2 = k$ for $k = 25, 50, 75$ on top of the feasible region. What is the largest possible value for k for which the graph of this equation still contains a point in the feasible region? Where is this point?

Describe any differences you found between optimizing this system of inequations containing nonlinear inequations and the linear programming problems in the chapter.

Project 9.4: Bifurcation and Systems

The recursive formula $x_n = 3.2x_{n-1}(1 - x_{n-1})$ can be looked at in different ways. Start the sequence at some value like 0.1, and watch what happens with $3.2\text{Ans}(1 - \text{Ans})$. After about 50 or so iterations you will notice that the answers have fallen into a pattern. Start with another value and you will probably get the same result. But there is one starting value that is quite different. Start with 0.6875 and describe what happens.

If you set up a system of equations, you can find the two-value pattern you saw with the first iteration. Explain how to solve a system when the input of one iteration becomes the output of the next iteration, or when $y = 3.2x(1 - x)$ and $x = 3.2y(1 - y)$. Explain why the value of 0.6875 doesn't lead to the same pattern, by showing that it is the solution to $x = 3.2x(1 - x)$.

The formula $x_n = 3.83x_{n-1}(1 - x_{n-1})$ exhibits slightly different behavior. Start with some value like 0.1, and find out what happens after a large number of iterations. Set up a system to solve for this pattern of numbers directly. Find the one number that leads to a constant cycle. Find a pair of numbers that leads to a two-cycle bifurcation like you saw in the first example. Explain why this equation would have a different behavior than the first equation.

Chapter Ten

POLYNOMIALS

Contents

Section 10.1: Finite Differences 452

We all have our differences

Section 10.2: Different Quadratic Forms 458

The parabola is back!!!

Section 10.3: Factored Polynomials... 463

Divide and concur

Section 10.4: The Quadratic Formula 469

Roots the quick way

Section 10.5: Applications and Algebraic Solutions..................................... 477

Polynomials in your world

Section 10.6: Higher Degree Polynomials... 482

Did they go to college?

Section 10.7: No Real Solutions... 488

No sense in being real all the time

Section 10.8: More About Finding Solutions.. 492

I didn't know they were lost

Section 10.9: Chapter Review.. 499

Assessing yourself

Section 10.10: Projects.. 501

Taking it one step further

Section 10.1: Finite Differences

What would happen if you deposited $100 into a savings account on your fourteenth birthday, and continued to deposit $60 on each birthday thereafter? If r is the annual interest rate, then the annual balances of your account would be as follows.

100	at 14 yr old,
$100(1 + r) + $**60**	at 15 yr old,
$100(1 + r)^2 + 60(1 + r) + $**60**	at 16 yr old,

and so on.

The money in your account will grow as the bank compounds interest and you deposit more money. If the interest rate is 6.5%, then immediately after your sixteenth birthday the account value can be represented as follows.

value of 1st deposit	+	value of 2nd deposit	+	new deposit	= Total
$100(1 + 0.065)^2$	+	$60(1 + 0.065)$	+	60	

or

$100(1.065)^2$	+	$60(1.065)$	+	60	= $237.32

Example 1: What similar bank deposit situation does $50(1.08)^2 + 70(1.08) + 90$ represent?

Solution: The expression can model the value of an account that earns 8% interest, beginning immediately after an original birthday deposit of $50, and two more birthday deposits of $70 and $90.

Example 2: Your friend Penny had a similar account worth $193.84 when she was sixteen. What interest rate did her three $60 deposits earn?

Solution: You need to find a value of x that satisfies the equation $60x^2 + 60x + 60 = 193.84$. What choice of x works? You can find out by graphing and locating the intersection of $y_1 = 60x^2 + 60x + 60$ and $y_2 = 193.84$. (See the graph on the left below.) Or you can find the value of x by graphing $y_1 - y_2$ and locating the positive x-intercept. (See the graph on the right below.)

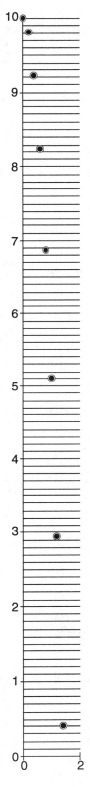

Method 1:

$y_1 = y_2$

$60x^2 + 60x + 60 = 193.84$

Method 2:

$y_1 - y_2 = 0$

$60x^2 + 60x + 60 - 193.84 = 0$

$60x^2 + 60x - 133.84 = 0$

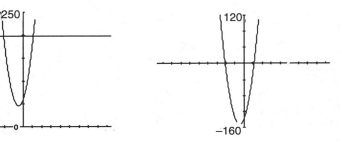

Only the positive x-value has any real meaning in this problem. Repeated zooming gives $x = 1.075$. Check this on your calculator. Therefore, the interest rate that provides $193.84 during this time span is 7.5%.

The equations for yours and Penny's accounts considered only 3 yr of deposits. They also had three **terms**. If the deposits continued for 5 yr, the equation would look like $y = 60x^4 + 60x^3 + 60x^2 + 60x + 60$. This is called a **polynomial** equation because it is the sum of terms whose variables have only positive whole-number powers. The highest power of x in this equation is 4, so it is called a 4th **degree** polynomial equation.

Falling Objects Activity

The picture at the left is a photograph taken of an object dropped from a height of 10 m. The photograph was taken in a dark room with a flash that fired every 0.20 sec. Carefully determine and record the heights of the ball at each flash, accurate to the nearest 0.01 m. Create a table like the one below and record this information. Make your measurements carefully and check them with others in your group. Accurate measurements are very important.

Time	0.0	0.2	0.4	0.6	. . .	. . .
Height	10.00					
D_1						
D_2						

Subtract each pair of consecutive heights (second height minus first height, third height minus second height, and so on) and record these as the third row of data. These are called the **first differences**. Repeat the process and find the differences in the first row of differences. These are called the **second differences**. Include them as the fourth row of your table of information. This process is called finding **finite differences**. You will use this table of information in the next section.

You can predict the degree of a polynomial that fits a set of data whose x-values are in an arithmetic sequence if you follow the steps below.

Step 1: Find the finite differences of the y-values by subtracting consecutive values.

Step 2: Check to see if the first differences, D_1, are all equal nonzero numbers. If this is so, then the polynomial that fits the data is linear.

Step 3: If the first differences are not all equal nonzero numbers, then calculate D_2, the finite differences of the D_1 values.

Step 4: Check the second differences, D_2. If they are all equal nonzero numbers, then the polynomial that fits the data points is second-degree.

Step 5: If not, continue. The polynomial has the degree n which matches the first D_n with equal nonzero numbers.

With measured data, the finite differences may be *nearly*, but not exactly, equal. Sometimes an approximate fit is the best you can do with measured data, and you will have to be content with *approximately* equal nonzero numbers in D_n.

Diagonals of Polygons Activity

Find an equation that expresses the relationship between the number of sides of a polygon and the number of diagonals.

a. The first step is to collect some data. Draw a four-sided polygon, a five-sided polygon, a six-sided polygon, and so on. Connect the nonconsecutive vertices of each polygon to form all the diagonals. Complete the chart.

Number of sides (s)	4	5	6	7	8	9
Number of diagonals (d)	2					

b. Use finite differences to predict the degree of the relationship. Because this data is not measured, but exact, you should find the differences in one of the levels of finite differences to be exactly equal.

c. Enter the data in your calculator and graph it. Choose one of the data points and call it (s, d).

d. Substitute the coordinates of point (s, d) from part c into the equation $d = as^2 + bs + c$ to get an equation in terms of a, b, and c.

e. Choose two other points and repeat the process from part d. You now have a system of three equations and three unknowns. Solve the system to find values for a, b, and c.

f. Using the values for a, b, and c from part e, write an equation expressing the relationship. Graph this equation to verify that it fits your data points.

g. Use your model to predict the number of diagonals in an octagon and the number in a dodecagon (12 sides).

h. Find the number of sides needed to have 230 diagonals.

When using the process developed in the above activity to find the equation, you must choose your points carefully. If the data is measured, as in the Falling Object Activity, your equation will most likely not fit all of the data points exactly. To get the best fit for all of the data points, choose three points that are not close together.

Problem Set 10.1

1. Meg Abux opens a savings account by depositing $10,000. The annual interest, i, is compounded monthly. At the end of the second month, $5,000 is added. At the end of the fourth month, $2,000 is added. (Nothing is added at the end of the first or third month.)

   a. Write an expression for the balance in the account at the end of the fourth month, using x to represent the multiplier $(1 + i/12)$.

   b. Find a good window of x-values for the graph. (Use common sense to estimate values for i, the interest rate.)

   c. Use your grapher to trace the graph of the curve and find the x-value needed to give a balance of $17,300 at the end of the fourth month.

   d. What is the annual interest rate, i?

2. Dr. Jeck L. Hyde takes 30 mg of a drug that will disappear from his blood at a rate of p percent per day.

   a. In writing an expression to represent the amount of the drug remaining in his blood, will you use $(1 + p)$ or $(1 - p)$ as your multiplier? Give a reason for your choice.

   b. Write an expression (using x as the multiplier) that gives the amount in his blood after three full days have passed.

   c. What x-value leaves 5 mg of the drug in his blood after three days?

   d. What percent p is removed each day?

3. Dr. Hyde takes 50 mg of a drug on day 1, 70 mg on day 2, and 90 mg on day 3. This drug disappears at a rate of q percent per day.

   a. Write an expression, using x as the multiplier $(1 - q)$, that gives the amount in his blood after 3 days.

   b. What x-value leaves 50 mg of the drug in his blood?

   c. What percent of the drug is removed each day?

4. a. The equation $s = 0.5n^2 + 0.5n$ generates triangular numbers. Create a table of values for this equation.

   b. Find the finite differences D_1 and D_2 between the consecutive values of s in your table.

n	1	2	3	4	5	6	7
s							

D_1						

D_2					

   c. What is the degree of this polynomial? How is this related to the finite differences?

   d. Why are triangular numbers (the s row above) called triangular? Answer in complete sentences.

5. The data below represents heights of an object during its fall. For 5a and 5b, compute the finite differences until one of D_1, D_2, and so on, are all *nonzero constants*.

a.

Time in seconds (t)	0	1	2	3	4	5	6
Height in meters (h)	80	95.1	100.4	95.9	81.6	57.5	23.6

b.

Time in seconds (t)	0	1	2	3	4	5	6
Height in meters (h)	4	63.1	112.4	151.9	181.6	201.5	211.6

c. Use what you know about the finite differences to predict the degree of the equation that you would use to model each data set.

d. Find the equation that will fit the data in 5a.

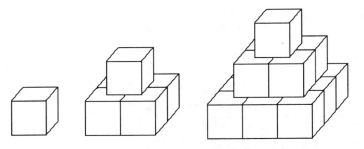

6. You can use blocks to build pyramids such as those shown above. Complete the table showing the number of layers in each pyramid and the number of blocks needed to build it. All pyramids are solid with no empty space inside.

a.

Layers (n)	1	2	3	4	5	6
Blocks (b)						

b. Use finite differences to find the degree of the relationship.

c. Write an equation for this relationship. (Hint: You will need to use four points to build your equation.)

d. Use your model to predict the number of blocks needed to build a pyramid eight layers high.

e. Graph and trace the curve to find the number of layers in a pyramid built with 650 blocks.

Section 10.2: Different Quadratic Forms

You have seen how polynomial equations can be used to represent bank balances, the levels of a drug in the bloodstream, geometric patterns, and other applications. Often you are able to use finite differences to find the polynomial equation that models a set of data. And you've learned that one way to solve a polynomial equation is to graph and trace. However, a polynomial equation can be written in a variety of different forms, and each form is useful (depending on what you want to do with the equation). In this section and the next, you will learn about three different forms in which you can express a polynomial equation.

Patterns of Squares Activity

Determine the number of 1-cm segments used to create each figure.

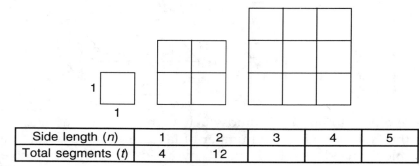

Side length (n)	1	2	3	4	5
Total segments (t)	4	12			

Calculate the finite differences until you have a common value. Find the equation (in terms of n and t) to fit this data. When you have found the equation, test the graph to see that it contains the data.

You might recognize the graph of your equation in the Patterns of Squares Activity as a parabola. You can write the equation of this parabola as $t = 2(n + 0.5)^2 - 0.5$, although this probably doesn't look like the equation you found. Are the two equations equivalent? How can you tell? Are there other forms for quadratic equations, and when is one form better than another? These are questions that you will explore in this section and the next.

One way to determine whether $t = 2(n + 0.5)^2 - 0.5$ and $t = 2n^2 + 2n$ are equivalent equations is to graph both of them to see if their graphs are the same. You may have to trace both graphs and check the coordinates. Another way is to use some algebra to remove the parentheses in the first expression.

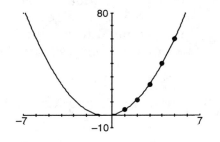

$2(n + 0.5)^2 - 0.5$	Original expression.
$2(n^2 + 0.5n + 0.5n + 0.25) - 0.5$	Multiply $(n + 0.5)(n + 0.5)$.
$2(n^2 + n + 0.25) - 0.5$	Add like terms.
$2n^2 + 2n + 0.5 - 0.5$	Multiply $2(n^2 + n + 0.25)$.
$2n^2 + 2n$	Add like terms.

This is the same equation that you found in the activity.

In the next section, you will explore a third popular form for this quadratic equation, $2n(n + 1)$. Following is a summary of the forms in which you can write a quadratic equation.

$y = ax^2 + bx + c$	**Polynomial Form**	$2n^2 + 2n$
$y = A(x - H)^2 + K$	**Vertex Form**	$2(n + 0.5)^2 - 0.5$
$y = A(x - R_1)(x - R_2)$	**Factored Form**	$2(n - 0)(n + 1)$

Problem Set 10.2

Use a "friendly" graphing window for most graphs in these problems. A background grid may also be helpful.

1. Each quadratic equation below is written in vertex form. Graph each function. Then remove parentheses to write each equation in polynomial form. Graph the new form of the quadratic equation to check that you removed the parentheses correctly.

    a. $y = (x - 2)^2 + 3$
    b. $y = (x + 4)^2 - 2$
    c. $y = 2(x - 5)^2 - 4$
    d. $y = {}^-0.5(x + 1)^2 + 4$
    e. $y = {}^-3(x - 4)^2$
    f. $y = 1.5(x - 0)^2 - 3$

    Write each equation without parentheses.

    g. $y = {}^-0.5(x + H)^2 + 4$
    h. $y = A(x - 4)^2$
    i. $y = A(x - H)^2 + K$

2. Write an equation in vertex form that describes each *transformation* of $y = x^2$. Next, use algebra to remove the parentheses and rewrite each equation in polynomial form. Finally, graph each form to make certain your equations are correct. Start *each* problem with $y = x^2$.

   a. Slide the graph 3 units left and then 2 units down.

   b. Reflect the graph over the *x*-axis, slide it 4 units right, and slide it 3 units up.

   c. Stretch the graph so that the *y*-values double, slide it 2 units right, and move it 4 units down.

   d. Multiply the *y*-values by −0.5, slide the graph 1.5 units left, and move it up 3 units.

   e. Stretch the graph by a factor of *A* vertically, slide it *H* units right, and slide it *K* units up.

3. Find the values of a, b, and c.

   a. $ax^2 + bx + c = 3x^2 + 2x - 5$

   b. $ax^2 + bx + c = 3x^2 + (2 + d)x + 14s^2$

   c. $ax^2 + bx + c = 2(x + 3)^2 + 4$

   d. $ax^2 + bx + c = -3(x - 5)^2 - 1$

4. Suppose $ax^2 + bx + c = A(x - H)^2 + K$. (Use the answer to Problem 1i to find the coefficients of x^2, x, and the constant.)

   a. $ax^2 + bx + c = \boxed{} x^2 + \boxed{} x + \boxed{}$.

   b. What is the relationship between a and A?

   c. Set the coefficients of the *x*-terms equal to each other, and solve for *H*. Substitute a for A, and find H in terms of a and b.

   d. Set the two constants equal to each other, and solve for *K*. Substitute your answers from 4b and 4c, and find an expression for K in terms of a, b, and c.

   e. Explain how you can check that your values give the same equation.

5. Use the results from Problem 4 to find the vertex of each parabola. Write each equation in vertex form. Check your work by graphing.

   a. $y = 3x^2 - 13x + 12$ b. $y = x^2 + 6x + 11$ c. $y = x^2 + 2x - 8$

   d. $h(t) = -16t^2 + 44t + 5$ e. $y = -2x^2 + 5x + 9$

6. The temperature you perceive often depends on the wind speed. This phenomenon is called the wind-chill factor. The following information is collected at a temperature reading of 30°F. At 5 mi/hr, the wind chill is 27°F; at 20 mi/hr, it is 4°F; and at 40 mi/hr, it is −5°F. Find a quadratic model for this data and locate the vertex.

7. The local outlet store charges $2 for a pack of AAA batteries. On the average, 200 packs are sold each day. A survey indicates that the sales will decrease by an average of 5 packs per day for each 10-cent increase in price.

   a. Use the information given to complete the row labeled "number sold."

Selling price	2.00	2.10	2.20	2.30	2.40
Number sold	200				
Revenue					
D_1					
D_2					

   b. Calculate the revenue using the selling price and the number sold. Then calculate the first and second differences.

   c. Write an equation that describes the relationship between the revenue, y, and the selling price, x, charged per pack.

   d. Graph the equation and find the maximum revenue. What selling price provides maximum revenue?

8. You are designing a rectangular garden and you need a fence to keep the varmints out. You have 80 m of fence and are trying to produce the largest possible area for your garden.

   a. Complete the following table for the widths provided.

Width	5	10	15	20	25
Length					
Area					

   b. Find an equation relating the area and the width of the garden.

   c. Which width provides the largest possible area? What is that area?

   d. Describe a situation that produces no area.

   e. Describe a situation that produces a negative area.

9. a. Use three points from your data in the Falling Object Activity to find an equation that will fit the curve.

   b. Put your equation in y_1 and set your graphing window to the values in the photograph. Record the window settings in your homework.

   c. Trace the curve and match the points on the photograph to points on your graph. Give the differences (residuals) for each point. Use the residuals to help you modify your equation to get the best fit you can.

Section 10.3: Factored Polynomials

You discovered that the formula for the number of diagonals in a polygon of n sides is $d = 0.5n^2 - 1.5n$. How can you find the number of sides if you are told there are 230 diagonals? You can graph and trace the curve until you find the point where the y-value is 230. Or you can make a table and look up the correct value there. Another technique is to write a new equation, $0.5n^2 - 1.5n = 230$. Then subtract 230 from each side to get $0.5n^2 - 1.5n - 230 = 0$. Graph this new equation. The solutions to this equation will be the x-values where the new graph crosses the x-axis. These values are called the **roots** of the equation. In this section, you will learn how to write equations of polynomials when you know the roots. You will also learn about one more form of a polynomial equation, the factored form, and how it relates to the roots of the equation.

Open-Topped Boxes Activity

You will need graph paper and scissors for this activity.

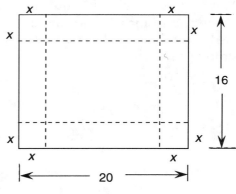

a. Cut several 16-unit-by-20 unit rectangles from your graph paper.

b. Construct open-top boxes with *all* possible integer x-value dimensions. (Construct the boxes by cutting a square from each corner and folding up the sides.)

c. Record the dimensions of each box and calculate the box's volume. Prepare a table showing the x-values and volumes of the boxes.

d. Use finite differences to find the degree of the relation. Write an equation that gives the volume V in terms of x, the side length of the removed square.

e. Graph the equation and determine the x-intercepts.(There are three.) Call these three values r_1, r_2, and r_3. If you make boxes using these values as x, what will they look like?

f. Graph the equation $y = (x - r_1)(x - r_2)(x - r_3)$, as well as your first equation. What are the similarities and differences? How can you alter the second equation to make the graphs of the equations identical?

Consider each graph pictured below. The x-intercepts have been marked.

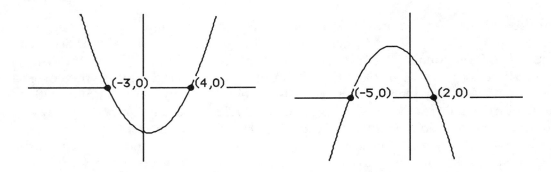

It should be no surprise that the y-coordinate is zero at each x-intercept. In fact, every point on the x-axis has a y-coordinate of zero. You will use this information and the **zero-factor property** to find x-intercepts.

Think of numbers that multiply to 0, $\square \bullet \bigcirc = 0$. Whatever numbers you substitute to make this statement true will have the following characteristic: *at least one of the factors must be zero.* Complete the following so that each statement is true.

$\boxed{} \bullet 16.2 = 0$ $3(\boxed{} - 4)(\boxed{} - 9) = 0$ $-1.4(x - 5.6)(x + 3.1) = 0$

(Ans. 0)   (Ans. either 4 or 9)   (Ans. either 5.6 or -3.1)

Example 1: Suppose $y = -1.4(x - 5.6)(x + 3.1)$. Look at the graph and the equation and name the x-intercepts. What are the coordinates of the vertex?

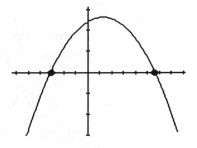

Solution: The x-intercepts will be the two x-values in the equation that make $y = 0$.

$0 = -1.4(x - 5.6)(x + 3.1)$

5.6 works because $-1.4(\mathbf{5.6 - 5.6})(\,5.6 + 3.1) = 0$.

-3.1 works because $-1.4(-3.1 - 5.6)(\mathbf{-3.1 + 3.1}) = 0$.

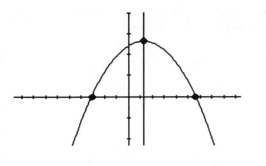

Because parabolas have reflection symmetry, the x-coordinate of the vertex is halfway between the x-coordinates of the intercepts (their average). Therefore the vertex has as its x-coordinate $\frac{(-3.1 + 5.6)}{2} = 1.25$.

You can substitute this value into the original equation to find the y-coordinate of the vertex: $y = -1.4(1.25 - 5.6)(1.25 + 3.1) = 26.4915$. Therefore, the vertex is at $(1.25, 26.4915)$.

So $H = 1.25$, $K = 26.4915$, and $A = -1.4$.

$y = A(x - H)^2 + K$ **Vertex Form** $y = -1.4(x - 1.25)^2 + 26.4915$

Expanding either the Factored Form or Vertex Form gives you

$y = ax^2 + bx + c$ **Polynomial Form** $y = -1.4x^2 + 3.5x + 24.304$

Example 2: Build an equation for a graph with x-intercepts at $-2.5, 7.5,$ and 3.2.

Solution: -2.5 makes $(x + 2.5) = 0$, 7.5 makes $(x - 7.5) = 0$, and 3.2 makes $(x - 3.2) = 0$. So the **Factored Form** $y = A(x - R_1)(x - R_2)$ is $y = A(x + 2.5)(x - 7.5)(x - 3.2)$.

You can choose different values for A and experiment to see what effect each choice will have on the graph. You will soon be able to predict the effect produced by different positive or negative values of A.

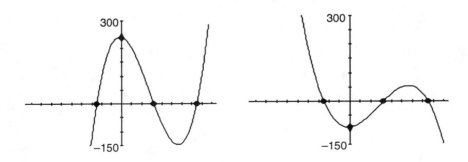

The equation of the graph on the left is $y = 4(x - 7.5)(x + 2.5)(x - 3.2)$. Notice that the x-intercepts are correct. The y-intercept has 0 as an x-value. Substituting $x = 0$ into the equation gives 240 as the y-intercept. The equation of the graph on the right has the same x-intercepts. The equation is $y = -1.5(x - 7.5)(x + 2.5)(x - 3.2)$. Substituting $x = 0$, you find the y-intercept is -90.

Problem Set 10.3

1. a. Find the x-intercepts and y-intercept of $y = 2.5(x - 7.5)(x + 2.5)(x - 3.2)$.

   b. Remove the parentheses and write the equation in polynomial form.

   c. Graph the polynomial form to make certain your work is correct.

2. A projectile is shot from the bottom of a well. It comes up to ground level after 0.7 sec and falls back to ground level again at 2.8 sec.

   a. Complete the equation of this graph using the points (0.7, 0) and (2.8, 0):

   $y = -4.9(\qquad)(\qquad)$. The height, (in meters), is given by y and the time is represented by x.

   b. Find the vertex. What is the real-world meaning of this value?

   c. Find the y-intercept. What is the real-world meaning of this value?

   d. If -4.9 is changed to a different nonzero number, what varies in the graph? What stays the same?

3. Find the x-intercepts and y-intercept for the graph of each equation, without actually graphing. If the equation represents a parabola, find the vertex. Check each answer by graphing.

   a. $y = -0.25(x + 1.5)(x + 6)$ b. $y = 3(x - 4)(x - 4)$

   c. $y = -2(x - 3)(x + 2)(x + 5)$ d. $y = 5(x + 3)(x + 3)(x - 3)$

4. Sketch a graph that has the given attributes.

   a. A quadratic equation with one x-intercept

   b. A quadratic equation with no x-intercepts

   c. A cubic equation with one x-intercept

   d. A cubic equation with two x-intercepts

5. a. Write the factored form of the equation for each graph. Make certain the graph passes through the points indicated.

i.

ii.

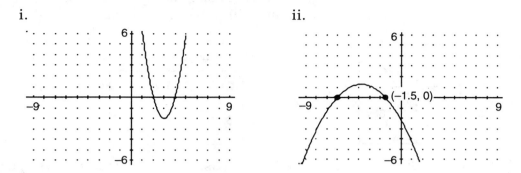

b. Write the polynomial form of the equation of each graph.

c. Write the vertex form of the equation of each graph.

6. Let $y_1 = x + 2$ and $y_2 = x - 3$. Graph y_1, y_2, and $y_3 = y_1 y_2$. How does the graph of y_3 compare to the graphs of y_1 and y_2?

7. a. Write the equation of the polynomial of least degree that contains the x-intercepts pictured.

b. Adjust the leading factor A so that it contains the y-intercept $(0, 180)$. This might take some exploring.

c. Write the equation that contains points that are exactly 100 units up from the graph pictured.

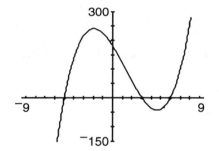

d. Write the equation that contains points that are exactly 4 units left of the points pictured.

8. a. Express the area of each large rectangle in factored form.

b. Express the area of each large rectangle in polynomial form.

i.

ii.

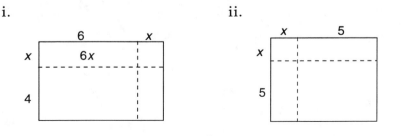

9. a. Complete the blanks for each figure.

   b. Find the missing expression (if there is one) and the area of each large rectangle in (i) factored form, and (ii) polynomial form.

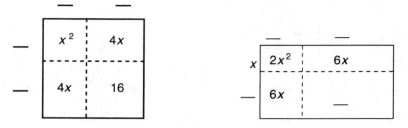

10. Write each polynomial in factored form. (Use area models if you wish, or graph the polynomials and look for x-intercepts.)

   a. $x^2 - 10x + 24$ b. $x^2 - 6x + 9$ c. $x^2 - 64$

   d. $x^2 - 2x - 120$ e. $4x^2 - 88x + 480$ f. $6x^2 - 7x - 5$

   g. $x^2 - (R_1 + R_2)x + R_1 R_2$ h. $a^2 + 2ab + b^2$

11. a. Is it possible to find a quadratic polynomial that contains the points $(-4, -2)$, $(-1, 7)$, and $(2, 16)$? Explain why or why not.

   b. Find a quadratic polynomial that has vertex $(-2, 3)$ and contains the point $(4, 12)$.

Section 10.4: The Quadratic Formula

Very few quadratic functions can be solved by factoring. Although you can always graph the function and trace to find the x-intercepts, you are often not able to find exact solutions. In this section, you will learn about an algebraic formula that you can always use to find the exact solutions to a quadratic function.

The polynomial $x^2 - 6x + 9$ is a perfect square because both factors are the same: $x^2 - 6x + 9 = (x - 3)^2$. Another perfect-square polynomial is $x^2 + 16x + 64$, because $x^2 + 16x + 64 = (x + 8)^2$.

Each large rectangle below is a pictorial representation of a perfect square. The areas of the smaller rectangles represent the terms of the polynomial, and the side lengths represent the factors.

$$(x + 5)(x + 5) = (x + 5)^2$$
$$= x^2 + 5x + 5x + 25$$
$$= x^2 + 10x + 25$$

	x	5
x	x^2	$5x$
5	$5x$	25

$$(a + b)(a + b) = (a + b)^2$$
$$= a^2 + ab + ab + b^2$$
$$= a^2 + 2ab + b^2$$

	a	b
a	a^2	ab
b	ab	b^2

Example 1: Suppose you start with an equation and want to find the x-values, or the roots, that satisfy the equation. If you already have a perfect square like $(x + 3)^2 = 16$, it's easy.

Solution:
$$x + 3 = \pm\sqrt{16}$$
$$x + 3 = \pm 4$$
$$x = \pm 4 - 3$$
$$x = 1 \text{ or } x = -7$$

Check this by calculating $(1 + 3)^2$ and $(-7 + 3)^2$.

Example 2: Find the x-intercepts (also called zeros) of an unstretched parabola with a vertex at $(-3, -16)$ that opens upward.

Solution: The graph $y = (x + 3)^2 - 16$ crosses the x-axis when

$$(x + 3)^2 - 16 = 0$$
$$(x + 3)^2 = 16$$

So the x-intercepts are at 1 and -7. Check this with a graph.

Solving quadratic equations is routine when the expression is already written as a perfect square or in *vertex form*. In general, when $y = A(x - H)^2 + K$ you can find the zeros, or roots, by using this process.

Start with $A(x - H)^2 + K = 0$ Replace y with zero.

$\qquad A(x - H)^2 = {}^-K$ Add ^-K to both sides.

$\qquad (x - H)^2 = \dfrac{^-K}{A}$ Multiply both sides by $\frac{1}{A}$.

$\qquad (x - H) = \pm \sqrt{\dfrac{^-K}{A}}$ Take the square root of both sides.

$\qquad x = H \pm \sqrt{\dfrac{^-K}{A}}$ Add H to both sides.

Notice that there are two zeros, $x = H + \sqrt{\dfrac{^-K}{A}}$ and $x = H - \sqrt{\dfrac{^-K}{A}}$.

Because all parabolas have a vertex and can be written in vertex form, you can use this formula to find the zeros of any parabola.

Example 3: Find the zeros, or x-intercepts, of $y = -3(x - 2)^2 + 5$

Solution: $x = H \pm \sqrt{\dfrac{^-K}{A}} = 2 \pm \sqrt{\dfrac{^-5}{^-3}} \approx 2 \pm 1.291 = 3.291, -0.709$

Suppose you want to find the x-intercepts and the equation is in polynomial form, $y = ax^2 + bx + c$. Either the equation must be changed to vertex form, or you need a modified formula that uses a, b, and c instead of A, H, and K. You have already made the connection between the coefficients of $ax^2 + bx + c$ and $A(x - H)^2 + K$ (Section 2, Problem 4).

$$A = a, \qquad H = \frac{-b}{2a}, \qquad \text{and} \qquad K = c - \frac{b^2}{4a}.$$

Start with $\quad x = H \pm \sqrt{\dfrac{-K}{A}}$ $\qquad\qquad$ The zeros in vertex form.

$$x = \dfrac{-b}{2a} \pm \sqrt{\dfrac{-(c - \dfrac{b^2}{4a})}{a}}$$ $\qquad$ Substitute for H, K, and A.

$$x = \dfrac{-b}{2a} \pm \sqrt{\dfrac{\dfrac{b^2}{4a} - c}{a}}$$ $\qquad$ Remove the parentheses.

$$x = \dfrac{-b}{2a} \pm \sqrt{\dfrac{\dfrac{b^2}{4a} - \dfrac{4ac}{4a}}{a}}$$ $\qquad$ Rewrite with a common denominator.

$$x = \dfrac{-b}{2a} \pm \sqrt{\dfrac{b^2 - 4ac}{4a^2}} = \dfrac{-b}{2a} \pm \dfrac{\sqrt{b^2 - 4ac}}{\sqrt{4a^2}} = \dfrac{-b}{2a} \pm \dfrac{\sqrt{b^2 - 4ac}}{2a}$$

$$x = \dfrac{-b \pm \sqrt{b^2 - 4ac}}{2a}$$

The Quadratic Formula	
Vertex form	Polynomial form
If $A(x - H)^2 + K = 0$, then the solutions are $x = H \pm \sqrt{\dfrac{-K}{A}}$	If $ax^2 + bx + c = 0$, then the solutions are $x = \dfrac{-b \pm \sqrt{b^2 - 4ac}}{2a}$

Example 4: Find the x-intercepts of $y = x^2 - 14x - 26$.

Solution:

$x^2 - 14x - 26 = 0 \qquad a = 1, b = -14,$ and $c = -26$

$$x = \dfrac{-(-14) \pm \sqrt{(-14)^2 - 4(1)(-26)}}{2(1)}$$ $\qquad$ (Be careful with the parentheses.)

$$x = \dfrac{14 \pm \sqrt{300}}{2}$$

$x = 7 \pm 0.5\sqrt{300}$ $\qquad\qquad$ (The **exact** answers.)

The x-intercepts are at $7 + 0.5\sqrt{300} \approx 15.66$ and $7 - 0.5\sqrt{300} \approx -1.66$. Do these values agree with the values found on the graph?

Some problems in this chapter involve objects under the influence of earth's gravity. The distance measurements of these projectile-motion problems are normally in either meters or feet. The initial coefficient depends on which system you are using. The equations are polynomials involving either t or x, depending on whether you use parametric or $y=$ form.

Example 5: Ovida Fentz hits a baseball so that it travels at a speed of 120 ft/sec and at an angle of 30° to the ground (horizontal). If her bat contacts the ball at a height of 3 ft above the ground, how far does the ball travel before it hits the ground?

Solution: You can model this situation best by looking at the motion of the ball parametrically. That is, break it into its horizontal and vertical components. This is like problems you have done before, except that the ball leaves the bat at an angle. Draw a picture and write equations for the x- and y-components of the motion.

$$\cos 30° = \frac{x}{120t} \qquad \sin 30° = \frac{y}{120t}$$

$$x = 120t \cos 30° \qquad y = 120t \sin 30°$$

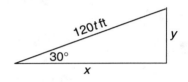

Because the x-direction of the motion is affected only by Ovida hitting the ball, the distance traveled in that direction will be given by $x = 120t \cos 30°$. The vertical motion is affected by Ovida hitting the ball, and also by the force of gravity pulling it down. In this case, the equation becomes $y = {}^{-}16t^2 + 120t \sin 30° + 3$. Notice that this is a second-degree polynomial. What is the meaning of the 3 in the equation? What is the meaning of the ${}^{-}16t^2$? If you want to find out when the ball hits the ground, you need to know when the y-value is 0. You can trace the graph, but now you also have the algebraic tools to solve the equation.

$$-16t^2 + 120t(0.5) + 3 = 0$$

Evaluate sin 30°.

$$-16t^2 + 60t + 3 = 0$$

Multiply.

$$a = {}^-16, b = 60, c = 3$$

Identify values of a, b, and c for the quadratic formula.

Substitute into the quadratic formula.

$$t = \frac{{}^-60 \pm \sqrt{60^2 - 4({}^-16)(3)}}{2({}^-16)}$$

$$t = {}^-0.049, 3.799$$

Evaluate quadratic formula and take the positive root. (Why do you ignore the negative root?)

To find how far the ball has traveled, substitute this t-value into the x-equation.

$$x = 120(3.799) \cos 30° = 394.84 \text{ feet.}$$

When an object is projected straight upward (like a rocket, or a ball thrown straight up), the situation can be modeled with one equation for y in terms of x.

Projectile motion equations:

One equation: Height versus time: $y = ax^2 + v_0x + s_0$, where

y = height in meters (feet), $a = {}^-4.9$ m/sec² or $^-16$ ft/sec²,

x = time in seconds, v_0 = initial speed in m/sec or ft/sec, and

s_0 = initial height in meters or feet.

Parametric: $x = v_0t \cos A + x_0$; $y = at^2 + v_0t \sin A + y_0$, where

x = horizontal, y = vertical, x_0 = horizontal start, y_0 = vertical start, $a = {}^-4.9$ or $^-16$, v_0 = initial speed, and A = initial angle.

Example 6: An object is projected upward with a velocity of 40 ft/sec from a starting height of 4 ft. When will the object hit the ground?

Solution: The height of the object at time t is found by $y = -16t^2 + v_0 t + s_0$ because the heights are in feet. The initial velocity, v_0, is 40 ft/sec and the initial height, s_0, is 4 ft. So the equation must be $y = -16t^2 + 40t + 4$. To find when the object will hit the ground, set $y = 0$. So $-16t^2 + 40t + 4 = 0$ and because $a = -16$, $b = 40$, and $c = 4$,

$$x = \frac{-b \pm \sqrt{b^2 - 4ac}}{2a} \text{ will become } t = \frac{-40 \pm \sqrt{(40)^2 - 4(-16)(4)}}{2(-16)} \text{ or}$$

$$t = \frac{-40 \pm \sqrt{1856}}{-32}. \text{ Therefore } t \approx -0.096 \text{ or } t \approx 2.596. \text{ Check this by}$$

graphing the equation. Because negative solutions make no sense in this problem, the time must be 2.596 seconds.

Sunburn Activity

The data in the table below was published in the *Mesa* (*Arizona*) *Tribune* on August 8, 1993. It gives the amount of time needed to redden untanned Caucasian skin at different times of the day based on the predicted weather for that day.

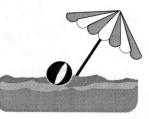

Time	9 A.M.	10 A.M.	11 A.M.	noon	1 P.M.	2 P.M.	3 P.M.	4 P.M.
Minutes	34	20	15	13	14	18	32	60

Plot the data and find an equation to fit the curve. Explain why you think your equation is the best. What is an appropriate domain for your equation? Use your equation to determine at what times skin will burn in 30 min. Do you think the equation would change for a different part of the country? Explain your reasoning.

Problem Set 10.4

Use either a graph or substitution to find each solution. Use your calculator to check solutions when possible. When appropriate, make a quick sketch of the graph in your homework for later reference.

1. Factor each polynomial.

   a. $4x^2 - 12x + 9$　　b. $x^2 + 5x + \dfrac{25}{4}$　　c. $x^2 - 2xy + y^2$

2. Solve for x.

   a. $(x - 2.3)^2 = 25$ b. $(x + 4.45)^2 = 12.25$ c. $(x - \frac{3}{4})^2 = \frac{25}{16}$

3. Rewrite each equation in polynomial form. Identify a, b, and c, and solve for x with the quadratic formula. Express each solution both in exact form and as a decimal approximation to the nearest 0.001.

   a. $3x^2 - 13x = 10$ b. $x^2 - 13 = 5x$ c. $3x^2 + 5x = -1$

   d. $3x^2 - 2 - 3x = 0$ e. $14(x - 4) - (x + 2) = (x + 2)(x - 4)$

4. Find the time and position when the projectile described by each equation reaches the ground.

   a. $x = 5t - 3$ b. $x = 7t + 2$ c. $x = 9$

      $y = -4.9t^2 + 5t + 7$ $y = -16t^2 + 2t + 100$ $y = -4.9t^2 - 3.17t + 470$

5. Write a quadratic polynomial for each situation described.

   a. Solutions 3 and $^-3$ b. Solutions 4 and $\frac{-2}{5}$ c. Solutions R_1 and R_2

   d. A projectile shot from the bottom of a well that reaches ground level at 1.1 sec and 4.7 sec.

6. Use the quadratic formula to find the x-intercepts (to the nearest 0.01) for $y = 2x^2 + 2x + 5$. Explain your dilemma. Is there a way to recognize this situation without using the formula? Find another equation that has no x-intercepts.

7. The table below gives the minimum stopping distance (in feet) required to stop a car traveling at the given speed on dry pavement.

Speed (mi/hr)	10	20	30	40	50	60	70
Stopping distance	19	42	73	116	173	248	343

   a. Write a quadratic equation that contains any three points in the data.

   b. Compare your equation to those of others. What conclusion can you draw from this?

   c. Describe a method for selecting data points that builds the most accurate model of the given information.

8. In Example 4, you found $7 + 0.5\sqrt{300}$ and $7 - 0.5\sqrt{300}$ as the solutions to $x^2 - 14x - 26 = 0$. Substitute these exact answers in for x to verify that they work.

9. A 20-ft ladder is leaning against a building.

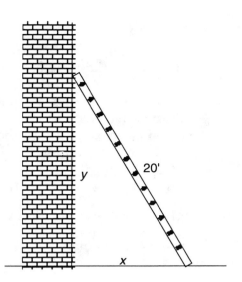

   a. Write an equation for y in terms of x.

   b. Find the height of the building if the ladder is 10 ft from the building.

   c. Find the distance of the foot of the ladder from the building if the ladder must reach 18 ft up the wall.

   d. Write out both the *name* and *statement of the formula* you used to write the equation in 9a.

10. The quadratic formula can be entered as a program in your calculator. This program can be elaborate or simple. Write a program that prompts the user to *input* values for a, b, and c for equations in the form $ax^2 + bx + c = 0$. The program should *calculate* the two solutions and *display* the answers.

11. Flying Freddy, the human cannonball, is fired out of a cannon at a speed of 40 ft/sec. The cannon is tilted at an angle of 60°. A 10-ft diameter net is hung 10 ft above the floor at a distance of 30 ft from the cannon.

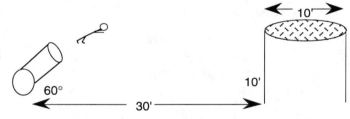

   Does Freddy land in the net? Record the equations you used to model this motion.

12. So far in this chapter you have looked at three different forms for a quadratic expression or equation. Discuss each of the forms, explaining why and in what situation you might prefer to use that form.

Section 10.5: Applications and Algebraic Solutions

So far in this chapter you have explored a variety of methods for solving quadratic equations. You have used graph-and-zoom techniques as well as several algebraic methods. In this section you will explore a variety of real-world applications for these techniques. Keep in mind that often there is more than one way to solve a problem. As you work the problems, share, compare, and discuss your methods with others.

Example 1: What interest rate provides a total value of $193.84 after three $60 deposits on Nick's fourteenth, fifteenth, and sixteenth birthdays?

Solution: In Section 10.1, you graphed and located the intersection of $y_1 = 60x^2 + 60x + 60$ and $y_2 = 193.84$ by tracing and zooming. (See the graph on the left below.) You also obtained the same solution for x by graphing $y_1 - y_2$ and locating the positive x-intercept. (See the graph on the right below.)

$$y_1 = y_2 \qquad\qquad \text{or} \qquad\qquad y_1 - y_2 = 0$$
$$60x^2 + 60x + 60 = 197.64 \qquad\qquad 60x^2 + 60x + 60 - 197.64 = 0$$
$$60x^2 + 60x - 137.64 = 0$$

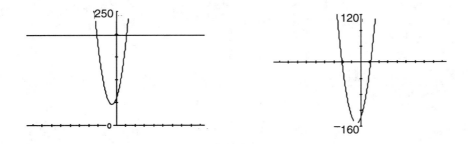

Instead of tracing and zooming, you could also find the solution by using the quadratic formula.

$$60x^2 + 60x - 133.84 = 0 \qquad\qquad a = 60, b = 60, c = -133.84$$

$$x = \frac{-60 \pm \sqrt{(60)^2 - 4(60)(-133.84)}}{2(60)} \approx 1.07501 \text{ or } -2.07501$$

Because you are looking for growth, the negative solution is **extraneous**, which means it has no meaning in this situation. Therefore, the annual interest rate is approximately 7.5%.

Example 2: An object is thrown vertically upward at 38 m/sec from a height of 55 m. Give the equation for its height. When does it hit the ground? How high does the object get?

Solution: The equation describing the height from the ground at any time t is

$$H(t) = -4.9t^2 + 38t + 55.$$

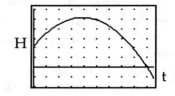

Ground level is the x-intercept, so use the quadratic formula to solve the equation when $H(t) = 0$.

$$t = \frac{-b \pm \sqrt{b^2 - 4ac}}{2a} = \frac{-38 \pm \sqrt{(38)^2 - 4(-4.9)(55)}}{2(-4.9)} = 9.002 \text{ or } -1.247$$

Again, the negative answer is extraneous, so the time in the air is approximately 9.002 seconds. The maximum height of the parabola is at the vertex (H, K). Because the vertex is located on the line of symmetry, the roots will be equally distant from that vertex on opposite sides. The average of these two roots will give the x-value of the point halfway between.

$$H = \frac{-1.247 + 9.002}{2} \approx 3.88.$$

Substitute this x-value into the original equation to find the y-value of the vertex, $K = -4.9(3.88)^2 + 38(3.88) + 55 \approx 128.67$.

Preliminary Edition

Making a Suitcase Activity

You will need graph paper and scissors for this activity.

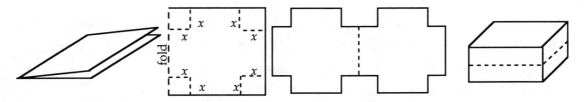

a. Fold a piece of paper in half as shown above. Then cut four equal-sized squares from the corners and fold your paper to form a box with a top. Determine the volume of the box.

b. What values of x would make a box with no volume? (There should be three such values.)

c. Use the x-values from part b to write an equation in factored form for the volume of the box.

d. Use the data from the box you made to determine the A-value for your equation. Graph your equation.

e. What value of x will give the box with the largest volume? What is the maximum volume?

f. Construct this maximum-volume box.

Problem Set 10.5

Solve each problem using algebraic manipulation and formulas.
When appropriate, you can check your solutions with a graph.

1. An object is dropped from the top of a building into a pool of water at ground level. The splash is 6.8 sec after the object is dropped. How high is the building in meters? In feet?

2. An object was projected upward and the following data collected.

Time in seconds (t)	1	2	3	4	5	6
Height in meters (h)	120.1	205.4	280.9	346.6	402.4	448.4

    a. Write the specific equation relating time and height for this object.

    b. What was the initial height? The initial velocity?

    c. At what time did the object reach its maximum height?

    d. What was the maximum height?

    e. When was the object 300 m high?

    f. When did the object hit the ground?

3. The local discount store charges $6.60 for a flashlight. On the average, 200 of them are sold each day. A survey indicates that the sales will decrease by an average of 10 flashlights per day for each 50-cent increase in price.

    a. Write an equation that describes the relationship between the revenue, y, and the selling price, x, charged per flashlight. (A table might help.)

    b. What selling price provides maximum revenue?

4. You are enclosing a rectangular area as a dog run. You have 80 ft of fence and want to build a pen with the largest possible area for your dog, so you build the dog run using an existing building as one side. Find the areas for some selected values of x.

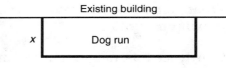

    a. Write an equation relating the area, y, and width, x.

    b. What width provides the largest possible area? What is that area?

5. a. Write a formula relating the greatest number of pizza pieces, y, you can obtain from x cuts.

    b. Use the formula to find the maximum number of pieces with five cuts and with ten cuts. Is there a greatest number of pieces?

One Cut   Two Cuts   Three Cuts

6. This 26 in. by 21 in. rectangle has been divided into two regions. The width of the unshaded region is x inches.

   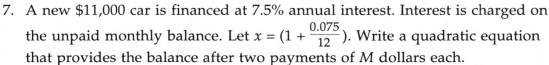

   a. Express the area of the shaded part as a function of x and graph it.

   b. Determine what values of x and A (area) make sense.

   c. Find the value of x that makes the two regions (shaded and unshaded) equal in area.

7. A new $11,000 car is financed at 7.5% annual interest. Interest is charged on the unpaid monthly balance. Let $x = (1 + \frac{0.075}{12})$. Write a quadratic equation that provides the balance after two payments of M dollars each.

8. The Math Club plans to sell mathematical T-shirts. They can purchase the shirts for $6.50 each. They surveyed 400 students to determine the highest price each would be willing to pay for a T-shirt. All 400 students indicated they would buy a shirt if the price were $8.00 or less, but only 208 students would buy shirts at $11.00.

Price	8.00	8.50	9.00	9.50	10.00	10.50	11.00
Number of students	400	373	344	313	280	245	208
Profit							

   a. Write an equation relating price charged and profit.

   b. Determine the price that will result in the maximum possible total profit.

   c. What price would result in a profit of $0.00?

9. The data in the table represents the amount of water in a draining bathtub and the amount of time since the plug was pulled.

Amount of water (L)	38.4	30.0	19.6	7.2
Time (min)	1	1.5	2	2.5

   a. Write an equation expressing liters (L), in terms of time (t).

   b. How much water was in the tub when you pulled the plug?

   c. How long did it take the tub to empty?

Section 10.6: Higher Degree Polynomials

Earlier in the chapter you looked at equations like $60x^2 + 60x + 60 = 149.544$. There are many interpretations of this equation. If you look at absorption of drugs taken daily, then the first term, $60x^2$, represents the amount of a 60-mg dosage remaining after two days. The second term, $60x$, represents the amount of the 60-mg dosage remaining after one day. The third 60 mg didn't have time to be absorbed by the body, so all of it is still present. The sum, 149.544 mg, represents the total amount remaining in the body after two days. If the absorption rate was 18% per day, then $x = (1 - 0.18)$.

Example 1: Suppose 60 mg of a drug is taken daily for three days. Then the dosage is reduced to 40 mg on the fourth day and 25 mg on the fifth day. Allowing for different absorption rates ($a\%$) for different people, let $x = 1 - a/100$. What is the expression that gives the amount in the system?

Solution:

60	at day 1
$60x + \mathbf{60}$	at day 2
$60x^2 + 60x + \mathbf{60}$	at day 3
$60x^3 + 60x^2 + 60x + \mathbf{40}$	at day 4
$60x^4 + 60x^3 + 60x^2 + 40x + \mathbf{25}$	at day 5

The first term, $60x^4$, gives the amount of the first day's dose that remains after four days. The second term, $60x^3$, gives the amount of the second day's dose that remains after three days, and so on.
Five different types of polynomials are used in this example.

$y = 60$ constant polynomial (zero degree)

$y = 60x + 60$ linear polynomial (1st degree)

$y = 60x^2 + 60x + 60$ quadratic polynomial (2nd degree)

$y = 60x^3 + 60x^2 + 60x + 40$ cubic polynomial (3rd degree)

$y = 60x^4 + 60x^3 + 60x^2 + 40x + 25$ 4th degree polynomial

Polynomials with degree 3 or more are called higher degree polynomials. Instead of continuing with $a, b, c, \ldots$, as coefficients, you can use subscripted variables.

Polynomial Equations of Degree n

$$y = a_n x^n + a_{n-1} x^{n-1} + a_{n-2} x^{n-2} + \ldots + a_2 x^2 + a_1 x + a_0$$

Where the leading coefficient $a_n \neq 0$, and exponents, $n, n - 1$, and so on, are positive integers.

Polynomials with real coefficients have graphs that have a y-intercept, possibly one or more x-intercepts, and other features like turning points (local maxima or minima). In this section you will discover how to make the connections between polynomials and their graphs, so that you can predict when different features will occur.

Paper Folding Activity

Take a sheet of paper and fold the upper left corner so that it touches some point on the bottom edge of the same sheet. Find the area of triangle A formed in the lower left corner of the paper. Find the distance along the bottom of the paper (x) that produces the triangle with the greatest area. In some detail, explain your strategy for finding the largest triangle.

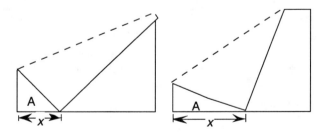

Example 2: The easiest connection to make may be between factors of the polynomial and the x-intercepts. (Zeros and roots are other names for the values at x-intercepts.) Find a polynomial that contains the x-intercepts $(3, 0)$, $(5, 0)$, and $(-4, 0)$.

Solution: This polynomial isn't quadratic because it has too many
x-intercepts. It could be a 3rd, 4th, 5th, or higher degree polynomial.
Consider a cubic equation, because that is the lowest possible degree
you can have with three roots. The expression $(x - 3)$ is zero when x
is 3, $(x - 5)$ is zero when x is 5, and $(x + 4)$ is zero when x is $^-4$.
Therefore, $y = A(x - 3)(x - 5)(x + 4)$ will work as the equation for
different nonzero choices of A.

This is the graph of
$y = A(x - 3)(x - 5)(x + 4)$
with A equal to 1.

Notice points D, E, and F are the three
required x-intercepts and point I is the
y-intercept $(0, 60)$. Do you see why it is 60?

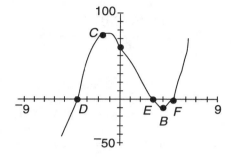

Point B is a **local minimum point** because it is the lowest point in its immediate
neighborhood of x-values. Point C is a **local maximum point** because it is the
highest point in its immediate neighborhood of x-values.

In the problems, you will have the opportunity to substitute other values for A
in the equation $y = A(x - 3)(x - 5)(x + 4)$ to see the effect. You will also explore
what happens with different exponents on the three factors. For example, what is
different and what is the same for $y = A(x - 3)(x - 5)(x + 4)^2$?

You can identify the degree of many polynomial graphs by looking at their
shapes. Every 3rd-degree polynomial has essentially one of the shapes shown
below. The first graph is $y = x^3$. It can be translated horizontally or vertically,
stretched, or flipped. The next two graphs are of the general cubic equation
$y = ax^3 + bx^2 + cx + d$. In the middle graph, a is positive. It is negative in the last
graph.

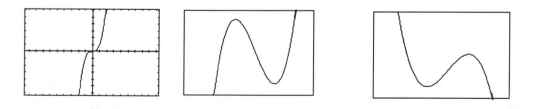

You should take time to graph several cubic equations. What you see will depend on your graphing window. You get a global view by selecting a large viewing screen. The global view gives you the end-behavior information about the graph at the right and left extremes of the x-axis, but tends to diminish individual features of the graph. It is similar to what happens to your view of an object as you move farther away from it.

Problem Set 10.6

1. a. Write a linear equation with x-intercept at $(4, 0)$.

    b. Write a quadratic equation with its only x-intercept at $(4, 0)$.

    c. Write a cubic equation with its only x-intercept at $(4, 0)$.

2. The graph for $y = 2(x - 3)(x - 5)(x + 4)^2$ has zeros at 3, 5, and -4 because they are the only possible values of x that make $y = 0$. This is a 4th-degree polynomial, but it has only three different x-intercepts. Graph each equation and name a graphing window that provides a complete graph.
    Complete graphs display all of the relevant features including local extrema.

    a. $y = 2(x - 3)(x - 5)(x + 4)^2$ b. $y = 2(x - 3)^2 (x - 5)(x + 4)$

    c. $y = 2(x - 3)(x - 5)^2 (x + 4)$ d. $y = 2(x - 3)^2 (x - 5)(x + 4)^2$

    e. Describe a connection between the exponent on a factor and what happens at that x-intercept.

3. Both graphs below are of the same polynomial function. The one on the left is not a complete graph.

    a. How many x-intercepts are there?

    b. What is the smallest possible degree for this polynomial?

    c. Write an equation of the graph pictured that includes the points $(0, 0)$, $(-5, 0)$, $(4, 0)$, $(-1, 0)$, and $(1, 216)$. You may have to use an exponent on a factor to get it right.

4. In this problem, you will investigate the graph of $y = A(x - 3)^n$ with different values of A and n.

   a. Suppose $n = 2$. Try different values of A and describe the effect of each on the graph.

   b. Suppose $A = {}^-2$. Try different values of n and describe the effect of each on the graph.

   c. What is the same about the graphs of $y = (x - 3)^2$ and $y = (x - 3)^4$? What is different?

   d. What is the same about the graphs of $y = (x - 3)^1$ and $y = (x - 3)^3$? What is different?

   e. Predict what the graph of $y = (x - 3)^2 (x - 5)^3 (x + 1)(x + 4)^2$ will look like. Verify your guess. This is an 8th degree polynomial with zeros $\{3, 3, 5, 5, 5, {}^-1, {}^-4, {}^-4\}$.

5. A 4th degree polynomial has the equation $y = ax^4 + bx^3 + cx^2 + dx + e$ for real values of $a, b, c, d,$ and e. Try different values for each of these coefficients. Be sure to include positive, negative, and zero values. Make a sketch of each different type of curve you get. Do not include the x-axis in your sketches. Compare graphs with others in the class and come up with six or more different shapes that describe all 4th degree functions.

6. True or false: Every polynomial equation has at least one real solution. Explain your answer. Modify the statement, if necessary, to make it true.

7. In each graph, $A = 1$ or -1. Write equations in factored form that will produce each graph.

a.

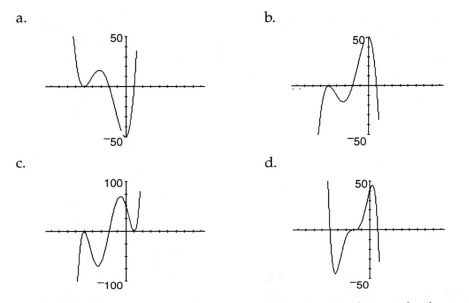

b.

c.

d.

e. Name the zeros of each polynomial in 7a–7d above. If a factor has degree n, list the zero n times.

8. The activity in this section relates the area of a triangle to the length of its base x. Explore the problem further by answering the following questions.

a. Use very careful measurements to find the area when the x-value is 3. Then find the area for an x-value of 6.

b. Name two x-values that produce an area of zero.

c. Given the equation $area = A(x - R_1)(x - R_2)(x - R_3)$, what do the results of 8b tell you about the problem?

d. Use the values from 8a and the equation from 8c to write two equations. Solve this system, and give the equation in factored form.

e. Graph your equation and find the maximum value for the area.

Section 10.7: No Real Solutions

You have explored several ways to solve quadratic equations. You can graph and zoom in to find the x-intercepts, you can make a table of values and zoom in numerically, or you can use the quadratic formula. But what happens if you try to use the quadratic formula on an equation whose graph has no x-intercepts?

Graph $y = x^2 + 4x + 5$. It has no x-intercepts. Using the quadratic formula you will get

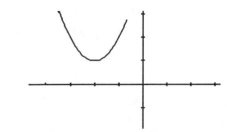

$$x = \frac{-4 \pm \sqrt{16 - 4(1)(5)}}{2} = \frac{-4 \pm \sqrt{-4}}{2}.$$

How do you take the square root of a negative number? This problem has bothered people for a long time. Since the 1500s, the square root of a negative number has been called an **imaginary number**. In the late 1700s, Euler introduced the symbol i to represent $\sqrt{-1}$. If you rewrite $\sqrt{-4}$ in its imaginary form, it is $\sqrt{4}\sqrt{-1} = 2i$. Therefore, the two solutions of the given equation are $\frac{-4 + 2i}{2}$ and $\frac{-4 - 2i}{2}$ or $-2 + i$ and $-2 - i$.

Numbers such as $\sqrt{-3}$ are usually rewritten as $i\sqrt{3}$ before performing any computations. Don't write $\sqrt{3}\, i$ because others can't tell whether i is or isn't under the radical.

Imagine a tank of water with a motorized device that creates waves that are 5 cm high from crest to trough. What happens to the waves when you add another similar device right next to it? Will the waves created be 10 cm? They may be, or there may be no waves at all, or they could be anything in between, like 2.5 cm or 7.5 cm. If the motors are synchronized, the waves will be 10 cm high. If they are running one quarter-cycle out of phase, then the waves will be about 7 cm high. Something similar happens when you combine a real number and an imaginary number.

The combination of a real number and an imaginary number creates a new type of number called a complex number. These are different than the numbers you have used before. They are numbers with a phase or a direction. You know that $5 + 5 = 10$, but $5 + 5i$ is not 10, any more than a place 5 km north and 5 km east of you is 10 km away. It is about 7 km to the northeast—a new direction altogether. If the second motor is one quarter-cycle out of phase, then you will end up with 7 cm waves in a slightly different pattern than the original waves. Complex numbers help describe many applications involving waves, including electrical systems, displacement of objects, the flow of air over and below an aircraft wing, and the flow of fluids around barriers. Using complex numbers actually enables you to model these situations more realistically.

The definition of an imaginary number can be extended a little by considering the meaning of square root. You know that $\sqrt{81} = 9$ because $9^2 = 81$, and likewise

$$\sqrt{-1} = i \text{ means } i^2 = -1$$

Example 1: Simplify the following numerical expressions, and write each as one complex number, using the same properties you have used for real numbers.

a. $3(2 - 4i)$ b. $2 - 4i + 3 + 5i$

c. $(2 - 4i) - (3 + 5i)$ d. $(2 - 4i)^2$

e. $(2 - 4i)(3 + 5i)$

Solution:

a. $3(2 - 4i) = \mathbf{6 - 12i}$ b. $2 - 4i + 3 + 5i = \mathbf{5 + i}$

c. $(2 - 4i) - (3 + 5i) = \mathbf{-1 - 9i}$

d. $(2 - 4i)^2$ e. $(2 - 4i)(3 + 5i)$

     $4 - 16i + 16i^2$ $6 + 10i - 12i - 20i^2$

     $4 - 16i + 16(-1)$ $6 - 2i + 20$

     $\mathbf{-12 - 16i}$ $\mathbf{26 - 2i}$

Did you notice that each of the answers is in the form $a + bi$? If b is zero, the number is an old real-number friend. If a is zero, but b isn't, the number is a pure imaginary number. In general, numbers of the form $a + bi$ are called **complex numbers**.

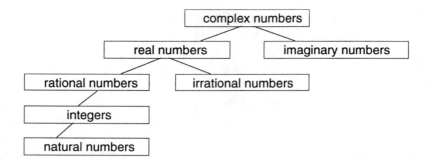

Problem Set 10.7

1. Solve each equation. Label each solution as real or nonreal (imaginary).
   Note: The nonreal answers always occur in pairs: $a + bi$ and $a - bi$. These are
   called **conjugate pairs**.

   a. $x^2 - 4x + 6 = 0$ b. $x^2 + 1 = 0$ c. $x^2 + x = -1$

2. Write a quadratic equation that has the given solutions.

   a. -3 and 5 b. -3.5 and -3.5

   c. $5i$ and $-5i$ d. $2 + i$ and $2 - i$

3. Write the lowest-degree equation with integer coefficients that has at least the
   given set of zeros and the given y-intercept.

   a. $-4, 5, -2, -2$ and y-intercept at -80.

   b. $-4, 5, -2, -2$ and y-intercept at 160.

   c. $\dfrac{1}{3}, \dfrac{-5}{2}, 0$ and y-intercept at 0.

   d. $-5i, -1, -1, -1, 4$ and y-intercept at 100.

4. Solve for x:

   a. $x^2 - 10ix - 9i^2 = 0$ b. $x^2 - 3ix = 2$

   c. Why don't the solutions to 4a and 4b come in conjugate pairs?

5. The quadratic equation $x = \dfrac{-b \pm \sqrt{b^2 - 4ac}}{2a}$ provides solutions to
   $ax^2 + bx + c = 0$. Make up some rules involving a, b, and c that determine each
   of the following conditions.

   a. The solutions (roots or zeros) are nonreal.

   b. The solutions are real.

   c. The solutions are equal.

6. Without using your calculator, sketch a graph of
$y = {}^-3(x + 2)^2 (x - 3)(x - 6) + 50$. (Hint: What happens when $x = {}^-2$ or 3 or 6?)
Verify your sketch with your calculator.

7. For x-values near 1 you can use the polynomial equation
$y = 0.0723 \left[6(x - 1) - 3(x - 1)^2 + 2(x - 1)^3 \right]$ as an approximation for log x.

   a. Sketch a graph of both $y = \log x$ and the polynomial equation for $0 \le x \le 2$.

   b. What is the most obvious root of the polynomial?

   c. Show that
   $$0.0723 \left[6(x - 1) - 3(x - 1)^2 + 2(x - 1)^3 \right] = 0.0723 \left[(x - 1)\left(6 - 3(x - 1) + 2(x - 1)^2 \right) \right]$$

   d. Find the roots of $6 - 3(x - 1) + 2(x - 1)^2 = 0$.

8. For 8a and 8b, graph each equation as y_1. Then let $y_2 = \left| y_1 \right|$. For 8c, you are
given the graph of y_1. Predict what the graph of y_2 will look like. Check your
work.

   a. $y_1 = 3x - 2$ b. $y_1 = (x - 4)^2$ c.

9. Write or adapt an existing calculator program that will provide solutions to
any quadratic equation with real-number coefficients. (**See APPENDIX 10C.**)

Section 10.8: More About Finding Solutions

This is the graph of $y = x^3 - 6x^2 + 11x - 6$. The graph indicates zeros at 1, 2, and 3. This brings up the question, how can you find the zeros when the equation is given as a polynomial, but the x-intercepts aren't as obvious?

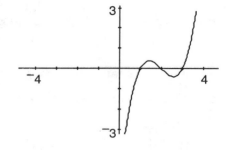

Can you use the graph and the information in the polynomial to help determine the zeros?

Even without referring to the graph, there is evidence that a factored form of $x^3 - 6x^2 + 11x - 6$ is $(x - 1)(x - 2)(x - 3)$ because $(x)(x)(x) = x^3$ and $(-1)(-2)(-3) = -6$.

Example 1: What are the zeros of $P(x) = x^5 - 6x^4 + 20x^3 - 60x^2 + 99x - 54$?

Solution: The graph has a cubic look and shows x-intercepts at 1, 2, and 3, which should mean that $(x - 1)(x - 2)(x - 3) = x^3 - 6x^2 + 11x - 6$ is a factor. The task is to find another factor so that

$(x^3 - 6x^2 + 11x - 6)(\text{ factor}) = x^5 - 6x^4 + 20x^3 - 60x^2 + 99x - 54$.

You can find another factor using division.

		$x^2 + 9$
Divide x^3 into x^5 to get x^2.	$x^3 - 6x^2 + 11x - 6$	$\overline{)\,x^5 - 6x^4 + 20x^3 - 60x^2 + 99x - 54}$
Multiply the divisor by x^2.		$x^5 - 6x^4 + 11x^3 - 6x^2$
Subtract and divide x^3 into $9x^3$.		$\overline{9x^3 - 54x^2 + 99x - 54}$
Multiply the divisor by 9.		$9x^3 - 54x^2 + 99x - 54$
The remainder is zero.		$\overline{0}$

Preliminary Edition

Division of polynomials is similar to the long division you learned in grade school, and is equally difficult. Both the original polynomial and the divisor are written in descending order of the powers of x. If any degree is missing, a term with 0 as coefficient should be inserted as a place holder. For example, you can write the polynomial expression $x^4 + 3x^2 - 5x + 8$ as $x^4 + 0x^3 + 3x^2 - 5x + 8$.

The remainder of zero means the divisor, $D(x)$, and the quotient, $Q(x)$, are both factors of the polynomial, $P(x)$. Thus, $P(x) = D(x) \cdot Q(x)$.

$$x^5 - 6x^4 + 20x^3 - 60x^2 + 99x - 54 = (x^3 - 6x^2 + 11x - 6)(x^2 + 9)$$
$$= (x - 1)(x - 2)(x - 3)(x^2 + 9)$$

Another way to find this missing factor is to have the calculator do the division for you, and graph the result. Graph

$$y = (x^5 - 6x^4 + 20x^3 - 60x^2 + 99x - 54)/(x^3 - 6x^2 + 11x - 6).$$

The result should look familiar. It is the parabola $y = x^2 + 9$. This means that the missing factor is $x^2 + 9$. Now that the polynomial is in factored form, you can easily find the zeros. You knew three of them from the graph. There are two more zeros to find because this is a 5th degree polynomial. They are contained in $x^2 + 9$. What values of x make $x^2 + 9$ equal zero?

$$x^2 + 9 = 0$$
$$x^2 = {}^-9$$
$$x = \pm\sqrt{-9} = \pm 3i$$

Therefore, the five solutions are 1, 2, 3, $3i$, and ${}^-3i$. Notice that the imaginary solutions are a conjugate pair. This means that if the coefficients of a polynomial are real numbers, and the polynomial has one imaginary root, then the conjugate of that imaginary root must also be a root.

Example 2: Find the zeros of $y = 6x^3 + 11x^2 - 17x - 30$.

Solution: All three zeros are real because the graph has three x-intercepts. By tracing or making a table you can find that both ${}^-2$ and $-\frac{3}{2}$ are solutions. The other root is somewhere between 1 and 2.
How can you find the exact solution without zooming?

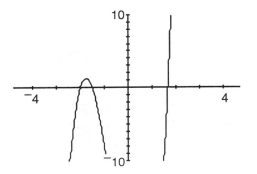

Instead of using guess-and-check, you can divide by the associated factors $(x + 2)$ and $(x + \frac{3}{2})$ using polynomial division, and reduce the expression

$$\frac{6x^3 + 11x^2 - 17x - 30}{(x + 2)(x + 1.5)}.$$

Another choice is a short cut called **synthetic division**. Synthetic division is based on using a **nested form** of the polynomial to evaluate it at particular x-values. This evaluation only involves multiplication and addition. As you can see in the right column below, $^-2$ is a solution because it makes the remainder equal to zero.

Long Division

$$\begin{array}{r} 6x^2 - 1x - 15 \\ x + 2 \overline{\smash{\big)}\, 6x^3 + 11x^2 - 17x - 30} \\ \underline{-6x^3 - 12x^2} \\ -1x^2 - 17x - 30 \\ \underline{1x^2 + 2x} \\ -15x - 30 \\ \underline{15x + 30} \\ 0 \end{array}$$

Synthetic Division

$$P(x) = 6x^3 + 11x^2 - 17x - 30$$

$^-2$	6	11	$^-17$	$^-30$
		$^-12$	2	30
	6	$^-1$	$^-15$	0

Synthetic division is a short cut to the long division process. We won't give a formal explanation of the technique. See if you can figure out the individual steps from the example.

The number furthest to the right in the last row of a synthetic division is the remainder, which in this case is 0. When the remainder in a division problem is zero, you know that the divisor is a factor. This means $^-2$ is a solution and the polynomial $6x^3 + 11x^2 - 17x - 30$ factors into the divisor $(x + 2)$ and the quotient $6x^2 - x - 15$. You could use any of the methods you've learned—simple factoring, quadratic formula, synthetic division, or graphing—to reduce the quotient even further. Study the synthetic division process with the other root, $^-1.5$.

-1.5	6	$^-1$	$^-15$
		$^-9$	15
	6	$^-10$	0

There is also a connection between the synthetic division and writing the equation as nested linear factors, such as

$$6x^2 - x - 15 = (6x - 1)x - 15 \text{ or}$$

$$6x^3 + 11x^2 - 17x - 30 = ((6x + 11)x - 17)x - 30.$$

See if you can figure out this connection.

$P(x) = (6x - 1)x - 15$

$P(-1.5) = (6\,(-1.5) - 1) \cdot -1.5 - 15$

$P(-1.5) = 0$

$$
\begin{array}{r|rrr}
-1.5 & 6 & -1 & -15 \\
     &   & -9 & 15 \\
\hline
     & 6 & -10 & 0
\end{array}
$$

You know that $\frac{-3}{2}$ is a solution because the remainder is again zero. The other factor is the remaining quotient $(6x - 10)$. Therefore the three zeros are -2, $\frac{-3}{2}$, and $\frac{5}{3}$. *Every polynomial function with degree n has exactly n complex zeros.* This means that all cubic equations have three roots and three factors. They may be repeated roots, such as the roots of $x^3 - 15x^2 + 75x - 125 = 0$, whose three roots are 5, 5, and 5. Check the graph! Two of the roots may be imaginary or complex, such as the roots of $x^3 + 5x^2 - 24x - 130 = 0$, whose three roots are 5, $-5 + i$, and $-5 - i$. Check the graph!

A Leaky Bucket Experiment Activity

Equipment Needed

A translucent plastic water container with a hole in the bottom (A one-liter plastic bleach bottle or soda bottle works well), a metric ruler, a marker, and a timing device.

Assignment of Tasks

Each member of the group should be assigned a task. One team member holds the bucket. A second team member keeps track of the time, the third team member reads the water level heights, and the fourth team member records the data.

Procedure

Make a mark on the side of the container at a height of 15 cm. The bucket holder should fill the container with water to this mark, keeping a finger on the hole and adjusting the water level with her finger if necessary. The water-level reader needs to hold the ruler next to the container, or he can attach the ruler to the container with some tape. Do not collect data until the water has emptied to the vertical part of the container, and quit before the water level reaches the rounded portion of the bottom.

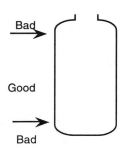

When the timekeeper says go, the person holding the bucket removes her finger from the hole and lets the water run freely out of the bucket. The team member with the timing device will call out the time every ten seconds. When she does this, the water-level reader reads the water level to the nearest millimeter. The recorder then records the data. Do this until the container is *nearly, but not completely*, empty.

Data Analysis

Sketch a graph of the data. Look at the graph and name the type of function represented by the data. Explain what physical properties or laws might predict this type of behavior. Use the method of finite differences to investigate your guess. Give the equation that you believe best fits the data. Add the graph of this equation to your data plot. On a separate graph, show the residuals of this fit.

From your work, predict when the container would be empty. How long will it take to drain if you started with the container filled to a height of 20.0 cm?

Problem Set 10.8

1. Division produces a quotient and often a remainder. Rewrite $P(x)$ in the form $P(x) = D(x) \cdot Q(x) + R$ where $D(x)$ is the given divisor, $Q(x)$ is the quotient, and R is the remainder. For example, $x^3 + 2x^2 + 3x - 4 = (x - 1)(x^2 + 3x + 6) + \dfrac{2}{x - 1}$.

   Remember that you must use zero coefficients for missing terms in synthetic division.

   a. $P(x) = 47$ and $D(x) = 11$

   b. $P(x) = 6x^4 - 5x^3 + 7x^2 - 12x + 15$ and $D(x) = x - 1$

   c. $P(x) = x^3 - x^2 - 10x + 16$ and $D(x) = x - 2$

2. Consider $y = x^5 - 6x^4 + 20x^3 - 60x^2 + 99x - 54$.

   a. Find $P(1)$ using synthetic division, and name the quotient polynomial so that $(x - 1) Q_1(x) = 0$.

   b. Use synthetic division on the quotient polynomial, and name a new $Q_2(x)$ so that $(x - 1)(x - 2) Q_2(x) = 0$.

   c. Use synthetic division on the latest quotient polynomial, and name a new $Q_3(x)$ so that $(x - 1)(x - 2)(x - 3) Q_3(x) = 0$.

   d. Find the two solutions of the quadratic quotient remaining by using the quadratic formula.

   e. Synthetic division can be done with your calculator by entering the program in **APPENDIX 10B**. Use this program to check your answers to 2a, 2b, and 2c.

3. a. How many zeros does $y = x^4 + 3x^3 - 11x^2 - 3x + 10$ have?

   b. Name the x-intercepts.

   c. Name the y-intercept.

   d. Write the polynomial in factored form.

4. As you trace to find the value of an x-intercept on a graph, you see the y-values jump from positive to negative when you pass over the root. By zooming in between these values, you find more and more accurate approximations for x. These actions can be automated once the low and high boundaries for x have been entered. The automation uses successive midpoints and is called the **bisection method**. Find the x-intercepts for each equation by using the program in **APPENDIX 10A**.

   a. $y = x^5 - x^4 - 16x + 16$ b. $y = 2x^3 + 15x^2 + 6x - 6$

   c. $y = 0.2(x - 12)^5 - 6(x - 12)^3 - (x - 12)^2 + 1$ d. $y = 2x^4 + 2x^3 - 14x^2 - 9x - 12$

5. Consider $y = x - \dfrac{x^3}{3!} + \dfrac{x^5}{5!} - \dfrac{x^7}{7!} + \ldots$ (The pattern continues.)

   a. Graph $y = x - \dfrac{x^3}{3!} + \dfrac{x^5}{5!} - \dfrac{x^7}{7!}$ and find the zeros.

   b. Graph $y = x - \dfrac{x^3}{3!} + \dfrac{x^5}{5!} - \dfrac{x^7}{7!} + \dfrac{x^9}{9!} - \dfrac{x^{11}}{11!}$ and find the zeros.

   c. Continue the pattern and describe what is happening.

6. As you move closer and closer to the end of the year, think about how you felt about your math class, working in groups and your ability to learn at the start of the school year. Has your perspective changed? Explain.

7. In this chapter you looked at a number of different ways to solve polynomial equations. Discuss at least three of the methods. What are the advantages and disadvantages of each method? Which method do you prefer? Why?

Section 10.9: Chapter Review

Problem Set 10.9

Some of the problems below are simple and straightforward, but most of them require investigation, thought, and checking your solutions along the way. You will need to use root-finding techniques such as graphing, the quadratic formula, and synthetic division. Share, compare, and work with others until you are sure that you understand the problem and have found the solution.

1. Given three noncollinear points, how many triangles can you draw? Given four points, no three of which are collinear, how many triangles can you draw? Given five points, no three of which are collinear, how many triangles can you draw? How many triangles can be drawn from n points, no three of which are collinear?

2. Each equation is written in polynomial form, vertex form, or factored form. Write each equation in the other two forms if possible.

   a. $y = 2(x - 2)^2 - 16$ b. $y = {}^-3(x - 5)(x + 1)$

   c. $y = x^2 + 3x + 2$ d. $y = (x + 1)(x - 3)(x + 4)$

   e. $y = 2x^2 + 5x - 6$ f. $y = {}^-(x + 7)^2 - 2$

3. Sketch a graph and label the coordinates of all zeros, local maxima and relative minima. (Each coordinate should be accurate to at least the nearest 0.001.)

   a. $y = 2(x - 2)^2 - 16$ b. $y = {}^-3(x - 5)(x + 1)$

   c. $y = x^2 - 3x + 2$ d. $y = (x + 1)(x - 3)(x + 4)$

   e. $y = x^3 + 2x^2 - 19x + 20$ f. $y = 5x^5 + 38x^4 + 79x^3 - 8x^2 - 102x + 36$

4. Write the equation of each graph.

a.

b.

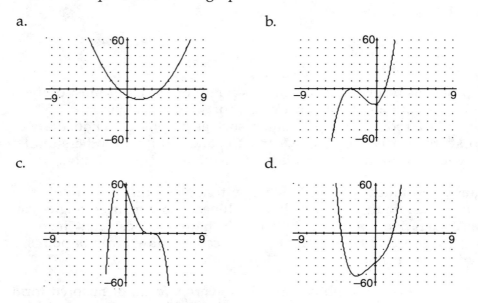

c.

d.

(Hint: One of the zeros occurs at $x = 3i$.)

5. A rectangular package must have a maximum combined girth and length of 108 inches (by postal regulations). This means $4x + y = 108$. Find the dimensions of the package with maximum volume. (Assume the cross-section is always a square with side length x.) Making a table might be helpful.

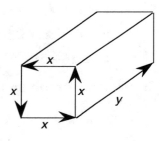

6. What ideas or topics were introduced in this chapter that you feel you do not quite understand, or see the purpose of? Give examples.

7. Find three problems in the chapter that you feel are representative of the chapter. Write out each problem and its solution. For each problem, explain why you feel it is representative of the chapter. Please use complete sentences.

Section 10.10: Projects

Project 10.1: Air Drag

Projectile motion involves air drag, which varies with temperature, humidity, and barometric pressure. The k-values in this model range from 0.01 to 0.25, as conditions become more severe.

$$x(t) = \frac{v_0}{k}(1 - e^{-kt})\cos\theta$$

$$y(t) = \frac{v_0}{k}(1 - e^{-kt})\sin\theta + \frac{32}{k^2}(1 - kt - e^{-kt}) + y_0$$

A baseball is hit from a point 3 ft above the ground with an initial velocity of 147 ft/sec at an angle of 21°. Find the range and maximum height of the ball using both the model from the chapter and the air-drag model above, with k equal to 0.08 (or 8% air drag).

Take a second look at the same situation with a horizontal wind of 20 ft/sec blowing against the path of the ball.

Without air drag, an object dropped from any height would continue to accelerate until it hit the ground. With air drag, the object accelerates but the acceleration is not constant. If an object falls long enough, the acceleration all but stops as the object reaches a maximum speed. This is called its terminal velocity, $v_T = \frac{w}{k}$, where w is the weight of the object in pounds.

Without air drag, the velocity at any time t is given by $-16t$, which continues to increase in magnitude as time increases. With air drag, the velocity model is quite different.

$$v(t) = \frac{w}{k}\left(1 - e^{-32kt/w}\right)$$

Compute the terminal velocity for a 0.5 lb baseball. How long does it take the baseball to reach this velocity? From what height should the ball be dropped to reach this velocity before it hits the ground?

Project 10.2: Least-Squares Polynomial Fit

In this chapter you have fit polynomials to data by selecting certain points to represent the set. Using this kind of selective approach, you can choose to go through those points or pockets that you feel are important and ignore some others. Using the same criteria as the least-squares line, you can also find a curve that treats each point as significantly as the rest and minimizes the sum of the squares of the residuals of all the data. (The derivations of these relationships involve the concept of derivatives and calculus, so for now you will have to accept that the formulas do indeed minimize the squares of the residuals.)

The quadratic fit involves finding three constants a, b, and c for $y = ax^2 + bx + c$. This means you must find three equations. First you make the sum of the residuals equal to zero. Then x times the residuals is also equal to zero, and finally x^2 times the residuals is equal to zero.

$$\sum_{i=1}^{n}(y_i - f(x_i)) = 0 \qquad \sum_{i=1}^{n} y_i = a\sum x_i^2 + b\sum x_i + cn$$

$$\sum_{i=1}^{n}(x_i y_i - x_i f(x_i)) = 0 \Rightarrow \sum_{i=1}^{n} x_i y_i = a\sum x_i^3 + b\sum x_i^2 + c\sum x_i$$

$$\sum_{i=1}^{n}(x_i^2 y_i - x_i^2 f(x_i)) = 0 \qquad \sum_{i=1}^{n} x_i^2 y_i = a\sum x_i^4 + b\sum x_i^3 + c\sum x_i^2$$

A chemical is added to make varnish smoother and easier to apply, but it also affects the drying time of the varnish. The following data were collected by adding the chemical to equal amounts of varnish, then recording how long it took before the varnish was dry to the touch. The amount of the additive, in grams, is recorded as x and the drying time, in hours, is recorded as y. Complete the table below and find each sum.

Sample number	x	x^2	x^3	x^4	y	xy	x^2y
1	1.0				8.5		
2	2.0				8.0		
3	3.0				6.0		
4	4.0				5.0		
5	5.0				6.0		
6	6.0				5.5		
7	7.0				6.5		
8	8.0				7.0		
Σ							

Use the sums from the table to write the systems of equations listed on the right above. Use matrices to find values of *a*, *b*, and *c* that give the best-fit quadratic equation for the data. Some calculators have polynomial fits as a statistical calculation. See **APPENDIX 10D** for instructions on how to use your calculator to check the results. If your calculator does not have the functions built in, then you will have to enter the program.

Project 10.3: Coefficient of Fit

The coefficient of correlation, *r*, used earlier in the course is a metric (measure) of the data, and not of the model used to fit the data. It exists only for linear data or data that can be linearized. A second coefficient, called the coefficient of fit, is "model dependent" and is based on the residuals. This measure will work for any data set after you find a model. It is a useful comparison for making a selection between models.

The Greek letter rho, ρ, is used for the coefficient of fit. As with the coefficient of correlation, it is the coefficient of fit *squared* that is a meaningful measure. The formula below has been coded into a calculator program found in **APPENDIX 10E**. The variables used in the formula are σ_y for the standard deviation of the *y* data and σ_r for the root mean square of the residuals. The standard deviation is the square root of the average of the squares of the differences between the values and the mean value. The root mean square is the square root of the average of the squares of the residuals. See Project 3.3 in Chapter 3 if you aren't familiar with standard deviation. σ is the Greek letter sigma.

The formula for **Coefficient of Fit** uses the standard deviation of the *y* data, σ_y, and the root mean square of the residuals, σ_r.

$$\sigma_y^2 = \frac{\sum_{i=1}^{n}(y_i - \bar{y})^2}{n} \qquad \sigma_r^2 = \frac{\sum_{i=1}^{n}(y_i - f(x_i))^2}{n}$$

The value is always between zero and one. A value of one is a perfect fit and a value of zero indicates no fit at all.

$$\rho^2 = \frac{\sigma_y^2 - \sigma_r^2}{\sigma_y^2}$$

A chemical is added to make varnish smoother and easier to apply, but it also has an effect on the drying time of the varnish. The following data were collected by adding the chemical to equal amounts of varnish, then timing until the varnish was dry to the touch. Find several different models for the data and make your choice for the *best*. Remember your first priority is that there be no pattern in the residuals.

Additive (grams)	1.0	2.0	3.0	4.0	5.0	6.0	7.0	8.0
Drying time (hours)		8.5	8.0	6.0	5.0	6.0	5.5	6.5	7.0

Project 10.4: Mandelbrot Set

The most famous of all fractal images is created using a recursive quadratic expression. Choose some value z, square it, and add a constant c. This becomes the new z-value. Repeat the process. One of two things will happen: either the value will "explode" up to infinity, or it will not. Let's look at two patterns: one for $z_1 = 0$ and $c = 0.5$, and one for $z_1 = 0$ and $c = -0.5$

$$z_2 = z_1^2 + 0.5 = 0.5 \qquad\qquad z_2 = z_1^2 - 0.5 = -0.5$$

$$z_3 = z_2^2 + 0.5 = 0.75 \qquad\qquad z_3 = z_2^2 - 0.5 = -0.25$$

$$z_4 = z_3^2 + 0.5 = 1.0625 \qquad\qquad z_4 = z_3^2 - 0.5 = -0.4375$$

$$z_5 = z_4^2 + 0.5 = 1.6289\ldots \qquad\qquad z_5 = z_4^2 - 0.5 = -0.3085\ldots$$

$$z_6 = z_5^2 + 0.5 = 3.1533\ldots \qquad\qquad z_6 = z_5^2 - 0.5 = -0.4048\ldots$$

$$z_{10} = z_9^2 + 0.5 = 144{,}131{,}442 \qquad\qquad z_{10} = z_9^2 - 0.5 = -0.3773\ldots$$

$$z_{big} = \text{very big} \qquad\qquad z_{big} = -0.3660254038\ldots$$

You should check this recursively on your calculator. What will happen if $z_1 = 0$ and $c = 0.25$? What will happen if c or z is a complex number, like $z_1 = 0$ and $c = -0.4 + 0.5i$? Note: If your calculator does not work with complex numbers, then use a matrix for $a + bi$, such as $[A] = \begin{bmatrix} a & -b \\ b & a \end{bmatrix}$.

```
[A]
        [[-.4  -.5]
         [.5   -.4]]
Ans²+[A]
        [[-.49  -.1 ]
         [.1    -.49]]
```

Then enter $[A]$ and recursively calculate the expression $\text{Ans}^2 + [A]$. Give an argument that explains why $\begin{bmatrix} a & -b \\ b & a \end{bmatrix}^2$ works like $(a + bi)^2$.

Preliminary Edition CHAPTER 10

What will happen if you choose to color a point black if it does not explode and white if it does? The result will be a coloring of a complex plane into a pattern that looks like the graph shown. Your project is to choose a small section on the boundary of the black area of this graph and create a graph of this section. You will find a program in **APPENDIX 11F** that will analyze every point in the window to determine if it is to be black or white. The program uses the fact that if a point gets more than 2 units from the origin, it will never come back. If it is still within 2 units after 50 iterations, then it will

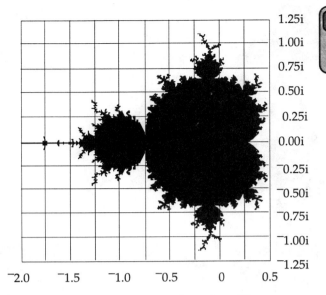

likely stay in. Look at this graph, and select a good window. Then run the program. Make a sketch of your result. Note any similarities between your graph and the original. Zoom in as many times as you wish and form a conclusion from your results.

Chapter Eleven

MORE PROBABILITY AND STATISTICS

Contents

Section 11.1: Permutations and Probability 508

        Learning to count with a tree

Section 11.2: Combinations and Probability 515

        When order doesn't really count

Section 11.3: Binomial Theorem 521

        Expanding quickly now

Section 11.4: Standard Deviation 527

        Let's measure the spread

Section 11.5: Normal Distribution 536

        When even the unusual can be normal

Section 11.6: Using the Normal Curve 543

        Don't go around this curve too fast

Section 11.7: Chapter Review 549

        Assessing yourself

Section 11.8: Projects 551

        More good problems

Section 11.1: Permutations and Probability

How many different outfits–consisting of a
sweater, pants, and shoes–could you wear if
you were to select from four different
sweaters, six different pairs of pants, and two
pairs of shoes?

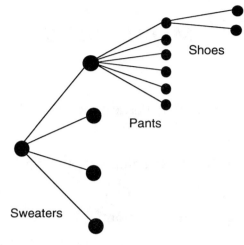

Each different outfit can be represented by a
path through a tree diagram. How many
outfits or paths are there? Each path is a
sequence of three segments representing a
sweater **and** a pair of pants **and** a pair of shoes.
This partial tree diagram pictures six pairs of
pants for each sweater, followed by two pairs
of shoes for each sweater/pants outfit.
(Drawing all 48 paths would be difficult and messy.)

Visualize a tree with four choices of sweaters and six different pants for each
sweater. Each of the 24 sweater/pants outfits can be matched with two pairs of
shoes. This extended tree has a sequence of sweater–pants–shoe along each of the
48 paths representing the 48 different outfits.

The total number of outfits with four choices, then six choices, and then two
choices can be found by drawing a tree diagram or by using the **counting
principle** ($4 \cdot 6 \cdot 2 = 48$ choices).

> The **counting principle:** Suppose there are n_1 ways to make the
> first choice, n_2 ways to make the second choice, n_3 ways to
> make the third choice, and so on. The product $n_1 \cdot n_2 \cdot n_3 \cdot \ldots$
> represents the total number of different ways (outcomes) in
> which the entire sequence of choices can be made.

The counting principle provides a method for finding the total number of
outcomes. However, the solutions will be more meaningful if you look for
patterns, and sketch or visualize a representative tree diagram.

Example 1:

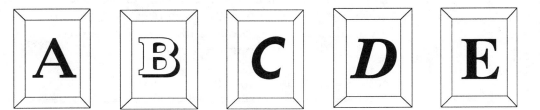

You have been asked to arrange five different pictures along a wall.

a. How many different ways can this be done?

b. What is the probability of any one of these outcomes?

c. Suppose you want to select and arrange any three of the five pictures in a row. How many different ways can this be done?

d. What is the probability of a particular outcome in this situation?

Solution:

a. Label the pictures A, B, C, D, and E. Choose one of the pictures, then choose one of the remaining four pictures, then choose one of the remaining three pictures, then choose one of the remaining two pictures, and then choose one of the remaining one picture. This can be done in $\underline{5} \cdot \underline{4} \cdot \underline{3} \cdot \underline{2} \cdot \underline{1} = 120$ ways.

b. Visualize a tree diagram with 120 different paths, each containing five branch segments. Because no path is more special than another, each is equally likely, and the probability of any single path, such as **CABED**, occurring is $\frac{1}{120}$. You can think of this as 1 path out of 120 total paths, or you can obtain this answer by multiplying the probabilities of each branch along the path:
$$\frac{1}{5} \cdot \frac{1}{4} \cdot \frac{1}{3} \cdot \frac{1}{2} \cdot \frac{1}{1} = \frac{1}{120}.$$

c. What if you only need to hang three of the pictures? Begin by choosing one of the original five pictures. Then choose one of the remaining four pictures, and then choose one of the remaining three pictures. This can be done in $\underline{5} \cdot \underline{4} \cdot \underline{3} = 60$ ways.

d. The probability of a particular order, such as **DAB**, occurring is $\frac{1}{60}$.
(One of the 60 paths, or $\frac{1}{5} \cdot \frac{1}{4} \cdot \frac{1}{3} = \frac{1}{60}$.)

> If $n_1, n_2, n_3, \ldots$ represent choice 1, choice 2, choice 3, $\ldots$
> along a path, the probability of the path occurring can be
> found by multiplying the probabilities for each choice
> (branch) along the path.
>
> $P(n_1 \text{ and } n_2 \text{ and } n_3 \text{ and } \ldots) = P(n_1) \bullet P(n_2) \bullet P(n_3) \ldots$

Factorial Function Activity

Investigate the ! **key** on your calculator. (The expression $n!$ is read "n factorial.")

a. Find the value of $n!$ for each choice of n:

n	1	2	3	4	5	6	7
$n!$							

b. What can you do to the answer to 6! to get 7! ?

c. What can you do to the answer to 6! to get 5! ?

d. What does 8! mean?

e. Describe a real-life situation involving 8!.

f. What happens when you try to compute 1.5! on your calculator?

g. What happens when you try to compute ($^-$3)! on your calculator?

h. What is the biggest n for which you can find $n!$ on your calculator? Explain why you think this is so.

i. What is the smallest n for which you can find $n!$?

j. Create and write a definition for $n!$ that seems to match the design of your calculator's factorial function.

k. Define $n!$ recursively.

The arrangements in Example 1 are called **permutations**. The *order* along each sequence is significant and once a choice is made, that choice cannot be used again in the same sequence.

> A **permutation** is an arrangement or selection of objects
> from a set when order is important.

In Example 1a, you permuted or arranged all five of the five pictures, $_5P_5 = 120$, and in Example 1b you permuted three of the five pictures, $_5P_3 = 60$, to obtain the total number of arrangements. The notation $_nP_r$ is read "n things permuted r at a time." See **APPENDIX 11A** for an explanation of how to compute permutations on your calculator.

Example 2: Suppose there are seven flute players in an ensemble. How many different arrangements of these players can be made for each given situation?

a. All seven players are seated in a row.

b. Any four players are selected to sit in a row.

c. All seven players are seated, but Fiona must be first and Steven must be seventh.

d. All seven players are seated, but Donald and Elizabeth must be next to each other.

Solution:

a. $_7P_7 = \underline{7} \cdot \underline{6} \cdot \underline{5} \cdot \underline{4} \cdot \underline{3} \cdot \underline{2} \cdot \underline{1} = 5040$. There are seven choices for the first chair, six choices remaining for the second chair, five for the third chair, and so on.

b. $_7P_4 = \underline{7} \cdot \underline{6} \cdot \underline{5} \cdot \underline{4} = 840$. There are only four slots or chairs to fill. There are seven choices for the first chair, six choices remaining for the second chair, five for the third chair, and finally four for the fourth chair.

c. <u>Fiona</u> _____ _____ _____ _____ _____ <u>Steven</u>. This arrangement means there is one choice for the first chair and one choice for the seventh chair. The other chairs can be filled in $_5P_5$ ways. Therefore, the counting principle suggests $\underline{1} \cdot \underline{5} \cdot \underline{4} \cdot \underline{3} \cdot \underline{2} \cdot \underline{1} \cdot \underline{1} = 120$ different arrangements. It is important that Fiona's and Steven's positions be established first. In general, you should take care of special circumstances first as you establish your counting scheme. *Don't start multiplying before you think about the meaning of the numbers in the sequence, or before you draw or visualize a tree diagram.*

d. One way of thinking through this arrangement is to consider Donald and Elizabeth as a unit or element. Imagine them actually tied together somewhere in the sequence.
___ • ___ • ___ • **DE** • ___ • ___ . Now there are six elements to be arranged in $_6P_6 = 720$ different arrangements. Multiply this number (720) by 2 because the unit could be either DE or ED in each of the 720 arrangements. Therefore, there are 1440 different arrangements with Donald and Elizabeth seated next to each other.

Sometimes the challenge is deciding which counting strategy to apply in a particular problem. You must think carefully about each problem. In the previous examples, you have used tree diagrams, the counting principle, and your calculator to find the number of permutations. Be sure to think about each problem, and avoid the temptation to blindly apply formulas.

Example 3:

a. How many different license plates are available if any three letters from the alphabet are followed by any three digits?

JTM 047

b. How many different license plates are available if either three letters are followed by three digits or three digits are followed by three letters?

Solution:

a. License plates allow multiple use of letters and digits, so $26 • 26 • 26 • 10 • 10 • 10 = 17,576,000$ represents the number of license plates available.

b. You could have either $26 • 26 • 26 • 10 • 10 • 10$ plates if the letters are first, or $10 • 10 • 10 • 26 • 26 • 26$ license plates if the digits are first. Therefore, there are 35,152,000 such plates.

An arrangement is not considered a permutation if letters and/or digits can be used more than once. The definition of a permutation states that it is an arrangement without replacement or, in this case, duplication. The license plate *MTM 351* is not a permutation.

Problem Set 11.1

1. a. In how many ways can the eight different math books for grades 1 through 8 be arranged on a shelf?

    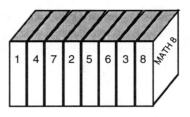

    b. How many ways can the books be arranged so that the Grade 5 book will be the right-most book?

    c. Use the answers from 1a and 1b to find the probability that the Grade 5 book will be the right-most book.

    d. Explain how to compute the probability in 1c using another method.

    e. What is the probability that the books can be arranged so that the last book is an even number? Explain how you determined this.

    f. How many ways can the books be arranged so that the books are in increasing order?

    g. How many ways can the books be arranged so that the books are out of order (not in strictly increasing order)?

    h. What is the probability that the books are out of order?

2. Evaluate each factorial expression. (Some answers will contain n.)

    a. $\dfrac{12!}{11!}$

    b. $\dfrac{7!}{6!}$

    c. $\dfrac{(n+1)!}{n!}$

    d. $\dfrac{n!}{(n-1)!}$

    e. $\dfrac{120!}{118!}$

    f. $\dfrac{n!}{(n-2)!}$

    g. Find n if $\dfrac{(n+1)!}{n!} = 15$

3. a. Describe a real-life situation involving $_7P_3$.

    b. Explain the relationship between $_7P_3$ and $\dfrac{7!}{4!}$.

    c. Describe several different ways to find the value of $_nP_r$.

4. The ten digits 0, 1, 2, 3, . . . , 9 are arranged randomly with no repetition of digits.

    a. How many different arrangements are possible?

    b. What is the probability that the number formed is greater than or equal to 7 billion?

    c. What is the probability that the number formed is divisible by 5?

    d. What is the probability that the 4, 5, and 6 are next to each other (in this order) in the number formed?

5. How many different 800 telephone numbers (1–800–_ _ _–_ _ _ _) are available? (The numbers 0 or 1 are not allowed in the first slot.)

6. A computer is programmed to list all of the permutations for *N* items. Compute *N*!. Figure out how long it will take for the computer to list all of the possibilities. Use an appropriate time unit for each answer (minutes, hours, days, or years).

N	Permutation (N!)	Time
5	120	0.00012 sec
10	3,628,800	3.6288 sec
12		
13		
15		
20		

7. You have purchased four tickets to a charity raffle. Only 50 tickets were sold. Three prizes will be awarded.

a. What is probability you will win *only* the first prize?

b. What is the probability you will win both first and second prize, but not third prize?

c. What is the probability you will win the second or third prize?

d. If the prizes are gift certificates for $25, $10, and $5, respectively, what is your expected value? Recall from Chapter 8 that the expected value is the sum of the products of the probability of each possible event times the value of that event.

Section 11.2: Combinations and Probability

This tree diagram pictures the possible outcomes when a coin is tossed three times.

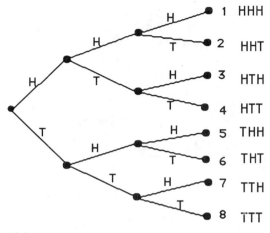

3Hs	One path
2Hs and 1T	Three paths
1H and 2Ts	Three paths
3Ts	One path

If you are not concerned about what order the heads and tails occur, then paths 2, 3, and 5 can be lumped together as (2 heads and 1 tail) and paths 4, 6, and 7 can be lumped together as (1 head and 2 tails).

The diagram and the counting principle both indicate $\underline{2} \cdot \underline{2} \cdot \underline{2} = 8$ equally likely outcomes; 2 choices, then 2 choices, then 2 choices.

The probabilities of the four different outcomes are as follows.

P (three Heads) $= \frac{1}{8}$ P (exactly two Heads) $= \frac{3}{8}$

P (exactly two Tails) $= \frac{3}{8}$ P (three Tails) $= \frac{1}{8}$

In this section you will develop a counting formula that you will use throughout this chapter. Understanding the connection between a tree diagram and the formula will help you understand the more complicated ideas to come. Think visually, and draw one or more representations for each problem you investigate.

Example 1:

At the first meeting of the International Club, the members are getting acquainted by introducing themselves and shaking hands. Each member shakes hands with every other member. How many handshakes are there in each of these situations?

a. Three people are in the room.

b. Four people are in the room.

c. Five people are in the room.

d. Fifteen people are in the room.

Solution:

The points (**vertices**) pictured can represent the three, four, or five people in a room and the lines (**edges**) can represent the handshakes. You can find the answer by counting, but as you add more people to the group it will become more difficult to draw and count the number of handshakes.

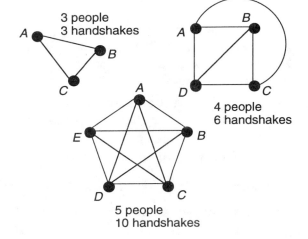

Four edges at each vertex in the five-person handshake solution might suggest that there are $4 \cdot 5$ edges. However, this means an edge like DB has been counted at vertex D and again at vertex B. Because DB is the same as BD, you are counting twice as many edges as the actual total. The handshake problem is an example of "a combination of five things taken two at a time," $_5C_2$. (Sometimes this is read as "five choose two.") The order in which two vertices are taken doesn't matter here and, because there are $_5P_2 = 20$ permutations of five vertices taken two at a time, you have

$$2 \cdot {_5C_2} = {_5P_2} \text{ or } {_5C_2} = \frac{_5P_2}{2} = \frac{20}{2} = 10.$$

The same pattern continues for 15 people (vertices). The edge between any two vertices represents a handshake. The value $_{15}P_2 = 210$ is twice as big as the number you want, so there are $_{15}C_2 = 105$ handshakes.

Preliminary Edition

> A **combination** is a selection of objects from a set in which order is not important.

Example 2:

Ann, Ben, Chang, and Dena are members of the International Club, and they have volunteered to be on a committee that will arrange a reception for foreign exchange students. Usually there are only three students on the committee. How many different three-member committees can be formed with these four students?

Solution:

Note that order isn't important in this case. **ABD** and **BDA** are the same committee and shouldn't be counted more than once.
The number of different committee combinations will be fewer than the $_4P_3 = 24$ listed arrangements. (This is always the case with committees.)

ABC	**ABD**	**ACD**	**BCD**
ACB	ADB	ADC	BDC
BAC	BAD	CAD	CBD
BCA	BDA	CDA	CDB
CAB	DAB	DAC	DBC
CBA	DBA	DCA	DCB

The four committees in the top row represent all the arrangements listed in each column. Therefore, the permutation total $_4P_3 = 24$ is six times larger than the combination needed. There are always fewer combinations of a set of elements than there are permutations of that set. The combination number $_4C_3$ represents a collection of three elements from a set of four, without regard to order. You have just seen that $_4P_3 = 6 \cdot {_4C_3}$. Therefore, $_4C_3 = 4$. What is the relationship between the 6 in this example and 3!?

Example 3:

Les Luhk seems to have the worst luck getting Saturday night dates. On the average he has a 10% success rate; that is, only 10% of the girls he asks to go out with him will accept. On a particular Saturday, he faxes requests to seven potential dates. (Are you beginning to understand part of his problem?) What is the probability that he will end up with *two* dates?

Solution:

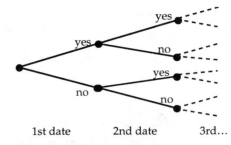

1st date   2nd date   3rd...

The tree diagram for this problem has seven stages (one for each potential date), and splits into two possibilities (success or failure) at each point on the path. This means there are $2 \cdot 2 \cdot 2 \cdot 2 \cdot 2 \cdot 2 \cdot 2 = 2^7 = 128$ possibilities. The question is, how many of the 128 separate paths contain 2 successes and 5 failures? Because order is not important, you can find the number of paths that fit this description by finding a combination number. There are $_7C_2$ or 21 branches. (Could you also compute $_7C_5$? Why or why not?) For any one of these paths, the probability is

$$0.1 \cdot 0.1 \cdot 0.9 \cdot 0.9 \cdot 0.9 \cdot 0.9 \cdot 0.9 = 0.0059049.$$

Multiply the number of these paths by the probability of each path to find the probability that Les will end up with exactly two dates.

$$21 \cdot 0.0059 = 0.124.$$

Therefore, the probability is 12.4% that he will end up with two dates.

Lottery Activity

Consider a state lottery called **Lotto 47**. Twice a week, players select six different numbers between 1 and 47, inclusive. The state Lottery Commission also selects six numbers from 1 through 47. Selection order doesn't matter, but a player needs to match all six numbers to win the Lotto.

a. For five minutes, write down as many different sets of six numbers as you can. Each number written should be from 1 to 47, inclusive.

b. As a class, determine a **Rand routine** that generates numbers in the list $\{1, 2, 3, \ldots, 47\}$.

c. Next, each member of the class stands up.

d. The teacher will generate a set of six random numbers. After the first number is generated, any person who does not have that number written anywhere in any set sits down.

e. The second number is generated. Any person who does not have the first and second number in the same set sits down.

f. Repeat step e until no one is standing or until you have generated six numbers. (If a number appears twice, simply skip it the second time.)

g. What is the probability that any one set of six numbers wins? At one dollar for each set of six numbers, how much have you invested during the five minutes?

h. What is the probability that someone in your class wins?

i. What was the total amount invested by the entire class in the five minutes?

j. What is the probability that someone in your school wins?

k. If each of the possible sets of six numbers are written on one-inch chips, and all the chips are laid end to end, how long will the line of chips be? (Use appropriate units, not inches.)

l. Write a paragraph or story that compares winning Lotto 47 with some other remote possibility. The numbers and probabilities should be the same.

Problem Set 11.2

1. a. What is the relationship between $_7P_2$ and $_7C_2$?

   b. What is the relationship between $_7P_3$ and $_7C_3$?

   c. What is the relationship between $_7P_4$ and $_7C_4$?

   d. What is the relationship between $_7P_7$ and $_7C_7$?

   e. Describe how you can find $_nC_r$ if you know $_nP_r$.

2. Evaluate each factorial expression.

   a. $\dfrac{10!}{3!7!}$ b. $\dfrac{7!}{4!3!}$ c. $\dfrac{15!}{13!2!}$ d. $\dfrac{7!}{7!0!}$

3. Find each combination number.

   a. $_{10}C_7$ b. $_7C_3$ c. $_{15}C_2$ d. $_7C_0$

4. Compare each answer in Problem 3 with the corresponding answer in Problem 2.

   a. Explain how $_{10}C_4$ is related to the factorial expression $\dfrac{10!}{4!6!}$.

   b. Find a different number r, for $_{10}C_r$, with the same answer as $_{10}C_4$.

   c. Explain why these two combination numbers are the same.

5. Express the relationship between each of these pairs. You may use tree diagrams, formulas, written statements, or another method of your choice.

   a. $_nP_r$ and $_{n+1}P_r$ b. $_nP_r$ and $_nP_{r+1}$ c. $_nC_r$ and $_{n+1}C_r$ d. $_nC_r$ and $_nC_{r+1}$

6. Imagine there are 20 students in the class, and the teacher will randomly select six students to give an oral report on "Using Probability in the Work Place." Noah and Rita are considering the possibility of working together on one report and hoping that the teacher will not call on both of them.

   a. How many different ways are there of selecting groups of six students?

   b. How many of these groups include both Noah and Rita?

   c. What is the probability that Noah and Rita will both be called upon to give their reports?

   d. What would you advise Noah and Rita to do, given this probability?

7. Suppose you are to answer any four of the seven essay questions on the history test and the teacher doesn't care in which order you answer them.

   a. How many different question combinations are possible?

   b. What is the probability that you include Essay 5 if you randomly select your combination?

8. A coin is tossed five times and it comes up heads four out of five times. In your opinion, is this a rare occurrence? Defend your position.

9. Data collected over the last ten years shows that it will rain sometime during 30% of the days in the spring.

   a. How likely is a week with exactly five rainy days?

   b. How likely is a week with exactly six rainy days?

   c. How likely is a week with exactly seven rainy days?

   d. How likely is a week with at least five rainy days? (To answer this question, you must add several paths.)

10. Write a short letter to Pika Lock Company and explain why their "combination locks" should be called "permutation locks." Be sure to tell them how a true "combination lock" should work.

Section 11.3: Binomial Theorem

Probability is an area of mathematics that is rich with patterns. Long-range patterns are used by insurance companies when computing rates, lottery commissioners when predicting prizes and revenue, casino owners when determining odds, meteorologists when predicting the weather, and pollsters when reporting survey results. You can describe random phenomena outcomes, in which there are two possible choices, using the laws of counting and probability. In this section you will learn about the binomial theorem and how it can be used to compute probabilities.

A tree diagram can show the different results that occur when flipping a coin three times. In this situation there are eight outcomes that are usually counted as four possibilities.

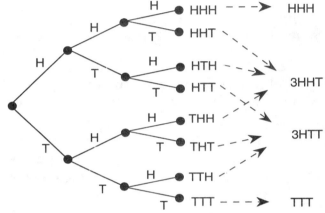

You can also use a binomial expansion to give you these counting numbers. At first glance, the expansion of the binomial $(H + T)^3$ or $(H + T) (H + T) (H + T)$ may not seem to be related to counting possible outcomes. To begin expanding this binomial, you multiply the H and T in the first pair with the H and T in the second pair:

$$(H + T) (H + T) = (HH + HT + TH + TT)$$

Then multiply each term of that result with the H and T in the third pair:

$$(HH + HT + TH + TT)(H + T) = HHH + HHT + HTH + HTT + THH + THT + TTH + TTT$$

Add similar terms, and write the result using exponents:

$$H^3 + H^2T + H^2T + HT^2 + H^2T + HT^2 + HT^2 + T^3$$

Combine again, and you will have $\mathbf{1}\ H^3 + \mathbf{3}\ H^2T + \mathbf{3}\ HT^2 + \mathbf{1}\ T^3$

How is this last expression related to the outcome shown in the tree diagram above?

This four-term polynomial is the result of expanding the binomial $(H + T)^3$. **Binomials** or two-term expressions like $(H + T)$ or $(1 + r)$ appear frequently in mathematics, and combination numbers show up in the expansion of binomials. The numbers 1, 3, 3, 1 from the expansion of $(H + T)^3 = \mathbf{1} H^3 + \mathbf{3} H^2T + \mathbf{3} HT^2 + \mathbf{1} T^3$ represent the coefficients of the expanded binomial, as well as totals for the different outcomes for three coins. The one path with no tails is represented by $_3C_0$; the three paths with one tail are represented by $_3C_1$; the three paths with two tails are represented by $_3C_2$; and the one path with three tails is represented by $_3C_3$. The 3 before the C represents the number of coins, which in this case is three.

Binomial Expansion Activity

There are many connections between a binomial expansion and combination numbers. In this activity, you will explore some of these connections.

a. Verify and complete the binomial expansions. The easiest way to do this is to multiply the previous result by $(H + T)$. For example, to expand $(H + T)^3$, first find $(H + T)^2$. Then multiply that result by $(H + T)$ to get the final result.

$$(H + T)^0 = \qquad\qquad 1$$
$$(H + T)^1 = \qquad\qquad \mathbf{1}\,H + \mathbf{1}\,T$$
$$(H + T)^2 = \qquad\qquad \mathbf{1}\,H^2 + \mathbf{2}\,HT + \mathbf{1}\,T^2$$
$$(H + T)^3 = \qquad\qquad \mathbf{1}\,H^3 + \mathbf{3}\,H^2T + \mathbf{3}\,HT^2 + \mathbf{1}\,T^3$$
$$(H + T)^4 = \qquad\qquad \text{complete this one}$$
$$(H + T)^5 = \qquad\qquad \text{complete this one}$$

b. The paths of a tree diagram for $(H + T)^5$ produce the combination numbers for five objects chosen one at a time, five objects chosen two at a time, and so on. Compute the combination numbers on your calculator.

The number of paths with 0 Tails $= {_5C_0} =$ _____
The number of paths with 1 Tail $\ = {_5C_1} =$ _____
The number of paths with 2 Tails $= {_5C_2} =$ _____
The number of paths with 3 Tails $= {_5C_3} =$ _____
The number of paths with 4 Tails $= {_5C_4} =$ _____
The number of paths with 5 Tails $= {_5C_5} =$ _____

c. i. Find the sum of the combination numbers (the coefficients) in each expansion in part a.

ii. What is the sum for $(H + T)^6$?

iii. What is the sum for $(H + T)^7$?

iv. What is the sum for $(H + T)^n$?

d. Arrange the combination numbers that appear in the expansions of $(H + T)^0$ through $(H + T)^7$ in part a in a triangular pattern as shown at the right. Keep the rows and columns organized. Copy the first five rows as shown and continue adding rows until you have a total of ten rows. This triangle is called **Pascal's triangle**. (Hint: You may find a connection between a combination number in a given row, and two combination numbers in the previous row.)

```
        1
      1   1
    1   2   1
  1   3   3   1
1   4   6   4   1
      . . .
```

e. Use the combination numbers from Pascal's triangle to write out the expansion of $(a + b)^{10}$.

f. Use the combination numbers from Pascal's triangle to name the first five terms of $(p + q)^{12}$.

g. Write the first three terms of the expansion $(a + b)^n$. What is the sixth term? What is the general term in terms of x? List the last three terms.

In this example you will see how combination numbers can be used to describe a natural phenomenon.

Example 1:

A hatching yellow-bellied sapsucker has a 0.58 probability of surviving to adulthood. Given a nest of 6 eggs, what are the respective probabilities for 0, 1, . . . , 6 birds to survive?

Solution:

The probability of survival or success is 0.58 for each hatching bird, so the probability of not surviving until adulthood is $1 - 0.58 = 0.42$. Some short cuts have been taken when expanding the binomial $(0.58 + 0.42)^6$. Look for patterns as you study the expansion.

$$_6C_0 \cdot 0.58^6 + {}_6C_1 \cdot 0.58^5 \cdot 0.42 + {}_6C_2 \cdot 0.58^4 \cdot 0.42^2 + {}_6C_3 \cdot 0.58^3 \cdot 0.42^3 + {}_6C_4 \cdot 0.58^2 \cdot 0.42^4$$
$$+ {}_6C_5 \cdot 0.58 \cdot 0.42^5 + {}_6C_6 \cdot 0.42^6$$

$$= 1 \cdot 0.58^6 + 6 \cdot 0.58^5 \cdot 0.42 + 15 \cdot 0.58^4 \cdot 0.42^2 + 20 \cdot 0.58^3 \cdot 0.42^3$$
$$+ 15 \cdot 0.58^2 \cdot 0.42^4 + 6 \cdot 0.58 \cdot 0.42^5 + 1 \cdot 0.42^6$$

$$= 0.038 + 0.165 + 0.299 + 0.289 + 0.157 + 0.045 + 0.005$$

Survival	0 birds	1 bird	2 birds	3 birds	4 birds	5 birds	6 birds
Exactly	4 %	16 %	?	29 %	16 %	5 %	0.5 %
At most	4%	20%	?	?	95%	99.5%	100%
At least	100%	?	?	?	?	5%	0.5%

The first row of this table comes directly from the terms of the expansion. Find the percentage that is missing. To find the probability that at most two birds survive, find the sum of the probabilities of zero, one, and two birds surviving. Complete the two values missing in the second row. To find the "at least" probabilities, you need to add the probabilities from the left. Complete the entries in the last row in the table. Why don't the "at most" and "at least" values for n birds add up to 100%? Make a statement about birds that incorporates the 20% entry located in the second row.

Free-Throw Activity

Using what resources you have available, attempt ten free-throw shots. If you don't have access to a real basketball hoop and basketball, be creative with what you have. If you make all ten (or zero) baskets, continue to shoot until you miss (or make) one. Use this information to calculate the experimental probability of your success on any given shot. Enter the program in **APPENDIX 11B**. When you run the program, you will be asked to enter p as your personal probability of success. The program will use p and the corresponding probability of failure $(1 - p)$ as it simulates 250 trials of this ten-shot experiment. Then it will display a histogram of the results.

Next, calculate the eleven theoretical probabilities for making each of zero to ten baskets based on your experimental probability. For example, if your probability of success is 30%, then the probability you will make 6 out of 10 shots is

$$_{10}C_6 \, (0.3)(0.3)(0.3)(0.3)(0.3)(0.3)(0.7)(0.7)(0.7)(0.7).$$

Why? Now multiply each of these 11 values by 250 and create a frequency histogram of the theoretical values. Sketch the calculator histogram next to the theoretical histogram. Then write a paragraph summarizing what this information tells you.

Problem Set 11.3

1. a. List the equally-likely outcomes if a coin is tossed twice.

   b. List the equally-likely outcomes if two coins are tossed once.

   c. Draw a tree diagram that pictures the answers to 1a and 1b.

   d. Describe the connection between the combination numbers $_2C_0 = 1$, $_2C_1 = 2$, $_2C_2 = 1$, and the results of your answers to 1a, 1b, and 1c.

   e. Give a real-world meaning to the equation
   $(H + T)^2 = \mathbf{1} \cdot H^2 + \mathbf{2} \cdot HT + \mathbf{1} \cdot T^2$

2. Expand each binomial, combining similar terms when possible.

    a. $(x + y)^4$ b. $(p + q)^5$ c. $(2x + 3)^3$ d. $(3x - 4)^4$

3. Enter the equation $y_1 = (8 \, {}_nC_r \, x) \, p^{(8 - x)}(1 - p)^x$ in your calculator.

    a. Find y_1 as x takes on the values $\{0, 1, 2, 3, \ldots, 8\}$ when $p = 0.50$. What is the sum of these nine values?

    b. Describe a method, using your calculator's statistics capabilities, that makes 3a easier. Make a scatter plot of (x, y).

    c. Find y_1 as x takes on the values $\{0, 1, 2, 3, \ldots, 8\}$ when $p = 0.55$. What is the sum of these nine values? Make a scatter plot of (x, y).

    d. Compare and describe the values of (x, y) created by this function as p increases in increments of 0.05.

4. Dr. Zeus is using a method of treatment that is 97% effective.

    a. What is the probability that there will be no failure in 30 treatments?

    b. What is the probability that there will be less than 3 failures in 30 treatments?

    c. Let x represent the number of failures in 30 treatments. Enter an equation in y_1 that will provide a table of values representing the probability $P(x)$ for any value of x.

    d. Use the equation and table from 4c to find the probability that there will be less than 3 failures in 30 treatments.

5. The university medical research team has developed a new test that is 88% effective at detecting a disease in its early stages. What is the probability that there will be more than 20 false readings in 100 applications of the test? (You may wish to enter and use the program in **APPENDIX 11C**.)

6. Suppose the probability that a penny chosen at random was minted before 1975 is 0.12.

    a. What is the probability that you will find 25 or more such coins in a 100-penny roll?

    b. What is the probability that you will find 25 or more such coins in two 100-penny rolls?

    c. What is the probability that you will find 25 or more such coins in three 100-penny rolls?

7. [The solution to this problem is used in the activity in Section 5.]

   a. Take the last two digits of your phone number, divide by 200 and add 0.25. Use this result as your probability of success, p, on one trial. Graph the binomial distribution showing the distribution of successes in 90 trials,

   $$y = (90\ _nC_r\ x)\ p^{(90-x)}(1-p)^x,$$ in the window given in **APPENDIX 11D**.

   b. The exponential equation (as you well know) is $y = ab^x$. The curve $y = ab^{x^2}$ can be used to approximate the binomial curve if you apply a horizontal shift to this equation so that it is not centered on the y-axis. Experiment with values of a and b until you can best match the binomial distribution graph. (Hint: The value of b will be slightly less than 1, and a can be found by looking at the maximum value for the first function.)

Section 11.4: Standard Deviation

Pulse rates are measured in beats per minute. A distribution of these rates for 50 cross-country runners might be quite different than that for 50 senior citizens, or 50 of your classmates. What is your pulse rate and how does it compare with the rates of others? What different statistical tools might be useful to describe similarities and differences of these distributions? Certainly measures of central tendency like the mean, median, and mode would be useful.

Deviations from an average pulse rate, the total range of rates, the amount of variability, and any measures which help describe the overall shape of a distribution are also valuable tools. To be useful, a measure of variability should be both universally acceptable and capable of measuring some dimension of the data. The standard deviation is the natural measure of spread (or dispersion) for certain types of distributions. In this section, you will discover how and why this is true.

Suppose the mean of several pulse rates is 72. Individual deviations, $x_i - \bar{x}$, for each data value, x_i, are listed in the table. The last column contains the squares of these individual deviations or $(x_i - \bar{x})^2$.

The standard deviation is the square root of the average entry

Data values	Pulse rates	Deviations $x_i - \bar{x}$	Squared deviations
x_1	64	$64 - 72 = {}^-8$	64
x_2	65	$65 - 72 = {}^-7$	49
x_3	70	$70 - 72 = {}^-2$	4
x_4	71	$71 - 72 = {}^-1$	1
x_5	73	$73 - 72 = 1$	1
x_6	79	$79 - 72 = 7$	49
x_7	82	$82 - 72 = 10$	100
		Total	268

in the last column, or $\sqrt{\dfrac{268}{7}}$. If all of the pulse rates were 72 beats per minute, the standard deviation would be zero. But, in fact, in most situations the data values differ from the mean value. Standard deviation is a way of averaging the amount of deviation from the mean.

Cord Length Activity

A cord measuring somewhere between 1.5 m and 2 m in length will be passed about the class. Use a meter stick to measure the length of this cord as accurately as you can. Don't share this measurement with your classmates, but instead record it on a scrap of paper. Place the record of your measurement in the envelope that came with the cord.

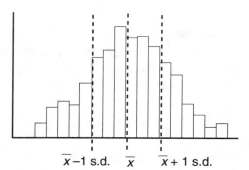

When everyone has recorded their measurements, enter the list of cord measurements in your calculator. Then create several histograms with different bar widths. Determine the bar width that gives the best picture, and make a sketch of this histogram. Find the mean value of the data and draw in a vertical line at the mean.

Now find the deviation of each measurement from the mean and then square each deviation. The mean value of the sum of the squares of the deviations is called the **variance** of the data. The units of this variance are centimeters squared, which is a little confusing because your cord measurements had nothing to do with area, so a number involving squaring measures of length doesn't make much sense. The square root of the variance remedies this units dilemma and is called the **standard deviation** of the data. The units of the standard deviation of the measured cords are centimeters. Now find the standard deviation of the data, and add two more vertical lines to your sketch: one that is one standard deviation above the mean, and another that is one standard deviation below the mean.

This standard deviation is a widely-used measure of spread that you can use in much the same way you have used the mean absolute deviation or MAD. One advantage of the standard deviation is that it is a built-in function on most calculators, computer spreadsheets, and analysis tools. See **APPENDIX 11E** for instructions on how to calculate standard deviation with your calculator so that you can concentrate on the meaning of this measure rather than on calculating the number. The lowercase Greek letter sigma (σ) is used for standard deviation.

> The **variance** of a data set is the mean of the sum of the squares of the deviations from the mean of the data.
>
> $$\sigma^2 = \frac{\displaystyle\sum_{i=1}^{n}(x_i - \bar{x})^2}{n}$$
>
> The **standard deviation** is a measure of spread used for data sets. It is equal to the square root of the variance.
>
> $$\sigma = \sqrt{\frac{\displaystyle\sum_{i=1}^{n}(x_i - \bar{x})^2}{n}}$$

Example 1:

Five hundred pennies were weighed. The individual penny masses varied from 2.7 g to 3.4 g. The following table gives the frequencies of each different mass in the set of 500 pennies.

Mass	2.7 g	2.8 g	2.9 g	3.0 g	3.1 g	3.2 g	3.3 g	3.4 g
Frequency	2	15	57	111	138	109	54	14

Find the mean and standard deviation of the data. How far from the mean is the weight of 2.7 g?

Solution:

Enter the data in the calculator as described in **APPENDIX 11E**. The mean is 3.0962 g, and the standard deviation is 0.1383 g. Take a moment to verify these values. A penny with a mass of 2.7 g is $\frac{3.0962 - 2.7}{0.1383} = 2.86$ standard deviations below the mean.

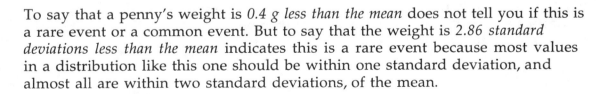

To say that a penny's weight is *0.4 g less than the mean* does not tell you if this is a rare event or a common event. But to say that the weight is *2.86 standard deviations less than the mean* indicates this is a rare event because most values in a distribution like this one should be within one standard deviation, and almost all are within two standard deviations, of the mean.

Any penny mass, x_i, can be converted to this standardized score for a comparative analysis. The calculation $\dfrac{x_i - \bar{x}}{\sigma}$ tells you how many standard deviations x_i is from the mean, providing a relative measure that allows you to compare one data set with another.

Example 2:

Rita scored 670 on a standardized math test and 740 on the verbal portion of the exam. The mean math score for all students was 550, with $\sigma = 80$. The mean verbal score was 610, with $\sigma = 95$. Which was the better score?

Solution:

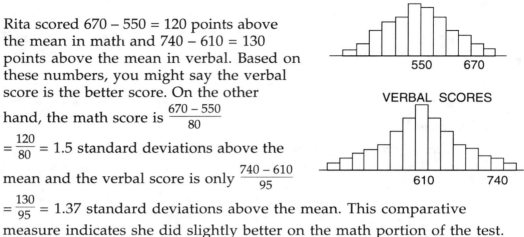

MATH SCORES

VERBAL SCORES

Rita scored $670 - 550 = 120$ points above the mean in math and $740 - 610 = 130$ points above the mean in verbal. Based on these numbers, you might say the verbal score is the better score. On the other hand, the math score is $\frac{670 - 550}{80}$

$= \frac{120}{80} = 1.5$ standard deviations above the mean and the verbal score is only $\frac{740 - 610}{95}$

$= \frac{130}{95} = 1.37$ standard deviations above the mean. This comparative measure indicates she did slightly better on the math portion of the test.

The mean is probably the most commonly-used measure of center, and the standard deviation is a measure of a distribution's spread about the mean. These two measures go together. The units of this measure of spread are the same as the units of the data. The standard deviation, like the mean, involves every value in the set, so it is strongly influenced by outliers. Therefore, this measure is very sensitive when the distribution of data is skewed. The strongest argument for using standard deviation is its close ties to a common type of distribution, the normal distribution. Because the spread of the data in such a distribution is quite predictable, you can use standard deviation to determine probabilities. You will soon learn, for example, that in a large set of cord length measurements, two-thirds of the data will be within one standard deviation of the mean. This means you could predict that the probability that the next measurement is within one standard deviation to be about 67%.

Example 3:

Dee Visor created an adapter which will plug into the lighter socket of a car to recharge a video camera. She plans to sell 10,000 adapters in the first year. Each unit uses several resistors, and Dee needs top-quality ones. She purchased a package of one hundred 4.7-ohm resistors from Impedance Inc. and a package of one hundred 4.7-ohm resistors from Electrical Obstructions. She tested all of the resistors and recorded the results in a table.

Resistance (Ohms)	4.697	4.698	4.699	4.700	4.701	4.702	4.703	4.704
Impedance Inc. (100 count)	5	9	17	27	21	13	3	5
Electrical Obstruction (100 count)	2	4	23	32	21	5	7	6

The first 5 in the table indicates that five of the Impedance Inc. resistors were found to be 4.697 ohms. Her specifications require that each resistor be no more than 0.002 ohms from its labeled value of 4.7 ohms. Which resistors should she order?

Solution:

She can only use resistors between 4.698 and 4.702 ohms, inclusive. Be certain you understand why before continuing. This means that out of the first package she must discard 5 + 3 + 5 = 13 resistors. The package from Electrical Obstructions contains 2 + 7 + 6 = 15 rejects. Based on this information you might recommend she buy from Impedance Inc. But further calculations show the first set has a standard deviation of 0.00165 ohms, while the second set has a standard deviation of 0.00155 ohms. The larger standard deviation for the Impedance Inc. set of resistors implies that the data for these resistors is more spread out. This could mean that over the long run, Dee would end up discarding more resistors from Impedance Inc.

Problem Set 11.4

1. a. Which of these sets of data would you expect to have the larger standard deviation? Explain your reasoning.

   5   23   36   48   63   or   112 115 118 119 121

   b. Calculate the mean and standard deviation of each set by using the definitions, rather than using the built-in function keys on your calculator.

   c. Multiply the data values in each of the two given sets by 10. Then find the mean and standard deviation of the new sets. How do these measures compare to those you found in 1b?

2. a. Select four numbers from the whole numbers 1 to 8, inclusive (repeats are allowed), so that they have the smallest possible standard deviation. Explain your thinking while making these selections.

   b. This time select four numbers so that they have the largest possible standard deviation. Explain your thinking.

3. Pierre, Hans, and Juanita have taken national language exams in French, German, and Spanish, respectively. Pierre scored 88, Hans scored 84, and Juanita scored 91. The national means and standard deviations for the tests are: French, $\bar{x} = 72$, $\sigma = 8.5$; German, $\bar{x} = 72$, $\sigma = 5.8$; and Spanish, $\bar{x} = 85$, $\sigma = 6.1$.

   a. Based on the information given, can you determine which test is most difficult? Why or why not?

   b. Which test do you suspect had the widest range of scores nationally? Explain your reasoning.

   c. Which of the three friends did *best* when compared to the national norms? Explain your reasoning.

4. Collect data from the sum of two six-sided dice rolled 99 times. (See APPENDIX 11F for a calculator simulation.)

   a. Find the mean and standard deviation of the sums.

   b. How many of the 99 sums are within one standard deviation of the mean?

   c. What percent of the data is within one standard deviation of the mean?

   d. What percent of the data is within two standard deviations of the mean?

5. Describe the standard deviation for each histogram and compare them. The domain of the horizontal axis is 50 to 100 in each diagram.

a.   b.   c.

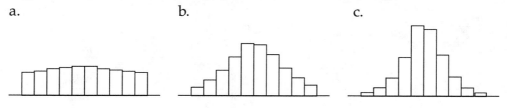

6. Consider the ages of the presidents and vice-presidents at inauguration.

   a. Predict the mean inaugural ages of the presidents and the vice-presidents. Which should have the larger standard deviation?

   b. Enter the two separate lists of data into your calculator and calculate the mean and standard deviation for each list.

   c. Use your calculator to graph two histograms of the data. Use the same scale for each graph.

   d. Create two new lists by converting each age to a standardized scale by calculating $\dfrac{x_i - \bar{x}}{\sigma}$.

   e. Describe the range of values in the new distributions.

   f. Graph the two histograms of these standardized distributions. Use an Xmin of ⁻3.5, Xmax of 3.5, and Xscl of 1.

   g. Compare and describe the graphs from 6f.

President	Age	Vice-pres	Age	President	Age	Vice-Pres	Age
Washington	57	Adams	54	Cleveland	55	Hobart	53
J. Adams	61	Jefferson	54	McKinley	54	Roosevelt	38
Jefferson	57	Burr	45	T. Roosevelt	42	Fairbanks	53
Madison	57	Clinton	66	Taft	51	Sherman	54
Monroe	58	Gerry	69	Wilson	56	Marshall	59
J. Q. Adams	57	Tompkins	43	Harding	55	Coolidge	49
Jackson	61	Calhoun	43	Coolidge	51	Dawes	60
Van Buren	54	Van Buren	51	Hoover	54	Curtis	69
W. Harrison	68	Johnson	57	F. D. Roosevelt	51	Garner	65
Tyler	51	Tyler	51			Wallace	53
Polk	49	Dallas	53			Truman	60
Taylor	64	Fillmore	49	Eisenhower	62	Nixon	40
Fillmore	50	King	67	Truman	61	Barkley	72
Pierce	48	Breckinridge	36	Kennedy	43	Johnson	53
Buchanan	64	Hamlin	52	L.B. Johnson	55	Humphrey	54
Lincoln	52	Johnson	57	Nixon	56	Agnew	51
A. Johnson	56	Colfax	46			Ford	60
Grant	46	Wilson	61	Ford	61	Rockefeller	66
Hayes	54	Wheeler	58	Carter	52	Mondale	49
Garfield	49	Arthur	51	Reagan	69	Bush	57
Arthur	50	Hendricks	66	Bush	64	Quayle	42
Cleveland	47	Morton	65	Clinton	45	Gore	43
B. Harrison	55	Stevenson	58				

7. Consider the number of heads when 15 fair coins are tossed all at once.

a. Use the binomial probability distribution, $P(x) = (15\ _n C_r\ x)\ p^{(15-x)}(1-p)^x$, to complete a table of theoretical results for 500 trials of this experiment. The middle row indicates results of one trial. Round off the frequencies (in row 3) to whole-number values.

Heads (x)	0	1	2	. . .	14	15	Total
P(x)	(0.5^{15})						= 1
Frequency	$500(0.5^{15})$			. . .			= 500

b. Create a histogram showing the total number of heads.

c. Find the mean and standard deviation of the number of heads.

d. How many of the 500 trials are within one standard deviation of the mean?

e. What percent of the data is within one standard deviation of the mean?

f. What percent of the data is within two standard deviations of the mean?

g. What percent of the data is within three standard deviations of the mean?

8. [The solution to this problem is used in the activity in Section 5.] Enter the equation for the binomial distribution $y_1 = (90 \, {}_nC_r \, x) \, p^{(90-x)}(1-p)^x$ using the window given in **APPENDIX 11D** and the same probability of success as you used in Problem 7, Section 3. Place the values from 0 to 90 into the data set. Your goal is to find the mean and standard deviation of the function values using the probabilities as frequencies. The calculator uses only integer values of frequency to compute the values needed. To approximate the frequencies, use the rounded-off part of 1000 times the probability. (See **APPENDIX 11G**.) Now find the mean and standard deviation of the data.

Section 11.5: Normal Distributions

Penny Punkuall has worked for many years as an actuary in the same office. It takes her an average of 23 min to get to work every day, with a standard deviation of 4.1 min. As she leaves her home, she notes that she must be at the office in 25 min. Because Penny uses public transportation, she cannot control the time it takes her to get to work. What is the probability that she will be late?

With no other information available, you will have to make some assumptions. What does this distribution of times look like? Is the distribution symmetric, or are her times all over the place like Figure c below? If you think her travel times are best represented by Figure b, this means some times are less and some are more than the average of 23 min. In fact, Figure b suggests the times are divided quite equally about the mean, and that generally her travel times are near the average of 23 min.

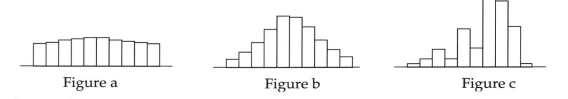

| Figure a | Figure b | Figure c |

The **normal distribution** is a common distribution that can also be used to determine probabilities. It is both symmetric and "bell-shaped" like a binomial distribution. In fact, the binomial distribution, $(p + q)^n$, becomes a normal distribution as the values of n grow increasingly large. Normal distributions and normal curves are used in many types of studies, some of which describe biological and psychological measurements. They were first applied to data by Gauss (1777–1855) to describe errors made by surveyors and astronomers as they remeasured the same quantities. In this section, you will be introduced to some properties of the normal distribution and the related normal curve.

In the last section, you found the mean penny mass was 3.1 g and the standard deviation was 0.2012 g for this distribution of 500 penny masses varying from 2.7 g to 3.4 g.

Mass	2.7 g	2.8 g	2.9 g	3.0 g	3.1 g	3.2 g	3.3 g	3.4 g
Frequency	2	15	57	111	138	109	54	14

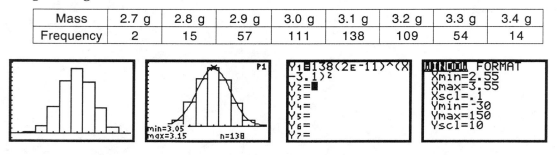

The equation $y = ab^{x^2}$ can be used to approximate or model this distribution. It requires a horizontal shift because the curve pictured is symmetric about the mean mass of 3.1 g. In the equation $y = ab^{(x - 3.1)^2}$ the 3.1 shifts the graph 3.1 g to the right.

The calculations below show how the values for a and b can be found. To find a, substitute the x- and y-values for the table entry for the mean value, (3.1, 138), into the equation:

$$138 = ab^{(3.1 - 3.1)^2} = ab^{(0)} \text{ means } a = 138 \text{ or } y = 138b^{(x - 3.1)^2}$$

Then substitute any other table entry to find the value of b. In this case, the entry (2.8, 15) was used.

$$15 = 138b^{(2.8 - 3.1)^2} \text{ or } 138b^{0.09} \text{ means } b = \sqrt[0.09]{\frac{15}{138}} \approx 2 \cdot 10^{-11}$$

$$\text{or } y = 138(2\text{E}{-}11)^{(x - 3.1)^2}.$$

In a normal distribution, the variable values are actually continuous rather than discrete, because it is as likely that a penny will weigh 3.2147883 g as 3.2 g.

Areas and Distributions Activity

The curve $y = 138(2\text{E}{-}11)^{(x-3.1)^2}$ models the distribution of penny masses. Find the area under this curve using the area program in **APPENDIX 11H**. When you run this program you must input a value for the left endpoint (or starting value), a value for the right endpoint (or ending value), and the number of subdivisions. The greater the number of subdivisions, the more accuracy in the answer (and the longer it takes to complete the calculation). For left endpoint 1, right endpoint 5, and 500 subdivisions you should get an area of approximately 49.18. Do this now.

A relative frequency distribution of this collection of pennies corresponds to the approximations given by $y = 2.8(2\text{E}{-}11)^{(x - 3.1)^2}$. The smaller coefficient 2.8 is the number that provides an area of 1 between the curve and the x-axis (138 divided by 49.18). Normal curves approximate histograms of probabilities. Because a probability distribution sums to 1, the area under a normal curve is 1, allowing you to answer probability questions.

Graph the equation
$$y = 2.8(2\text{E}{-}11)^{(x-3.1)^2}$$
on your calculator. What is the maximum value of this function? Use the area program in **APPENDIX 11H** to find the area values in the table. Verify the entries in the following table by using the endpoint values and number of subdivisions indicated.

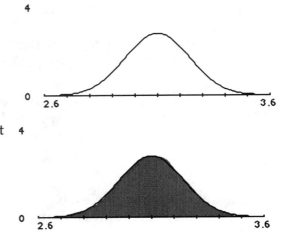

Start	2.6	2.6	2.6	2.6	1	0
End	3.6	3.6	3.6	3.6	5	6
Subdivisions	10	100	1000	10,000	1000	1000
Area	0.9089	0.9896	0.9985	0.9993	0.9989	0.9989

The pattern and information pictured in the table shows that by choosing a larger interval, or by using more subdivisions, the area increases towards 1. Now use the same program to find the area under the curve when x is greater than 3.3. You will need to decide how much accuracy is needed for the solution and then choose your values accordingly. As a general rule of thumb, you will need about 10^n divisions to get n digits of accuracy. You will find the approximate area is 0.0803. How close is the estimate using 100 subdivisions? This means the probability is that $\frac{0.0803}{0.999} = 0.0804$ or 8.04% (or about 1 out of 13) of the pennies will weigh more than 3.3 grams. Describe how you can use this answer to determine the probability of a penny weighing less than or equal to 3.3 grams.

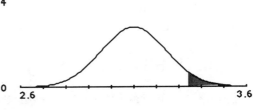

In a histogram, the sum of the column heights is the total number in the distribution. Similarly, the area under the distribution curve represents all of the numbers involved in the distribution. In the last activity, you found the area under the curve using the area program. You were faced with the problem that this curve has no endpoints because it approaches zero asymptotically. Because the curve seems to drop so quickly toward zero, you may have assumed that the area beyond a certain point was minimal.

Example 1:

Professor Ty Tration at Whatts Amatta U recently gave a chemistry test. He found that the distribution of test scores fit the curve $y = 21(0.991)^{(x-82)^2}$. Use his model to find frequencies of the scores listed in this table.

Score	65	70	75	80	82	85	90	95	100
Freq									

What is the mean and standard deviation of the scores?

Solution:

Enter *all* scores and frequencies from 62 to 102 (inclusive) by using the equation to reconstruct the data set. Some of the frequency values predicted by the model are listed below. (See **APPENDIX 11I** for one way to enter the data quickly and accurately.) It is very unlikely that these are the actual scores and frequencies in the distribution, but they must be close to the actual data if the curve fits the distribution.

Score	65	70	75	80	82	85	90	95	100
Freq	2	6	13	20	21	19	12	5	1

Check with your calculator to see that the table is correct, that the standard deviation is 7.4 points, and that the mean is 82. In a symmetric data set the mean is always in the middle. In general, 99.99% of the area is within four standard deviations (in each direction) from the mean. Look at the area under the curve $y = 21(0.991)^{(x-82)^2}$ from $82 - 4(7.4) \approx 52$ to $82 + 4(7.4) \approx 112$. You should find the area is about 391. (Check this on your own.) [You will continue this example in the problem set.]

The mean determines the symmetrical center of the curve or distribution, but it does not control the steepness of the curve. The slope, which is determined by the standard deviation of the distribution, controls the width or spread of the curve. If two normal curves have the same mean, the taller and more narrow graph is the one with the smaller standard deviation. Below are three normal distributions with a mean of 50. The vertical scales are adjusted so the curves are all the same height. (Looking at the y-scales, you can see that the graph on the left would be the tallest graph if the same y-scales were used for each graph.) Note that at a distance of one standard deviation from the mean the graphs all have the same relative height.

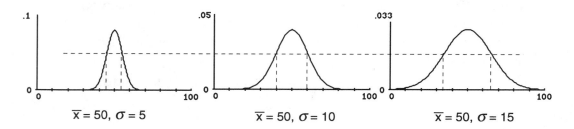

$\overline{x} = 50, \sigma = 5$ $\overline{x} = 50, \sigma = 10$ $\overline{x} = 50, \sigma = 15$

All normal curves are symmetric about their means, and bell-shaped as in the curves above. Their tails fall off very rapidly. The two points where the curvature changes are each located one standard deviation away from the mean. In general, 68% of all data described by a normal distribution falls within one standard deviation of the mean, 95% of the data falls within two standard deviations, and 99.7% falls within three standard deviations of the mean. This information given by the standard deviation determines the shape, height and width of any normal distribution.

Problem Set 11.5

1. The mean height of an adult male gorilla is 5 ft 8 in., with a standard deviation of 2.8 in.

    a. Sketch the graph of a normal distribution of gorilla heights. Shade the portion of this graph that indicates heights that are greater than 6 ft.

    b. Sketch the graph of a normal distribution of gorilla heights if instead the standard deviation is 3.2 in.

    c. Compare your sketches and explain your reasoning.

2. The life span of a tribble has a mean value of 28 days, with a standard deviation of 4 days. Sketch the normal curve for a life span distribution. Shade the portion of the curve where tribbles live 24 to 28 days.

3. Chocolate Frosted Sugar Bombs are packaged in 16-oz boxes. The filling machine is set to put 16.8 oz in the box, with a standard deviation of 0.7 oz. Sketch a graph of the normal distribution curve and shade the portion of boxes that are under the required weight.

4. Water collected from several different locations and depths of a lake will likely have a normal distribution of pH values. The pH of a solution measures the strength of the acidity of that solution. The mean value plus or minus one standard deviation is defined to be the pH range of the lake. Lake Fishbegon has a pH range of 5.8 to 7.2. Shade those portions of the normal curve that are outside this range.

5. Professor Ty Tration's distribution of test scores fit the curve $y = 21(0.991)^{(x-82)^2}$. This distribution has a mean of 82 and standard deviation of 7.4. In Example 1 you found the area under the curve to be 391. Use the area program to find the percentages of the total area as specified in a–c.

   a. Within one standard deviation of the mean.

   b. Within two standard deviations of the mean.

   c. Within three standard deviations of the mean.

6. a. Convert the equation $y = 21(0.991)^{(x-82)^2}$ to a normal curve by finding a value of a in $y = a(0.991)^{(x-82)^2}$ that provides an area of 1 under the curve.

   b. Use your new equation to find the percent of the data within one standard deviation of the mean.

   c. Use your new equation to find the percent of the data within two standard deviations of the mean.

   d. Use your new equation to find the percent of the data within three standard deviations of the mean.

7. The following data was collected from 493 college women.

Height (cm)	148–50	150–52	152–54	154–56	156–58	158–60	160–62	162–64
Frequency	2	5	9	15	27	40	52	63

Height (cm)	164–66	166–68	168–70	170–72	172–74	174–76	176–78	178–80
Frequency	66	64	53	39	28	16	9	5

   a. Find the mean and standard deviation of the heights.

   b. Sketch the histogram of the given data.

   c. Write the equation that approximates the histogram based on the model $y = ab^{x^2}$.

   d. Find the equation for a normal curve based on this data.

8. a. Find the mean and standard deviation of the data below that represents the pulse rates of 50 people.

66	75	83	73	87	94	79	93	87	64
80	72	84	82	80	73	74	80	83	68
86	70	73	62	77	90	82	85	84	80
80	79	81	82	76	95	76	82	79	91
82	66	78	73	72	77	71	79	82	88

   b. Sketch a histogram of the data.

   c. Sketch a normal distribution curve that approximates the histogram. Write the equation of this curve.

   d. Find the equation for a normal curve based on this data.

   e. Based on this information, would you say that these pulse rates are normally distributed? Why or why not?

Section 11.6: Using the Normal Curve

Mayor Polly Tishon just learned that there are 4700 unemployed working-age adults in her town. Should she be concerned? This depends on a number of variables, such as the size of her town and how many people are usually unemployed at any given time. If data over the last five-year interval indicates a mean of 4000 unemployed working-age adults, with a standard deviation of 500, she may have a legitimate concern. The current unemployment, however, may be just part of other normal changes in the community, or it may be a result of a new trend. How unusual is the unemployment figure of 4700? Even though the data may not be a perfect normal distribution, she can still use a normal distribution curve as a good model to make predictions and decisions about this situation.

You already know the normal curve equation with total area of 1 can be modeled by $y = ab^{x^2}$. In Problem 6 of Section 11.5, you were asked to find the coefficient a in $y = a(0.991)^{(x-82)^2}$. The coefficient a, the value of the base, and the shift of the mean provide the particular model to fit the data. How is the value of a determined for this function? How is the value of the base, 0.991, determined for this function? The standard deviation must be involved because this measure determines the shape of the curve.

Normal Curve Equation Activity

Do you recognize the mean and standard deviation of the unemployment statistics in the equation $y_1 = (\frac{1}{500\sqrt{2\pi}}) (1 - \frac{1}{2(500)^2})^{(x-4000)^2}$? Enter this equation into your calculator and graph the normal curve in the window pictured. Now calculate the values of

$$a = \frac{1}{\sigma\sqrt{2\pi}} \text{ and } b = 1 - \frac{1}{2(\sigma)^2} \text{ where } \sigma = 500.$$

Confirm this equation. Then graph $y_2 = 0.0007979(0.999998)^{(x-4000)^2}$.

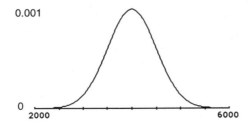

Check that the two graphs and table entries for $2000 \leq x \leq 6000$ are the same. Use the program in **APPENDIX 11H** with a starting value of 2000, an ending value of 6000, and 500 divisions. Where did 2000 and 6000 come from? In a normal distribution there will be hardly any area beyond four standard deviations from the mean. In fact, you should find the area under this curve is 0.9979, or approximately 1, as expected.

The area under this curve to the right of 4700 unemployed people will provide the probability of this event. That is, if the number of unemployed is distributed normally, the area to the right of the vertical line represents the probability that more than 4700 will be unemployed. Use the program with a starting value of 4700, an ending value of 6000, and 500 divisions.

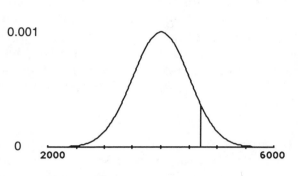

When you complete these calculations, you will find that under normal conditions, the probability of this event happening is 8%. Write up an explanation for Mayor Polly Tishon that she can use to help her address the situation for the media.

Finding the probability or likelihood of an event takes a good understanding of the normal curve and its geometric properties. Observe the different approaches as you work on the examples and problems in this section. Sometimes the information is reversed in a problem—the probability is given and you need to find the interval of values that should represent the event. To solve these problems you will use a program to find endpoints of the interval. The program is designed to match the given area (probability) with the interval at the left end of the normal curve. This means you will need to reinterpret some of the problems.

Example 1:

Chuck O'Latt wishes to advertise the abundance of chips in his cookies. The research division at his factory has calculated that the mean number of chips in a cookie is 22.5, with a standard deviation of 4.5 chips. Chuck wants to advertise a number that will accurately represent 95% of the cookies sold. How many chips should he advertise?

Solution:

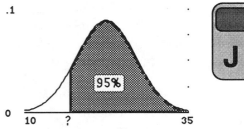

The program Chuck is using (reprinted for you in **APPENDIX 11J**) will always find the right end of an interval, so Chuck should consider the unshaded portion of the graph pictured here. When he runs the program, he will give 0.05 as the percent. Do you see why? Remember, the probability of an event being true and the probability of it not being true must always add up to one. The program gives a value of 15.12 chips. Check this! He can probably advertise that "all cookies have at least 15 chips," but you know that only 95% or more of all his cookies have at least 15 chips.

In Example 1 you were given the area (probability) to the right of a line, but you adjusted and worked with the region left of that line. Frequently you will need to use the symmetry of the curve to find the values that you are looking for.

Example 2:

Inventor Cray Z. Eyedea invented an apparatus for cold sufferers to wear when trying to get a good night's sleep. The unit must fit tightly about the nose. Because noses come in such a big range of sizes, Cray knows it is probably only feasible to produce units to fit 80% of the population. Medical research shows that the mean adult nose is 2.41 cm long, with a standard deviation of 0.34 cm. What range of sizes will Cray's apparatus fit?

Solution:

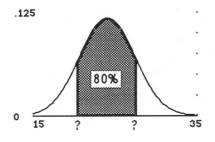

The fairest way to fit 80% of the targeted population is to choose a range that is centered on the mean. Because of the symmetry of the curve, he knows that the area left of the shaded region must be the same as the area to the right of the shaded region. The three areas are 0.10, 0.80, and 0.10 because 0.10 + 0.80 + 0.10 = 1.00. Try using the program with the value $\bar{x} = 2.41$, $\sigma = 0.34$, and a probability of 0.1. Remember the program requires that you furnish the probability of the left-most region. When you run the program you will get an error message because the program formula is limited. The program requires *that the standard deviation entered is greater than 2.*

Cray thinks quickly and converts all measurements to millimeters. This makes the mean length 24.1 mm and the standard deviation 3.4 mm. He enters the values $\bar{x} = 24.1$, $\sigma = 3.4$, and probability of 0.1 and the program provides him with an answer of 19.9 mm. This is the nose measurement at the right end of the left-most region. The lower deviation from the mean is $24.1 - 19.9 = 4.2$ mm and, because of the curve's symmetry, he finds the upper deviation value by adding to the mean: $24.1 + 4.2 = 28.3$ mm. So, to fit 80% of the population he must make his device adjust to fit noses between 1.99 cm and 2.83 cm. Gesundheit!

Problem Set 11.6

1. Penny Punkuall has worked for many years as an actuary in the same office. By her calculations, it takes her an average of 23 min to get to work every day, with a standard deviation of 4.1 min. As she leaves her home one day, she notes that she must be at the office in 25 min. What is the probability that she will be late?

2. The "You Gotta Be Nuts" candy bar has an average weight of 75.3 g, with a standard deviation of 4.7 g.
   a. What weight should the company advertise to be truthful 80% of the time? (Write a complete sentence using your numerical answer.)
   b. What weight should the company advertise to be truthful 90% of the time? (Write a complete sentence using your numerical answer.)
   c. What weight should the company advertise to be truthful 95% of the time? (Write a complete sentence using your numerical answer.)

3. Acorns will fall around the base of a tree in a somewhat normal distribution with a standard deviation of 20 ft (away from the base.)
   a. What is the probability that an acorn will land more than 50 ft from the tree?
   b. What is the probability that an acorn will land more than 75 ft from the tree?

4. Three hundred equal samples were taken from Lake Asidreign. An indicator solution was used to find that 225 of the samples were in the pH range from 5.5 to 6.5. The mean pH was calculated at 6.0. What is the standard deviation of the samples? How did you find your solution?

5. Makers of "Sweet Swallows" 100% fruit drink have found that their filling machine will fill a bottle with a standard deviation of 0.75 oz. The control on the machine will change the mean value, but not affect the standard deviation.
   a. Where should they set the mean so that 90% of the bottles have at least 12 oz in them?
   b. If a fruit drink bottle can hold 13.5 oz before overflowing, what percent of them will overflow at the setting suggested in 5a?

6. Assume the probability of high school students needing corrective lenses is 28%.

   a. What is the probability that exactly 25 out of 95 students would need corrective lenses?

   b. In how many of 1000 groups of 95 students would you expect to find exactly 25 students needing corrective lenses?

   c. Repeat this calculation for all values from 0 to 95. Put these into a data set with x-values between 0 and 95 inclusive and y-values as the frequency of the event. (See **APPENDIX 11F** to automate this calculation.)

   d. Find the standard deviation of this set of data.

   e. Compare this number to $\sqrt{95(0.28)(0.72)}$.

7. Enter the two functions in your calculator for binomial distributions and the normal curve. Use the variables N, P, S, and M in your equations. Here N is the number of trials, P is the probability of success, S is the standard deviation, and M is the mean.

$$y_1 = (N\,_nC_r\,x)P^x(1-P)^{(N-x)}$$

$$y_2 = (\frac{1}{S\sqrt{2\pi}})(1-\frac{1}{2S^2})^{(x-M)^2}$$

   a. Complete the table below by calculating $M = NP$ and $S = \sqrt{NP(1-P)}$

N	47	64	150	Your choice	Your choice
P	0.3	0.8	0.18	0.61	Your choice
M					
S					

   b. Store the first column values in the proper variables, and graph the equations using a range that will give integer values along the x-axis on your calculator.

   c. Repeat 7b for the other four columns. Make a statement about your observations.

Section 11.7: Chapter Review

Problem Set 11.7

1. Twelve candidates (seven males and five females) for a job are to be called into a room one at a time.

   a. How many different interview orders are possible?

   b. If the interview order is generated randomly, what is the probability that the first five candidates will be female?

2. Stamin Blackwood just picked up his bridge hand of thirteen cards. He has ten red cards and three black cards. The first ten cards he picked up were red. How unusual is this? Explain in detail so that Stamin will understand your answer.

3. Anna Chovey can take exactly 20 more orders before closing. She has enough pepperoni for 16 more pizzas. On a typical night, 65% of her pizzas are pepperoni. What is the probability that she will be short if she doesn't apply the pepperoni conservatively? (Hint: You will need to add four calculations for this answer.)

4. Rewrite each expression without parentheses.

   a. $100(1 - x)^8$ b. $600(1 + x/12)^5$

5. The height of each adult in Normalville was measured to the nearest inch. Find the mean and standard deviation of the heights. Make a statement about the meaning of the standard deviation in this problem.

Height	60	61	62	63	64	65	66	67	68	69	70	71	72	73	74	75
Frequency	1	1	4	6	8	10	9	8	13	10	5	6	6	3	6	3

6. The height of all adults in Bigtown is normally distributed with a mean of 167 cm and a standard deviation of 8.5 cm. Sketch a graph of the distribution curve of these heights, and shade the portion of that graph showing the percent of people shorter than 155 cm.

7. Find the probability of guessing exactly six right answers out of ten true/false questions. Describe your solution process.

8. Write expressions involving x, n, and ! that are equivalent to

   a. nCr b. nPr

9. Find the probability of guessing seven or more correct answers on a ten-question multiple-choice quiz if each question has five choices.

10. Six-foot U. S. males between the ages of 18 and 24 have a mean weight of 175 lb. Their weights are normally distributed with a standard deviation of 14 lb.

a. What percentage of these males weigh between 180 lb and 200 lb?

b. What percentage of these males weigh less than 160 lb?

c. Find two weights so that 90% of all these males are included between them.

d. Find the equation of a normal curve which will provide a probability distribution representing this information.

Section 11.8: Projects

11.1 Trinomial Distribution

In the chapter you looked at binomial distributions. When there are three options instead of two, the situation is similar but different. Begin this project by expanding the trinomials here. Note that the first answer will have 6 terms, the second will have 10 terms, and the third will have 15 terms.

$$(x + y + z)^2 \qquad\qquad (x + y + z)^3 \qquad\qquad (x + y + z)^4$$

Make some generalizations about $(x + y + z)^n$, including a formula involving factorials for the coefficients of the terms.

The probability of a passenger buying a first-class airline ticket is 0.05, and the probability that she will buy a business-class ticket is 0.08. If 81 seats are sold, then what is the probability that there are exactly 4 in first class, 6 in business class, and 71 in coach? A plane has 100 seats, 10 in first class, 10 in business class, and 80 in coach. Explain how to find the probability that any of the three sections will be overfilled if 81 seats were sold. What is the probability that both first class and business are overfilled?

11.2 Normal Curves and e

The formula used in this chapter for a normal distribution comes with the stipulation that you should only use it with a standard deviation greater than two. This is a rather unusual condition, but it is because the formula is only approximate. The actual formula is $\frac{1}{\sigma\sqrt{2\pi}} e^{-(x-\bar{x})^2/2\sigma^2}$, which uses the constant e for continuous exponential growth. (If you do not know what e is, then see Project 7.3.) Compare the graph of this equation with the equation in the chapter. Make sketches of both equations with $\bar{x} = 50$ for three different standard deviations, $\sigma = 10$, $\sigma = 3$, and $\sigma = 0.5$.

Select a problem from Section 11.6 and solve it again using the new formula. How much error was involved with the formula given in the chapter?

11.3 Skewed Data

A normal curve is balanced on both sides of the mean. If the mean of a normal distribution is 50, then the probability that a value is between 20 and 30 is the same as its being between 70 and 80. Not all data is so evenly distributed. One example of "skewed data" is called a **Poisson distribution**. In this project you will study a binomial distribution with a low probability of success (less than 0.01), using enough trials so that you might be likely to get more than 10 successes.

Find the probability of a real-world event with a low likelihood of happening (like being hit by lightning while playing golf in a thunderstorm) and make a graph of the binomial curve for many such events. Do some calculations to prove that the probability is not evenly distributed about the mean value. What are the implications of this skewedness? Write a lesson to help others understand a Poisson distribution.

11.4 Helping Out

Go to counseling, administrative, or food services in your school and offer to gather some information on a topic or issue of their choosing. Collect the data and provide them with graphs and an interpretation of the data collected. Be sure to indicate in your written report how the data was collected and why you chose that particular method of collecting the data.

An important part of collecting information is designing the question so that it is unbiased. Have several people read your question and decide if the question has a bias. For example, here are two biased questions: "Do you believe we should have capital punishment and the government should devalue human life and kill prisoners for some crimes?" and "Do you believe we should have capital punishment and save taxpayers thousands of dollars each year confining a prisoner who has no chance of parole?" They are phrased in such a way as to lead persons toward one side or the other of an issue. Modify your question until there is no bias present.

Chapter Twelve

FUNCTIONS AND RELATIONS

Contents

Section 12.1: The Inverse Variation Function.. 554

      About face

Section 12.2: Rational Functions 560

      Is this an irrational choice?

Section 12.3: Refining the Growth Model 566

      This might be chaotic

Section 12.4: Functions Involving Distance 573

      Watch out Pythagoras

Section 12.5: The Circle and Ellipse 579

      More than a simple distortion

Section 12.6: The Parabola 587

      Focus this time

Section 12.7: The Hyperbola 592

      Hyper what?

Section 12.8: The General Quadratic 598

      The big boss

Section 12.9: The Rotation Matrix 604

      You say your head is already spinning?

Section 12.10: Chapter Review 609

      Assessing yourself

Section 12.11: Projects 611

      More good problems

Section 12.1: The Inverse Variation Function

You probably know from experience that a lighter tree climber can crawl farther out on a limb than a heavier climber can.

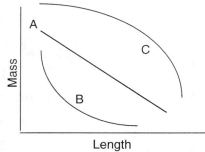

If a stick or pole is held so that some of it hangs over the edge of a table, the amount hanging over the edge should control the amount of force or mass that can be applied at the end of the pole. What would a graph of (*length*, *mass*) look like where the mass amount is applied to a length of pole until it breaks? Is the relationship linear like that pictured in graph A, or more like one of the curves? The next activity will give you a chance to collect data and experiment with this relationship.

The Breaking Point Activity

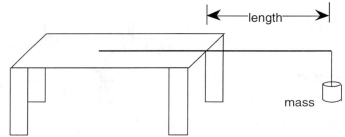

You will need several pieces of spaghetti, a small film canister, some string or thread, some weights (M&Ms, pennies, or other *small* measures of mass), and tape. Lay a piece of the spaghetti on a desk or table so that its length is perpendicular to one of the sides of the table and one end extends off the edge of the table. (See the diagram at the right.) Attach the string to the film canister so that you can suspend it from one end of the spaghetti. You may need to tape the string or thread to the spaghetti. Then place your mass weights in the container one at a time until the spaghetti breaks. Record the number of mass weights and the length from the table edge to the end of the spaghetti. Repeat the experiment several times, each time changing the length of the extension. Make a graph of (*length*, *number of mass weights*). Is the relationship linear? If not, describe the appearance of the graph. Use guess-and-check to write an equation that is a good fit to the plotted data.

Corey Ekt and Misty Ake were each asked to enter equations on the classroom view screen that would graph $y = \frac{2}{3}x - 4$. Corey entered $Y_1 = (2/3)x - 4$ and Misty entered

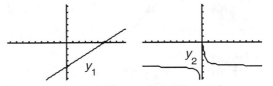

$Y_2 = 2/3x - 4$. The graphs are pictured. Which is correct? Although Misty Ake entered the equation incorrectly, her result is an unusual graph. It is an example of a rational function, which you will be learning about in this section. A **rational function** is one that can be written as the quotient of two polynomials, $f(x) = \frac{p(x)}{q(x)}$. The denominator polynomial must be of degree 1 or more. Misty's rational function is $f(x) = \frac{2}{3x} - 4$ (or $\frac{2}{3x} - \frac{4 \cdot 3x}{3x} = \frac{2 - 12x}{3x}$). In this example, $p(x) = 2 - 12x$ and $q(x) = 3x$.

The parent rational function $f(x) = \frac{1}{x}$ demonstrates features that are characteristic of more complicated examples. You should graph this function on your calculator, and verify the discussion that follows. The graph is made up of two pieces. One part occurs where x is negative and the other where x is positive. Notice that there is *no value* for this function when $x = 0$.

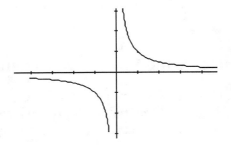

Complete a table similar to this for x-values close to 0. A vertical line at $x = 0$ is called a **vertical asymptote** because the function approaches this line as x gets closer to 0.

−1	−0.1	−0.01	−0.001	*x*	0.001	0.01	0.1	1
−1				*y*				1

Now complete a table for x-values toward the extreme ends of the axis. As x approaches extreme values at the left and right ends of the x-axis, the graph approaches the horizontal axis. The horizontal line $y = 0$ is called a **horizontal asymptote** because the function approaches it as x takes on extreme values. This asymptote is a global or end behavior of the function. In general, the **end behavior** of a function is its behavior for x-values that are large in absolute value.

−10000	−1000	−100	−10	*x*	10	100	1000	10000
			−0.1	*y*	0.1			

If you think of $y = \frac{1}{x}$ as a parent function, then $y = \frac{1}{x} + 1$, $y = \frac{1}{x - 2}$, and $y = 3\left(\frac{1}{x}\right)$ are typical examples of transformed rational functions. Do you remember what happens to a function when x is replaced with $(x - 2)$? Both graphs below are of the function $y = \dfrac{1}{x - 2}$. Frequently, rational function graphs on the calculator may include a vertical-like drag line that *is not part of the graph*. However, it will look much like the graph of the vertical asymptote. See if you can figure out how, why, or when the calculator will draw in a drag line. The graphs below were created on a TI-82. The domain of the graph on the left is $^-4.7 \le x \le 4.7$, and the domain of the graph on the right is $^-5 \le x \le 5$.

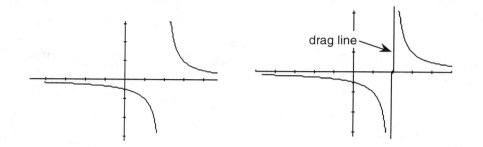

Increase the Percentage Activity

Your group will need about 200 tokens (chips, markers, or beans) in two colors, such as dark beans and light beans. Start by counting out 70 dark beans and 30 light beans. Calculate the percentage of light beans by computing the fraction

$$\frac{\text{number of light beans}}{\text{total number of beans}}.$$

Record your results in a table like this as you continue adding ten more light beans to the pile and recalculating the percentage each time.

Number of light beans added (x)	0	10	20	30	x	. . .
Total number of light beans						
Total number of beans						
Percent of the total that are light (y)	30%					. . .

Write a paragraph that responds to the following questions: How many beans must you add to reach 60%? How many must you add to reach 75%? 90%? Will you ever reach 100%? Why or why not?

Start over again with 70 dark beans and 30 light beans, and record your results each time after *removing* 5 light beans.

Number of light beans removed (x)	0	5	10	15	x	. . .
Total number of light beans						
Total number of beans						
Percent of the total that are light (y)	30%					. . .

Plot the values (*number of light beans added or removed, percent of light beans*) from each table on the same graph. Use negative values for x in the second table, and enter the percentages in decimal form. Your domain should include $-30 \le x \le 60$, and your range should include $0 \le y \le 1$ (decimal versions of the percentage values). Is the data linear? Write an equation involving x that describes the data values. What conclusions can you now add to your earlier paragraph?

Problem Set 12.1

1. Use $f(x) = \dfrac{1}{x}$ as the parent function. Sketch a graph and write an equation for each transformation of $f(x)$.

   a. Slide it two units up.

   b. Slide it three units right.

   c. Slide it one unit down and four units left.

   d. Stretch it to twice its present vertical height.

   e. Stretch it to three times its horizontal width, and shift it up one unit.

2. Write altered forms of the equation $y = \dfrac{1}{x}$ so that its graph has the specified characteristics.

   a. A horizontal asymptote at $y = 2$ and a vertical asymptote at $x = 0$.

   b. A horizontal asymptote at $y = -4$ and a vertical asymptote at $x = 2$.

   c. A horizontal asymptote at $y = 3$ and a vertical asymptote at $x = -4$.

3. Write a rational equation to describe each graph. Some equations will need stretch factors. Assume that each grid mark represents one unit.

   a.   b.

c.   d.

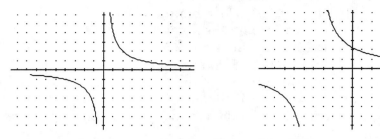

4. Police air patrols help monitor the flow of traffic on busy expressways. Explain how an air patrol officer with a stopwatch and calculator can determine the speed of a vehicle on a highway with marks placed every 0.25 mi.

5. This graph pictures the number of milliliters of a pure acid that must be added to 55 mL of a 38% acid solution to raise the solution up to 64%.

   a. How many milliliters of pure acid were in the original solution?

   b. Write an equation for each pictured function. Use x for the number of added milliliters of pure acid.

   c. Find x when the solution is at 64%.

   d. Describe the end behavior of the curved graph.

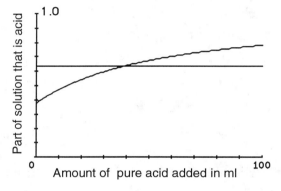

6. If a basketball team's present record is 42 wins and 36 losses, how many consecutive games must it win so that its winning record reaches 60%?

7. In a 1 gal container of 2% milk, two percent of the liquid is fat. How much of the liquid would need to be emptied and replaced with pure fat so that the container could be labeled as whole (4%) milk?

8. a. Graph $y = \dfrac{2x - 13}{x - 5}$.

   b. Graph $y = \dfrac{3x + 11}{x + 3}$.

c. Use synthetic or long division and rewrite each fraction above. The result should be an equation in the form $y = a \pm \dfrac{b}{q(x)}$ for some values of a, b, and $q(x)$. Graph each new equation.

d. Compare the graphs in 8a and 8b with the results of 8c. Describe any differences.

e. Describe each graph in terms of translations and stretches of the parent function.

Section 12.2: Rational Functions

Rational functions create interesting and very different kinds of graphs than those you have studied previously. Although it is difficult to find real-world applications for some of these functions, their graphs are fun to explore and may give you new insights into algebraic concepts. The graphs of these functions are always in two or more parts if you look at a nonrestricted domain. This is because the denominator, a polynomial function, will be equal to zero for at least one x-value, and the function will be undefined at that point. Sometimes it may be difficult to see the different parts of the graph because they may be separated only by a missing point. Other times you will see two parts that look very similar—one part may look like a reflection or rotation of the other part. Or you may get multiple parts that each look totally different.

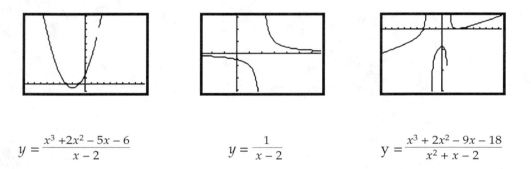

$$y = \frac{x^3 + 2x^2 - 5x - 6}{x - 2}$$

$$y = \frac{1}{x - 2}$$

$$y = \frac{x^3 + 2x^2 - 9x - 18}{x^2 + x - 2}$$

In this section you will explore local and end (or global) behavior of a rational function, and learn how to predict some of the features of a rational function's graph by studying the equation. By definition, a rational function can always be written as a quotient of two polynomials, and the polynomial in the denominator must contain the variable. You will notice that when closely examining a rational function it is often helpful to look at the equation in factored form.

Predicting Asymptotes and Holes Activity

In this activity you will consider the graphs of four rational functions and their local behavior at (and near) $x = 2$.

Find a match between each graph and rational function listed below. Use a "friendly" window as you graph and trace each equation. Describe the unusual occurrences at and near $x = 2$ and try to explain the equation feature that makes the graph look like it does. (You will not actually see the hole pictured in the last graph unless you turn off your coordinate axes.)

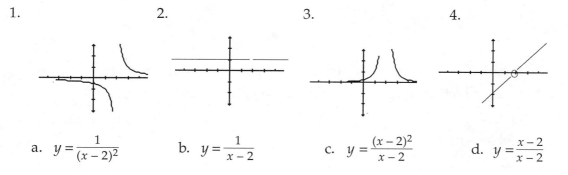

1.   2.   3.   4.

a. $y = \dfrac{1}{(x-2)^2}$ b. $y = \dfrac{1}{x-2}$ c. $y = \dfrac{(x-2)^2}{x-2}$ d. $y = \dfrac{x-2}{x-2}$

Name a rational-function equation for each graph below and write a few sentences that explain the appearance of the graph.

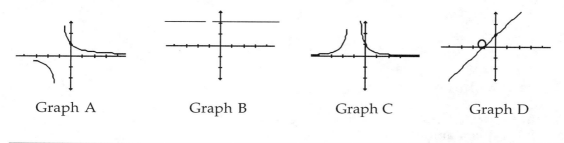

Graph A   Graph B   Graph C   Graph D

You have already considered $y = \dfrac{1}{x}$, some transformations of this function, and some of the peculiarities involving graphs of more complicated rational functions. You know that $y = \dfrac{1}{x}$ has both horizontal and vertical asymptotes. What do you think the graph would look like if you added x to $\dfrac{1}{x}$? Reflect on this question for a minute. Then graph $y = x + \dfrac{1}{x}$.

Example 1: Describe the graph of $y = x + \frac{1}{x}$.

Solution: The values of $\frac{1}{x}$ are added to the values of x rather than being added to zero. This means the graph has an asymptote at x instead of at the x-axis. The graph of $y = x + \frac{1}{x}$ has a **slant asymptote** whose equation is $y = x$.

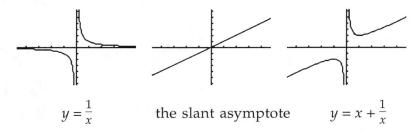

$$y = \frac{1}{x}$$ the slant asymptote $$y = x + \frac{1}{x}$$

Constant Volume Activity

Measure the inside radius and filled height of a cylinder that contains a given amount of water (or sand, salt, or other substance). Then carefully pour the entire contents into another cylinder with a different radius. The volume of the contents of the cylinders will remain constant throughout the activity, but the container radii and corresponding heights will vary. Repeat this process for several different cylinders and record the data pair (*radius, height*) for each container.

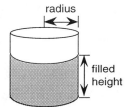

Radius						
Height						

Plot the data on your calculator and confirm that this is not a linear relation. Find a regression model that is a good fit for your data. Remember that correlation coefficients, residual plots, and sums of squares of residuals are good tools to help you with this decision.

Compare your model with $y = \frac{k}{x}$, $y = \frac{k}{x^2}$, and $y = \frac{k}{x^3}$, and so on. If possible, write your equation in one of the given forms. Explain why you think your (*radius, height*) data is an inverse, inverse square, or inverse cube relationship.

Problem Set 12.2

1. Predict what each graph will look like. Then use your calculator with a "friendly" graphing window to confirm your thinking. Make a sketch of each graph.

   a. $y = x - 2 + \dfrac{1}{x}$

   b. $y = {}^-2x + 3 + \dfrac{2}{x}$

   c. $y = 3 + \dfrac{x - 2}{x - 2}$

   d. Describe any asymptotes or holes in the graphs in 1a through 1c. Explain why each asymptote or hole occurs.

2. Graph each equation on your calculator, and make a sketch of the graph on your paper. Use a "friendly" graphing window. Indicate any asymptotes or holes on your sketches.

   a. $y = \dfrac{(5 - x)}{(x - 5)}$

   b. $y = \dfrac{3x + 6}{x + 2}$

   c. $y = \dfrac{(x + 3)(x - 4)}{x - 4}$

   d. Describe any asymptotes or holes in the graphs in 2a through 2c. Explain why each asymptote or hole occurs.

3. Write an equation for each graph. Assume each grid mark represents one unit. Note the position of each **hole**.

   a.   b.   c.

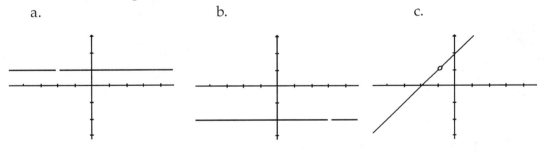

   (Note: Your calculator will not show the small circle in the graph for 3c. The circle was added to make the hole location more visible.)

4. a. Predict what the graph of $y = {}^-x + \dfrac{4}{x-3}$ will look like. Confirm your prediction by graphing.

    b. Describe the global behavior of the graph. (Use a large graphing window.)

    c. Describe the behavior of the graph near $x = 3$. (Use a small graphing window.)

    d. Show the algebra manipulations needed to rewrite the expression ${}^-x + \dfrac{4}{x-3}$ as $\dfrac{{}^-x^2 + 3x + 4}{x-3}$.

    e. What are the roots of ${}^-x^2 + 3x + 4 = 0$? Of $\dfrac{{}^-x^2 + 3x + 4}{x-3} = 0$?

5. The two graphs pictured below show the same function. The left graph is a global look, and the right graph a local look, at the function.

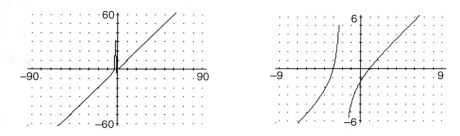

    a. List all the important facts you can about the graph.

    b. Find the equation of the apparent line in the first graph.

    c. Give an example of an equation with an asymptote at $x = {}^-2$.

    d. Give a polynomial with roots at $x = {}^-3$ and $x = 1$.

    e. Write an equation for the function. Graph it to check your answer.

6. The two graphs pictured below are of the same function. Write an equation for this function.

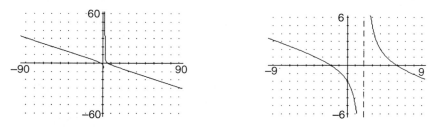

7. Consider the graph of $y = \dfrac{(x-1)(x+4)}{(x-2)(x+3)}$.

   a. Describe local-behavior oddities of the graph.

   b. Describe the global behavior of the graph.

   c. Sketch the graph.

8. Solve each equation for x and describe your solution process.

   a. $\dfrac{2}{x-1} + x = 5$ b. $\dfrac{2}{x-1} + x = 2$ c. $\dfrac{x-3}{x+2} \geq 2$

9. A machine drill removes a 2-in. radius core from a cylinder. Suppose you want the amount of material left after the core is removed to remain constant. The table below compares the height and outer radius (x) needed if the volume of the hollow cylinder is to remain the same.

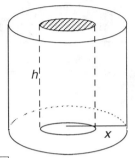

Radius (x)	2.5	3.0	3.5	4.0	4.5	5.0	5.5	6.0	6.5
Height (h)	56.6	25.5	15.4	10.6	7.8	6.1	4.9	4.0	3.3

   a. Plot the points (x, h) and draw a smooth curve through them.

   b. Explain what happens to the height of the figure as the radius gets smaller. How small can x be?

   c. Write the formula for volume in terms of x and h.

   d. Solve the formula in 9c for h. What function describes the height in terms of x?

   e. What is the fixed volume?

Section 12.3: Refining the Growth Model

You have studied growth recursively and explicitly since the beginning of the course. Until now you have assumed that the rate of growth, r, remained constant over time, which meant you used the recursive equations

$$u_n = u_{(n-1)} + r \cdot u_{(n-1)} \text{ or } (1 + r) \cdot u_{(n-1)}$$

and the explicit formula

$$u_n = u_0 (1 + r)^n$$

to model the growth of populations or money, or the decay of radioactive elements. As you have seen, the result either increased to infinity or decreased to zero, as pictured below.

Ecosystems are complicated and generally require sophisticated assumptions regarding population growth. Environmental situations rarely support unlimited growth. Because of space and resource limitations, or competition between individuals or species, certain environments may only support a population up to a limiting value, L. For example, a large field may provide enough food to feed 500 healthy rabbits. If presently there are no rabbits living in the field, what would you expect to happen if you introduced 100 rabbits to the area? What would happen if you introduced 700 rabbits to the field? Any representative model should include both the growth rate of the rabbits and the survival rate, which is partially dependent on the total food supply. As the population exceeds or approaches the limiting value, the growth rate of the rabbit population may slow because they are no longer healthy, or because some will simply leave the area in search of more food.

When you sketch a (*time, population*) graph, it might show slower growth (or decay) as the population approaches the limiting number. This means the actual growth rate isn't a constant value like r or 6%, but rather is a function related to the present population. You have seen graphs with a limiting value or horizontal asymptote, such as the pine tree population, medicine levels in the bloodstream, and chlorine levels in a pool. Each of these involve both adding to, and subtracting from, the preceding value.

Net growth is affected by births, deaths, immigration and emigration. If you assume that the next population u_n will have a net growth that depends on the present population size $u_{(n-1)}$, then the net growth rate will be a function of the population, written $f(u_{(n-1)})$. This changes the simple growth model of $u_n = u_{(n-1)} + r \cdot u_{(n-1)}$ in which the rate, r, is a constant, to a growth model with a changeable rate.

Variable Rate Activity

Part 1: Consider the rabbits discussed earlier. When food and space is unlimited the population growth rate of the rabbits is 20% or 0.20. The population that can be supported is 500 rabbits. Complete each statement and write a sentence explaining the statement.

1. When the population is less than 500, the growth rate should be . . . .

2. When the population is more than 500, the growth rate should be . . . .

3. When the population is very small, the rate should have a value near . . . .

4. When the population is 500, the rate should have a value of . . . .

Write an equation of a line that contains the points (*population, rate*) by using (0, 0.20) and (500, 0). If this is a model of the *rate* based on population, what is the rate when the population is 100? What is the rate when the population is 700? (Answer each question using complete sentences.)

Part 2: Extend this activity by finding the line that gives the variable rate for each situation below. Test some values in your model to find the rates and check that the values make sense.

1. An unrestricted growth rate of 0.20 and a population limit of 1000.

2. An unrestricted growth rate of 0.30 and a population limit of 500.

3. An unrestricted growth rate of 0.20 and a population limit of *L*.

4. An unrestricted growth rate of *r* and a population limit of *L*.

Show that your solution to situation 4 is equivalent to the model $y = r\left(1 - \dfrac{x}{L}\right)$.

If you use more formal sequence notation, the variable rate function can be written as $f(u_{(n-1)}) = r\left(1 - \dfrac{u_{(n-1)}}{L}\right)$. This growth rate function is used in the population model formulated in the nineteenth century by the Belgian mathematical biologist, Verhulst. This model with a variable rate is

new population = old population + net growth rate • old population.

$$u_n = u_{(n-1)} + r\left(1 - \dfrac{u_{(n-1)}}{L}\right)u_{(n-1)}.$$

Example 1: Suppose the unrestricted growth rate (r) of a deer population on a small island is 12% annually and the island limit (L) is 2000 deer. Find the net growth rate for one year for each of the following initial populations. Use the net rate function

$$f(u_{(n-1)}) = r\left(1 - \dfrac{u_{(n-1)}}{L}\right).$$

a. 0   b. 300   c. 1000   d. 1500   e. 3000

Solution: The function for the rate will be $0.12\left(1 - \dfrac{u_{(n-1)}}{2000}\right)$. For each of the given populations the growth rate will be as follows.

a. $0.12\left(1 - \dfrac{0}{2000}\right) = 0.12$ or 12%

b. $0.12\left(1 - \dfrac{300}{2000}\right) = 0.102$ or 10.2%

c. $0.12\left(1 - \dfrac{1000}{2000}\right) = 0.06$ or 6%

d. $0.12\left(1 - \dfrac{1500}{2000}\right) = 0.03$ or 3%

e. $0.12\left(1 - \dfrac{3000}{2000}\right) = -0.06$ or −6%

In the example the population grew at the unrestricted rate of 12% when the population was very small. As the population became larger, the rate decreased, causing the population to grow at a slower rate. When you examine a population that exceeds the limit, the rate is a decay rate rather than a growth rate.

Example 2: Because *new population = old population + net growth rate • old population*, the equation $u_n = u_{(n-1)} + r\left(1 - \dfrac{u_{(n-1)}}{L}\right)u_{(n-1)}$ implies that the net growth rate is variable. Use this equation to find the next year's deer population with the values for r, L, and $u_{(n-1)}$ from Example 1.

Solution: The population function and the values from Example 1 give $u_n = u_{(n-1)} + 0.12\left(1 - \dfrac{u_{(n-1)}}{2000}\right)u_{(n-1)}$. For each of the given populations, the next year's population will be as follows.

a. $u_n = 0 + 0.12\left(1 - \dfrac{0}{2000}\right)0 = 0$ deer

b. $u_n = 300 + 0.12\left(1 - \dfrac{300}{2000}\right)300 = 330.6$ or 331 deer

c. $u_n = 1000 + 0.12\left(1 - \dfrac{1000}{2000}\right)1000 = 1060$ deer

d. $u_n = 1500 + 0.12\left(1 - \dfrac{1500}{2000}\right)1500 = 1545$ deer

e. $u_n = 3000 + 0.12\left(1 - \dfrac{3000}{2000}\right)3000 = 2820$ deer

Example 3: Suppose the present deer population is 300. Use a 12% unrestricted growth rate and a carrying capacity or maximum population of 2000 deer to find the population after 50 years. Make a graph showing (*time, population*) over the next 50 years.

Solution: The recursive function to predict deer population is

$$u_n = u_{(n-1)} + 0.12\left(1 - \dfrac{u_{(n-1)}}{2000}\right)u_{(n-1)}.$$

A seed value or start value of 300 for $n = 0$ gives $u_{50} \approx 1976$. The graph shows the population as it grows toward the horizontal asymptote or capacity of 2000 deer.

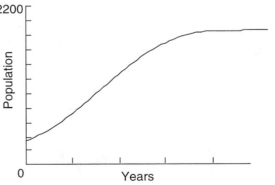

Problem Set 12.3

1. Suppose that a population of size P grows by the amount $0.08(1 - \frac{P}{500})P$ each year.

    a. What is the real-world meaning for the 0.08 and the 500?

    b. If the initial population is 50, what will the population be next year?

    c. Find the populations at 5, 15, 25, . . . , 65 years.

    d. What is the long-run population?

    e. Sketch a graph of this population model.

2. Bacteria grown in a culture dish are provided with plenty of food, but a limited amount of growing space. Eventually the population will become overcrowded, even though there is plenty of food. The bacteria grow at a rate of 125% each week. The initial population is 50 and the capacity of the dish is 5000. Give the net rate and population after 20 weeks.

3. The expression $d + 0.35(1 - \frac{d}{750})d$ will give the number of daisies growing in the median of the highway. Presently there are about 100 daisies. Write a paragraph or two explaining what will happen. Explain and support your reasoning.

4. The following information was gathered on the number of grasshoppers in a vacant lot.

Year	1984	85	86	87	88	89
Population	3283	4365	5603	6895	8104	9107

Year	90	91	92	93	94
Population	9843	10330	10626	10796	10890

Experiment with different unrestricted rates and limiting populations to best model the population of grasshoppers.

5. Suppose next year's state deer population in millions is generated by

$$u_n = u_{(n-1)} + 0.60\left(1 - \frac{u_{(n-1)}}{5}\right)u_{(n-1)} - 0.8$$

where u_0 represents the present deer population of 7 million. Assume the annual harvest rate is 0.8 million.

   a. What happens in the long run?

   b. Change the harvest rate several times and look at the resulting long-run population values and how the population approaches these values. Explain how the number harvested affects the growth and the long-run values.

6. Suppose the weeds in Dan D. Lyon's yard have an unrestricted annual growth rate of 210%, with a limit of 10,000 weeds. This year he has calculated that there are 100 weeds in his yard.

   a. Find the population six years from now.

   b. Give the population for years 34, 35, 36, 37, 38, and 39.

   c. Sketch a graph of the first ten years.

   d. Provide and describe a theory about this situation.

7. Kermit T. F. started a frog pond in his back yard with only two frogs. The population limit of the pond is 470 frogs. The annual rate of unrestricted frog population growth is 295%. Study the population numbers for the first 20 years. Based on these values, without using the function, can you predict the population for year 21? Why or why not?

8. A mathematical study of ecology would not be complete without considering predator and prey relationships. Here is one possible model where the population of the prey (rabbits) and the population of the predator (foxes) depend partially on each other.

$$new\ rabbit = rabbit\ (1 + 0.04 - 0.002fox)$$

$$new\ fox = fox\ (1 + 0.001rabbit - 0.03)$$

- where 4% is the growth rate of rabbits if there are no foxes.

- 3% is the death rate of foxes if there are no rabbits.

- the $-0.002fox$ and $+0.001rabbit$ represent a proportional decline of rabbits and increase of foxes because of "the encounters" between the two species.

a. Suppose initially there are 38 rabbits, 15 foxes, and each time period is 1 mo. Graph the populations over a 40-mo period.

b. Study this model by using different initial values. Keep a record of your values, your observations, and any peaks and valleys. Try to explain the population patterns. Is there a steady state under the proper conditions?

Section 12.4: Functions Involving Distance

Imagine a timed competition where you carry an empty pail from point A to a pool where you fill the pail, and then quickly move to empty it at point B. Luck, physical fitness, common sense, staying calm, and a little mathematics will make a difference. A path of shortest length should help minimize the effort, distance, and time involved. It's difficult to imagine that anyone would travel 5 m straight down from A, then 20 m along the edge of the pool, and finally 7 m up to B. What is the shortest distance from point A, to the pool edge, to point B?

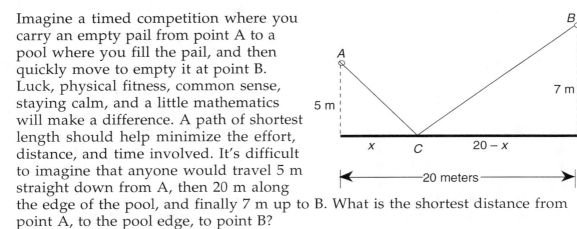

Water Pail Activity

Part A. Find the location of point C, which is x meters from the end of the pool, so that AC + CB is the shortest path possible. Solve this problem by making a scale drawing on graph paper. Use 5 cm, 7 cm, 20 cm, and x cm as the distances. Find the total length of AC + CB for several different values of x and record your data. What is the best location for C so that the total length is as short as possible? Is there more than one best location? Describe at least two alternative methods for finding this solution. For one of your methods use the Pythagorean theorem to find an equation. Make a scale drawing of your solution.

Part B. You can move faster with an empty pail than you can when it is filled. Certainly this might have implications for winning the water-pail contest if the amount of water you empty out at point B is important enough to be recorded. This means you must move carefully so as not to spill water. Suppose you can carry an empty pail at a rate of 1.2 m/sec and you can carefully carry a full pail at a rate of 0.4 m/sec. Go back to the data collected in Part A and find the time needed for each value of x. Now find a solution to the activity so that you minimize the time from point A, to the pool edge, to point B. What is your minimum time? Describe your solution process.

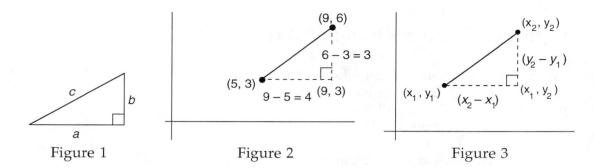

Figure 1   Figure 2   Figure 3

Here is a quick review of some distance and parametric concepts. Figure 1 represents the usual statement of the Pythagorean theorem, $a^2 + b^2 = c^2$, where the legs of the right triangle are of lengths a and b, and the hypotenuse has a length c. Figure 2 shows how to calculate the distance between two points that are located at (5, 3) and (9, 6). The horizontal distance between the points is 4 and the vertical distance between them is 3. Using the Pythagorean theorem, the distance between the two points is $\sqrt{4^2 + 3^2}$ or 5, so the points are 5 units apart. Figure 3 shows the general case. If two points are located at (x_1, y_1) and (x_2, y_2), then $a^2 + b^2 = c^2$ is equivalent to

$$(x_2 - x_1)^2 + (y_2 - y_1)^2 = (distance\ between\ the\ two\ points)^2.$$

> The distance between two points located at
> (x_1, y_1) and (x_2, y_2) is $\sqrt{(x_2 - x_1)^2 + (y_2 - y_1)^2}$.

If (x, y) is any point located on the circumference of a circle, its distance from the center (0, 0) is $\sqrt{(x - 0)^2 + (y - 0)^2}$ or the $radius = \sqrt{x^2 + y^2}$. You have previously used this information to write the equation of a unit circle $x^2 + y^2 = 1$ or $y = \pm\sqrt{1 - y^2}$.

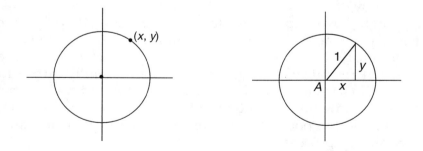

Because $\cos A = \frac{x}{1}$ and $\sin A = \frac{y}{1}$, you can use the parametric equations $x = \cos t$ and $y = \sin t$ to graph a unit circle. The parameter t represents degree measure, and if the range of t-values is $0° \le t \le 360°$, you will get one complete rotation or the graph of a circle. The parameter t can also represent time. The range $0 \le t \le 360$ could represent one revolution occurring in 360 sec. What would the range of t-values be if one revolution occurs in 36 seconds? In 20 seconds?

Example 1: Simulate the motion of an object as it completes one 5-ft radius circle in 20 sec.

Solution: $x = 5 \cos Bt$ and $y = 5 \sin Bt$ provide the correct radius. Now you need to find a value for B that changes 20 sec to degrees. This means you want $Bt = 360°$ when $t = 20$ sec.

Time (sec)	Angle (deg)	x (ft)	y (ft)
0	0	5	0
5	90	0	5
10	180	−5	0
15	270	0	−5
20	360	5	0

$$B \cdot 20 \text{ sec} = 360°$$

$$B = 18°/\text{sec}$$

When $B = 18°/\text{sec}$, the graph of the two equations shows one complete rotation in 20 sec. You should test this by setting $0 \le t \le 20$ in your graphing window. Remember, the parameter t now represents time in seconds.

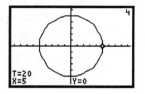

Trace this graph and notice the beginning point of the circle. Then replace t with $(t - 2.5)$ in each equation. Again trace and identify the beginning point of the circle. What would you substitute for t if you want the circle to begin at the bottom-most point?

Problem Set 12.4

1. A patient must be rushed from an off-shore oil rig to a doctor in the nearest town.

   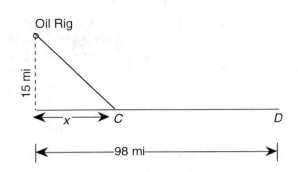

   a. Where should the boat meet the ambulance so that the trip to the doctor at point D is the shortest possible distance?

   b. How far must the boat travel? How far must the ambulance travel?

   c. Suppose the boat can move at 23 mi/hr and the ambulance can travel at 70 mi/hr. Where should the boat meet the ambulance so that the trip time is as short as possible? How far does the boat travel at this speed? How far does the ambulance travel?

2. A 10-m pole and a 13-m pole are 20 m apart at their bases. A wire connects each pole top with a point on the ground between them.

   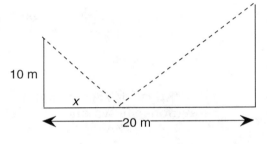

   a. Make a table of values for (x, *wire length*) and graph the relationship.

   b. What values of x and *wire length* make sense in this situation?

   c. Where should a wire be fastened to the ground so that a minimum length is used to connect the pole tops and the ground?

3. A 24-ft ladder is held upright against a wall. The top of the ladder slides down the wall while the foot of the ladder is dragged outward along the ground at a steady rate of 2 ft/sec.

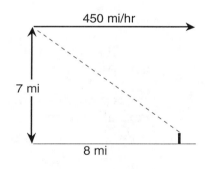

24 ft

2 ft/sec

   a. How long will it take before the entire ladder is lying on the ground?

   b. Find the height of the ladder top at 1-sec intervals while the ladder slides down the wall.

Time (sec)	0	1	2	. . .
Height (ft)	25			

   c. Does the ladder slide down the wall at a steady rate of 2 ft/sec? Explain.

   d. Write parametric equations that model the specified variable.

      i. The location of the foot of the ladder.

      ii. The location of the top of the ladder.

   e. Write a complete explanation of the rate at which the ladder slides down the wall.

4. You are standing on the ground and spot an airplane flying in your direction at 450 mi/hr. (What is the rate in mi/sec?) The plane flies at a constant height of 7 mi.

   450 mi/hr

   7 mi

   8 mi

   a. How long before the plane flies 8 mi and is directly overhead?

   b. Write an equation that gives the actual distance between you and the plane. (Ignore your height.)

   c. Use the equation from 4b to complete the following table.

Time (sec)	0	1	5	10	20	30	
Ground distance (mi)	8 mi						0 mi
Actual distance (mi)							7 mi

   d. Graph (*time, actual distance*).

5. a. Write an equation that provides a graph of the distance between the point (5, −3) and any point (x, y) on the parabola $y = 0.5x^2 + 1$.

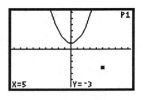

   b. What is the minimum distance and at what point (x, y) does it occur?

6. Sandra Noi is riding on a 100-ft diameter Ferris wheel that can complete one revolution every 30 sec. The wheel is 5 ft from the ground at its lowest point. Her little sister Ann is screaming at her while standing 90 ft away from the base of the Ferris wheel.

   a. Use a graphing window that provides a counterclockwise circular motion and also pictures Ann Noi. Write parametric equations that will simulate Sandra's Ferris wheel ride starting at a point one-fourth of the way to the top.

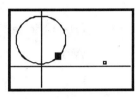

   b. Ann throws the family car keys toward Sandra just as she starts moving again. The initial velocity of the keys is 55 ft/sec, the initial angle of release is 70°, and the keys are released at a height of 4 ft. Write equations to simulate the path of the keys. Does it look like Sandra can catch the keys?

   c. Write an equation picturing (*time, distance between keys and Sandra*). Will the keys be close enough for Sandra to catch them? How close do they get? At what time are they the closest?

7. A tack is embedded in a tire with a 30-in. (2.5 ft) radius. The car is moving forward at 25 ft/sec.

   a. If the tack starts at the ground, how long does it take before it is on the ground again?

   b. Write parametric equations that simulate the position of the tack relative to the ground during the time $0 \text{ sec} \le t \le 5 \text{ sec}$.

   c. Sketch the graph of the tack position (*horizontal distance, height of tack*) over a time period of 5 sec.

Section 12.5: The Circle and Ellipse

The orbital paths of the earth around the sun, the moon around the earth, and satellites around the earth are examples of an important mathematical curve—the ellipse. A stream of water forced into the air from a pressurized hose, the path of a ball thrown from deep center field towards home plate, the path of a kicked football, and the cables hanging between the towers of the Golden Gate Bridge are all examples of the parabola. The design of nuclear cooling towers, transmission gears, and LORAN navigation systems all depend on the hyperbola.

Students of mathematics have studied **conic sections** since the early Greeks. These interesting planar mathematical curves—the circle, ellipse, parabola, and hyperbola—are classified as conic sections because each can be created by slicing a cone. A mathematical cone is formed when two lines meet at an acute angle, and one of the lines is rotated around the other (the axis).

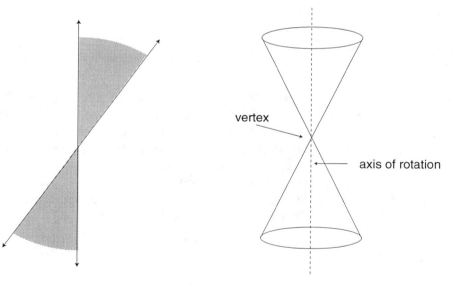

Rotation of one line about another   Mathematical Cone

In this section you will investigate circles and ellipses. A **circle** is a set of points P located a constant distance r from a fixed point C. The fixed point is called the **center** and the constant distance is called the **radius**. Two equivalent symbolic descriptions of a circle are $\left| P - C \right| = r$ and $PC = r$.

Construct a Circle and an Ellipse Activity

You will need a ruler for this activity. Draw a
point near the center on a paper. Choose a distance
of less than 10 cm. Use your ruler to locate 12 or
more points at that distance from your fixed point.
Connect the points with a smooth curve. Explain
$PC = r$ in terms of your drawing.

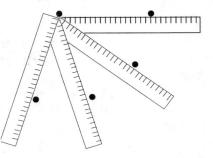

The Ellipse

An **ellipse** is a set of points P such that the sum of
the distances from two fixed points F_1 and F_2 is always a constant length, d. That
is, $F_1P + F_2P = d$. The two fixed points are called **foci**.

You will need
two rulers for this
activity. Fold a
paper in half
along its length.
Locate the center
of the crease.
Draw and label
two points, F_1 and
F_2, in the crease

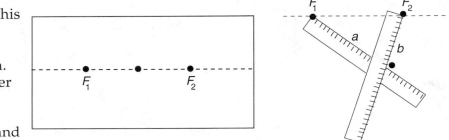

so they are equal distances from the center. Now choose a length, d, which is
greater than the distance between F_1 and F_2 and less than 25 cm. Think of two
numbers, a and b, that add up to your selected distance. Using both rulers, find a
point that is a units from one point and b units from the other point. Think of
two new numbers, a and b, that add up to your selected distance. Locate a point
that is a units from one point and b units from the other point. Repeat this
process with other choices of a and b until you have enough points to define the
shape. Connect the points with a smooth curve. Explain $F_1P + F_2P = d$ in terms of
your drawing.

If a point represented by (x, y) is a generic point anywhere on
the circumference of a unit circle, solving $x^2 + y^2 = 1^2$ for y
gives

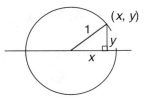

$$x^2 + y^2 = 1^2$$

$$y^2 = 1 - x^2$$

$$y = \pm\sqrt{1 - x^2}$$

Using the same logic, the equation of a circle centered at the origin with a radius of r units will satisfy the relation $x^2 + y^2 = r^2$. You can enter the two functions $y = \pm\sqrt{r^2 - x^2}$ to produce the graph with your calculator. The parametric equations $x(t) = r \cos t$ and $y(t) = r \sin t$ also produce the same graph in parametric mode. Take a moment now to explain to yourself why this is so.

You can shift a graph horizontally and vertically by replacing x with $x - h$ for some number h and replacing y with $y - k$ for some number k.

A circle with the center located at point (h, k) with a radius of r

has the equation $(x - h)^2 + (y - k)^2 = r^2$ or $\begin{cases} x(t) = r \cos t + h \\ y(t) = r \sin t + k \end{cases}$.

Example 1: Write the equation of a circle that has a center at $(3, -2)$ and that is tangent to the line $y = 2x + 1$.

Solution: If the line is tangent to the circle, then it is perpendicular to a diameter of the circle at the point of tangency. The tangent line has a slope of 2, so a line containing the diameter will have a slope of $-1/2$, and it will pass through the center of the circle $(3, -2)$. Therefore, one form of its equation is $y = \frac{-1}{2}(x - 3) - 2$. You will find that this line intersects the tangent line at $(-0.6, -0.2)$. Do this now. The distance between $(-0.6, -0.2)$

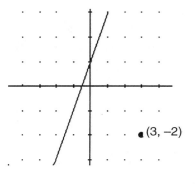

and the center is $\sqrt{16.2} \approx 4.0249223595$. Check that this is true. Therefore, the equation of this circle is

$$(x - 3)^2 + (y + 2)^2 = 16.2 \text{ or } \begin{cases} x(t) = 4.025 \cos t + 3 \\ y(t) = 4.025 \sin t - 2 \end{cases}$$

If you stretch a circle horizontally and vertically by the same amount, you will still have a circle. However, if the horizontal stretch is different than the vertical stretch, the resulting figure is an **ellipse**. A circle is to an ellipse as a square is to a rectangle.

Example 2: Write the equation of an ellipse that is centered at the origin, is six units tall, and is four units wide.

Solution: You can start with a unit circle, $x^2 + y^2 = 1$. This circle has a diameter of 2 and can be stretched vertically by a factor of 3 to make it 6 units tall. To make it 4 units wide you must stretch it horizontally by a factor of 2. You can accomplish this using either strategy shown.

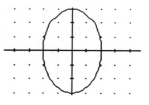

Function Transformation:

Replace y with $\frac{y}{3}$ and x with $\frac{x}{2}$.

$$\left(\frac{x}{2}\right)^2 + \left(\frac{y}{3}\right)^2 = 1 \text{ or } \frac{x^2}{4} + \frac{y^2}{9} = 1$$

Parametric Transformation:

$$\begin{cases} x(t) = 2\cos t \\ y(t) = 3\sin t \end{cases}$$

Solve the nonparametric form for y, graph both the positive and negative roots, and check that this is the correct ellipse.

$$\left(\frac{x}{2}\right)^2 + \left(\frac{y}{3}\right)^2 = 1$$

$$\left(\frac{y}{3}\right)^2 = 1 - \left(\frac{x}{2}\right)^2$$

$$\frac{y}{3} = \pm\sqrt{1 - \left(\frac{x}{2}\right)^2}$$

$$y = \pm 3\sqrt{1 - \left(\frac{x}{2}\right)^2}$$

An **ellipse** with the center shifted to the point (h, k) with a horizontal stretch of a and a vertical stretch of b has the equation $\left(\frac{x-h}{a}\right)^2 + \left(\frac{y-k}{b}\right)^2 = 1$ or

$$\begin{cases} x(t) = a\cos t + h \\ y(t) = b\sin t + k \end{cases}.$$

Shine On Activity

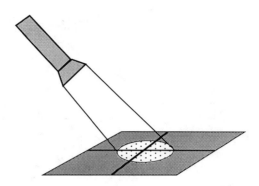

Draw an x- and a y-axis at the center of a sheet of graph paper. Shine a flashlight on your graph paper at an angle. For better results, the room should be quite dark. Try to align the major axis of the ellipse formed by the beam with one axis of the paper. Now carefully trace the edge of the beam as someone holds the light steady. (If you have a ring stand and clamps available, use them to hold the flashlight steady.) You might start by placing four points to help the light holder stay on target. Collect the coordinates of 20 points from the graph and find an equation that fits the data as closely as you can. Name the lengths of both the major and minor axes. Finally, verify that the coordinates of some of your collected points do satisfy your equation.

Problem Set 12.5

1. Graph each circle on your calculator. Sketch the graph on your paper and label the radius and center.

    a. $x^2 + y^2 = 4$

    b. $(x - 3)^2 + y^2 = 1$

    c. $(x + 1)^2 + (y - 2)^2 = 9$

    d. $x^2 + (y - 1.5)^2 = 0.25$

    e. $\begin{cases} x(t) = 2\cos t + 1 \\ y(t) = 2\sin t + 2 \end{cases}$

    f. $\begin{cases} x(t) = 4\cos t - 3 \\ y(t) = 4\sin t \end{cases}$

2. Write nonparametric and parametric equations for each graph.

   a.

   b.

   c.

   d.

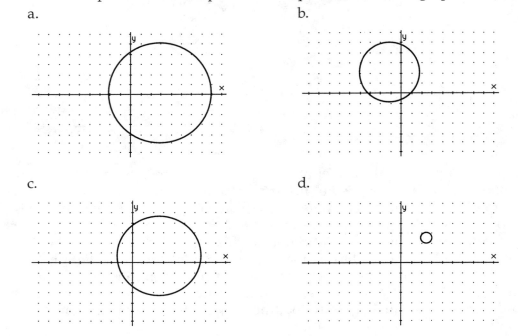

3. Sketch a graph of each equation. Label the four vertices (extreme points on each axis) of each ellipse.

   a. $\left(\frac{x}{2}\right)^2 + \left(\frac{y}{4}\right)^2 = 1$

   b. $\left(\frac{x-2}{3}\right)^2 + \left(\frac{y+2}{1}\right)^2 = 1$

   c. $\left(\frac{x-4}{3}\right)^2 + \left(\frac{y-1}{3}\right)^2 = 1$

   d. $y = \pm 2\sqrt{1 - \left(\frac{x+2}{3}\right)^2} - 1$

   e. $\begin{cases} x(t) = 4\cos t - 1 \\ y(t) = 2\sin t + 3 \end{cases}$

   f. $\begin{cases} x(t) = 3\cos t + 3 \\ y(t) = 5\sin t \end{cases}$

4. Write nonparametric and parametric equations for each graph.

   a.

   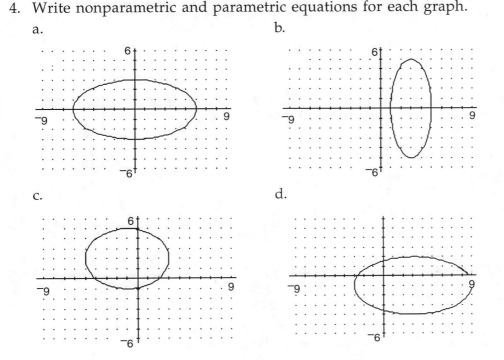

   b.

   c.

   d.

5. Planets, moons, and comets all move in elliptical orbits. Johannes Kepler was
   the first European to think that planets moved in elliptical rather than
   circular orbits around the sun. He worked as an assistant to the astronomer
   Tycho Brache and was able to check his hypotheses because he had access to
   Brache's astronomical data, considered to be the finest pretelescope data.
   Without Brache's data he might have stayed with his first hypothesis—that
   the planets moved in circular orbits which lay on spheres that could be
   circumscribed around regular polyhedra. The polyhedra were supposed to lie
   between the planets.

   Suppose a grid is laid down on the solar system in the plane of a comet's orbit,
   with the origin at the location of the sun and the *x*-axis through the longer
   axis of the orbit as in the diagram. The table gives the approximate position of
   a comet circling the sun.

   a. Find the best equation to match the data.

   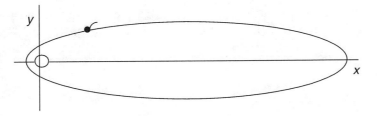

x	−2.1	12.9	62.6	244.5	579.3	778.1	900.1	982.4	923.4	663.0	450.0	141.6
y	5.5	16.3	31.5	54.6	62.0	51.6	36.1	10.9	−31.5	−59.2	−62.8	−44.5

    b. Find the y-value when the x-value is 493.0 AUs.

    c. What is the farthest distance of the comet from the sun?

    d. If the sun, which is now at the origin, were at the opposite end of the ellipse, what would its coordinates be?

6. a. Construct an ellipse by using a string, ruler, two tacks, a pencil, and graph paper fastened to a piece of cardboard. Use the tacks to fasten a 16 cm string at F_1 and F_2, the foci of the ellipse.

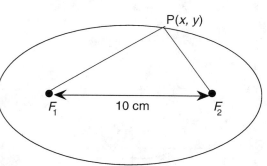

    b. If the midpoint of F_1 and F_2 is (0, 0), what are the coordinates of the left-most and right-most points? These are called the vertices at the ends of the major (longer) axis.

    c. What are the coordinates of the top-most and bottom-most points? These are called the vertices at the ends of the minor (shorter) axis.

    d. Write an equation that represents this ellipse.

    e. Use your equation from 6d and graph the distance relation $PF_1 + PF_2$. Describe the values of $PF_1 + PF_2$.

7. Visualize constructing the ellipse pictured on the right with two tacks and a string.

    a. How long will the string be?

    b. Where will you place the tacks?

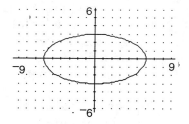

8. The moon's greatest distance from the earth is 252,710 mi and its least distance is 221,643 mi. Write an equation that describes the moon's orbit about the earth.

9. A point moves in the plane so that the sum of its distances from (−2, 1) and (4, 1) is always 10 units. What is the equation of the path of this point?

Section 12.6: The Parabola

The designs of telescope lenses, spot lights, and other paraboloid reflecting surfaces are based on a remarkable property of parabolas—a ray that travels parallel to the axis will strike the surface of the parabola or paraboloid and reflect toward the **focus**. Likewise, when a ray from the focus strikes the curve, it will reflect in a ray that is parallel to the axis.

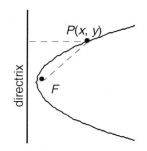

> A **parabola** is a set of points P that are equally distant from a fixed point F and a fixed line l. The fixed point is called a **focus** and the line is called a **directrix**.

Construct the Parabola Activity

You will need two rulers for this activity. Fold a paper in half along its length. Draw a line l in the lower half of the paper so that it is perpendicular to the crease. Draw a point F above this line and on the crease. With one ruler find and measure a point P that is straight up from the line l, and use the other ruler to measure an equal distance from the point F. Repeat this point-location process until you have plotted enough points to define the shape. Draw a smooth curve to connect the points. You can see from the drawing that the distance from point P to point F is the same as the distance from point P to line l.

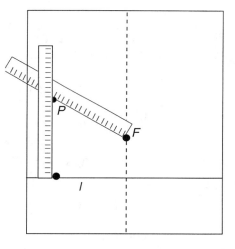

You have studied the parabola on several different occasions, and you have seen many applications of parabolas. However, in this section you will study it from a different perspective and learn about two important features of the parabola—the **focus** and the **directrix**. Remember, from the definition the distance from a point P on the curve to the focus, F, is always the same as the perpendicular distance from that point P to the directrix l.

How can you locate the focus of a parabola? Suppose the parabola is horizontal and located with its vertex at the origin. It has a focus inside the curve at a point $(f, 0)$. The vertex is on the curve, so it should be as far from the focus as it is from the directrix. This means the equation of the directrix is $x = {}^-f$. Supply the reasons for each step in this derivation.

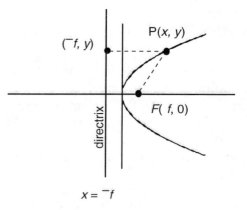

$$\sqrt{(x - f)^2 + (y - 0)^2} = \sqrt{(x + f)^2 + (y - y)^2}$$

$$\sqrt{(x - f)^2 + y^2} = \sqrt{(x + f)^2 + (0)^2}$$

$$(x - f)^2 + y^2 = (x + f)^2$$

$$x^2 - 2fx + f^2 + y^2 = x^2 + 2fx + f^2$$

$$y^2 = 4fx$$

This means the coefficient of the linear variable x is $4f$ where f is the directed distance from vertex to focus.

Example 1: Consider the equation $y^2 = x$.

a. Draw the graph, and write the equation of this graph after each transformation has been performed.

  i.   Stretched vertically by a factor of 3.

  ii. Then shifted horizontally 2 units.

  iii. Then shifted vertically $^-4$ units.

b. Where is the focus of $y^2 = x$?

c. What is the equation of the directrix of $y^2 = x$?

The final graph will look like the one pictured below on the right.

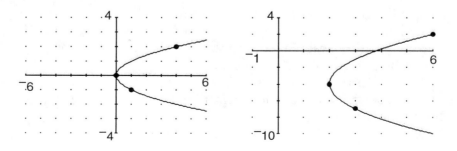

Solution: The original function contains the points (0, 0), (4, 2), and (1, −1). When stretched vertically, the points become (0, 0), (4, 6), and (1, −3). When translated horizontally, the points become (2, 0), (6, 6), and (3, −3). Finally, the last shift moves the points to (2, −4), (6, 2) and (3, −7).

Start with $y^2 = x.$

The vertical stretch is $\left(\frac{y}{3}\right)^2 = x.$

The horizontal translation is $\left(\frac{y}{3}\right)^2 = (x - 2).$

The vertical translation is $\left(\frac{y + 4}{3}\right)^2 = (x - 2).$

When you look at this same process parametrically, begin with $\begin{cases} x(t) = t^2 \\ y(t) = t \end{cases}$. Stretch 3 vertically $\begin{cases} x(t) = t^2 \\ y(t) = 3t \end{cases}$, then 2 units right $\begin{cases} x(t) = t^2 + 2 \\ y(t) = 3t \end{cases}$, and finally 4 units down $\begin{cases} x(t) = t^2 + 2 \\ y(t) = 3t - 4 \end{cases}$.

A **vertical parabola** with the vertex shifted to the point (h, k) with a horizontal stretch of a and a vertical stretch of b has the

equation $\left(\frac{y - k}{b}\right) = \left(\frac{x - h}{a}\right)^2$ or $\begin{cases} x(t) = at + h \\ y(t) = bt^2 + k \end{cases}$.

A **horizontal parabola** under the same conditions has the

equation $\left(\frac{y - k}{b}\right)^2 = \left(\frac{x - h}{a}\right)$ or $\begin{cases} x(t) = at^2 + h \\ y(t) = bt + k \end{cases}$.

You can use the general form $y^2 = 4fx$ to locate the focus and directrix of the equation $y^2 = x$. The coefficient of the linear variable x is $4f$. This means $4f = 1$, the focus is at $(\frac{1}{4}, 0)$, and the directrix has the equation $x = -\frac{1}{4}$.

Now locate the focus and directrix of the image $\left(\frac{y + 4}{3}\right)^2 = (x - 2)$

or $(y + 4)^2 = 9(x - 2)$. This means $4f = 9$ or $f = 2.25$ and both the focus and directrix will be 2.25 units from the vertex (2, −4). Therefore, the directrix of the image is at $x = -0.25$ and the focus is (4.25, −4).

The Rolling Ball Activity

Tape graph paper to a board or clipboard. Lay this on a table and prop one end up with two books. Practice rolling a large ball bearing from the lower left of the board so that it rolls up the board and back down, leaving at the lower right. When you can do this consistently, tape a sheet of carbon paper (black side down) over the graph paper. Roll the ball bearing one more time. Then remove the carbon paper and draw x- and y-axes on the graph paper wherever you believe they belong. Carefully locate several points on the curve left by the carbon paper trace. Find the equation that best fits the data.

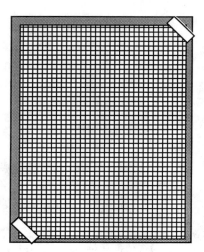

Did you assume the curve was a parabola or half an ellipse? Give a reason for your choice. Make a plot of the residuals. Now test the other curve option and plot its residuals. Using your residual plots, describe which is the better choice. Write the equation that best fits the data.

Problem Set 12.6

1. Sketch a graph of each equation. Label the vertex, focus, and directrix.

   a. $\left(\dfrac{x}{2}\right)^2 + 5 = y$

   b. $(y + 2)^2 - 2 = x$

   c. $-(x + 3)^2 + 1 = 2y$

   d. $2y^2 = {}^-x + 4$

   e. $\begin{cases} x(t) = 4t - 1 \\ y(t) = 2t^2 + 3 \end{cases}$

   f. $\begin{cases} x(t) = 3t^2 + 3 \\ y(t) = 5t \end{cases}$

Preliminary Edition

2. Write the equation of each parabola. Name the focus and directrix. (In the four problems, at least one equation should be written in nonparametric form, and at least one equation should be written in parametric form.)

a.

b.

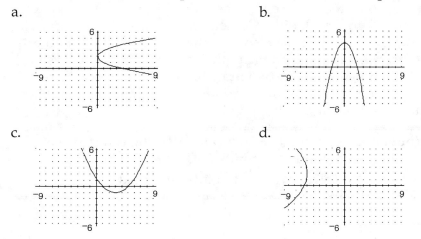

c.

d.

3. The pilot of a small boat charted a course so that her boat would be the same distance from an upcoming rock as it was from the shoreline. Describe and explain the path of the boat.

4. a. Describe the graph represented by $\sqrt{(x - 0)^2 + (y - 3)^2} = \sqrt{(x - x)^2 + (y + 1)^2}$.

   b. Rewrite the equation by solving for y.

   c. Graph the equation.

5. a. Describe the graph represented by

   $$\sqrt{(x - 2.5)^2 + (y - y)^2} = \sqrt{(x - 3.5)^2 + (y - 4)^2}.$$

   b. Rewrite the equation by solving for y.

   c. Graph the equation.

6. Find the function that describes a parabola containing the points (3.6, 0.764), (5, 1.436), and (5.8, −2.404).

7. Find the equation of a circle that contains the points (2, 4), (−5, 5), and (−6, −2). (There are several ways to solve this problem. None of them are very easy.)

Section 12.7: The Hyperbola

The last of the conic sections, the hyperbola, was named by the third century B.C. by the Greek mathematician, Apollonius. Comets travel in orbits that are either parabolic, elliptical, or hyperbolic. In fact, comets that come close to another object, but never return, are on a hyperbolic path. The two light shadows on a wall next to a circular lamp shade form two branches of a hyperbola. Similarly, a sonic-boom shock curve formed along the ground by a plane traveling faster than sound is actually one branch of a hyperbola.

> A **hyperbola** is a set of points P so located that the difference of the distances from two fixed points F_1, F_2 remains constant: $\left|F_1P - F_2P\right| = d$. The two fixed points are called **foci**.

Construct the Hyperbola

Fold a paper in half along its length. Draw two points, F_1 and F_2, in the crease at equal distances from the center of the crease. Select a length that is less than the distance between the points. Think of two numbers, a and b, whose difference is your selected length. Using two rulers,

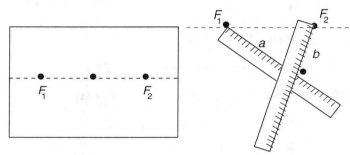

find a point that is a units from F_1 and b units from F_2. Repeat this with other choices of a and b until you have located enough points to define the shape. Connect the points with a smooth curve. Be sure the difference between a and b remains constant. Explain $\left|F_1P - F_2P\right| = d$ in terms of your drawing.

Example 1: Graph the **unit hyperbola**, $x^2 - y^2 = 1$.

Solution: To graph this as a function of y, you must first solve for y.

$x^2 - y^2 = 1$

$-y^2 = 1 - x^2$ or $y^2 = x^2 - 1$

$y = \pm\sqrt{x^2 - 1}$

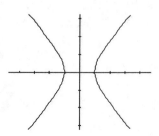

If you include the graphs of $y = x$ and $y = {}^-x$ you will notice that they pass through the vertices of a square with corners at $(1, 1)$, $(1, {}^-1)$, $({}^-1, {}^-1)$, and $({}^-1, 1)$. As you zoom out, the hyperbola approaches the two lines, which are called asymptotes of the hyperbola.

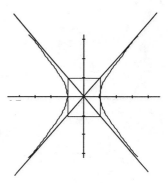

Before you move on, consider the graph and features of $y^2 - x^2 = 1$. Find the similarities to, and differences from, the graph of $x^2 - y^2 = 1$.

The equation of a hyperbola looks much like the equation of the ellipse except that the terms are not both positive. For example, the equation $\left(\frac{y}{4}\right)^2 - \left(\frac{x}{3}\right)^2 = 1$ is a hyperbola while $\left(\frac{y}{4}\right)^2 + \left(\frac{x}{3}\right)^2 = 1$ is an ellipse.

Example 2: Graph $\left(\frac{y}{4}\right)^2 - \left(\frac{x}{3}\right)^2 = 1$.

Solution: To graph this as a function of y, you must first solve for y.

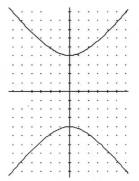

$$\left(\frac{y}{4}\right)^2 - \left(\frac{x}{3}\right)^2 = 1$$

$$\left(\frac{y}{4}\right)^2 = 1 + \left(\frac{x}{3}\right)^2$$

$$\left(\frac{y}{4}\right) = \pm\sqrt{1 + \left(\frac{x}{3}\right)^2}$$

$$y = \pm 4\sqrt{1 + \left(\frac{x}{3}\right)^2}$$

When you sketch a hyperbola by hand, you will find it easier if you sketch the asymptotes first. You can do this by first drawing a rectangle centered at the origin that measures six units across and eight units high. Look at the equations and you will recognize where these dimensions came from. Do you see how the square contained in the unit hyperbola has been stretched? Draw the diagonals of this rectangle, and extend them outside the rectangle. These lines are asymptotes of the curve. Now add the curve so that it touches the center of the side of the rectangle and swings out asymptotically to the diagonal lines. If you write the equations of these two asymptotes and graph them on your calculator, you will see that the hyperbola does approach them asymptotically. The asymptotes provide you with an end-behavior model of the hyperbola.

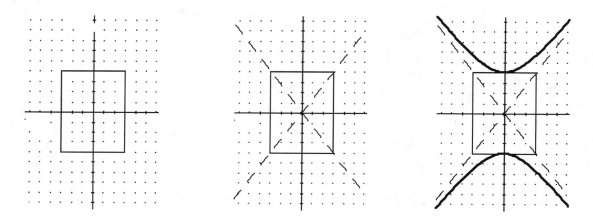

When you create parametric equations from a two-variable relation, your first choice is critical because you must begin by defining one of the two variables as a function of t. The other variable is defined by the original relation. Sometimes the geometry of the situation helps you to make this first assignment—as with circles. Sometimes logic helps—as with parabolas. With the hyperbola, start with the equation of the **unit hyperbola**, $x^2 - y^2 = 1$ and define x as $\dfrac{1}{\cos t}$. Substitute this x-value into the unit equation.

$$\left(\frac{1}{\cos t}\right)^2 - y^2 = 1$$
Replace the x.

$$-y^2 = 1 - \left(\frac{1}{\cos t}\right)^2$$
Add the fraction to both sides.

$$y^2 = \left(\frac{1}{\cos t}\right)^2 - 1$$
Multiply both sides by $^-1$.

$$y^2 = \left(\frac{1}{\cos^2 t}\right) - \left(\frac{\cos^2 t}{\cos^2 t}\right)$$
Find a common denominator.

$$y^2 = \left(\frac{1 - \cos^2 t}{\cos^2 t}\right)$$
Add the fractions.

$$y^2 = \left(\frac{\sin^2 t}{\cos^2 t}\right)$$
Because $\sin^2 t + \cos^2 t = 1$.

$$y^2 = \tan^2 t$$
Because $\dfrac{\sin t}{\cos t} = \tan t$.

$$y = \tan t$$
Take the square root of both sides.

Preliminary Edition CHAPTER 12

A **hyperbola** with the center shifted to the point (h, k) with a horizontal stretch of a and a vertical stretch of b would have the equation

$$\left(\frac{x-h}{a}\right)^2 - \left(\frac{y-k}{b}\right)^2 = 1 \text{ or } \begin{cases} x(t) = \dfrac{a}{\cos t} + h \\ y(t) = b \tan t + k \end{cases}$$

or the equation

$$\left(\frac{y-k}{b}\right)^2 - \left(\frac{x-h}{a}\right)^2 = 1 \text{ or } \begin{cases} x(t) = a \tan t + h \\ y(t) = \dfrac{b}{\cos t} + k \end{cases}.$$

Example 3: Write the equation for the graph.

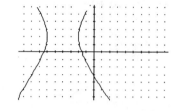

Solution: The center is between the vertices at the point $(-4, 2)$. The horizontal radius, $a = 2$, is the distance between the center and a vertex. The value of b is more difficult to find. Here are several options.

i.   You can choose to work backwards by first sketching the asymptotes and then drawing the rectangle to find the value of b.

ii. You can experiment with your calculator to find the best value.

iii. You can choose a point and solve for b symbolically.

Whatever your choice (go ahead and try them all), you should find b to be 3. Now the proper form of the equation is either

$$\left(\frac{x+4}{2}\right)^2 - \left(\frac{y-2}{3}\right)^2 = 1 \text{ or } \begin{cases} x(t) = \dfrac{2}{\cos t} - 4 \\ y(t) = 3 \tan t + 2 \end{cases}.$$

Either equation should provide the graph of the pictured hyperbola.

Problem Set 12.7

1. Sketch a graph of each hyperbola. Label each vertex and write the equation of each asymptote.

   a. $\left(\dfrac{x}{2}\right)^2 - \left(\dfrac{y}{4}\right)^2 = 1$

   b. $\left(\dfrac{y + 2}{1}\right)^2 - \left(\dfrac{x - 2}{3}\right)^2 = 1$

   c. $\left(\dfrac{x - 4}{3}\right)^2 - \left(\dfrac{y - 1}{3}\right)^2 = 1$

   d. $y = \pm 2\sqrt{1 + \left(\dfrac{x + 2}{3}\right)^2} - 1$

   e. $\begin{cases} x(t) = \dfrac{4}{\cos t} - 1 \\ y(t) = 2 \tan t + 3 \end{cases}$

   f. $\begin{cases} x(t) = 3 \tan t + 3 \\ y(t) = \dfrac{5}{\cos t} \end{cases}$

2. Write the equation of each hyperbola in both nonparametric and parametric form. Write the equation of each asymptote.

   a.   b.

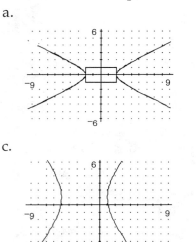
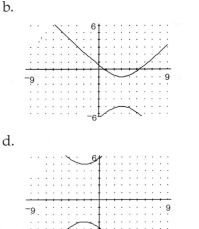

   c.   d.

3. Each branch of a hyperbola has a focus. You can locate these foci by rotating the rectangle about its center so that opposite corners lie on the line of symmetry, which contains the vertices of the hyperbola. From the diagram you can see that

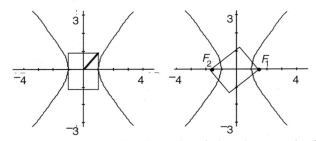

the distance from the origin to a focus is one-half the length of the diagonal of the rectangle.

   a. Find the foci for $x^2 - y^2 = 1$.

   b. Find the foci for $\left(\dfrac{y + 2}{1}\right)^2 - \left(\dfrac{x - 2}{3}\right)^2 = 1$.

4. A point moves in the plane so that the difference of its distances from (−2, 1) and (4, 1) is always ten units. What is the equation of the path of this point?

5. Graph and write the equation of a hyperbola that has an upper vertex at (−2.35, 1.46) and is asymptotic to the line $y = 1.5x + 1.035$.

6. Find the smallest vertical distance between $y = \pm 2\sqrt{1 + \left(\dfrac{x+2}{3}\right)^2} - 1$ and its asymptote at each of the following values of x.

Value of x	5	10	20	40
Distance				

7. A receiver can determine the distance to a homing transmitter by its signal strength, but cannot find the direction. The following distances (in miles) were gathered as the car receiver traveled due north.

Car	0.0	2.0	4.0	6.0	8.0	10.0	12.0	14.0	16.0
Transmitter	9.82	7.91	6.04	4.30	2.92	2.55	3.54	5.15	6.96

a. Find the equation of the hyperbola that best fits the data.

b. Name the center of this hyperbola.

c. What does this point tell you?

8. Find a problem that you have encountered in this chapter that you cannot solve. Write out the problem and as much of the solution as you can. Then, clearly explain what is keeping you from solving the problem. Be as specific as you can.

Section 12.8: The General Quadratic

Circles, parabolas, ellipses, and hyperbolas are called quadratic curves (or 2nd degree curves) because 2 is the highest power on either of the variables. One general equation form can be used to generate all of the quadratic curves you have studied in this chapter.

> The general quadratic equation has the form
> $$Ax^2 + Bxy + Cy^2 + Dx + Ey + F = 0,$$
> where A, B, and C are not all zero.

In this section you will solve the general quadratic equation for y so that you can use your calculator to graph it. You will also convert between the general quadratic form and the center-vertex form of a graph.

Example 1: Solve for y and sketch the curve $4x^2 - 9y^2 + 144 = 0$. Then put the equation in center-vertex form.

Solution:

Solve for y:

$$-9y^2 = -4x^2 - 144$$

$$y^2 = \frac{4}{9}x^2 + 16$$

$$y = \pm\sqrt{\frac{4}{9}x^2 + 16}$$

Put the equation in center-vertex form:

$$4x^2 - 9y^2 = -144$$

$$\frac{4x^2 - 9y^2}{-144} = 1$$

$$\frac{y^2}{16} - \frac{x^2}{36} = 1$$

Now you can use your calculator to graph the y-form equation, or you can use sketching techniques you learned in previous sections to graph the equation in center-vertex form. When Dx or Ey terms are present in the general quadratic equation $Ax^2 + Bxy + Cy^2 + Dx + Ey + F = 0$, the process of writing a center-vertex form is a little more complex.

The general form $x^2 + y^2 - 14x + 33 = 0$ does not tell you much about its graph. But the same equation written in its center-vertex form, $(x - 7)^2 + y^2 = 16$, indicates a circle with center at $(7, 0)$ and a radius of 4 units. One way to show the two equations are equivalent is to expand the binomial $(x - 7)^2 + y^2 = 16$.

$(x - 7)(x - 7) + y^2 = 16$	Definition of squaring.
$x^2 - 7x - 7x + 49 + y^2 = 16$	Expand the binomial.
$x^2 - 14x + 49 + y^2 = 16$	Combine terms.
$x^2 + y^2 - 14x + 33 = 0$	Equation in general form.

Reversing the process is called **completing the square**. It involves "discovering" the number (49 in this example) that will make the trinomial a perfect square. By using $(x \pm h)^2 = x^2 \pm 2hx + h^2$ you can find the numbers needed to complete the squares and convert equations to the center-vertex form. The key is recognizing that the coefficient of the linear term, $-14x$, is twice the value of h. This means h must be -7.

$x^2 + y^2 - 14x + 33 = 0$	
$x^2 - 14\,x + y^2 = -33$	Separate the variables.
$x^2 - 14x + 49 + y^2 = -33 + 49$	Add 49 to both sides of the equation.
$(x - 7)^2 + y^2 = 16$	Write the trinomial in perfect-square form.

The completing-the-square procedure uses the familiar expansion for perfect-square binomials, $(x \pm h)^2 = x^2 \pm 2hx + h^2$.

Example 2: Rewrite each of these polynomials so that the expressions involving the variable x are perfect-squares.

a. $x^2 - 10x + 25 = y$ b. $x^2 - 10x = y$ c. $x^2 - 10x + 14 = y$

Solution:

a. This one is easy because $x^2 - 10x + 25$ is already the same as $(x - 5)^2$. The $(x \pm h)^2 = x^2 \pm 2hx + h^2$ pattern is expressed as $(x - 5)^2 = x^2 - (2)(5)x + 5^2$. Therefore, an equivalent equation is $(x - 5)^2 = y$.

b. The expression on the left needs the additional term "25" so that it is equivalent to $(x - 5)^2$.

$x^2 - 10x + \mathbf{25} = y + \mathbf{25}$ Add 25 to both sides of the equation.

Note that the square of half the coefficient of x, or $\left(\dfrac{-10}{2}\right)^2$, is the same as 25. Therefore, an equivalent equation written as a perfect square is $(x - 5)^2 = y + 25$.

c. $x^2 - 10x + 14 = y$ Start with the given equation.

$x^2 - 10x = y - \mathbf{14}$ Subtract the constant from both sides.

$x^2 - 10x + \mathbf{25} = y - 14 + \mathbf{25}$ Add $\left(\dfrac{-10}{2}\right)^2$ to both sides.

$(x - 5)^2 = y + 11$ An equivalent equation.

In the next example, which requires this completing-the-square process, you will obtain the expressions $A(x - h)^2$ and $B(y - k)^2$ that are present in the familiar center-vertex form for these quadratic equations.

Example 3: Graph the equation $y^2 - 4x + 6y + 1 = 0$.

Solution:

$y^2 + 6y = 4x - 1$ Separate the variables.

$y^2 + 6y + 9 = 4x - 1 + 9$ Add 9 to both sides

                            $\left(\dfrac{6}{2} = 3 \text{ and } 3^2 = 9\right)$.

$(y + 3)^2 = 4x + 8$ Simplify.

$(y + 3)^2 = 4(x + 2)$ Factor the expression on the right (**center-vertex form**).

$y + 3 = \pm\sqrt{4(x + 2)}$ Take the square root of both sides.

$y = \pm 2\sqrt{x + 2} - 3$ Subtract 3 from both sides (**$y=$ form**).

The final two steps in this example show you how to change the equation into $y=$ form once you have obtained the center-vertex form. However, if you only want to graph a relation and don't need information about the center or focus, you can obtain the $y=$ form more directly by using the quadratic formula.

The Quadratic Formula

Vertex form	Polynomial form
If $A(x - H)^2 + K = 0$, then the solutions are $x = H \pm \sqrt{\dfrac{-K}{A}}$.	If $ax^2 + bx + c = 0$, then the solutions are $x = \dfrac{-b \pm \sqrt{b^2 - 4ac}}{2a}$.

Example 3 revisited: Solve the equation $y^2 - 4x + 6y + 1 = 0$ using the quadratic formula.

Solution:

$y^2 - 4x + 6y + 1 = 0$ The original equation (a quadratic in the variable y).

$y^2 + 6y - 4x + 1 = 0$ Identify the formula constants as $a = 1$, $b = 6$, and $c = {}^-4x + 1$.

$$y = \frac{{}^-b \pm \sqrt{b^2 - 4ac}}{2a} = \frac{{}^-6 \pm \sqrt{6^2 - 4(1)\left({}^-4x + 1\right)}}{(2)(1)}$$

You should check that this equation is the same as $y = \pm\sqrt{4(x + 2)} - 3$. Do you see why they are equivalent?

Example 4: Graph $x^2 + 4y^2 - 10x + 16y + 37 = 0$

Solution: This requires that you complete the square for both variables.

$x^2 - 10x + 4y^2 + 16y = {}^-37$

$(x^2 - 10x) + 4(y^2 + 4y) = {}^-37$

$(x^2 - 10x + 25) + 4(y^2 + 4y + 4) = {}^-37 + 25 + 16$

$(x - 5)^2 + 4(y + 2)^2 = 4$

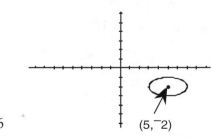

(5, ⁻2)

$$\frac{(x-5)^2}{4} + \frac{(y+2)^2}{1} = 1 \qquad\qquad \textbf{center-vertex form}$$

$$\frac{(y+2)^2}{1} = 1 - \frac{(x-5)^2}{4}$$

$$(y+2) = \pm\sqrt{1 - \frac{(x-5)^2}{4}}$$

$$y = \pm\sqrt{1 - \frac{(x-5)^2}{4}} - 2 \qquad\qquad \textbf{\textit{y}= form}$$

The problems will help you understand the examples, let you practice the completing-the-square process, and give you the opportunity to use the quadratic formula.

Problem Set 12.8

1. Rewrite each equation in the general quadratic form as defined in the beginning of this section.

   a. $(x+7)^2 = 9(y-11)$

   b. $\dfrac{(x-7)^2}{9} + \dfrac{(y+11)^2}{1} = 1$

2. Find the values for a, b, c, d, and e as you complete the square for $15x^2 + 21x$.

   a. $15x^2 + 21x = 15(x^2 + ax)$ $\qquad\qquad\qquad$ $(15a = 21)$

   b. $15(x^2 + ax) = 15(x^2 + 2bx)$ $\qquad\qquad\qquad$ $(2b = a)$

   c. $15(x^2 + 2bx) = 15(x^2 + 2bx + c) - 15c$ $\qquad$ $(b^2 = c)$

   d. $15(x^2 + 2bx + c) - 15c = 15(x^2 + 2bx + c) - d$ $\quad$ $(15c = d)$

   e. $15(x^2 + 2bx + c) - d = 15(x + e)^2 - d$ $\qquad$ $(\sqrt{c} = e)$

3. Identify each equation as true or false. If it is false, correct it to make it true.

   a. $y^2 + 11y + 121 = (y + 11)^2$ $\qquad\qquad$ b. $x^2 - 18x + 81 = (x - 9)^2$

   c. $5y^2 + 10y + 5 = 5(y + 1)^2$ $\qquad\qquad$ d. $4x^2 + 24x + 36 = 4(x + 6)^2$

4. Match each equation to one of the graphs. Assume all grid marks represent one unit.

   a. $9x^2 + 4y^2 - 36 = 0$

   b. $x^2 - 4y^2 - 8x = 0$

   c. $3x^2 - 30x + 5y + 55 = 0$

   d. $x^2 + y^2 + 2x - 6y - 15 = 0$

   i.

   ii.

   iii.

   iv.

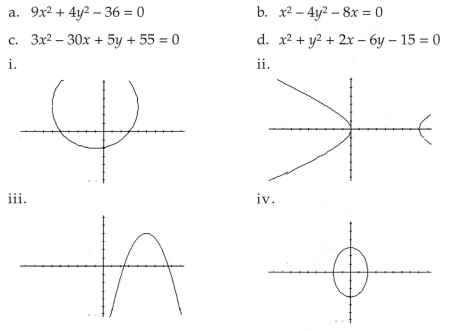

5. Rewrite each equation in center-vertex form, and identify the curve.

   a. $25x^2 - 4y^2 + 100 = 0$

   b. $4y^2 - 10x + 16y + 36 = 0$

   c. $4x^2 + 4y^2 + 24x - 8y + 39 = 0$

   d. $3x^2 + 5y^2 - 12x + 20y + 8 = 0$

6. Rewrite each equation in $y=$ form by solving for y with the quadratic formula. Graph each curve.

   a. $25x^2 - 4y^2 + 100 = 0$

   b. $4y^2 - 10x + 16y + 36 = 0$

   c. $4x^2 + 4y^2 + 24x - 8y + 39 = 0$

   d. $3x^2 + 5y^2 - 12x + 20y + 8 = 0$

7. The towers of this parabolic suspension bridge are 400 m apart and 50 m above the suspended roadway. The cable is 4 m above the roadway at the halfway point. Write an equation that models the parabolic shape of the cable.

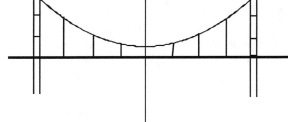

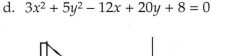

8. Explain in your own words the difference between the center-vertex form and the $y=$ form of a quadratic equation. Under what circumstances would you want to use each of these forms?

Section 12.9: The Rotation Matrix

Without some kind of graphing utility you would find it very difficult to graph a conic section that is rotated off the horizontal and vertical axes like the one at the right. The graph comes from the equation

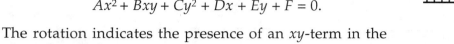

$$Ax^2 + Bxy + Cy^2 + Dx + Ey + F = 0.$$

The rotation indicates the presence of an xy-term in the general equation.

Example 1: Solve for y and graph the conic equation determined by $16x^2 - 24xy + 25y^2 - 60x - 80y + 100 = 0$.

Solution: You can solve for y by using the quadratic formula $ay^2 + by + c = 0$. The first step is to identify the coefficients a, b, and c.

$$\boxed{25}\; y^2 + \boxed{(-8 - 24x)}\; y + \boxed{16x^2 - 60x + 100} = 0$$

$$y = \frac{-b \pm \sqrt{b^2 - 4ac}}{2a}\;;\; a = 25,\, b = -80 - 24x,\, c = 16x^2 - 60x + 100$$

$$\text{Graph } y = \frac{-(-80 - 24x) \pm \sqrt{(-80 - 24x)^2 - 4 \cdot 25(16x^2 - 60x + 100)}}{(2 \cdot 25)}.$$

Your graph should match the ellipse pictured and described above.

Transformations and Matrices Activity

a. Draw a coordinate axis such that its origin is near the center of a piece of graph paper. Mark two points, A and B, which are close to each other and located in the first quadrant. You will increase your accuracy if you don't place A and B too close to the origin. Use a straightedge to connect each point to the origin.

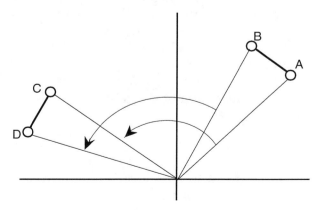

Select an arbitrary angle of rotation, θ. Do not choose θ equal to 45° or 90°. Use a compass or ruler and protractor to locate points C and D. Points C and D should be the images of points A and B after they are rotated $\theta°$ counterclockwise about the origin. Find the coordinates of points C and D as accurately as you can.

b. Find the matrix that will transform segment AB to segment CD by placing the coordinates of the points A, B, C, and D into the second and third matrices shown below. Then use an inverse matrix to find the entries of the first (transformation) matrix. Multiply to check your answer.

$$\begin{bmatrix} e & f \\ g & h \end{bmatrix}\begin{bmatrix} A_x & B_x \\ A_y & B_y \end{bmatrix}=\begin{bmatrix} C_x & D_x \\ C_y & D_y \end{bmatrix}$$

c. Find the sine and cosine of the rotation angle θ that you used to locate points C and D. Determine a connection between the entries of the first (transformation) matrix in the above equation, and your sine and cosine values. Form a conjecture about a matrix that will rotate a graph $\theta°$ counterclockwise about the origin. Compare your results with those of others.

The drawing shows the images after rotating points (1, 0) and (0, 1) $\theta°$ counterclockwise about the origin. The point (1, 0) rotates into $(\cos \theta, \sin \theta)$. Do you see why? The point (0, 1) rotates into (a, b). Use the fact that the two triangles (drawn to the x-axis) are congruent. Rename a and b in terms of $\cos \theta$ and $\sin \theta$. Then substitute your expressions in for a and b in the matrix $\begin{bmatrix} \cos \theta & a \\ \sin \theta & b \end{bmatrix}$.

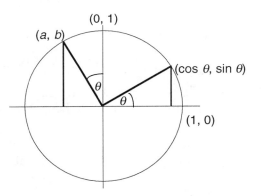

The **general rotation matrix** for a counterclockwise rotation through an angle of $\theta°$ is $\begin{bmatrix} \cos \theta & -\sin \theta \\ \sin \theta & \cos \theta \end{bmatrix}$.

Example 2: Rotate the point (5, 2) counterclockwise 60° with respect to the origin.

Solution:

$$\begin{bmatrix} \cos 60° & -\sin 60° \\ \sin 60° & \cos 60° \end{bmatrix} = \begin{bmatrix} 0.5 & -0.866 \\ 0.866 & 0.5 \end{bmatrix}$$

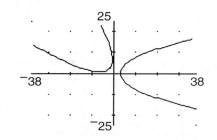

$$\begin{bmatrix} 0.5 & -0.866 \\ 0.866 & 0.5 \end{bmatrix}\begin{bmatrix} 5 \\ 2 \end{bmatrix} = \begin{bmatrix} 0.768 \\ 5.33 \end{bmatrix}$$

Check to see if you can enter and calculate this solution more directly in your calculator using $\begin{bmatrix} \cos 60° & -\sin 60° \\ \sin 60° & \cos 60° \end{bmatrix}\begin{bmatrix} 5 \\ 2 \end{bmatrix} = \begin{bmatrix} 0.768 \\ 5.33 \end{bmatrix}$.

You can verify your results by finding the distance from each point to the origin and by finding the angle measured from the positive ray of the x-axis to the ray of each point.

$$\sqrt{5^2 + 2^2} = 5.385$$ $$\sqrt{0.768^2 + 5.33^2} = 5.385$$

$$\tan^{-1}\left(\frac{2}{5}\right) = 21.8°$$ $$\tan^{-1}\left(\frac{0.768}{5.33}\right) = 81.8°$$

The new point is the same distance from the origin and has been rotated 60° further from the x-axis.

Example 3: Rotate the parabola $\begin{cases} x(t) = 3t^2 + 3 \\ y(t) = 5t \end{cases}$ counterclockwise 135°.

Solution:

$$\begin{bmatrix} \cos 135° & -\sin 135° \\ \sin 135° & \cos 135° \end{bmatrix}\begin{bmatrix} 3t^2 + 3 \\ 5t \end{bmatrix}$$

$$\approx \begin{bmatrix} -2.1t^2 - 3.5t - 2.1 \\ 2.1t^2 - 3.5t + 2.1 \end{bmatrix}$$

Verify this result by graphing the original parabola $\begin{cases} x_1 = 3t^2 + 3 \\ y_1 = 5t \end{cases}$ and the image

parabola $\begin{cases} x(t) = -2.1t^2 - 3.5t - 2.1 \\ y(t) = 2.1t^2 - 3.5t + 2.1 \end{cases}$. In general, the image equations $\begin{bmatrix} x_2 \\ y_2 \end{bmatrix}$ can be

directly written in your calculator because

$$\begin{bmatrix} \cos\theta & -\sin\theta \\ \sin\theta & \cos\theta \end{bmatrix} \begin{bmatrix} x_1 \\ y_1 \end{bmatrix} = \begin{bmatrix} x_1\cos\theta - y_1\sin\theta \\ x_1\sin\theta + y_1\cos\theta \end{bmatrix}.$$

This means after parametric equations for x_1 and y_1 are entered, you can graph the image by entering

$$x_2 = x_1\cos\theta - y_1\sin\theta \text{ and } y_2 = x_1\sin\theta + y_1\cos\theta.$$

However, if you cannot change to parametric form you must replace each x and y in the equation with the rotated equivalent. This is demonstrated in the following example.

Example 4: Rotate the hyperbola $x^2 - y^2 = 1$ counterclockwise 90° about the origin.

Solution: Replace each x and y in the equation $x^2 - y^2 = 1$.

$(x\cos 90 - y\sin 90)^2 - (x\sin 90 + y\cos 90)^2 = 1$

$(x \bullet 0 - y \bullet 1)^2 - (x \bullet 1 + y \bullet 0)^2 = 1$

$y^2 - x^2 = 1$ (This is the rotated hyperbola.)

Problem Set 12.9

1. Find the rotation matrix for each angle. Round off decimals to the nearest thousandth.

   a. 30° counterclockwise   b. 147° counterclockwise

   c. 270° counterclockwise   d. 213° clockwise

2. Rotate the triangle formed by (1, −2), (4, 5), and (7, −2) counterclockwise 90°. Give the coordinates of the new vertices, and sketch both the original and rotated triangle on a grid.

3. Rotate the ellipse $x = 3 \cos t$ and $y = 2 \sin t$ through an angle of 30°.

   a. Graph both curves

   b. Write the parametric equations of the image curve.

4. Rotate this triangle 180° counterclockwise about the origin.

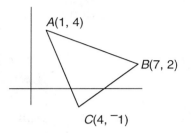

   a. Name the new vertices.

   b. What composition of reflections gives the same image?

5. Sketch this figure on graph paper, and enter the vertices in $[B] = \begin{bmatrix} 3 & 6 & 6 & 3 \\ 1 & 1 & 3 & 3 \end{bmatrix}$. For each choice of $[A]$, find the matrix result after multiplying $[A]\,[B]$. Graph the images, and identify a transformation involved.

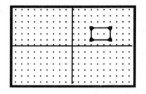

   i. $[A] = \begin{bmatrix} 1 & 0 \\ 0 & -1 \end{bmatrix}$ ii. $[A] = \begin{bmatrix} -1 & 0 \\ 0 & 1 \end{bmatrix}$ iii. $[A] = \begin{bmatrix} 0 & -1 \\ 1 & 0 \end{bmatrix}$

   iv. $[A] = \begin{bmatrix} -1 & 0 \\ 0 & -1 \end{bmatrix}$ v. $[A] = \begin{bmatrix} 0 & 1 \\ 1 & 0 \end{bmatrix}$

6. a. Predict the graph of $x_1 = \tan t$ and $y_1 = \dfrac{1}{\cos t}$.

   b. Describe what the equations for $x_2 = x_1 \cos \theta - y_1 \sin \theta$ and $y_2 = x_1 \sin \theta + y_1 \cos \theta$ accomplish when $\theta = -50°$.

   c. Draw the graphs.

7. Graph $xy = 4$. Find the equation of its image after a rotation of 45°. (Use the replacements for x and y described in Example 4.)

8. a. Write parametric equations that will draw the larger equilateral triangle on your calculator.

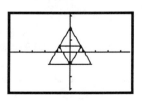

   b. Write parametric equations that will transform the larger triangle into the smaller triangle.

Section 12.10: Chapter Review

Problem Set 12.10

1. How many ounces of pure sugar must you add to a 20-oz container of a 12% sugar solution so that it is at least 42% sugar?

2. Describe how to section or slice a mathematical cone to produce each of the following.
   a. Circle   b. Ellipse   c. Parabola   d. Hyperbola

   e. Point   f. One line   g. Two lines

3. a. Write the center-vertex equation for this graph.

   b. Write the parametric equations for this graph.

   c. Name the center and foci.

   d. Write the general quadratic form of the equation for this graph.

   e. Write the parametric equations of the graph after a rotation through an angle of 75°.

   f. Write the general quadratic for the equation of this rotated graph.

4. a. Write the equations of the asymptotes of this graph.

   b. Write the general quadratic equation for this hyperbola.

   c. Write a function that will give the *vertical distance* between the asymptote with positive slope and the upper branch of the hyperbola as a point moves to the right from the origin.

   d. Use the function from 4c to complete the missing table values.

x	0	1	2	10	. . .	20
Distance						

5. a. Graph $y = \dfrac{2x - 14}{x - 5}$.

    b. What are the horizontal and vertical asymptotes of this function?

    c. Write a distance function that records the vertical distance between a point moving on the graph and the horizontal asymptote.

    d. Use the function from 5c to complete the missing table values.

x	0	3	5	10	. . .	20
Distance						

6. How can you alter the equation of $y = \dfrac{2x - 14}{x - 5}$ so that the graphs are the same except for a hole when $x = {}^-3$? Verify this by graphing the equation on your calculator.

7. Ellen drove at a steady speed for the first 2 mi on her way to school. After glancing at her watch she drove 20 mi/hr faster during the remaining 3.5 mi. How fast did she drive during the two portions of this trip if the total time involved was 10 min? Explain your solution process.

8. Eric cycled 34 mi on his bike and then ran the last 13 mi in the "World's Most Common" competition. On a good day he can run fast and bike fast. On a bad day he does them both slowly. Overall, his average bike speed is consistently 11 mi/hr faster than his average running speed.

    a. Write a function relating (*average running speed, total time*).

    b. Draw the graph of this function and describe the features of the graph.

    c. What values of x and y make sense?

    d. If Eric's total time for this event was 5 hr, what was his average running time?

9. What was the most interesting concept you learned about in this chapter? Explain it in such a way as to be convincing that you have *learned* it.

Section 12.11: Projects

12.1: Going Downhill Fast

Design an activity to determine a relationship between the tilt (or degree of slant) of a long tube and the time it takes a ball to travel the length of the tube. Use the following questions as a guide as you write up the activity, collect the data, and complete the activity. What should a graph of the relation (*angle, time*) look like? As the tube angle becomes steeper, what is the effect on the time it takes a ball to roll through the tube? What angles make sense? Will the graph have an *x*-intercept? A *y*-intercept? What meaning can be attached to the intercepts? To the slope?

12.2: Basketball

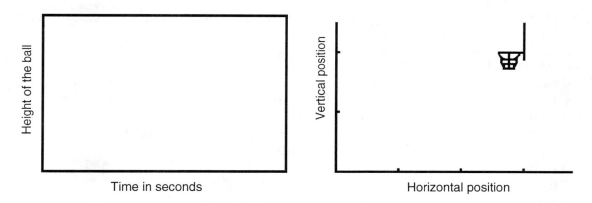

Sketch a graph of (*time, height*) for a typical free-throw attempt. Your graph should show what is happening over a period of 10 sec. Then sketch the typical path of a successful free throw. Do some research. What are the distances involved? How high is the rim? What is the floor distance from the free-throw line to the front rim? What is the diameter of the basket? What is the length of the bracket that fastens the basket to the backboard? Collect some data for a shooter (perhaps yourself) that provides the height of the ball at release, the angle at release, typical maximum height, and the time from release until the ball reaches the basket.

Using your data, write parametric equations that will simulate a successful free throw. Write a report on this project that includes the information collected, your data, equations, and graphs. Your description should also indicate how you collected information, list some of the problems involved, and how you solved the problems.

12.3: Jeep in the Desert

A jeep gets 10 mi/gal and can carry no more than 50 gal of gasoline. In order to cross 1000 mi of desert the jeep must make partial trips and leave gas at certain points across the desert. Find the least amount of gas needed to cross the desert.

12.4: Piston Pressure

In this project you will investigate the relationship between the volume of air in a piston and the amount of pressure on the trapped column of air. Use a set of masses and a large (50 cc) medical syringe with one end sealed (closed). Dangle a heavy thread into the syringe so that you can more easily push the piston down to somewhere between the 25 cc and 50 cc marks. Then remove the thread and let the piston rise back up until it stops moving. Record this ending volume and pair it with a mass of 0. Continue by carefully adding various mass amounts to the top of the piston, push down, and let the piston rise. Record (*mass, volume*) for 12 to 20 data points. To increase the accuracy of your experiment, repeat the process and record a new list of volume readings as you use the same mass amounts.

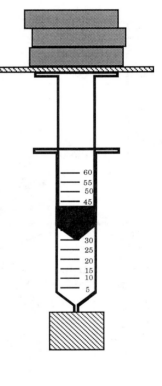

Mass	0	0.5 kg	1 kg	. . .
Volume 1				
Volume 2				
Pressure				
Average volume				

At this point you could plot the data and try to write a best-fit equation for the (*mass, volume*) data. But this relationship might be quite difficult to determine. An easier alternative will be to convert mass to pressure, then plot calculated points involving (*pressure, volume*), and, finally, write a best-fit equation for this (*pressure, volume*) relationship. The conversion calculations will seem messy, but the function might be easier to determine after you make the conversions.

1. Convert the mass placed on the syringe into force (pressure) by multiplying the mass (in kg) by 9.8 m/sec^2.

2. Divide the result by the cross-sectional area of the syringe (in cm^2). Use πr^2 to find the area of the opening of the cylinder.

3. Now add the air pressure in the room. Use 10 N/cm^2 for the air pressure if you do not know the actual barometric pressure in the room. N is measured in Newtons. If you have a barometer, then find the mercury height (in mm) and multiply it by 0.01333 to find the air pressure in the room.

Example Calculation: $0.5 \text{ kg} \cdot 9.8 \dfrac{\text{m}}{\text{sec}^2} \div 4.9 \text{ cm}^2 + 10 \dfrac{\text{N}}{\text{cm}^2} = 11 \dfrac{\text{N}}{\text{cm}^2}$

Make a graph by plotting the (*pressure, volume*) data. Write a short paragraph responding to the following questions. Based on your graph, what pressure would be needed to reduce the volume to zero? What would the volume be if the pressure was zero? Write an equation that fits the (*pressure, volume*) data you collected in the Piston Activity. Explain the process you used to discover this equation.

Chapter Thirteen

TRIGONOMETRIC FUNCTIONS

Contents

Section 13.1: Defining the Circular Function.. 616

     It's really about "Froggie went a-ridin'"

Section 13.2: Other Periodic Functions 624

     Again and again and again

Section 13.3: Combinations of Functions 630

     Math and music together

Section 13.4: The Law of Sines and Law of Cosines............................... 636

     Will I need a lawyer?

Section 13.5: Trigonometry Equations and Inverse Functions........................ 644

     Another look at (y, x)

Section 13.6: Polar Curves.. 651

     Is it getting colder in here?

Section 13.7: Polar Coordinates and Complex Numbers...................................... 658

     And still another name for a point

Section 13.8: Chapter Review.. 669

     Assessing yourself

Section 13.9: Projects.. 672

     Some more good problems

Section 13.1: Defining the Circular Function

Have you ever wondered how the exact time of sunrise or sunset is known for each day even years in advance? Or have you been curious about what gives each musical instrument its unique sound? The water depth caused by the tide at the ocean shoreline, the motion of a young child on a swing, your height as you ride a Ferris wheel, and the number of hours between sunrise and sunset each day are predictable. In this chapter you will study mathematical functions that help to explain these phenomena and other cyclical or repetitive motions.

Anne Fibian and the Paddle Wheel Activity

While swimming along, a frog by the name of Anne Fibian reaches out and grabs onto a paddle of a ten-meter diameter paddle wheel. The axle of this wheel is at the water level. Anne is immediately lifted from the surface of the river and begins her journey clinging tightly to the paddle. The wheel is slowly spinning at one revolution every 6 min. This means that Anne will be underwater for 3 min during each rotation. Your first task is to cut out a paper model for the wheel, using a 1 cm = 1 m scale, and draw a frog on the edge of your wheel. Then use your wheel and a ruler to collect data to complete the table below. The times are in seconds. The height from the surface of the water is in meters (centimeters for your model) and may be either positive (above the water) or negative (below the water). What is the meaning when the height is zero?

Time	0 sec	30	45	60	90	120	135	150
Height	0 m							

Time	180	240	270	300	360	420	480	540
Height								

Time	600	660	720	780	840	900
Height						

Enter this data into your calculator and plot a (*time, height*) graph. With the calculator in DEGREE mode, find the transformations needed to make the parent curve $y = \sin x$ best fit the data. Use your model to calculate Anne's height after 315 sec. Use your model to find at least three times when Anne is close to 4 m under water. Write a short report which includes a graph and the answers to the above questions.

The initial definition of the sine function found in Chapter 6 is no longer adequate, because the ratio of the opposite side to the hypotenuse in a right triangle cannot help you find the sines of angles whose measures are greater than 90°. In this section, you will use what you discovered in the Paddle Wheel Activity to extend the definition.

Example 1: Use your calculator to find the sine of each angle.

a.   sin 30°   b.   sin 150°   c.   sin 210°   d.   sin 330°

Solution: Using your calculator, you will get sin 30° = sin 150° = 0.5, and sin 210° = sin 330° = ⁻0.5. How can each of these angles have sines that are either 0.5 or ⁻0.5?

a.   Imagine a lily pad stuck on Anne's paddle wheel 1 m from the center. After 30 sec, the wheel has rotated 30°. To find the height of the lily pad above the water, draw a triangle like the one shown.

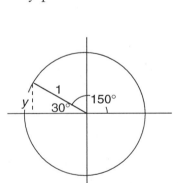

$\sin 30° = \frac{y}{1}$

$y = \sin 30° = 0.5$

The distance from the surface of the water to the lily pad is the sine of the angle.

b.   After 150 sec, the paddle wheel has rotated 150°. To determine the height of the lily pad above the water, draw a right triangle by dropping a perpendicular to the x-axis. Again, the angle you use to find the height is 30°. This acute angle within the triangle is called the **reference angle**.

$\sin 30° = \frac{y}{1}$

$y = \sin 30° = 0.5$

This angle has the same sine as a 150° angle, and again the sine represents the vertical distance of the lily pad from the surface of the water.

c. After 210 sec, the paddle wheel has rotated 210°. The triangle again has a reference angle of 30°.

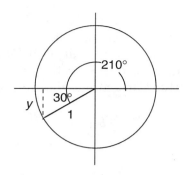

$$\sin 30° = \frac{y}{1}$$

$$y = \sin 30° = 0.5$$

Because the lily pad is underwater, the answer must be negative, so $y = {}^{-}0.5$.

This means that sin 210° represents the vertical distance below the surface of the water.

d. After 330 sec, the paddle wheel has rotated 330°. Repeating the previous steps, you again work with a 30° reference angle.

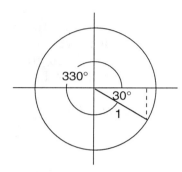

$$\sin 30° = \frac{y}{1}$$

$$y = \sin 30° = 0.5$$

Because the lily pad is under water, the answer should be negative, so $y = {}^{-}0.5$ and $\sin 330° = {}^{-}0.5$.

Notice that the sine of the angle through which the paddle wheel has turned, automatically tells you the distance from the surface and whether the lily pad is above or below the water. So the sine of angle A can be defined as the distance from the surface of the water to a lily pad stuck 1 m from the center of a paddle wheel after it has rotated $A°$ counterclockwise from the surface of the water.

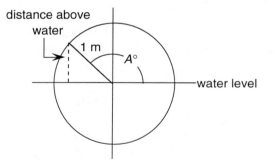

A more mathematical definition of the sine of an angle is as follows.

> The sine of an angle A is the y-coordinate of a point rotated $A°$ counterclockwise about the origin from the positive x-axis on a circle with a radius of 1 unit.

The domain of the function sin A is measured in degrees and, because the paddle wheel can keep rotating, the measure of the angle can increase beyond 360°. In the activity, the time Anne spent on the wheel was directly related to the angle through which the wheel turned. Because the wheel was turning before Anne got on, both the time and the angle can be negative values. This means that you can find the sine of any positive or negative angle. If the measure of angle A is negative, for example $A = {}^-30°$, then this point is located 30° before Anne got on and started to rotate. Another way to think of this is that the point has been rotated 30° clockwise about the origin from the positive x-axis on a circle with radius 1 unit.

Also, because the lily pad repeats the exact same journey each time around, the graph of the sine of the angle will repeat itself over and over again. Explain why the graph shows this endless journey of the lily pad.

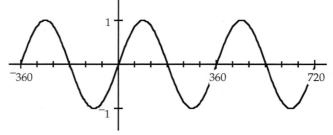

Your graph of Anne's distance from the surface of the water in the Anne Fibian and the Paddle Wheel Activity had an equation similar to $y = 5 \sin x$. What is the role of the 5 in the equation? How does the graph of Anne's distance from the surface compare to the graph of the lily pad's distance from the surface? Graph both of the equations on the same axis to see.

Because you know that you can find the sine for any angle, it is also reasonable to assume that the cosine and tangent also can be defined for any angle.

Example 2: Use a calculator to find the cosine of each angle.

a. 150°

b. 320°

Compare each result to the cosine of the reference angle.

Solution:

a. According to the calculator, cos 150° = ⁻0.866.

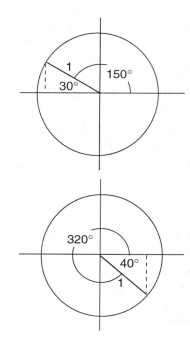

The reference angle is 30°. In the triangle shown, you can see that cos 30° = $\frac{x}{1}$. Because this x-value will be negative, you must change the sign. This means cos 150° = ⁻cos 30° = ⁻0.866.

b. According to the calculator, cos 320° = 0.766.

The reference angle is 40° and the triangle suggests the equation

$$\cos 40° = \frac{x}{1}.$$

$x = 0.766$

Therefore cos 320° = cos 40° = 0.766

Notice in each case the cosine of the angle is equal to the x-coordinate of the point on the circle. With respect to the paddle wheel example, this means that when the lily pad (which is stuck one meter from the center of the paddle wheel) has rotated $A°$ counterclockwise, the cosine of the angle gives its horizontal distance from the center of the wheel. Positive numbers mean the lily pad is to the right of the center, and negative numbers mean it is to the left of the center.

Here is a more mathematical definition of cosine.

> The cosine of an angle A is the x-coordinate of a point rotated $A°$ counterclockwise about the origin from the positive x-axis on a circle with radius 1 unit.

Again, you can visualize a negative angle, such as ⁻40°, as the point located 40° before the lily pad started to rotate. This will identify the same point as does a rotation of 320°. In the problems, you will revise your definition of the tangent of an angle.

Problem Set 13.1

1. Use your calculator to find each value. Then draw paddle-wheel diagrams to show the meaning of the value. Name the reference angle.

   a. sin 85°   b. cos 147°   c. sin 280°   d. cos 310°   e. sin ⁻47°

2. a. Carefully sketch a graph of $y = \sin x$ for $0° \leq x \leq 360°$ on your paper.

   b. Predict how the graph of $y = \sin x + 2$ will compare to the graph of $y = \sin x$. Verify your prediction with your calculator, and record a sketch of the graph.

   c. Predict how the graph of $y = \sin(x - 180°)$ will compare to the graph of $y = \sin x$. Verify your prediction with your calculator, and record a sketch of the graph.

   d. Predict how the graph of $y = 2 \sin(x - 180°) + 3$ will compare to the graph of $y = \sin x$. Verify your prediction with your calculator and record a sketch of the graph.

3. As the paddle wheel turns, the slope of a line joining the lily pad to the center changes.

   a. Determine the x- and y-coordinates that correspond to each position of the lily pad. Record these values in a table like the one below. (Remember, the coordinates of the lily pad are the cosine and sine of the rotation angle of the wheel.)

Angle A	0°	30°	60°	90°	120°	150°	180°
x-coordinate							
y-coordinate							
Slope							
Tan A							

Angle A	210°	240°	270°	300°	315°	330°	360°
x-coordinate							
y-coordinate							
Slope							
Tan A							

   b. To find the slope of these lines, you can use the coordinates of the lily pad's location and the coordinates of the center of the wheel (the origin). So the slope is equal to the ratio $\frac{y\text{-coordinate}}{x\text{-coordinate}}$. Compute the slope of the line between the lily pad and the center for each angle, and record the results in the table.

c. The slope is the same as the ratio of the leg lengths of the reference triangle. Why? What is another name for the ratio of the leg lengths of a right triangle?

d. Find the tangent of each angle in the table. Compare the tangent values to the slopes. What do you notice?

e. Write a definition of the tangent of angle A using the lily-pad-and-paddle-wheel scenario.

4. a. Carefully sketch a graph of $y = \tan x$ for $0° \leq x \leq 360°$.

   b. What happens at $x = 90°$? Explain why this is so.

   c. Why are $\tan 40°$ and $\tan 220°$ the same? Explain in terms of your definition of tangent.

When a portion of the graph of a function like sine or tangent repeats over and over again, it is called **periodic**. The **period** of such a function is the length of the x-interval required for the graph of one complete cycle before the graph begins to repeat itself.

5. Graph each function and name its period.

   a. $y = \sin x$ b. $y = \cos x$ c. $y = \tan x$ d. $y = \sin 2x$ e. $y = \tan 3x$

6. a. On your calculator, graph $y = \sin ax$ with a-values of 1, 2, 3, 4, and 5. Write a sentence explaining how the value of a affects the period of the sine graph.

   b. What is the period of $y = \sin ax$?

7. a. Using what you discovered in Problem 6, predict the period of $y = \tan 2x$. Use your calculator to verify or revise your answer.

   b. Predict the period of $y = \tan \frac{1}{3}x$. Use your calculator to verify or revise your answer.

   c. How does the period change compare to other transformations you have studied?

8. Determine the period for each graph below. Next, find any vertical stretches. Then find the horizontal or vertical shifts, if any. Finally, write an equation for each graph. There may be more than one correct equation. Verify each equation with your calculator.

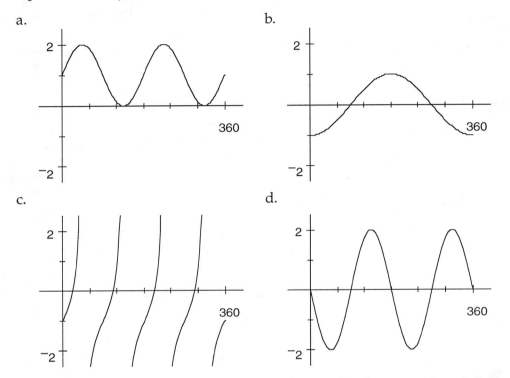

a.

b.

c.

d.

9. A plane flying 300 mi from Detroit to Chicago has been put in a holding pattern above the Chicago airport. The holding pattern is a circle with a diameter of 20 mi, which the plane completes every 15 min. Complete the following steps to write an equation that models the distance of the plane from Detroit as a function of time.

   a. What is the period of this motion?

   b. What vertical stretch is needed to show the diameter of 20 mi?

   c. What shift is needed to show the 300 mi between airports?

   d. Write an equation modeling the plane's distance from Detroit while it is flying in this holding pattern.

Section 13.2: Other Periodic Functions

Many situations are accurately and conveniently modeled with the sine, cosine, or tangent functions. However, in some applications the equation or model can be written more concisely if you use variations on these original three functions. These new functions share many common properties with the basic trigonometric functions, but they also have some interesting properties of their own.

Example 1: Bill Durr has been hired to construct a collection of ramps for InTune Piano Movers. The ramps must be built with a 7° incline angle. The movers need ramp heights of 20 cm, 35 cm, 47 cm, 75 cm, and 100 cm. Find the length of the boards that Bill will need for the inclined surface of each ramp.

Solution: Bill makes a drawing of a ramp. He labels the height of the ramp h and the length of the board b. For each ramp, the angle is 7°. Bill writes this equation.

$$\sin 7° = \frac{h}{b}$$

Because he needs to know the length of the board, he solves for b and gets

$$b = h \cdot \frac{1}{\sin 7°}.$$

Now he can find the length of each board by substituting the different height measures.

$$20 \cdot \frac{1}{\sin 7°} = 164.1 \text{ cm} \qquad 35 \cdot \frac{1}{\sin 7°} = 287.2 \text{ cm} \qquad 47 \cdot \frac{1}{\sin 7°} = 385.7 \text{ cm}$$

$$75 \cdot \frac{1}{\sin 7°} = 615.4 \text{ cm} \qquad 100 \cdot \frac{1}{\sin 7°} = 820.6 \text{ cm}$$

As you can see, each equation involves the reciprocal of the sine function. This reciprocal is called the **cosecant** function, abbreviated **csc**. So another way to write Bill's final equation is $b = h \cdot \csc 7°$.

Likewise, the reciprocal of the cosine has a special name, **secant**, abbreviated **sec**. And the reciprocal of the tangent is the **cotangent** or **cot**.

$$\text{secant } A° = \sec A° = \frac{1}{\cos A°} \qquad \text{cosecant } A° = \csc A° = \frac{1}{\sin A°}$$

$$\text{cotangent } A° = \cot A° = \frac{1}{\tan A°}$$

Your calculator does not have special keys for these reciprocal functions. So you must convert them to sin, cos or tan in order to enter them on your calculator. One way to do this is to use the reciprocal key (x^{-1}). To enter csc x, you can enter $(\sin x) \boxed{x^{-1}}$.

Reciprocal Function Graph Activity

In this activity, you will explore the graphs of the reciprocal trigonometric functions.

a. Graph $y = \sin x$ and $y = \csc x$ in the same graphing window. Carefully sketch the graph of each function on your paper. Compare the y-values of sin x and csc x for several different x-values. How does the range for sin x compare to the range for csc x? What is the period of the cosecant curve? (Note: The cosecant curve has vertical asymptotes that are not actually part of the graph. The function actually breaks at these values and starts up again on the other side. However, it may appear that the asymptotes are drawn on your screen. These "fake asymptotes" or "drag lines" occur when the calculator connects points from the top and bottom of the screen. If your window is set so that a pixel has the exact value of the asymptote, then there will be no drag line drawn. Otherwise, the calculator will connect the pieces of the graph.) Where are the asymptotes located? How can you explain these with reference to the ramp-building example above?

b. Graph $y = \cos x$ and $y = \sec x$ in the same graphing window. Carefully sketch the graph of each function on your paper. What is the period of the secant curve? Where are the vertical asymptotes? Describe the similarities and differences between the secant graph and the cosecant graph. (Hint: Look at the similarities and differences of the sine and cosine graphs.)

c. Graph $y = \tan x$ and $y = \cot x$ in the same graphing window. Carefully sketch the graph of each function on your paper. What is the period for the cotangent curve? Where are its vertical asymptotes? How does it compare to the graph of the tangent? Explain.

Graphs of the reciprocal functions may be transformed in the same ways as those of the other functions you have studied. In the problems, you will practice writing equations for both transformed reciprocal functions and the basic trigonometric functions.

In the activity, you found the graphs of secant and cosecant were transformations of each other. This was also true for the sine and cosine graphs. This means you can always write the equation of a sine curve in at least two different ways.

Example 2: Write three different equations of this graph.

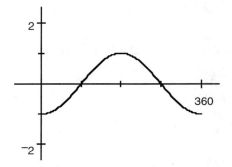

Solution:

a. You can think of this graph as a sine curve that has been shifted to the right by 90°. This gives an equation of $y = \sin(x - 90°)$.

b. You can also think of this graph as a sine curve that has been flipped over the x-axis and shifted to the left by 90°. This gives an equation of $y = {}^-\sin(x + 90°)$.

c. This is also a cosine curve that has been flipped over the x-axis, $y = {}^-\cos x$.

Because the sine and cosine functions are periodic, you can shift their graphs either left or right to get the same image. Find three more correct answers. Be sure to graph them on your calculator to verify that each equation gives the same graph.

Problem Set 13.2

1. Draw a sketch of this function on your paper and label it $f(x)$. Then sketch a graph of $\dfrac{1}{f(x)}$ on the same axis.

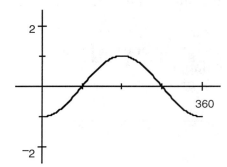

2. Find at least two different equations for each graph.

a.

b.

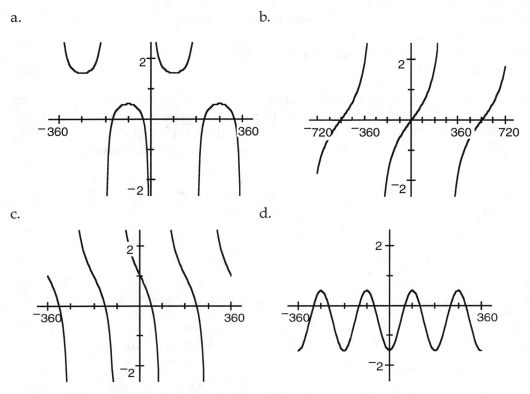

c.

d.

3. a. What effect does the value of d have on the graph of $y = \sin x + d$? Be specific.

   b. What effect does the value of a have on the graph of $y = a \sin x$? Be specific.

   c. What effect does the value of b have on the graph of $y = \sin bx$? Be specific.

   d. What effect does the value of c have on the graph of $y = \sin (x - c)$? Be specific.

   e. Use what you have discovered to sketch a graph of $y = 2 \sin 3x + 4$. Verify your sketch on your calculator.

4. a. A small bug is crawling counterclockwise around the rim of a 24-in. diameter tire. The rim is 15 in. in diameter. The slow-moving bug is now at its maximum height, and is crawling at a constant rate of one-fourth of a revolution per minute. Write an equation and sketch a graph modeling the bug's height from the ground over the next 20 min.

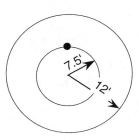

b. Suppose instead that the bug is crawling counterclockwise around this square picture frame. The square has side lengths of 24 in and the bug is crawling at a constant rate of one-fourth of a revolution per minute. If the bug is now 6 ft from the floor, sketch a graph of its (*time, height from floor*) over the next 20 min.

5. Annie Thropolagist is standing 20 m from the base of a cliff. Looking through her binoculars, she sees the remains of ancient cliff dwellings in the cliff face. To map the area, she must know the height of the dwellings above the canyon floor. Annie holds her binoculars at eye level, 1.5 m above the ground.

   a. Write an equation which relates the angle at which she holds the binoculars to the height of the object she sees.

   b. The top of the cliff is at an angle of 58°. How high is the cliff?

   c. Annie sees ruins at angles of 36° and 40°. How high are the ruins?

   d. If cliff swallows built a nest in the cliff face 10 m above the canyon floor, at what angle should Annie focus her binoculars to observe the birds?

6. The chart below shows the number of hours between sunrise and sunset, on the dates indicated, in Columbus, Ohio, which is located at 40° latitude.

Date	Hours	Date	Hours	Date	Hours	Date	Hours
21 Dec	9.246	14 Feb	11.283	10 Apr	13.667	4 June	15.017
26 Dec	9.533	19 Feb	11.517	15 Apr	13.850	9 June	15.017
31 Dec	9.650	24 Feb	11.717	20 Apr	14.033	14 June	14.983
5 Jan	9.783	1 Mar	11.950	25 Apr	14.217	19 June	14.933
10 Jan	9.917	6 Mar	12.183	30 Apr	14.383	24 June	14.867
15 Jan	10.083	11 Mar	12.400	5 May	14.530	29 June	14.750
20 Jan	10.267	16 Mar	12.617	10 May	14.667	4 July	14.633
25 Jan	10.450	21 Mar	12.833	15 May	14.783	9 July	14.517
30 Jan	10.650	26 Mar	13.050	20 May	14.883	14 July	14.367
4 Feb	10.867	31 Mar	13.250	25 May	14.950	24 July	14.200
9 Feb	11.083	5 Apr	13.467	30 May	14.983	29 July	14.017

   a. Graph (*day, hours of daylight*) and find an equation of a best-fit curve. Use December 31 as day zero.

   b. Which day will have the least amount of daylight? How many hours of daylight is this?

   c. Describe what you think a graph for Homer, Alaska, at 60° latitude would look like compared to this graph.

7. The table below shows the maximum safe speed for a vehicle traveling around a curve and the angle of "banking" on the curve.

banking angle

Angle	1°	2°	3°	4°	5°	6°	7°
Speed	26.2	37.0	45.4	52.4	58.6	64.2	69.4

a. Plot a graph of (*banking angle, speed squared*).

b. Try to fit the data with a sine curve. Check the residuals for your curve. What do the residuals imply?

c. Try to fit the data with a tangent curve. Check the residuals for your curve. What do the residuals imply?

d. What does your best-fit equation and its graph imply about a road banked at an angle of 90°?

8. Parametric equations $x = 5 \cos Bt$ and $y = 5 \sin Bt$ can be used to simulate a circular motion on a circle with a radius of 5 ft. The circle starts at $(-5, 0)$ and finishes at the same point 20 sec later, where $B = 18°/\text{sec}$ and t is replaced with $(t - 10)$.

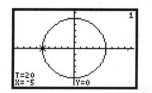

a. Graph this simulation in a "friendly" window with a factor of 2.

b. Write a function which models the distance of the cursor from the left margin of the window during the interval $0 \le t \le 20$.

c. Draw a graph of the function you wrote in 8b.

d. Write a function that models the distance of the cursor from the bottom margin of the window during the interval $0 \le t \le 20$.

e. Draw a graph of the function you wrote in 8d.

9. Find another function that has the same graph as each function named below.

a. $y = \cos(90 - x)$ e. $y = \sin(-x)$

b. $y = \sin(90 - x)$ f. $y = \tan(-x)$

c. $y = \tan(90 - x)$ g. $y = \sin(x + 360)$

d. $y = \cos(-x)$ h. $y = \cos(90 + x)$

Section 13.3: Combinations of Functions

Some applications require a combination of more than one function to make a realistic model. The sound produced by a musical instrument is actually the combination of several different sounds. In order to accurately reproduce an instrumental sound on an electronic synthesizer, you must specify the relative strengths of each of the individual component sounds and pitches. Each of these individual pitches can be represented by a sine function, and these sine functions are literally added together to create the desired effect.

Each band or orchestra instrument has its own characteristic sound. Flutes and violins sound very different even if they are playing the same note. One reason for this is that as each instrument plays a note, like an A, it also plays the next higher A and E, and several other notes that form its overtone series. The individual notes and overtones are difficult to hear and are present in varying degrees of loudness for different instruments. The graphs and equations below show a flute and a violin playing the same A above middle C.

The fundamental period for both graphs is the same. This period is determined by the term $A \sin 440x$, which represents the basic tone. The "bumps" in the graphs are caused by the overtones, which correspond to the remaining terms in the equations. The coefficients of these terms indicate the loudness of each overtone and, because the coefficients differ, the heights of these bumps also differ. Both equations are composed of several different sine functions. The numbers 440, 880, 1320, 1760, and so on, are the frequencies of the tones (measured in cycles per second). All of the frequencies are multiples of the basic frequency, 440. One cycle is completed when $\sin 440x = \sin 360°$, and this occurs when the period is $\frac{360}{440}$, or when $x = 0.82$ seconds. The variable x is a measure of time and y represents the loudness or amplitude of the sound.

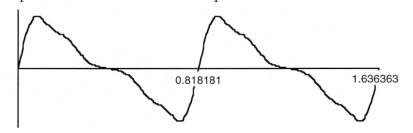

Flute: $y = 16 \sin 440x + 9 \sin 880x + 3 \sin 1320x + 2.5 \sin 1760x + 1.0 \sin 2200x$

The flute equation contains five different terms. The first term, 16 sin 440x, is the fundamental tone—and the loudest tone, because its coefficient, 16, is the largest coefficient. Notice that, by comparison, the coefficients on the other terms are much smaller. This gives the flute its characteristic clear sound.

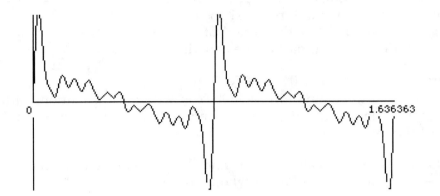

Violin: y = 19 sin 440x + 9 sin 880x + 8 sin 1320x + 9 sin 1760x + 12.5 sin 2200x + 10.5 sin 2640x + 14 sin 3080x + 11 sin 3520x + 8 sin 3960x + 7 sin 4400x + 5.5 sin 4840x + 1.0 sin 5280x + 4.5 sin 5720x + 4.0 sin 6160x + 3 sin 6600x

The violin sound for the same note is much more complicated, containing fifteen different pitches. The coefficients of some of the other tones are quite large compared to the initial term. This makes the violin sound more complex. Each musical instrument will have its own typical sound and graph. Different musicians will affect the sound of the note slightly, and also the shape of the graphs, but the basic shape will remain the same. You might try entering these equations in your calculator and reproducing the graphs. Then modify the coefficients of some of the terms and observe how the graph is affected.

Period Search Activity

What is the period of a function created by adding two sine functions together? How can you predict the graph of the sum of two different sine functions? In this activity you will investigate how the period of a function depends on the periods of each part of the equation.

a	b	Period
1	2	
2	3	
3	6	
2	4	
4	12	

a. Set your graphing window to $0° \leq x \leq 720°$ and $-2 \leq y \leq 2$. Mark the x-axis in units of $180°$. You will graph equations of the form $y = \sin ax + \sin bx$. Use the pairs of a- and b-values listed in the table. Then record the period for each pair.

b. Write a statement that explains how to find the period of a function $y = \sin ax + \sin bx$ where a and b are whole numbers.

c. Set your graphing window to $0° \leq x \leq 3600°$ and $-2 \leq y \leq 2$. Mark the x-axis in units of $360°$. Graph equations of the form $y = \sin ax + \sin bx$. This time the values of a and b are fractions. Record the period for each (a, b) pair. To see one complete cycle of the function, you may need to increase Xmax.

a	b	period
$\frac{1}{2}$	$\frac{1}{4}$	
$\frac{1}{2}$	$\frac{1}{3}$	
$\frac{1}{2}$	$\frac{1}{5}$	
$\frac{5}{6}$	$\frac{3}{4}$	
$\frac{5}{8}$	$\frac{3}{10}$	

d. Write a statement that explains how to find the period of a function $y = \sin ax + \sin bx$ when a and b are fractions. It may be helpful to rewrite each period as a multiple of $360°$. For example, if the period is $720°$, write it as $2 \cdot 360°$.

e. Predict the period for $y = \sin \frac{2}{3}x + \sin 4x + \sin \frac{1}{8}x$. Explain your reasoning.

Problem Set 13.3

1. Find an equation and graphing window that provides exactly one cycle of a sine wave during a span of 45 days. (Hint: Find B in $y = \sin Bx$ so that one cycle is completed at $x = 45$ days.)

2. Some people believe three aspects of their lives are governed by rhythmic cycles. These are the physical cycle of 23 days, the emotional cycle of 28 days, and the intellectual cycle of 33 days. These biorhythm cycles supposedly begin on the day you are born and continue throughout your life.

   a. Determine your age in terms of days.

   b. Write equations for each of the three cycles. In these equations, the period will be in terms of days and x will represent the number of days since your birth. Use an amplitude, or maximum height, of 1 for each cycle.

   c. Plot the three cycles for one month starting with today. Write a paragraph describing what these cycles predict for you during the next month.

   d. What is the period of the graph of the sum of the cycles? In other words, what is the length of time before all three cycles have the same y-value as they do at your starting time?

3. a. Carefully graph $y_1 = \cos^2 x$ and $y_2 = \sin^2 x$ on your calculator screen.

   b. Complete a table of values for the sum of y_1 and y_2.

x	0°	30°	60°	90°	120°	150°	. . .
$\cos^2 x + \sin^2 x$							

   Describe what a plot of all possible pairs from the above table would look like. Explain what it means if you connect these points with a smooth curve.

   c. Graph $y = \cos^2 x + \sin^2 x$ on your calculator. Look at the graph, or a table generated from this equation, and complete the following statement: $\cos^2 x + \sin^2 x = \underline{\hspace{1cm}}$ for all x. A statement such as this one that is always true is called an **identity**.

4. A popular amusement park ride is the double Ferris wheel. Sandra Noi is on the ride. Each small wheel takes 20 sec to make a single rotation. The two-wheel set takes 30 sec to revolve once. The dimensions of the ride are as shown at the right.

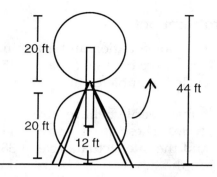

a. Sandra gets on at the foot of the bottom wheel. Write an equation that will model her position as this wheel spins around.

b. The entire ride (two-wheel set) starts rotating at the same time that the two smaller wheels begin to rotate. Write an equation that models the height of the center of Sandra's wheel as the entire ride revolves.

c. Because the two motions occur simultaneously, you can sum the two equations to write a final equation for Sandra's position. Write this equation.

d. During a 5-min ride, how many times is Sandra within 6 ft of the ground?

5. a. Graph $y_1 = \cos^2 x$ and $y_2 = \sin^2 x$ on your calculator screen.

b. Complete a table of values for the difference between y_1 and y_2.

x	0°	30°	60°	90°	120°	150°	. . .
$\cos^2 x - \sin^2 x$							

Describe what a plot of all possible pairs from the above table would look like. Explain what it means if you connect these points with a smooth curve.

c. Graph $y = \cos^2 x - \sin^2 x$. What other equation would give the same graph?

d. State what you discovered in 5c as an identity.

6. Graph $y = 2 \sin x \cos x$ on your calculator. What other equation would give the same graph? State your results as an identity.

7. a. Graph $y = (\sin x - \cos x)^2$ on your calculator. What other equation, without a horizontal shift, would give the same graph?

b. Expand the right side of the equation and use the identities you discovered in Problems 5 and 6 to write an equivalent expression.

8. Do the following tasks for each equation.

    i.   Carefully sketch a graph on your paper.

    ii. Write another equation that would provide the same graph.

    iii. Show algebraically why each pair forms an identity.

a. $y = 1 - \cos^2 x$ (Hint: Problem 3c should help.)

b. $y = \tan^2 x + 1$

   (Hint: substitute $\frac{\sin^2}{\cos^2} + 1$ for $\tan^2 x + 1$ and find a common denominator.)

c. $y = \sec x - \sin x \tan x$

d. $y = \dfrac{1}{\sin^2 x} - \dfrac{1}{\tan^2 x}$

9. If two musicians are playing tones that differ slightly in frequency, they create a sometimes annoying pulsing pattern of loud and soft sounds called beats. At times the two tones cancel each other out, and at times they combine to make a louder sound. The number of beats (or pulses) per second is called the **beat frequency** and good musicians know how to use this beat frequency to tune their instruments. Create a graph of the combined tones 440 cycles/sec and 442 cycles/sec and use it to find the beat frequency.

Section 13.4: The Law of Sines and the Law of Cosines

Two pilots are flying over Chicago. One is cruising at 400 mi/hr on a heading of 105° and the other is cruising at 450 mi/hr on a heading of 260°. How far apart are they after two hours? This question involves familiar rate/time relationships, but

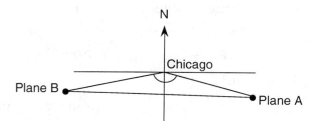

the triangle formed by the paths is not a right triangle. In this section you will discover useful relationships involving the sides and angles of non-right or **oblique** triangles and apply them to situations much like the distance problem presented here.

Oblique Triangle Activity

Draw an acute triangle. Label the angles A, B, and C. Label the side opposite angle A as a, the side opposite angle B as b, and the side opposite angle C as c. Draw the altitude from the vertex of angle A to side a. Label this h.

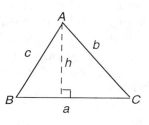

a. The altitude h separates the original triangle into two right triangles, one containing angle B and the other containing angle C. Use your knowledge of right triangle trigonometry to write an expression involving $\sin B$ and h, and one with $\sin C$ and h. Now combine the two expressions by eliminating h. Write this new expression as a proportion with $\sin B$ in one of the numerators. The result should be a proportion in this form: $\dfrac{\sin B}{?} = \dfrac{?}{?}$.

b. Now draw the altitude from angle B to side b and label it j. Repeat part a using trigonometric expressions involving j, $\sin C$ and $\sin A$. The result should be a proportion in this form: $\dfrac{\sin C}{?} = \dfrac{?}{?}$.

c. Compare the proportions that you have written. They can be combined into one extended proportion $\dfrac{?}{?} = \dfrac{?}{?} = \dfrac{?}{?}$. Fill in the numerators and denominators of this expression.

d. Draw a second acute triangle and carefully measure all of the angles and side lengths. Verify that your expression from part c is true.

e. Draw an obtuse triangle and measure all of the angles and side lengths. Verify that your expression from part c is still true.

Example 1: The Cliffs of Insanity rise vertically from the beach. The beach slopes gently down to the water at an angle of 3° from the horizontal. Lying at the water's edge, 50 ft from the base of the cliff, Cliff Scaylor determines that the top of the cliff is at an angle of 70° from where he is lying. How high is the cliff?

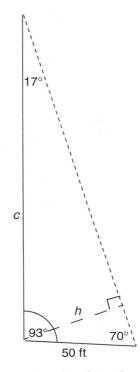

Solution: Make a diagram of the situation. Do you see where the 93° and 17° angles come from? This is not a right triangle but you can make two right triangles by drawing in the altitude from the vertex of the 93° angle to the opposite side. Label the length of this altitude h.

The height of the cliff is the hypotenuse of one of the two right triangles. Using the 17° and 70° angles you can write

$$\sin 17° = \frac{h}{c} \text{ and } \sin 70° = \frac{h}{50}$$

or $h = c \sin 17°$ and $h = 50 \sin 70°$.

Substituting for h gives $c \sin 17° = 50 \sin 70°$.

Solving for c gives $c = \frac{50 \sin 70°}{\sin 17°}$ or 160.7 ft.

The length of the altitude that you added to the diagram was not involved in the final calculations. The final equation can be written as $\frac{\sin 17°}{50} = \frac{\sin 70°}{c}$. This relationship, the ratio of the sine of an angle to the length of the opposite side, is constant throughout the triangle. This means you can draw the altitude to any side and get the same relationship for the other sides and angles in the triangle. This relationship is called the **Law of Sines**. You can use the **Law of Sines** to find missing parts of triangles.

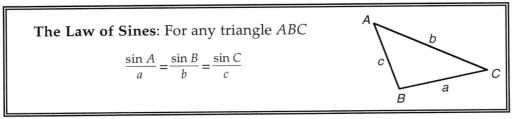

The Law of Sines: For any triangle ABC

$$\frac{\sin A}{a} = \frac{\sin B}{b} = \frac{\sin C}{c}$$

Example 2: Find the length of side *a*.

Solution: Use the Law of Sines.

$$\frac{\sin 52.5°}{a} = \frac{\sin 72.6°}{18}$$

$$18 \sin 52.5° = a \sin 72.6°$$

$$a = \frac{18 \sin 52.5°}{\sin 72.6°}$$

$$a \approx 15.0$$

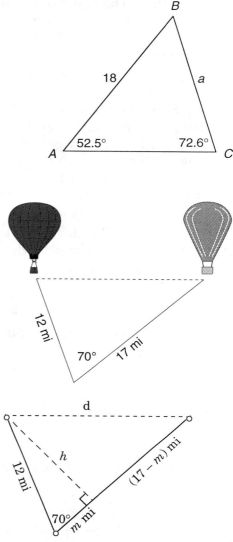

Example 3: The air traffic controller at Plainfield Airport observes that two hot air balloons are at the same altitude. One is 12 mi from the airport and the other is 17 mi away. If the angle between the balloons is 70°, how far apart are they?

Solution: In this case the Law of Sines does not help. You only know one angle, and if you try to set up an equation using the Law of Sines you will have more than one variable. (Take a minute now to confirm this.) So you must try something else. Again, draw an altitude to form two right triangles. This time draw it from the balloon on the left to the opposite side of the triangle so that one of the right triangles formed contains the 70° angle. (You could also draw from the balloon on the right.) The 17 mi side has been split into two parts. Label one part *m* and the other part 17 − *m*. Label the altitude *h*. You can now write two equations using the Pythagorean theorem.

$$m^2 + h^2 = 12^2 \text{ and } (17 − m)^2 + h^2 = d^2$$

$$m^2 + h^2 = 144$$
$$\text{and } 289 − 34m + m^2 + h^2 = d^2 \qquad \text{Multiply and expand.}$$

$$h^2 = 144 − m^2 \qquad\qquad\qquad \text{Solve the first equation for } h^2.$$

$289 - 34m + m^2 + 144 - m^2 = d^2$ Substitute for h^2 in the second equation.

$289 + 144 - 34m = d^2$ Combine like terms.

From the right triangles you can write $\cos 70° = \frac{m}{12}$ or $m = 12 \cos 70°$. Substitute for m in the equation to get

$d^2 = 289 + 144 - 34(12 \cos 70°)$

$d \approx 17.1$ mi   Take the square root of both sides.

The procedure followed in Example 3 is lengthy and complicated, but it can be repeated any time you know two sides and the included angle in a triangle and wish to find the length of the third side. Notice that the expression for d^2 could also be written as $17^2 + 12^2 - 2(17)(12)\cos 70°$, which looks a lot like the Pythagorean theorem (with the exception of the last term). This extra term is twice the product of the sides and the angle between them. In general form, this modified Pythagorean relationship is called the **Law of Cosines**.

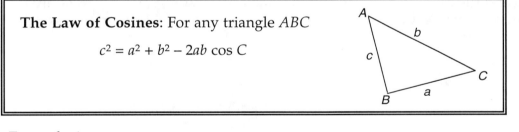

The Law of Cosines: For any triangle ABC

$$c^2 = a^2 + b^2 - 2ab \cos C$$

Example 4:

a. Use the Law of Cosines to find the length of the unknown side.

b. Use the Law of Sines to find the measure of angle A.

Solution:

a. Use the Law of Cosines to find the length of the unknown side.

$c^2 = 3^2 + 2.5^2 - 2(3)(2.5) \cos 28°$

$c^2 = 9 + 6.25 - 15 \cos 28°$

$c^2 \approx 2.01$, so $c \approx 1.42$.

b. Use the Law of Sines to find the measure of angle A.

$$\frac{\sin 28°}{1.42} = \frac{\sin A}{3}$$

$$1.42 \sin A = 3 \sin 28°$$

$$\sin A = \frac{3 \sin 28°}{1.42} \approx 0.9945$$

$$A = \sin^{-1}(0.9945) \approx 84°$$

To find the measure of the last angle, use the fact that the three angles sum to 180°:

$$B = 180° - 28° - 84° = 68°$$

You may have noticed that as you completed the calculations in Example 4 with the rounded-off approximation for c, you did not get the same answer for the measure of angle A. In general, you should use all of the decimals shown on your calculator and only round off at the end. An easy way to do this is to store the values in your calculator as you get them. That way, all decimals will be used in further calculations. Round off your final answer to the desired number of decimal places.

In deciding which law to use first, consider which triangle parts you know, and their relationships to each other. Then use the law which involves those given parts and the missing part you want to find. In all cases, you need to verify that the answers you get make sense in the context of the problem, or on a sketch of the triangle.

Problem Set 13.4

1. Find the measure of each unknown angle and the length of each unknown side.

a.

b.

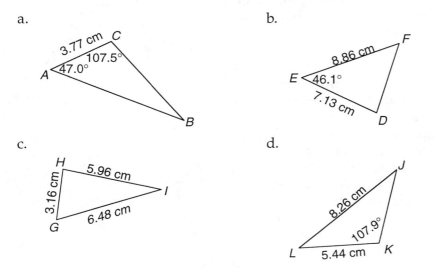

c.

d.

2. Describe how you know whether to use the Law of Sines or the Law of Cosines to solve for an unknown part of a triangle. What situations are most appropriate for each one? Refer to your work in Problem 1.

3. Two pilots are flying over Chicago. One is cruising at 400 mi/hr on a heading of 105° and the other is cruising at 450 mi/hr on a heading of 260°. How far apart are they two hours later?

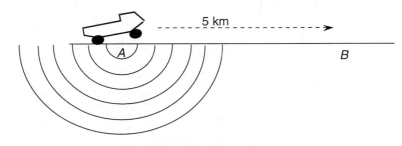

4. The Thumper is a truck used to find underground deposits. The entire body of the truck can raise itself off the ground, and then, at the press of a button, the truck crashes down to the ground. Sonic sensing equipment times the echo of the vibration to determine the distance to any underground phenomenon such as a cave, an oil pocket, a different density of rock, and so on. From a sounding at point A, the truck locates an underground chamber 7 km away. Moving to point B, 5 km from point A, the truck takes a second sounding and finds the chamber is 3 km away from that point. What can you determine about the location of the underground chamber?

5. The Pinched Finger Folding Chair Company is considering changing the angle where the legs meet to 50° to improve chair stability. The rear leg is 55 cm long and is attached to the front leg at a point 75 cm from the foot. How far apart will the legs be spread at the floor?

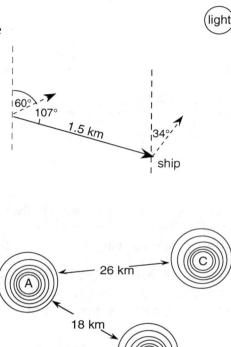

6. The SS *Minnow* was lost at sea in a deep fog. Moving at a heading of 107° degrees, the skipper sighted a light at a bearing of 60°. The same light reappeared through the fog after the skipper had sailed 1.5 km on his initial course. The second sighting of the light was at a heading of 34°. What is the position of the boat relative to the light at the time of the second sighting? Find both the heading and the distance.

7. Triangulation can be used to locate airplanes, boats, or vehicles that transmit a signal from a radio or a cellular phone. By measuring the strength of the signal at three fixed receiving locations, the distances can be found and the direction calculated. Receiver B is located 18 km from receiver A in a direction of 122° from north. Receiver C is located 26 km from receiver A in a direction of 80° from north. The signal from source D to receiver A indicates a range of 15 km. From source D to receiver B is 8 km, and from source D to receiver C is 25 km. What is the direction from A to the source? (Hint: You might try making a scale drawing of this situation. Then use your compass to get a general idea of the location of D before starting the calculations.)

8. One way to calculate distances to nearby stars is to measure the angle to the star at six-month intervals. A star is measured at a 42.13204° angle from the ecliptic (the plane of the earth's orbit). The angle is 42.13226° from the ecliptic six months later.

The diameter of the earth's orbit is 296,000,000 km ($3.13 \cdot 10^{-5}$ light years). What is the distance to the star?

9. In real life the Thumper truck
   problem is more complicated than
   described in Problem 4, because it is
   actually a three-dimensional
   problem that must be solved with
   three noncollinear soundings.
   Suppose you know the underground
   pocket is 7.2 km, 4.8 km, and 12.0 km
   from sites A, B, and C, respectively.
   Point B is 10.2 km from A at a
   heading of 23° from north and point
   C is 13.3 km from B at a heading of
   253° from north. Find the depth of
   the pocket, the direction from C to
   the pocket, and the distance from C
   to the point on the ground above the pocket.

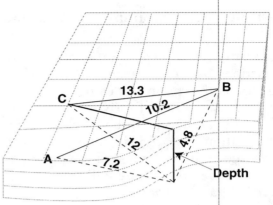

Section 13.5: Trigonometry Equations and Inverse Functions

Tides are caused by gravitational forces or attractions between the earth, the moon, and the sun as the moon circles the earth. The height of the water at a river mouth varies during the tide cycle. If the height is defined by the equation $h(t) = 7.5 \sin 30t + 15$, where t is measured in hours, when is the height 11.5 ft? How long before the tide will be at that height again? What is the cycle length modeled by this equation? These are important questions if you visit or live near the ocean, or if in your occupation you will be studying tide cycles.

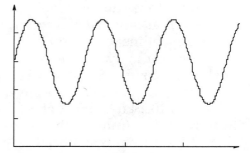

What is the meaning of 11.5 in the equation $11.5 = 7.5 \sin 30t + 15$? How do you solve for t? The graph above shows several different times when the water depth is at 11.5 ft, but if you calculate the inverse sine on your calculator you will only get one of these answers. This is because the calculator is a function tool, so it will only give you one output for any input. You will need to interpret the calculator results to find the other solutions. In the next example you will see that the calculator answer for an inverse function is not always the angle that you're looking for.

Example 1: Find the indicated angle.

Solution: Use the Law of Sines.

$$\frac{\sin 27°}{40} = \frac{\sin B}{77.5}$$

$$40 \sin B = 77.5 \sin 27°$$

$$\sin B = \frac{7.5 \sin 27°}{40}$$

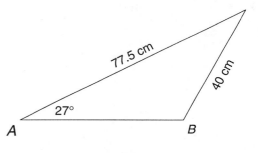

The calculator answer is $B \approx 61.6°$. But this answer doesn't make sense for the diagram. The angle should be obtuse, not acute. In this case, the calculator has given you the reference angle of the correct answer. The obtuse angle with the same sine as 61.6° is $180 - 61.6$ or 118.4°.

You can avoid this difficulty by using the Law of Cosines instead. However, you will first have to find the length of the bottom side of the triangle and then use the Law of Cosines again to find the angle at B. This is a much longer process, but if you don't know whether the angle you are seeking is acute or obtuse, it will be your only choice.

Suppose a mass is suspended from a spring. The mass is then pulled down slightly, stretching the spring. When released, the mass will move up and down. In reality, the displacement gradually decreases and finally the mass returns to rest. However, if the original displacement is small, then this decrease in its motion will be much slower and can be ignored during the first seconds of the oscillation. The height of the mass in relation to its resting position is given by a sine or cosine function. In general, the equation $y = A \sin B(x - C)$ or $y = A \cos B(x - C)$ provides this height. A is called the amplitude of the oscillation, or maximum distance from the resting position. B is the frequency of the motion, usually given in degrees per second. Here $360°$ represents one entire cycle of motion, and C is the phase shift. If the mass starts at a position other than where the parent curve begins, you must shift the curve horizontally to properly model the start of the motion.

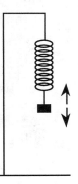

Example 2: A mass is pulled 3 cm from its resting position and then released. It makes ten complete bounces in 8 sec. At what times during the first 2 sec was the mass 1.5 cm above its resting position?

Solution: First write the equation. The amplitude of the vibration is 3 because the mass is pulled down 3 cm. The frequency is 10 cycles (or $10(360)°$) in 8 sec, or $450°/\text{sec}$. Because the motion starts at the bottom, the graph could be a standard sine curve that has been shifted one-quarter of a period to the right. (See the graph below.) A better alternative is to use the cosine curve, which starts at its maximum value, because you can simply flip it over the x-axis to get the correct starting position. This equation is $y = {}^-3 \cos 450x$. Now you can find the time when the height, y, is 1.5 cm.

One method is to graph the equations $y_1 = {}^-3 \cos 450x$ and $y_2 = 1.5$ and look for the points of intersection. From the graph you can see there are five. You have several options for finding them. You can zoom in on the points or use the built-in intersection finder in your calculator. Another method is to solve the equation formed by equating the two y-values.

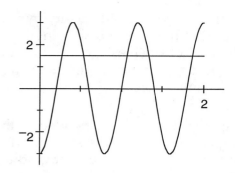

$${}^-3 \cos 450x = 1.5$$

$$\cos 450x = \frac{1.5}{{}^-3} \qquad\qquad \text{Divide by } {}^-3.$$

$$450x = \cos^{-1}(-0.5) \qquad\qquad \text{Calculate the inverse cosine.}$$

$$450x = 120$$

$$x = 0.266667 \text{ sec} \qquad\qquad \text{Divide by } 450.$$

This is the answer at the first intersection. The next solution comes at the next angle with cosine equal to $\cos 120°$. That angle is $240°$.

$$450x = 240° \quad \text{so } x = 0.533333 \text{ sec}$$

Because the function is periodic, the other three answers will come at one-period intervals to these two original answers. Adding the period of 0.8 sec gives the next two answers. Adding another period will give the final answer. The complete set of answers is

$$x = 0.266667, 0.533333, 1.066667, 1.333333, 1.866667 \text{ sec}.$$

In many cases equations involving trigonometric functions can be most easily solved with a calculator graph.

Example 3: The first mass is pulled down 3 cm from its resting position and released. A second mass is pulled 4 cm down from its resting position. It is released just as the first mass passes its resting position on its way up. When released, the second mass makes 12 complete bounces in 8 sec. At what times during the first 2 sec of its motion will the two masses be at the same height?

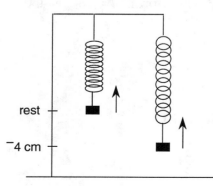

Solution: The equation for the second mass has an amplitude of 4. The frequency is 12(360°) in 8 sec or 540°/sec. The curve is again a cosine graph with a vertical flip. However, the period is 2/3 seconds so the equation is $y = -4 \cos 540x$. The equation for the first mass must be modified because it is now at the resting point when you begin timing. The sine curve is at a height of zero when x is zero so it will be easier to use a sine equation $y = 3 \sin 450x$ for this mass.

Graph both equations in the same window. You can see that they intersect six times during the first 2 sec. In this case, setting the two equations equal to each other is no help, because you can't get rid of the sines and cosines or combine the variables. Your best bet is to use your calculator. Instead of looking for the intersections of the curves you could make a third equation $y_3 = y_1 - y_2$. Graph only this equation. You can find the solutions where y_3 intersects the x-axis.

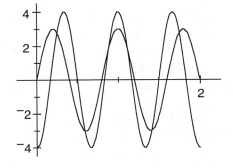

Now you need to find the roots of y_3. Using your calculator's built-in root finder or solver (**See APPENDIX 13A**), you get these six answers: $x = 0.248411, 0.589580, 0.884027, 1.115973, 1.410420, 1.751589$. Check to be sure that you can find them.

Inverse Trigonometric Functions Activity

Have you ever graphed the inverse of a sine or cosine graph? Can you visualize what such a graph would look like? You probably recall that (x, y) and (y, x) are inverses of each other. This activity will help you discover and explain some interesting features of the graphs of trigonometric functions and relations and their inverses.

Enter the A-values in this table into a calculator data list and use the list functions to calculate the other table entries.

A	0°	5°	10°	15°	20°	25°	. . .	90°	95°	100°	. . .	450°
Sin A												
Sin⁻¹(sin A)												

a. Plot the points $(A, \sin A)$ on your calculator screen. You should see a familiar graph. Record a sketch of this on your paper.

b. Plot the points $(\sin A, \sin^{-1}(\sin A))$ on your calculator screen. (You will need to redefine your window when you do this.) Is this graph a function? Compare the number of points plotted to the number of actual data points in your lists. Trace the graph and look through your data lists and then explain what has happened. Record a sketch of this on your paper.

c. Your first point plot, $(A, \sin A)$, was a graph of points from the sine function. Inverse relations are formed by switching the x- and y-coordinates of the points. Now graph the inverse sine by switching the coordinates. Use window values of $^{-}1.5 \le x \le 1.5$ and $^{-}100 \le y \le 360$. Create a plot of $(\sin A, A)$. Use the smallest mark on your calculator to mark these points. Is this graph a function? Explain. Now add a plot of the points $(\sin A, \sin^{-1}(\sin A))$ to your calculator screen using a different mark. Describe the similarities and differences in the two data plots. Why do you suppose the calculator gives only restricted values in the plot of $(\sin A, \sin^{-1}(\sin A))$?

d. In previous work you discovered that $f^{-1}(f(x)) = x$. Is this true for the sine function? Study the values and graph of $(A, \sin^{-1}(\sin A))$. Describe and explain the relationship between A and $\sin^{-1}(\sin A)$. You may need more angles, including negative angles, to be confident of your conclusions.

e. Now investigate the inverse cosine by following steps similar to those above. Again, you may need to use more angles, including negative angles, to be confident of your conclusions.

f. Draw accurate graphs of the $\sin^{-1}x$ and $\cos^{-1}x$ functions. Write a few sentences about each, explaining the domain and range of each function.

Problem Set 13.5

1. Find the measure of the indicated angle in each triangle.

a.   b.

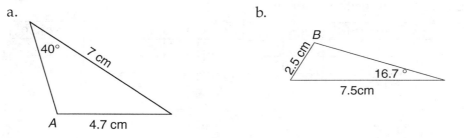

2. Use parametric mode on your calculator to answer each question. However, do not expect to find a window that will give you a good view of simultaneous graphs of these functions and their inverses.

   a. Graph $x_{1T} = T$, $y_{1T} = \sin T$ and its inverse relation $x_{2T} = \sin T$, $y_{2T} = T$. What range of T-values will give the same graph for the inverse as $y = \sin^{-1} x$ in function mode? Record a sketch of both parametric graphs.

   b. Graph $x_{1T} = T$, $y_{1T} = \sin 2T$ and its inverse relation. What range of T-values makes the inverse a function? Record a sketch of both parametric graphs.

   c. Graph $x_{1T} = T$, $y_{1T} = \sin \frac{1}{2}T$. What range of T-values make the inverse a function? Record a sketch of both parametric graphs.

   d. In 2b and 2c the period of the original function was changed. How does this period affect the range of the inverse function?

3. The height of the water (measured in feet) at a river's mouth varies during the tide cycle. The water height is $h(t) = 7.5 \sin 30t + 15$, where t is measured in hours. If you use $t = 0$ for the present time, during what time intervals over the next 48 hr is the river depth 11.5 ft or more?

4. As a pendulum swings, a graph of (*time, its height above its resting position*) follows a sine or cosine curve. Though the height is never below this resting position, it is customary to refer to the heights on one side of the swing as negative values and on the other side as positive values. The pendulum on Mark Tyme's grandfather clock makes 12 complete swings in 10 sec and its height is 1 cm above the resting level at each end of the swing.

   a. Write an equation which models the height of a swinging pendulum relative to its resting position.

   b. How many times during a one-minute interval does the pendulum pass through the resting position? Start the time interval when the pendulum is at the farthest point from its resting position.

5. A mass hanging from a spring is pulled 2 cm down from its resting position and released. It makes 12 complete bounces in 10 sec. At what times during the first 3 sec was it 0.5 cm below its resting position?

6. Two masses are each hanging at rest from different springs. They are each pulled down 2.5 cm and then released. The first mass makes eight complete bounces in 8 sec while the second makes ten bounces in 8 sec.

   a. During the first 3 sec, how many times are the two springs at the same height?

   b. During what percent of the first 3 sec are the springs within 1 cm of each other?

7. Find the first five positive x-values that make each equation true.

 a. $\sec x = -2.5$

 b. $(\csc x - \cot x)(\sec x + 1) = 0.8$

8. Carefully describe similarities and differences between $(\sin x, x)$ and $y = \sin^{-1}x$.

9. Household electric appliances plug into wall outlets. In the United States, most electric circuits supply 110 volts at 60 cycles/sec. (Actually the maximum voltage is $110\sqrt{2}$).

 a. Use the sine (or cosine) function and write an equation for (*time, voltage*) that models this information.

 b. Sketch and label a graph picturing three complete cycles.

10. a. The time between high and low tide in a river harbor is approximately 7 hr. The high-tide depth of 16 ft occurs at noon and the average river depth is 11 ft. Write an equation modeling this (*time, depth*) relationship.

 b. If a boat requires at least 9 ft of water, find the next two time periods when the boat will not be able to enter the harbor.

Section 13.6: Polar Curves

It's time to let your hair down, have fun, be creative, and at the same time learn about a very different kind of graphing that's related to trigonometric ratios.

In this section you will discover and use a coordinate system where surprisingly simple equations give very interesting graphs. For example, $r = 4$ is the equation of a circle. Elegant and complicated-appearing graphs, like the one pictured here, are frequently based on very simple relationships. You'll be surprised and intrigued by the variety of graphs and equations you will encounter.

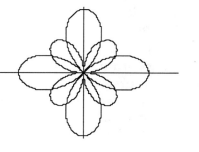

Graph the semicircle $y = \sqrt{16 - x^2}$ in a "friendly" window and then watch the (x, y) coordinates appear as you trace around the semi-circle. (See **APPENDIX 13B** to set your calculator for graphing and displaying coordinates in polar coordinate form.) As you trace this graph, the angle values change but the radius value remains constant. Can you explain why?

This relationship can be expressed with an equation in polar coordinates, using the variables r and θ to describe the graph. Polar equations are usually written as $r = f(\theta)$, where r is a distance from the origin and θ is an angle measured counterclockwise from the positive ray of the horizontal axis. Coordinates of points are given as (θ, r). Remember that a negative angle is measured clockwise from the positive ray of the horizontal axis.

Example 1: Graph the polar equation $r = 4$.

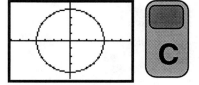

Solution: This is the set of points 4 units from the origin—a circle with radius 4. There is no θ in this equation, so no matter what your angle measures, the point will be 4 units from the origin. (See **APPENDIX 13C** for help with graphing polar equations.)

θ	0°	30°	45°	60°	90°	. . .
r	4	4	4	4	4	. . .

Example 2: Graph the polar equation $r = 3 \cos 2\theta$ with $0 \le \theta \le 360$.

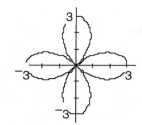

Solution: As you graph this equation on your calculator, you should see the four-petal rose that is pictured. To understand how this graph was formed, look at a table of (θ, r). To plot a point given in polar coordinates, imagine standing at the origin. Rotate yourself through the angle (for example, 30° counterclockwise from the positive ray of the horizontal axis). Then imagine walking straight out from the origin and placing a point at distance r. If r is positive, walk forward. If r is negative, walk backward. As θ increases from 0° to 360°, use this technique to locate points (θ, r) on the curve and then connect them with a smooth curve. Try drawing this graph on polar graph paper. What is the role of the coefficient 3 in the equation?

θ	r
0°	3.00
10°	2.81
20°	2.30
30°	1.50
40°	0.52
50°	−0.52
. . .	. . .

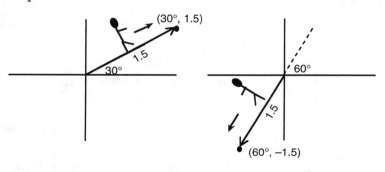

Rose Curve Activity

Take another good look at the equation, window, and graph for the four-petal rose in Example 2. Why four petals? Why the rose or flower shape? Concentrate on the connection between the trace numbers displayed on your calculator and the points. This beautiful graph comes from an equation that can be generalized as $r = a \cos n\theta$. In this activity, you will investigate Rose Curves, their symmetries, and the relationship between the number of petals and the value of n.

a. Graph the family of curves $r = 3 \cos n\theta$ with $n = 1, 2, 3, 4, 5$, and 6. Write statements that describe the curves for even n and odd n.

b. Graph the family of curves $r = 3 \sin n\theta$ with $n = 1, 2, 3, 4, 5$, and 6. Write statements that describe the curves for even n and odd n. How do these differ from the curves graphed in part a?

c. Find a way to graph a rose with only two petals. Explain why your method works.

d. Find a connection between the polar graph $r = a \cos n\theta$ and the associated function graph $y = a \cos n\theta$. Can you look at the graph of $y = a \cos n\theta$ and predict the shape and number of petals in the polar graph? Explain.

If you apply the Pythagorean theorem to the figure at the right, $r^2 = x^2 + y^2$ or $r = \sqrt{x^2 + y^2}$. Also, $\tan \theta = \frac{y}{x}$ or $\theta = \tan^{-1} \frac{y}{x}$. The actual value of θ depends on the quadrant in which the point (x, y) is located. These two equations allow you to convert between polar and rectangular forms. However, because many of the curves are not functions in the rectangular coordinate system, you cannot always easily solve the equations for y. By using the information in the drawing, you can also define two other equations, $x = r \cos \theta$ and $y = r \sin \theta$, which will help you understand the link between parametric and polar equations.

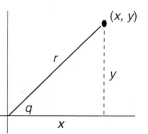

Example 3: Convert the polar equations to rectangular form.

a. $r = 4$

b. $r = 2 \cos \theta + 2$ (The graph of this equation is called a **cardioid**. You will explore this curve in the Problem Set.)

Solution:

a. Replace r with $\sqrt{x^2 + y^2}$, which gives you $\sqrt{x^2 + y^2} = 4$, or $x^2 + y^2 = 16$. Do you recognize this as the equation of a circle in rectangular form centered at the origin with radius 4? However, because a circle is not a function, it will take two equations, $y = \pm\sqrt{16 - x^2}$, to graph the entire circle.

b. Replace r with $\sqrt{x^2 + y^2}$ and $\cos\theta$ with $\dfrac{x}{r}$ or $\dfrac{x}{\sqrt{x^2 + y^2}}$ to get

$$\sqrt{x^2 + y^2} = 2\,\frac{x}{\sqrt{x^2 + y^2}} + 2.$$

$$x^2 + y^2 = 2x + 2\sqrt{x^2 + y^2}\qquad\text{Multiply by }\sqrt{x^2 + y^2}.$$

$$x^2 - 2x + y^2 = 2\sqrt{x^2 + y^2}\qquad\text{Subtract }2x.$$

$$(x^2 - 2x + y^2)^2 = 4(x^2 + y^2)\qquad\text{Square both sides.}$$

This is as good as it gets. After all this effort, you still haven't solved the equation for y. You might be able to find some points by choosing an x-value and then solving the resulting equation for y, but even that won't be easy. Certainly the polar form of this graph is easier to work with than the rectangular (function) form. The parametric form, however, is quite manageable.

If $r = 2\cos\theta + 2$ is given as the polar equation, you can use the equations $x = r\cos\theta$ and $y = r\sin\theta$. Just substitute $2\cos\theta + 2$ for r and t for θ to get $x = (2\cos t + 2)\cos t$ and $y = (2\cos t + 2)\sin t$.

The spiral is another curve that is easy to graph in polar form. Graph the equation $r = 0.01\theta$. Try using a larger range of values for θ. What happens? You may want to zoom out on your graph to see more.

Change your range of θ-values to include negatives. What happens? Can you explain why? You will continue this exploration in the exercise.

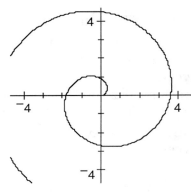

Problem Set 13.6

1. The coordinates (30°, 2) and (−150°, −2) identify the same point. Give two additional sets of polar coordinates that also name this point.

2. Give two additional sets of polar coordinates which locate the same point as (60°, −3).

3. a. Complete a table, like the one below, for the curve $r = 3 \cos 3\theta$
   for $0° \leq \theta \leq 360°$. Try to find a calculator process that makes this task easier.

θ	0°	5°	10°	15°	20°	25°	30°	35°	40°	45°	50°	55°
r												

60°	65°	70°	75°	80°	85°	90°	95°	100°	105°	110°	115°	. . .

   b. Draw this graph on polar graph paper. Be sure to connect the dots in a smooth curve as θ grows from 0° to 360°.

4. a. Graph the spiral $r = 0.01\theta$ using $0 \leq \theta \leq 360$.

   b. Graph the equation $r = -0.01\theta$ using $-360 \leq \theta \leq 0$. How does this compare to the original graph? Explain why this happens.

   c. Graph the equation $r = -0.01\theta$ using $0 \leq \theta \leq 360$. How does this compare to the original graph? What transformation has been performed?

   d. Graph the equation $r = 0.02\theta$ using $0 \leq \theta \leq 360$. How does this compare to the original graph? What transformation has been performed?

5. The family of curves $r = a(\cos \theta \pm 1)$ and $r = a(\sin \theta \pm 1)$ are called cardioids because they somewhat resemble a heart shape.

   a. Graph the cardioids $r = \cos \theta + 1$ and $r = \cos \theta - 1$. How do they differ?

   b. Graph the cardioid $r = \sin \theta + 1$. How does it differ from those graphed in 5a?

   c. Graph the cardioids $r = 2(\cos \theta + 1)$, $r = 3(\cos \theta + 1)$, $r = 0.5(\cos \theta + 1)$ on the same set of axes. How does the value of a affect the graph of
   $r = a(\cos \theta + 1)$?

6. A special microphone called a cardioid microphone is designed to pick up sound at equal intensity levels from any points on a cardioid around the microphone. The microphone is oriented so that the dimples of these curves are directed toward the audience and the ensemble is placed around the large curve of the cardioid shape.

a. Draw pictures of several cardioids like those in Problem 5c. Explain why this type of microphone will not pick up audience noise as well as the sound from the performers, even if the audience is actually closer to the microphone.

b. A quintet of musicians is to perform around a cardioid microphone. After placing the microphone, they decide that they should be evenly spaced on the cardioid shown at the right. What is the distance from the microphone for each performer?

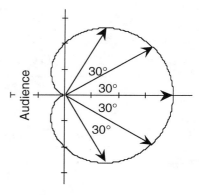

7. Write an equation for each graph. It may take more than one equation in some cases. Be sure to indicate your range of θ-values.

a.

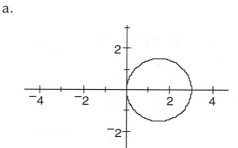

b.

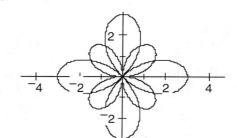

c.

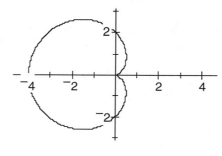

d.

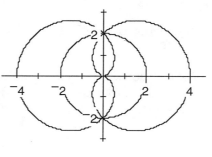

8. Graph each equation and name an interval for θ that provides a complete graph.

a. $r = 3 \cos 2.5\theta$

b. $r^2 = 4 \cos 2.5\theta$

c. $r = 3 \sin 7\theta + 4 \cos 2\theta$

d. $r = \cos(4 \sin 2\theta)$

e. $r^2 = \sin \dfrac{5\theta}{8}$

Section 13.7: Polar Coordinates and Complex Numbers

In Chapter 10 you solved equations with nonreal or complex solutions of the form $a + bi$. Complex numbers, like $3 + 4i$, cannot be graphed on the number line, but they can be graphed on a coordinate plane using either rectangular or polar coordinates. In the graph below, the horizontal axis is called the **Real Axis**, and the vertical axis is called the **Imaginary Axis**.

A complex number $a + bi$, has (a, b) as its rectangular coordinates. This means $3 + 4i$ is located at the point with rectangular coordinates $(3, 4)$. The real part of the complex number $3 + 4i$ is 3 and the imaginary part is $4i$. These coordinates can be changed to polar form using the conversion equations found in the previous section.

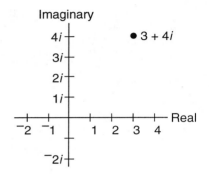

$$r = \sqrt{a^2 + b^2}, \ \theta = \tan^{-1}\frac{b}{a}$$

Example 1: Rewrite each complex number using polar coordinates.

a. $3 + 4i$

b. $^-3 - 4i$

Solution:

a. The complex number $3 + 4i$ is located in the first quadrant. You can find $\theta = \tan^{-1}\frac{4}{3} \approx 53.13°$, a first quadrant angle, and $r = \sqrt{3^2 + 4^2} = 5$. Therefore, the real part is $5 \cos 53°$ and the imaginary part is $5i \sin 53°$. So the number can be written as $5 \cos 53° + 5i \sin 53°$.

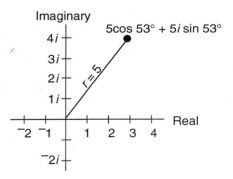

b. The complex number $^-3 - 4i$ is located in the third quadrant. Again, calculate the θ-value using $\tan^{-1}\frac{^-4}{^-3} \approx 53.13°$. In this case the angle is a reference angle, and the third quadrant angle is 233.13°. The r-value is the same as in part a, so the polar form of $^-3 - 4i$ is 5 cos 233.13° + 5i sin 233.13°.

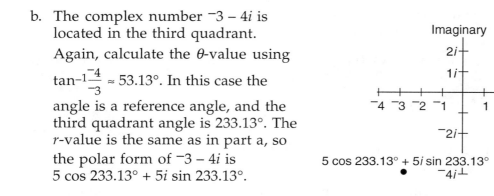

5 cos 233.13° + 5i sin 233.13°

The value r is called the absolute value or **modulus** of the number. The **polar form** of a complex number is $r \cos \theta + ri \sin \theta$, which is commonly written as $r(\cos \theta + i \sin \theta)$.

Multiplication of Complex Numbers Activity

In this activity you will discover a pattern involving multiplication of complex numbers written in polar form. Though a bit complicated at first, this important discovery will allow you to easily multiply and divide complex numbers, raise them to any power, and graph powers of complex numbers.

a. Multiply each pair of complex numbers and write your answer in $a + bi$ form. (Remember, $i^2 = -1$.)

i. $(2 + 3i)(3 + i)$ ii. $(1 + 4i)(3 - 2i)$ iii. $(-1 + 2i)(3 - 4i)$

b. Convert $2 + 3i$ and $3 + i$ to polar form. (See **APPENDIX 13D** for assistance.) Convert the product of these numbers to polar form. (See part ai.) Do this for each product in part a. Find a relationship between the angles of the two factors and the angle of their product. This relationship should be true for all three problems. Describe the relationship between the r-values (absolute values) of the factors and the r-value of the answer.

c. Study the following multiplication of $a(\cos \theta + i \sin \theta)$ and $b(\cos \Phi + i \sin \Phi)$.

$(a \cos \theta + ai \sin \theta)(b \cos \Phi + bi \sin \Phi)$

$= ab \cos \theta \cos \Phi + abi \cos \theta \sin \Phi + abi \sin \theta \cos \Phi + abi^2 \sin \theta \sin \Phi$

$ab(\cos \theta \cos \Phi - \sin \theta \sin \Phi) + abi(\cos \theta \sin \Phi + \sin \theta \cos \Phi)$

d. Set your calculator in function mode. Let $\theta = 45°$ and graph $y_1 = \cos 45° \cos x - \sin 45° \sin x$. This is a graph of the real part of your temporary answer.

Compare your graph with the graph of $y = \cos x$. Modify the equation $y = \cos x$ so that the graphs match.

Choose another value for θ and repeat this graph/modify process until you can complete this identity:

$\cos \theta \cos \Phi - \sin \theta \sin \Phi =$ _____

e. Let $\theta = 45°$ and graph $y_1 = \cos 45° \sin x + \sin 45° \cos x$. This is a graph of the imaginary part of the temporary answer.

Compare your graph with the graph of $y = \sin x$. Describe a modification of the equation $y = \sin x$ so the graphs match.

Choose another value for θ and repeat the graph/modify process until you can complete this identity:

$\cos \theta \sin \Phi + \sin \theta \cos \Phi =$ _____

f. Complete the following definition for multiplication of complex numbers in polar form: $(a \cos \theta + ai \sin \theta)(b \cos \Phi + bi \sin \Phi) =$ _____

Now multiply $4.25(\cos 23.4° + i \sin 23.4°)$ and $2.5(\cos 32.5° + i \sin 32.5°)$. Write your answer in polar form and then convert it to $a + bi$ form. Carefully explain your procedure.

Example 2:

a. Use the results of this activity to rewrite $(5(\cos 47° + i \sin 47°))^2$ without an exponent.

b. Rewrite $(5(\cos 47° + i \sin 47°))^3$ without an exponent.

Solution:

a. $(5(\cos 47° + i \sin 47°))^2$

$= (5(\cos 47° + i \sin 47°))(5(\cos 47° + i \sin 47°))$
$= 25(\cos(47° + 47°) + i \sin(47° + 47°))$
$= 25(\cos 94° + i \sin 94°)$

b. $(5(\cos 47° + i \sin 47°))^3$

$= (5(\cos 47° + i \sin 47°))^2 (5(\cos 47° + i \sin 47°))^1$
$= (25(\cos 2 \cdot 47° + i \sin 2 \cdot 47°))(5(\cos 47° + i \sin 47°))$
$= 125(\cos(2 \cdot 47° + 47°) + i \sin(2 \cdot 47° + 47°))$
$= 5^3(\cos 3 \cdot 47° + i \sin 3 \cdot 47°)$

Preliminary Edition

This example suggests a generalization for powers and roots of complex numbers.

$$[r(\cos \theta + i \sin \theta)]^n = r^n(\cos n\theta + i \sin n\theta)$$

Example 3: Find the three cube roots of 1.

Solution: 1 can be expressed as the complex number $1 + 0i$, or
$1(\cos 0° + i \sin 0°)$, or $1(\cos 360° + i \sin 360°)$, or
$1(\cos 720° + i \sin 720°)$ and so on, or with any other multiple of 360°.

Raise each of these representations to the 1/3 power (the cube root).

$$1^{1/3} \cos\left(\left(\frac{1}{3}\right)0°\right) + i \sin\left(\left(\frac{1}{3}\right)0°\right) = 1(\cos 0° + i \sin 0°) = 1 + 0i$$

$$1^{1/3} \cos\left(\left(\frac{1}{3}\right)360°\right) + i \sin\left(\left(\frac{1}{3}\right)360°\right) = 1(\cos 120° + i \sin 120°) = {}^-0.5 + 0.866$$

$$1^{1/3} \cos\left(\left(\frac{1}{3}\right)720°\right) + i \sin\left(\left(\frac{1}{3}\right)720°\right) = 1(\cos 240° + i \sin 240°) = {}^-0.5 - 0.866$$

The next multiple of 360 gives

$$1\left(\cos\left(\frac{1}{3}\right)1080° + i \sin\left(\frac{1}{3}\right)1080°\right)$$

$$= 1(\cos 360° + i \sin 360°)$$

$$= 1(\cos 0° + i \sin 0°)$$

and solutions are repeated for any other multiple of 360. Therefore, there are only the three unique answers. Confirm this before you move on.

Graph the three roots on the complex plane. Notice how the roots are evenly distributed around the origin. If you connect each point to the origin, there is 120° between each of these connectors. This symmetry of the roots can help you to predict the location of the complex roots of a number.

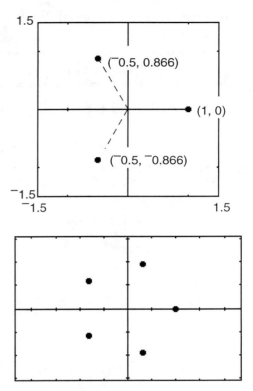

Example 4: Find the fifth roots of 32. How many are there? Where are they?

Solution: First write 32 as a complex number, 32 + 0i, and then convert to polar form: 32(cos 0° + i sin 0°). Other forms of this same number are
32(cos 360° + i sin 360°),
32(cos 720° + i sin 720°), and so on, using other multiples of 360°. Take a moment to confirm this. Now apply the generalization [r(cos θ + i sin θ)]^n = r^n(cos $n\theta$ + i sin $n\theta$) using $n = \frac{1}{5}$ and the first five choices of θ: 0, 360, 720, 1080, and 1440. The five roots are

$$32^{1/5}\cos\left(\left(\frac{1}{5}\right)0°\right)+i\sin\left(\left(\frac{1}{5}\right)0°\right)=2(\cos 0°+i\sin 0°)=2+0i=2$$

$$32^{1/5}\cos\left(\left(\frac{1}{5}\right)360°\right)+i\sin\left(\left(\frac{1}{5}\right)360°\right)=2(\cos 72°+i\sin 72°)=0.618+1.902i$$

$$32^{1/5}\cos\left(\left(\frac{1}{5}\right)720°\right)+i\sin\left(\left(\frac{1}{5}\right)720°\right)=2(\cos 144°+i\sin 144°)=-1.618+1.176i$$

$$32^{1/5}\cos\left(\left(\frac{1}{5}\right)1080°\right)+i\sin\left(\left(\frac{1}{5}\right)1080°\right)=2(\cos 216°+i\sin 216°)=-1.618-1.1761i$$

$$32^{1/5}\cos\left(\left(\frac{1}{5}\right)1440°\right)+i\sin\left(\left(\frac{1}{5}\right)1440°\right)=2(\cos 288°+i\sin 288°)=0.618-1.9021i$$

Notice that the angles for each root are incremented by 72°. If you plot them on the complex plane using a "friendly" window, the five points will be evenly distributed around the origin.

Until now you have only looked at plotting complex numbers as points. Now you will consider an extension for graphing **complex functions**. Complex functions involve variables that represent complex numbers. They are usually written with the variable z to distinguish them from functions of real numbers. It is not possible to graph a complex-valued function (a function that has complex numbers as outputs) in the same way as you graph something like $y = x^2$. You would need two dimensions for the independent variable z and two others for the dependent variable $f(z)$. You would need four dimensions to graph $w = z^2$ because w and z each represent a complex number. However, functions related to $w = z^2$ can be graphed. One way is to plot the result of repeated iteration on a point, which you will do in the next activity. The other is by graphing the numbers produced at each step of the iteration. You will explore this approach in Example 5.

Prisoners and Escapees Activity

You know that many recursive functions involving real numbers approach a long-run limiting value. Other recursive functions seem to grow infinitely large. This is also the case for functions involving complex variables. In this activity you will graph the results of iterating $z_n = \left(z_{(n-1)}\right)^2$, using many different seed values.

a. Label a region on your graph paper like that shown. Note that the spaces are labeled, not the lines. In other words, each square will have coordinates similar to the pixels on a calculator screen.

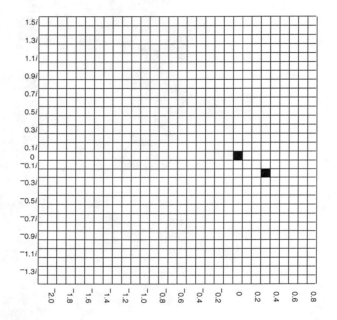

b. Choose a point. The coordinates of the point are the real and imaginary parts of the complex number. For example, the point (0.3, ⁻0.2) represents the number $0.3 - 0.2i$. Use this number as the seed for your recursive formula. It will probably be easiest to change to polar form for squaring. (See **APPENDIX 13D** for help in changing forms.) After several squarings you will notice one of two things happening: either the modulus will shrink to nearly zero, or it will become extremely large. If your seed number causes the function to go to zero, then color the associated square black. If your seed number causes the function to grow very large, then color it a different color.

Two sample points have been colored for you in the above grid. The point (0.3, ⁻0.2) becomes (⁻33.6°, 0.36) in polar form. Repeated squaring gives (⁻67°, 0.13), (⁻134°, 0.0169), and then (90.5°, 0.00028). The modulus is headed to zero so the point is colored black. Work together with your group to check all of the points. Use any patterns you discover to lessen the number of points you actually have to compute.

c. Describe the location of the points that go to zero. These points make up the **Prisoner Set**; they will never leave this region, no matter how many times you iterate. Describe the location of the points that grow infinitely large. These points make up the **Escape Set**; they keep moving farther and farther away as the iteration progresses. Describe the boundary of the prisoner and escape sets. These boundary points form a **Julia Set,** and they remain on the boundary between prisoners and escapees no matter how many times they are iterated.

The second graphing method for recursively defined complex functions is to plot each number that is generated as the function is iterated.

Example 5: Graph the points generated by $z_n = \begin{cases} 0 & n = 1 \\ \pm\sqrt{z_{(n-1)} + i} & n > 1 \end{cases}$.

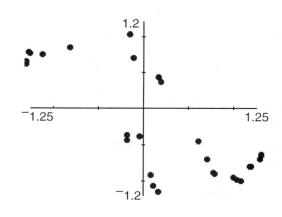

Solution: The $\pm$ in the second line of the formula indicates that you should take either the positive or negative root as you iterate the function. You could flip a coin each time to decide which root to choose. The table shows a possible set of the first ten numbers generated. If you try to generate some points for this function, you will probably get a different set, because your coin will indicate the negative root at different steps than the author's did. However, your points should appear to land on the same shape.

Real	Imaginary	Real	Imaginary
0.7071	−0.7071	−0.0989	1.1371
−1.1302	0.7552	−0.1873	−0.3660
0.1145	−1.069	0.7718	−0.8849
1.0457	−0.9894	1.1850	−0.7953
−1.2832	0.7752	1.2915	−0.6950

Initially, a random set of points appears on the graph. As you continue plotting many more points, a definite shape emerges. This plot shows the result of more than 10,000 iterations. (See **APPENDIX 13E** for a program to generate a plot similar to this.)

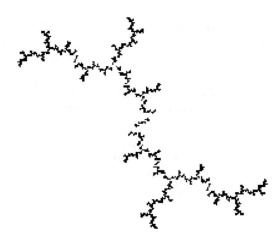

By changing the value of the constants, you can create many other interesting and beautiful shapes. See the Projects section for some further investigation of this topic.

Problem Set 13.7

1. Plot each complex number.

   a. $2 + 2i$ b. $-1 + i$ c. $0 - i$ d. $4 - 3i$ e. $-3 - 2i$

2. Convert each number in Problem 1 to polar form.

3. Find and plot all of the cube roots of 8.

4. Find and plot all of the fifth roots of 1.

5. Perform the indicated complex arithmetic. You may want to change some of the numbers to polar form before doing the arithmetic. Write your answers in rectangular form.

   a. $(3 - 5i) + (2 + 7i)$ b. $(2 + i\sqrt{12})^3$ c. $(4(\cos 27° + i \sin 27°))^{-1}$

   d. $(4 + 4i)(3 - 3i)^{-1}$ e. $\dfrac{1}{-4 + 4i}$

   f. $6(\cos 36° + i \sin 36°) \cdot 2(\cos 54° + i \sin 54°)$

6. a. Plot $(1 + i)$, $(1 + i)^2$, $(1 + i)^3$, $(1 + i)^4$, $(1 + i)^5$, $(1 + i)^6$, and $(1 + i)^7$ on the same complex plane. What will happen to the points as you continue to raise $(1 + i)$ to higher powers?

   b. Repeat 6a using $(0.5 + 0.5i)$. What will happen to the points as you continue to raise $(0.5 + 0.5i)$ to higher and higher powers?

   c. Explain the differences and similarities in the results of 6a and 6b.

7. Parametric equations and graphs provide easy access and interesting connections to roots and powers of complex numbers. Explore this idea with the complex number $-1 - i$.

a. Find r and θ in the expression $r(\cos\theta + i\sin\theta)$ representing the polar form of $(-1 - i)$.

b. Write the polar form for $(-1 - i)^T$. In this situation the parameter represents the power of the complex number.

c. Write parametric equations representing the polar form you found in 7b using $x = r^T \cos T\theta$ and $y = r^T \sin T\theta$. Complete a table of values for $0 \le T \le 10$.

T	0	1	2	3	4	5	6	7	8	9	10
x											
y											

d. Find a window that includes the points in the table and graph the parametric equations using a Tstep of 1. Be sure to square up the window. Trace the graph and locate the points listed in the table. What do these points represent?

e. Now graph and trace the same equations using a Tstep of 0.1. What do these points represent?

f. Using complete sentences, explain the shape of the graph.

8. a. Repeat parts a–f from Problem 7 using the complex number $(0.5 + 1.732i)^{463}$. This time use $0 \le T \le 12$.

b. Predict and then verify the point determined by $(0.5 + 1.732i)^{463}$. Explain why this point is the same as one of those listed in the table in Problem 7c.

9. a. In Example 4 of this section you found the fifth roots of 32. Do this again using the parametric equations $x = 2\cos\left(\frac{360T}{5}\right)$ and $y = 2\sin\left(\frac{360T}{5}\right)$. Explain the table values and your graph.

b. Find and graph the sixth roots of 32 using parametric equations.

10. a. Iterate the function $z_n = \sqrt[3]{z_{(n-1)}}$. Start with $z_0 = 1 + i$ and plot the value of the function at each step of the iteration. Continue until you can confidently describe what will happen to the value of the function in the long run.

b. Repeat 10a using $z_0 = -0.5 + 0.5i$.

c. Repeat 10a using any other point of your choice as z_0.

d. What generalizations can you make about iterating this function?

11. Construct on graph paper a grid like that in the Prisoner and Escapee Activity. Find the three points on the grid which locate the three cube roots of 1 that were found in Example 2. Mark these three points with different colors. Iterate locations that approximately form a circle passing through the roots with the function $z_n = z_{(n-1)} - \dfrac{z^3 - 1}{3z^2}$. Use the program in **APPENDIX 13F** to do this. Each location will eventually iterate to one of the three roots. Color the location with the same color as this root. When you have finished, choose a point between two different colored points and iterate it. What happens? Try another. You should find that between each pair of different-colored points, there lies a point of the third color. The "border" between the regions is as complicated as the edge of the Julia set you saw earlier. In fact, there is no real border because between any two points that go to different roots, there is a point that goes to the third root.

Section 13.8: Chapter Review

Problem Set 13.8

1. For each equation state the period and name one other equation that has the same graph.

   a. $y = 2 \sin 3(x - 30°)$ b. $y = {}^{-}3 \cos 4x$ c. $y = \sec 2x$ d. $y = ({}^{-}2x) + 1$

2. Write an equation for each graph.

   a.   b.

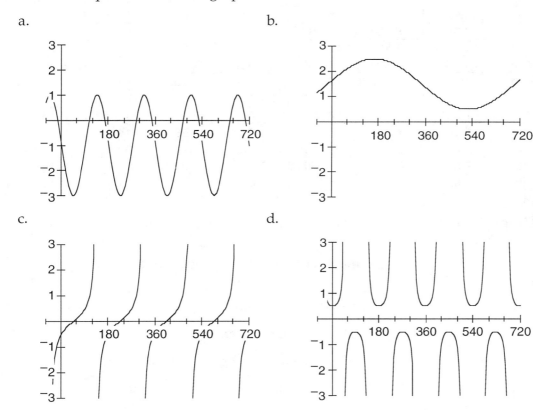

   c.   d.

3. The table below shows the number of hours of daylight in Winnipeg, Manitoba (at 50° latitude) on the dates indicated.

Date	hours	Date	hours	Date	hours	Date	hours
21 Dec	8.250	26 Mar	13.450	24 June	16.133	22 Sep	11.267
26 Dec	8.383	31 Mar	13.750	29 June	15.983	27 Sep	10.983
31 Dec	8.550	5 Apr	14.050	4 July	15.800	2 Oct	10.667
5 Jan	8.750	10 Apr	14.350	9 July	15.600	7 Oct	10.417
10 Jan	8.983	15 Apr	14.633	14 July	15.367	12 Oct	10.083
15 Jan	9.217	20 Apr	14.900	19 July	15.133	17 Oct	9.800
20 Jan	9.483	25 Apr	15.400	24 July	14.867	22 Oct	9.533
25 Jan	9.767	30 Apr	15.400	29 July	14.617	27 Oct	9.267
30 Jan	10.050	5 May	15.633	3 Aug	14.317	1 Nov	9.017
4 Feb	10.350	10 May	15.833	8 Aug	14.033	6 Nov	8.783
9 Feb	10.650	15 May	16.000	13 Aug	13.750	11 Nov	8.600
14 Feb	10.967	20 May	16.150	18 Aug	13.433	16 Nov	8.417
19 Feb	11.267	25 May	16.250	23 Aug	13.150	21 Nov	8.267
24 Feb	11.583	30 May	16.333	28 Aug	12.833	26 Nov	8.167
1 Mar	11.900	4 June	16.367	2 Sep	12.533	1 Dec	8.100
6 Mar	12.217	9 June	16.367	7 Sep	12.217	6 Dec	8.033
11 Mar	12.533	14 June	16.317	12 Sep	11.917	11 Dec	8.167
16 Mar	12.833	19 June	16.233	17 Sep	11.600	16 Dec	8.133
21 Mar	13.150						

a. Graph (*date, hours of daylight*) and determine the equation for your best-fit curve.

b. Which day will have the most daylight? How many hours of daylight is this?

c. On which days will there be equal amounts of daylight and darkness?

4. a. Graph $y_1 = \sec^2 x$ and $y_2 = \tan^2 x$ on the same axis.

   b. Describe the relationship between these two graphs as an identity.

5. Find the length of each unknown side and the measure of each unknown angle.

a.

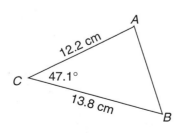

b.

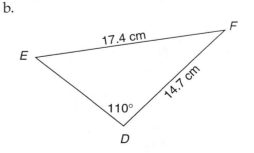

6. When trying to solve for an unknown side or angle of a triangle, how do you decide whether to use the Law of Sines or the Law of Cosines?

7. When a spaceship is launched into earth orbit it follows a sinusoidal path around the earth. The axis of this sine curve is the equator. Suppose that ten minutes after the launch from Florida, a spaceship is at its greatest distance from the equator, 100 mi. It makes a complete revolution of the earth in 105 min. Write an equation to model the path of the spaceship. How far from the equator was the launch site? How many times will the spaceship pass over the launch site during a three-day flight?

8. State two sets of polar coordinates that name the same point as $(40°, 5)$.

9. Graph the equation $r = 2(\cos \theta + 1)$ for $0 \leq \theta \leq 360°$.

   a. What equation will reflect this graph across the y-axis?

   b. What equation will rotate the graph 90° counterclockwise?

10. Plot each complex number.

    a. $3 + 4i$
    b. $-2 - i$
    c. $2(\cos 30° + i \sin 30°)$
    d. $(4 - i)^2$
    e. $(4(\cos 48° + i \sin 48°))^{(1/4)}$
    f. i^6

11. Iterate the function $z_n = (z_{(n-1)})^3$. What are the possible results for various values of z_0?

Section 13.9: Projects

Project 13.1: More on Julia Sets

Repeat the Julia set activity from Section 13.7 with $z_n = \begin{cases} 0 & n = 1 \\ \pm\sqrt{z_{(n-1)} - c} & n > 1 \end{cases}$

using $c = {}^-0.5 + 0.5i$. On your graph paper mark off a 30-by-30 grid using a scale of $^-1.5 \le x \le 1.5$ and $^-1.5 \le y \le 1.5$. Iterate each location through the function $z_n = (z_{n-1})^2 + c$. Color each prisoner point black.

Repeat the investigation again using $c = {}^-1 + 0i$. Based on these examples, describe the connection between the Julia set and the prisoner set. How are the two equations related to each other?

Use the program in **APPENDIX 13E** to plot more points in the Julia set. Compare your graphs. Experiment with other values of c. If possible print out a copy of your favorite Julia set and record the equation used to graph it.

Project 13.2: A Dampened Sine Curve

In Section 13.5 you modeled the motion of springs and pendulums using sine curves. In each case, the assumption was made that the amplitude of the motion did not decrease over time. This is not actually true. The motion gradually decreases in amplitude until the object comes to rest. In this project you will investigate this phenomenon.

Set up a pendulum with a protractor at the top. Start the string at a 20° angle from the center. Determine the period of the pendulum. Begin the experiment again and record the angle of the swing after each one, or at regular intervals of swings, until the pendulum is nearly at rest. Determine the height of the pendulum at each of these angles.

Plot the data (*time, height*) and draw a smooth sine curve to fit the points. Draw another curve which connects the tops of the curves. Find an equation which models this curve. Use this as the amplitude for the dampened sine function which will model the entire motion.

Preliminary Edition

Project 13.3: Design a Picnic Table

Your task is to accurately describe the pieces of lumber needed to build a picnic table like that shown below. Determine the lengths of all pieces, as well as the angles which need to be cut. Make scale drawings of all pieces.

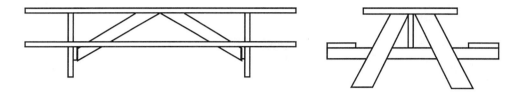

Project 13.4: Sum and Difference Identities.

Write an expression for the length of d using the distance formula. Write another expression for d using the Law of Cosines on the isosceles triangle with vertex C. Equate these expressions. Expand and look for ways use the identity $\sin^2 x + \cos^2 x = 1$ to reduce the equation as much as possible. Solve this for $\cos C$ in terms of $\sin A$, $\cos A$, $\sin B$, and $\cos B$. Because angle C is equal to angle A minus angle B, complete the following identity: $\cos (A - B) = $ ___. Test your new formula by finding $\cos (110° - 30°)$.

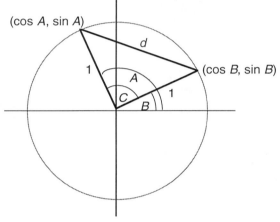

a. In your formula for $\cos (A - B)$, replace B with ^{-}B and rewrite the identity now for $\cos (A + B)$. Look at the graphs of $\cos {}^{-}x$ and $\sin {}^{-}x$ from 0 to 360. How can you rewrite $\cos {}^{-}B$ without a negative angle? How can you rewrite $\sin {}^{-}B$ without a negative angle? What is your new formula for $\cos (A + B)$ without using negative angles?

b. Study these statements:

$\sin x = \cos (90° - x)$. Graph both sides to see that this is true.

$\sin (A - B) = \cos (90° - (A + B)) = \cos ((90° - A) - B)$

Use the identity from part a to write an identity for $\sin (A - B)$.

c. Use the identity from part b and a similar argument as in part c to find an identity for $\sin (A + B)$.

d. Use your identities to find exact values for $\cos 75°$ and $\sin 15°$.

Appendices

FOR TI-80, TI-81, TI-82, AND TI-85 GRAPHICS CALCULATORS

Contents

Chapter Zero Appendices.. 676

Chapter One Appendices... 691

Chapter Two Appendices... 709

Chapter Three Appendices 711

Chapter Four Appendices 723

Chapter Five Appendices... 737

Chapter Six Appendices... 745

Chapter Seven Appendices.. 749

Chapter Eight Appendices... 760

Chapter Nine Appendices.. 770

Chapter Ten Appendices.. 781

Chapter Eleven Appendices 790

(There are no Chapter Twelve Appendices.)

Chapter Thirteen Appendices... 799

Chapter Zero Appendices

APPENDIX 0A80: MODE Settings

Press MODE to display a screen like the one shown at the right. The settings indicated are the ones that will be used most often in this course. If these settings are not selected, follow the steps below to change the settings.

1. Use the arrow keys to position the cursor on top of the setting you want to choose.

2. Press ENTER to register this selection.

3. When you have the settings you want, press 2nd [QUIT] to exit from the MODE screen.

Following are explanations of each setting.

First line—These settings determine the format of the numbers displayed by the calculator. **Norm** is the normal form of the number. It will display as many digits as will fit on the screen (10). **Sci** is the scientific-notation form of the number. In scientific notation, the decimal point is positioned so that there is only one digit to its left. The number is multiplied by a power of 10 to compensate for this move.

Second Line—This setting determines the number of decimal places shown. **Float** means as many places as will fit on the screen will be shown. The number settings are used if you wish to limit the number of decimal places shown. For example, setting this at **2** is useful if you are doing calculations with money.

Third Line—This setting indicates the type of angle measure to be used when doing calculations with trigonometric functions. **Degree** indicates degree measure, while **Radian** indicates another measuring unit called radian measure. In this course you will be using degree mode.

Fourth Line—Use this setting to display a fraction as a mixed number (**a b/c**) or improper fraction (**b/c**).

Fifth Line—Use this setting to **AUTOSIMP** (automatically simplify fractions) or to **MANSIMP** (manually simplify fractions).

Preliminary Edition

Sixth Line—This setting indicates the form of an equation. **Func** means that your equations will be entered in the form "y = some expression involving x." **Param** means that you will enter two equations, one for x and one for y, both involving a third variable t.

Seventh Line—This setting indicates how the calculator will draw graphs. **Connected** means that it will connect the points as it calculates them. **Dot** means that it will simply plot points on the screen, and not connect them.

Eighth Line—If you have several equations entered, this setting indicates whether they will be graphed **Sequentia**lly or **Simul**taneously.

APPENDIX 0A81: MODE Settings

Press [MODE] to display a screen like the one shown at the right. The settings indicated are the ones that will be used most often in this course. If these settings are not selected, follow the steps below to change the settings.

1. Use the arrow keys to position the cursor on top of the setting you want to choose.

2. Press [ENTER] to register this selection.

3. When you have the settings you want, press [2nd] [QUIT] to exit from the MODE screen.

Following are explanations of each setting.

First line—These settings determine the format of the numbers displayed by the calculator. **Norm** is the normal form of the number. It will display as many digits as will fit on the screen (10). **Sci** is the scientific-notation form of the number. In scientific notation, the decimal point is positioned so that there is only one digit to its left. The number is multiplied by a power of 10 to compensate for this move. **Eng** is engineering notation. This is similar to scientific notation, except that the powers of 10 are always multiples of 3. You will not use this form in this course.

Second Line—This setting determines the number of decimal places shown. **Float** means as many places as will fit on the screen will be shown. The number settings are used if you wish to limit the number of decimal places shown. For example, setting this at **2** is useful if you are doing calculations with money.

Third Line—This setting indicates the type of angle measure to be used when doing calculations with trigonometric functions. **Deg** indicates degree measure, while **Rad** indicates another measuring unit called radian measure. In this course you will be using degree mode.

Fourth Line—This setting indicates the form of an equation. **Function** means that your equations will be entered in the form "$y =$ some expression involving x." **Param** means that you will enter two equations, one for x and one for y, both involving a third variable t.

Fifth Line—This setting indicates how the calculator will draw graphs. **Connected** means that it will connect the points as it calculates them. **Dot** means that it will simply plot points on the screen, and not connect them.

Sixth Line—If you have several equations entered, this setting indicates whether they will be graphed **Sequen**tially or **Simul**taneously.

Seventh Line—This setting indicates whether or not the calculator will plot a grid of dots on your screen. This is similar to having the grid markings on graph paper or just using blank paper.

Eighth Line—This setting indicates which of two methods will be used by the calculator to indicate the position of a point on the graph. **Rect** will give the standard x- and y-coordinates (horizontal and vertical position). **Polar** will give the location by specifying an angle and a distance from the center of the graph.

APPENDIX 0A82: MODE Settings

Press MODE to display a screen like the one shown at the right. The settings indicated are the ones that will be used most often in this course. If these settings are not selected, follow the steps below to change the settings.

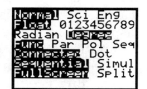

1. Use the arrow keys to position the cursor on top of the setting you want to choose.

2. Press ENTER to register this selection.

3. When you have the settings you want, press 2nd [QUIT] to exit from the MODE screen.

Following are explanations of each setting.

First line—These settings determine the format of the numbers displayed by the calculator. **Normal** is the normal form of the number. It will display as many digits as will fit on the screen (10). **Sci** is the scientific notation form of the number. In scientific notation, the decimal point is positioned so that there is only one digit to its left. The number is multiplied by a power of 10 to compensate for this move. **Eng** is engineering notation. This is similar to scientific notation, except that the powers of 10 are always multiples of 3. You will not use this form in this course.

Second Line—This setting determines the number of decimal places shown. **Float** means as many places as will fit on the screen will be shown. The number settings are used if you wish to limit the number of decimal places shown. For example, setting this at **2** is useful if you are doing calculations with money.

Third Line—This setting indicates the type of angle measure to be used when doing calculations with trigonometric functions. **Degree** indicates degree measure, while **Radian** indicates another measuring unit called radian measure. In this course you will be using degree mode.

Fourth Line—This setting indicates the form of an equation. **Func** (Function) means that your equations will be entered in the form "$y =$ some expression involving x." **Par** (Parametric) means that you will enter two equations, one for x and one for y, both involving a third variable t. **Pol** (Polar) means that you enter an equation with r specifying a distance from the center of the graph in terms of an angle. **Seq** (Sequence) means you can graph sequences that are defined recursively or explicitly.

Fifth Line—This setting indicates how the calculator will draw graphs. **Connected** means that it will connect the points as it calculates them. **Dot** means that it will simply plot points on the screen, and not connect them.

Sixth Line—If you have several equations entered, this setting indicates whether they will be graphed **Sequential**ly or **Simul**taneously.

Seventh Line—**Full Screen** uses the entire screen for the graph or as the HOME screen. **Split** displays your current graph on the upper half of the screen and uses the lower half of the screen as the HOME screen.

APPENDIX 0A85: MODE Settings

Press [2nd] [MODE] to display the MODE screen like the one at the right. The settings indicated are the ones that will be used most often in this course. If your calculator does not display these, follow the steps below to change settings.

1. Use the arrow keys to position the cursor on top of the setting you want to choose.

2. Press [ENTER] to register this selection.

3. When you have the settings as desired, press [EXIT] to exit from the MODE screen.

Following are explanations of each setting.

First line—These settings determine the format of the numbers displayed by the calculator. **Normal** is the normal form of the number. It will display as many digits as will fit on the screen (12). **Sci** is the scientific notation form of the number. In scientific notation, the decimal point is positioned so that there is only one digit to its left. The number is multiplied by a power of 10 to compensate for this move. **Eng** is engineering notation. This is similar to scientific notation, except that the powers of 10 are always multiples of 3. You will not use this form in this course.

Second Line—This setting determines the number of decimal places shown. **Float** means as many places as will fit on the screen will be shown. The number settings are used if you wish to limit the number of decimal places shown. For example, setting this at **2** is useful if you are doing calculations with money. The 0 and 1 at the end of the list are for 10 and 11 digits of display.

Third Line—This setting indicates the type of angle measure to be used when doing calculations with trigonometric functions. **Degree** indicates degree measure, while **Radian** indicates another measuring unit called radian measure. In this course you will be using degree mode.

Fourth Line—This setting allows you to change from rectangular coordinates to polar coordinates. It is used with complex numbers.

Fifth Line—This setting indicates the form of an equation. **Func** (function) means that your equations will be entered in the form "y = some expression involving x." **Pol** (Polar) means that you enter an equation with r specifying a distance from the center of the graph in terms of an angle. **Par** (Parametric) means that you will enter two equations, one for x and one for y, both involving a third variable t. **DifEq** (Differential Equations) means you can graph equations that are defined in terms of derivatives of functions (calculus stuff).

Sixth Line—This setting is used to select different number systems. Choices are base 10 (**Dec**imal), base 2 (**Bin**ary), base 8 (**Oct**al), or base 16 (**Hex**adecimal).

APPENDIX 0B80: Calculation Keys—Includes a Fraction Function

To perform any arithmetic calculation, enter it, and press ENTER to calculate the answer.

Exponents may be entered in several ways. If you wish to square a number, a variable, or an expression, you can use the x^2 key. It is located in the left-hand column of keys. To use it, enter the number, variable, or expression to be squared. Then press x^2 ENTER. If you are entering an expression, be sure to enclose it in parentheses.

What you enter: What you see:

17 x^2 ENTER

There is also a special key for cubing a number (raising it to the third power). It is not found on any of the regular keys, but must be accessed by using a menu. First type the number or expression that you want to raise to the third power. Press MATH and you will see a screen like the one at the right. Then press 3 and an exponent 3 will appear next to your number. (You can also use the arrow keys to position the cursor on choice 3.) Press ENTER to calculate the answer.

You can also use the caret key, ∧ , located in the right-hand column of keys, before any number, variable, or expression you want to enter as an exponent. Be sure to use parentheses around any exponent that involves more than just one number. For example, to enter the fractional-exponent expression $3^{2/3}$, type 3 ∧ (2/3).

What you enter:

2 [∧] 5 [ENTER]

What you see:

```
2^5
            32
■
```

Example 3 in Section 2 asks that 0.275 be written as a fraction. The TI-82 contains a function that will make this conversion directly. Enter 0.275, and press [MATH] [1] (Frac), and the calculator will display $\frac{11}{40}$.

What you enter:

0.275 [FRAC] [4] [FRAC] [ENTER]

What you see:

```
0.275▶FRAC
            11/40
■
```

Editing/Replay: The replay, or last entry key ([2nd] [ENTRY]), reprints the previous entry on the screen. Then you can edit what's displayed on the screen by typing over, inserting ([2nd] [INS]), or deleting ([DEL]) to change the expression.

Storing a value for a variable: You can store a specific value in each of the variable locations on your calculator. For example, 17 [STO] X [ENTER] assigns 17 as the temporarily value of x. Any expression containing the variable x, such as x^2, $-x^2$, $\sqrt{x+4}$, or $3.5x - 4.7$, will be evaluated at $x = 17$.

```
17→X
            17
X²
            289
-X²
           -289
■
```

APPENDIX 0B81: Calculation Keys—No Fraction Function

To perform any arithmetic calculation, type it in, and press [ENTER] to calculate the answer.

Exponents may be entered in several ways. If you wish to square something, you can use the x^2 key. This is located in the left column of keys. To use it, enter the number to be squared, then press [x^2] [ENTER].

What you enter:

17 [x^2] [ENTER]

What you see:

```
17²
            289
■
```

There is also a special key for cubing a number (raising it to the third power). It is not found on any of the regular keys, but must be accessed by using a menu. First type the number or expression that you want to raise to the third power.

Press [MATH] and you will see a screen like the one at the right. Then press 3 and an exponent 3 will appear next to your number. (You can also use the arrow keys to position the cursor on choice 3.) Press [ENTER] to calculate the answer.

```
MATH NUM HYP PRB
1:▶Frac
2:▶Dec
3:³
4:³√
5:×√
6:fMin(
7↓fMax(
```

You can also use the caret key, [∧], located in the right-hand column of keys, before any number, variable, or expression you want to enter as an exponent. Be sure to use parentheses around any exponent that involves more than just one number. For example, to enter the fractional-exponent expression $3^{2/3}$, type 3 [∧] (2/3).

What you enter:

What you see:

2 [∧] 5 [ENTER]

```
2^5
              32
■
```

Editing/Replay: The replay (the up arrow from the cluster of four direction arrows) or last entry key ([2nd] [ENTRY]) allows you to reprint the previous entry on the screen. Then you can edit what's displayed on the screen by typing over, inserting ([INS]), or deleting ([DEL]) to change the expression.

Storing a value for a variable: You can store specific values in each of the variable locations on your calculator. For example, 17[STO] X [ENTER] assigns 17 as the temporarily value of x. Any expression containing the variable x, such as x^2, $-x^2$, $\sqrt{x + 4}$, or $3.5x - 4.7$, will be evaluated at $x = 17$.

```
17→X
              17
X²
             289
-X²
            -289
■
```

APPENDIX 0B82: Calculation Keys—Includes a Fraction Function

To perform any arithmetic calculation, type it in, and press [ENTER] to calculate the answer.

Exponents may be entered in several ways. If you wish to square something, you can use the x^2 key. This is located in the left column of keys. To use it, enter the number to be squared, then press the $\boxed{x^2}$ and [ENTER].

What you enter:

What you see:

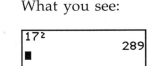

```
17²
             289
■
```

17 $\boxed{x^2}$ [ENTER]

There is also a special key for cubing a number (raising it to the third power). It is not found on any of the regular keys, but must be accessed by using a menu. First type the number or expression that you want to raise to the third power. Press the MATH key and you will see a screen like that at the right.

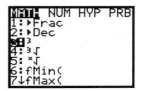

Then press 3 and an exponent 3 will appear next to your number. (You can also use the arrow keys to position the cursor on choice 3 and press \x(ENTER).) Press ENTER to calculate the answer.

You can also use the caret key, ∧, located in the right-hand column of keys, before any number, variable, or expression you want to enter as an exponent. Be sure to use parentheses around any exponent that involves more than just one number. For example, if there is a fraction in an exponent ($3^{2/3}$), type 3 ∧ (2/3).

What you enter: What you see:

2 ∧ 5 ENTER

```
2^5
           32
■
```

Example 3 in Section 2 asks that 0.275 be written as a fraction. The TI-82 contains a function that will make this conversion directly. Enter 0.275, and press MATH 1 (Frac), and the calculator will display $\frac{11}{40}$.

What you enter: What you see:

0.275 MATH 1 (Frac) ENTER

```
0.275▸Frac
          11/40
■
```

Editing/Replay: The replay, or last entry key (2nd [ENTRY]), reprints the previous entry on the screen. Then you can edit what's displayed on the screen by typing over, inserting (2nd [INS]), or deleting (DEL) to change the expression.

Storing a value for a variable: You can store specific values in each of the variable locations on your calculator. For example, 17 STO X ENTER assigns 17 as the temporarily value of x. Any expression containing the variable x, such as $x^2, -x^2, \sqrt{x+4}$, or $3.5x - 4.7$, will be evaluated at $x = 17$.

```
17→X
           17
X²
          289
-X²
         -289
■
```

APPENDIX 0B85: Calculation Keys—Includes a Fraction Function

To perform any arithmetic calculation, type it in, and press ENTER to calculate the answer.

Exponents may be entered in several ways. If you wish to square something, you can use the x^2 key. This is located in the left column of keys. To use it, enter the number to be squared, then press the x^2 ENTER.

What you enter: What you see:

```
17²
        289
■
```

17 x^2 ENTER

You can also use the caret key, $\wedge$, located in the right-hand column of keys, before any number, variable, or expression you want to enter as an exponent. Be sure to use parentheses around any exponent that involves more than just one number. For example, if there is a fraction in an exponent ($3^{2/3}$), type 3 $\wedge$ (2/3).

What you enter: What you see:

```
2^5
        32
■
```

2 $\wedge$ 5 ENTER

Example 3 in Section 2 asks that 0.275 be written as a fraction. The TI-85 contains a function that will make this conversion directly.

What you enter: What you see:

0.275 2nd [MATH] F5 (MISC) MORE F1 (FRAC) ENTER

```
0.275▶Frac
           11/40
```

Editing/Replay: The replay, or last entry key (2nd [ENTRY]), reprints the previous entry on the screen. Then you can edit what's displayed on the screen by typing over, inserting (2nd [INS]) or deleting (DEL), as you change the expression.

Storing a value for a variable: You can store specific values in each of the variable locations on your calculator. For example, 17 STO X ENTER assigns 17 as the temporarily value of x. Any expression containing the variable x such as $x^2, -x^2, \sqrt{x+4}, 3.5x - 4.7$ will be evaluated at $x = 17$.

```
17→X
        17
X²
        289
-X²
        -289
■
```

APPENDIX 0C80, 81, 82, 85: Scientific Notation

In Example 4, part a, the decimal point in the number 6,240,000 must move six places from the end of the number to the space between the 6 and the 2. Therefore, $6{,}240{,}000 = 6.24 \cdot 10^6$. Verify this by changing your calculator to scientific mode and entering the number 6240000. The calculator will display 6.24E6. (See **APPENDIX 0A** if you've forgotten how to change modes.)

In Example 4, part b, you must move the decimal point in the number 0.004819 three places to the right to the space between the 4 and the 8. Therefore, $0.004819 = 4.819 \cdot 10^{-3}$. Verify this by entering .004819 while your calculator is in scientific mode. The calculator will display 4.819E–3.

To convert from scientific notation to normal notation, reverse the above process. Sometimes you can verify the conversion with your calculator. Set your calculator in normal mode and enter the number $5.37 \cdot 10^3$ in scientific notation. (To enter a number in scientific notation, type in 5.37, and press EE followed by the exponent. You must press 2nd on the TI-80 and TI-82 before [EE].) The calculator displays the number in normal form, 5370. However, if your number has more digits than will fit on the display, the calculator will leave it in scientific notation.

APPENDIX 0D80: The Window Key

Press WINDOW to display the current settings for the window variables. For the coordinate axis at the right, the window values might be those shown on the screen below.

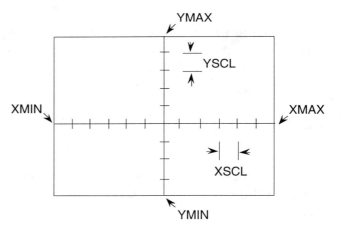

```
WINDOW
 XMIN=-6
 XMAX=6
 XSCL=1
 YMIN=-4
 YMAX=5
 YSCL=1
```

Changing the Window Settings

To change one of the values on this screen, use the arrow keys to position the cursor on the value to be changed, and type over the old value. When you finish changing these settings, press 2nd [QUIT].

Pressing Y= or another one of the top-row keys will also allow you to exit from the WINDOW screen.

When setting values for XMIN and XMAX or for YMIN and YMAX, be certain that the minimum value is less than the maximum value. If it isn't, an error message will appear. When choosing settings for XSCL and YSCL, choose values that will place tick marks far enough apart that they will be easy to distinguish. A value of 0 for either scale will place no marks on the axis. This is useful when you are just plotting points. (Otherwise, it can be difficult to distinguish the marks on the axis from the plotted points.)

The TI-80 table functions ([TblSet] and [TABLE]) will allow you to look at the coordinate pairs that will or should be pictured in a graphing window. If you have an equation in Y=, you can quickly investigate table values to help determine the correct graphing window. Using TblSet, you can determine the starting x-value (TblMin) and increment for x (ΔTbl) in your table. Press 2nd [TABLE] to see the table for the equation entered.

APPENDIX 0D81: The Range Key

Press the RANGE key to display the current settings for the Range variables. For the coordinate axis at the right, the window values might be those shown on the screen below.

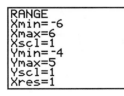

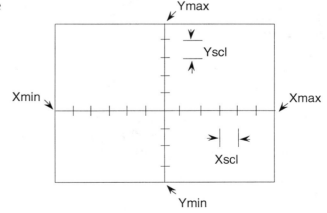

(Xres indicates the precision with which the calculator graphs an equation. Set Xres at 1, the most precise setting.)

Changing the Range Settings

To change one of the values on this screen, use the arrow keys to position the cursor on the value to be changed, and type over the old value. When you finish changing these settings, press 2nd [QUIT].

Pressing Y= , or another one of the top-row keys, will allow you to exit from the RANGE screen.

When setting values for Xmin and Xmax or for Ymin and Ymax, be certain that the minimum value is less than the maximum value. If it is not, an error message will appear. When choosing settings for Xscl and Yscl, choose values that will place tick marks far enough apart so that they will be easy to distinguish. A value of 0 for either scale will place no marks on the axis. This is useful when just plotting points. Otherwise, it can be difficult to distinguish the marks on the axis from the plotted points.

APPENDIX 0D82: The Window Key

Press WINDOW to display the current settings for the window variables. For the coordinate axis at the right, the window values might be those shown on the screen below.

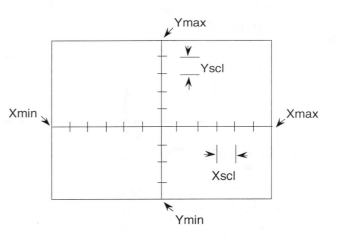

```
WINDOW FORMAT
 Xmin=-6
 Xmax=6
 Xscl=1
 Ymin=-4
 Ymax=5
 Yscl=1
```

Changing the Window Settings

To change one of the values on this screen, use the arrow keys to position the cursor on the value to be changed and type over the old value. When you finish changing these settings, press 2nd [QUIT].

Pressing $\boxed{\text{Y=}}$, or another one of the top-row keys, will allow you to exit from the WINDOW screen.

When setting values for Xmin and Xmax or for Ymin and Ymax, be certain that the minimum value is less than the maximum value. If it is not, an error message will appear. When choosing settings for Xscl and Yscl, choose values that will place tick marks far enough apart so that they will be easy to distinguish. A value of 0 for either scale will place no marks on the axis. This is useful when just plotting points. Otherwise, it can be difficult to distinguish the marks on the axis from the plotted points.

The TI-82 table functions ([TblSet] and [TABLE]) will allow you to look at the coordinate pairs that will or should be pictured in a graphing window. If you have an equation in $\boxed{\text{Y=}}$, you can quickly investigate table values to help determine the correct graphing window. Using TblSet, you can determine the starting x-value (TblMin) and increment for x (ΔTbl) in your table. Press $\boxed{\text{2nd}}$ [TABLE] to see the table for the equation entered.

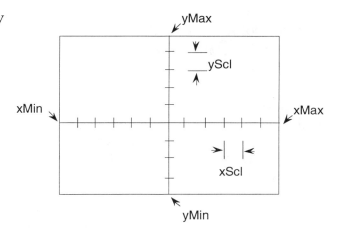

APPENDIX 0D85: The Range Key

Press $\boxed{\text{GRAPH}}$ $\boxed{\text{F2}}$ (RANGE) to display the current settings for the window variables. For the coordinate axis at the right, the window values might be those shown on the screen below.

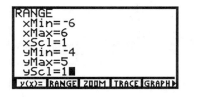

Changing the Range Settings

To change one of the values on this screen, use the arrow keys to position the cursor on the value to be changed, and type over the old value. When you finish changing these settings press EXIT .

Pressing F1 (Y =), or another one of the top-row keys, will allow you to exit from the Range screen.

When setting values for xMin and xMax or for yMin and yMax, be certain that the minimum value is less than the maximum value. If it is not, an error message will appear. When choosing settings for the scales, choose values that will place marks far enough apart so that they will be easy to distinguish. A value of 0 for either scale will place no marks on the axis. This is often handy when just plotting points. Otherwise, it can be difficult to distinguish the marks on the axis from the plotted points.

APPENDIX 0E80, 81, 82: The Absolute Value Function

The symbol for absolute value is $|an\ expression|$. The key on the calculator is labeled ABS , and it requires you to put the contents between the absolute value bars into parentheses, like ABS (*an expression*).

APPENDIX 0E85: The Absolute Value Function

The symbol for absolute value is $|an\ expression|$. It can be found in the 2nd [MATH] F1 (NUM) F5 (abs), and it requires you to put the contents between the absolute value bars into parentheses, like abs (*an expression*).

Commands like conversion to a fraction and absolute value are located several layers deep and it is time consuming to retrieve them even when you remember where they are. An option on the TI-85 is to create your own custom user menu and put such commands in an easy-to-access location. Press 2nd [CATALOG] then press F3 (CUSTOM). Since the little triangle is pointing at "abs", if you now press F1 it will become the first option on your custom menu. Now press Z or . and you will move to the end of the alphabet. Press and hold the down arrow until you locate the command

▶Frac. Press F2 to store this on the custom menu. Now press EXIT . Whenever you press CUSTOM these commands will be one keystroke away.

Chapter One Appendices

APPENDIX 1A80: Plotting Points

You can plot points on your calculator using the Pt-On(and 2nd [ENTRY] commands. Set the graphing window to [0, 7, 1, 0, 10, 1]. Press 2nd [DRAW] 0 (GRIDOFF) ENTER to turn the grid off.

Select 2nd [DRAW] POINTS 1 (Pt-On() and complete the command by entering the coordinates of your first point.

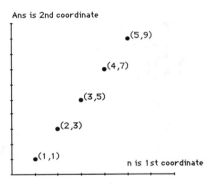

Pt-On(1,1) ENTER.

Press CLEAR to return to the HOME screen.

Press 2nd [ENTRY], and edit to get Pt-On(2,3).

Repeat until all points are plotted.

APPENDIX 1A81: Plotting Points

You can plot points on your calculator screen using the Pt-On(and Replay commands. Set the graphing window to [0, 7, 1, 0, 10, 1]. Select GRIDOFF in the MODE menu.

Select [2nd] [DRAW] [3] (Pt-On() and complete the command by entering the coordinates of your first point.

Pt-On(1,1) [ENTER]. (The comma is [ALPHA] [.])

Press [CLEAR] to return to the HOME screen.

Replay with the up arrow and edit to get Pt-On(2,3).

Repeat until all points are plotted.

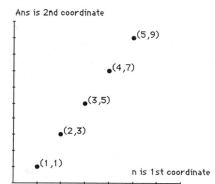

APPENDIX 1A82: Plotting Points

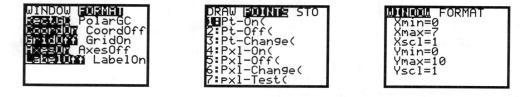

You can plot points on your calculator screen using the Pt-On(and [2nd] [ENTRY] commands. Set the graphing window to [0, 7, 1, 0, 10, 1]. Select GridOff in [WINDOW] FORMAT menu.

Select [2nd] [DRAW] POINTS [1] (Pt-On() and complete the command by entering the coordinates of your first point.

    Pt-On(1,1) and press [ENTER].

Press [CLEAR] to return to the HOME screen.

Press [2nd] [ENTRY], and edit to get Pt-On(2,3).

Repeat until all points are plotted.

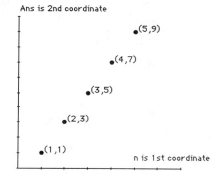

APPENDIX 1A85: Plotting Points

You can plot points on your calculator screen using the PtOn(command. Set the graphing window to [0, 7, 1, 0, 10, 1]. Press [GRAPH] [MORE] [F3] (FORMT) and select GridOff.

Press 2nd [CATALOG]. Select the PtOn(command and move it to F3 in your custom menu. Then enter the command and the coordinates for your first point.

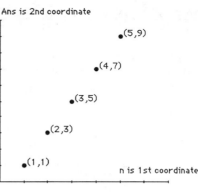

Ans is 2nd coordinate

PtOn(1,1) ENTER

Press CUSTOM F3 to return to the HOME screen.

Then press 2,3) to get PtOn(2,3).

Repeat until all points are plotted. Press CLEAR to remove the menu bar from the bottom of the screen.

APPENDIX 1B80: Scatter Plot Data Points:

The TI-80 STAT menu is the best choice for plotting points on the screen because the coordinates are stored in memory as a data set and can be replotted easily. Follow the procedure outlined below.

  i.   Clear Y= .

  ii. Enter the points as data.

      Type STAT 1 (EDIT).

      (If a list needs to be cleared, move the cursor on top of the list name and press CLEAR ENTER .)

      Enter the x-coordinates in L1 and the y-coordinates in L2.

  iii. Set the plot mode.

      Type 2nd [STAT PLOT] 1 (Plot 1 . . .).

      Select ON, (⋯), L1, L2, ▪.

  iv. Set the graphing window and press GRAPH .

You should see the points on the calculator screen. They can be replotted again when needed in a different graphing window by repeating step iv. Or the entire procedure can be repeated with new coordinates.

If you get a plot error, check to make sure that you have the same number of values in L1 as in L2. In order to stop the calculator from plotting this set of data forever, you will need to turn off the plot in the STAT PLOT menu. (Press 2nd [STATPLOT] 4 (PlotsOff).)

APPENDIX 1B81: Scatter Plot Data Points

The TI-81 STAT menu is the best choice for plotting points on the screen because the coordinates are stored in memory as a data set and can be replotted easily. Follow the procedure outlined below.

    i. Clear $\boxed{\text{Y=}}$.

    ii. Clear the data file.

         Press $\boxed{\text{2nd}}$ [STAT] DATA $\boxed{2}$ (ClrStat) $\boxed{\text{ENTER}}$.

```
ClrStat
          Done
■
```

    iii. Enter the points as data.

         Press $\boxed{\text{2nd}}$ [STAT] DATA $\boxed{1}$ (EDIT).

         Enter the (x, y) coordinates.

```
DATA
x1=■
y1=1
```

    iv. Set the graphing window.

    v. Make the scatter plot.

         Press $\boxed{\text{2nd}}$ [STAT] DRAW $\boxed{2}$ (Scatter) $\boxed{\text{ENTER}}$.

```
ClrStat
          Done
Scatter■
```

You should see the points on the calculator screen. They can be replotted again when needed in a different graphing window by repeating steps iv and v. Or the entire procedure can be repeated with new coordinates.

To change the points or add more points, go back to step iii to make corrections or additions to the list. To delete a point, move the cursor left over the equal sign of the point and press $\boxed{\text{DEL}}$.

Note: If you change your data and do not clear the screen (by changing some number in the range), then both the old points and the new points will appear. Simply type $\boxed{\text{2nd}}$ [DRAW] $\boxed{1}$ (ClrDraw) $\boxed{\text{ENTER}}$ and go to step v.

APPENDIX 1B82: Scatter Plot Data Points

The TI-82 STAT menu is the best choice for plotting points on the screen because the coordinates are stored in memory as a data set and can be replotted easily. Follow the procedure outlined below.

i. Clear $\boxed{Y=}$.

ii. Enter the points as data.

Type $\boxed{STAT}$ $\boxed{1}$ (EDIT).

(If a list needs to be cleared, move the cursor on top of the list name and press $\boxed{CLEAR}$ $\boxed{ENTER}$.)

Enter the *x*-coordinates in L1 and the *y*-coordinates in L2.

iii. Set the plot mode.

Press $\boxed{2nd}$ [STAT PLOT] $\boxed{1}$ (Plot 1 . . .).

Select ON, (⌐∵), L1, L2, ▫.

iv. Set the graphing window and press $\boxed{GRAPH}$.

You should see the points on the calculator screen. They can be replotted again when needed in a different graphing window by repeating step iv. Or the entire procedure can be repeated with new coordinates.

If you get a plot error, check to make sure that you have the same number of values in L1 as in L2. In order to stop the calculator from plotting this set of data forever, you will need to turn off the plot in the STAT PLOT menu. (Press $\boxed{2nd}$ [STATPLOT] $\boxed{4}$ (PlotsOff).)

APPENDIX 1B85: Scatter Plot Data Points

The TI-85 STAT menu is the best choice for plotting points on the screen because the coordinates are stored in memory as a data set and can be replotted easily. Follow the procedure outlined below.

i. Clear $\boxed{Y=}$.

ii. Enter the points as data.

Press $\boxed{STAT}$ $\boxed{F2}$ (EDIT) $\boxed{ENTER}$ $\boxed{ENTER}$.

(If a list needs to be cleared, press $\boxed{F5}$ (CLRxy).)

Enter the x- and y-coordinates of each data point.

iv. Set the graphing window.

v. Make the scatter plot.

Press $\boxed{STAT}$ $\boxed{F3}$ (DRAW).

Press $\boxed{F2}$ (Scatter).

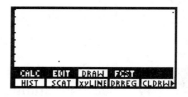

You should see the points on the calculator screen. They can be replotted again when needed in a different graphing window by repeating Steps iv and v. Or the entire procedure can be repeated with new coordinates.

APPENDIX 1C80: The Recursive Routine

The TI-80 is a hand-held computer. As with all computers, routines can be written or edited, stored, and executed when needed. Commands are entered from a menu. (For example, if you want the command END, you will find it in a menu. At times, in these appendices, you will find the TI-80 program printed exactly as you will see it on your calculator. At other times the program may be the same as one for another calculator, in which case the commands may look slightly different than what you see on your calculator screen. The TI-80 has only upper-case characters, so it is sometimes difficult to discern which are commands coming from some menu and which are variables which have been typed in. For example, L2 could be the variable L times 2, or it could be list 2 from the stat set. One is right and one is wrong. Typing a command with the alpha keys will mean something different to the calculator. You need to become familiar with the calculator commands. By pressing the $\boxed{PRGM}$ key when writing or editing a program, you can access many new commands. Below is the list of commands available on the TI-80.

As written here, the RECUR program will seed 3 as the starting term, generate exactly six terms, and display the results. The display can be a listing of the terms and/or points plotted. Include the blank line in your program. Enter the code in the left-hand column, the result in the right-hand column will be displayed on your calculator screen.

What you enter:

PRGM ▶ ▶ 1 RECUR ENTER

3 ENTER   ***

PGRM 4 ALPHA N , 1 , 6) ENTER

PGRM ▶ 1 2nd ANS ENTER

ENTER

2 2nd ANS ENTER   ***

PGRM 5 2nd QUIT   ***

What you see:

PROGRAM:RECUR

:3

:FOR(N,1,6)

:DISP ANS

:

:2ANS

:END

Following is an explanation of how the program works.

PROGRAM:RECUR

:3	Sets initial term at 3.
:FOR(N,1,6)	The sequence is u_1 to u_6.
:DISP ANS	Displays calculated terms.
:	A blank line.
:2ANS	The recursive routine.
:END	That's all folks!

Press PGRM 1 (RECUR) ENTER to execute the program. You will see the sequence 3, 6, 12, 24, 48, 96 displayed on the calculator screen, or you may get an error message if one or more of the commands have been entered incorrectly. The three lines marked *** will need to be altered when you work with a different sequence. Use PGRM EDIT 1 (RECUR) to edit and 2nd [QUIT] to save.

Later you can add PT-ON(N,ANS) in place of the blank line if you want to graph the points. (Be sure to define an appropriate graphing window.) The first point will have coordinates (1, seed value). This new command can take the place of the original blank line in the program. For real-world applications, you may prefer to see the original or initial value on the y-axis. If you change line 2 to :FOR(N,0,6), you will get the sequence $u_0, u_1, u_2, \ldots$.

APPENDIX 1C81: The Recursive Routine

The TI-81 is a hand-held computer. As with all computers, routines can be written or edited, stored, and executed when needed. The calculator stores many programs. Commands are entered from a menu. (For example, if you want the command Goto, you will find it in a menu.) Typing the word with the alpha keys will mean nothing to the calculator. By pressing the PRGM key when writing or editing a program, you can access many new commands. Here is the list of commands that are available on the TI-81.

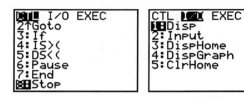

As written here, the RECUR program will seed 3 as the starting term, generate exactly six terms, and display the results. The display can be a listing of the terms and/or points plotted. Include the blank line in your program. Enter the code on the left-hand column, and you will see what's in the right-hand column displayed on your calculator screen.

What you enter:

PRGM ▸ 1 RECUR ENTER

1 STO N ENTER

3 ENTER ✳✳✳

PGRM 1 1 ENTER

PGRM ▸ 1 2nd Ans ENTER

ENTER

2 2nd Ans ENTER ✳✳✳

PGRM 4 ALPHA N ALPHA , 6) ENTER ✳✳✳

PGRM 2 1

2nd QUIT

What you see:

PRGM1:RECUR

:1→N

:3

:Lbl 1

:Disp Ans

:

:2Ans

:IS>(N,6)

:Goto 1

Here is an explanation of how the program works:

PRGM1:RECUR
:1→N	Starts the sequence at u_1.
:3	Sets $u_1 = 3$.
:Lbl 1	Establishes a loop.
:Disp Ans	Displays calculated terms.
:	A blank line.
:2Ans	The recursive routine.
:IS>(N,6)	Adds 1 to N (skips next line if N>6).
:Goto 1	Continues by looping to Lbl 1.

By pressing $\boxed{\text{PGRM}}$ $\boxed{1}$ (RECUR) $\boxed{\text{ENTER}}$ you can execute the program. You should see the sequence 3, 6, 12, 24, 48, 96 displayed on the calculator screen, or you may get an error message if one or more of the commands have been entered incorrectly. The loop defined by the pair of commands Lbl 1 and Goto 1 allows the display of several terms. The IS>(N,6) command adds 1 to the value of N, and if N is more than 6, the next program step is skipped.

The three lines marked with *** will need to be altered when you work with a different sequence. Press $\boxed{\text{PRGM}}$ EDIT $\boxed{1}$ (RECUR) to edit and $\boxed{\text{2nd}}$ [QUIT] to save.

Later you can add Pt-On(N,Ans) in place of the blank line to display the points in an appropriate graphing window. The first point will have coordinates (1, seed value). This new command can take the place of the original blank line in the program. For real-world applications, you may prefer to see the original or initial value on the y-axis. If you start with 0→N, this will produce $u_0, u_1, u_2, \ldots$.

APPENDIX 1C82: The Recursive Routine

With the TI-82 you have two choices. You can enter the short program below or you can use the built-in sequence mode. It is strongly recommended that you start by using the RECUR program, After you feel confident using this program, you may want to learn how to use the sequence mode.

One of the advantages of this program is that you can make all the settings in one place, rather than in three places. As with all computers, routines can be written or edited, stored, and executed when needed. Commands are entered from menus. (For example, if you want the command Disp, you will find it in a menu. Typing the word with the alpha keys will mean nothing.) Many new commands can be accessed while writing or editing a program by pressing the $\boxed{\text{PRGM}}$ key. Here is the listing of some commands that are available.

```
CTL I/O EXEC        CTL I/O EXEC        CTL I/O EXEC
1:If                8:Pause             1:Input
2:Then              9:Lbl               2:Prompt
3:Else              0:Goto              3:Disp
4:For(              A:IS>(              4:DispGraph
5:While             B:DS<(              5:DispTable
6:Repeat            C:Menu(             6:Output(
7↓End               D↓prgm              7↓getKey
```

As written here, the RECUR program will seed 3 as the starting term, generate exactly six terms, and display the results. The display can be a listing of the terms and/or points plotted. Include the blank line in your program. Enter the code on the left-hand column, and you will see what's in the right-hand column displayed on your calculator screen.

What you enter:	What you see:
PRGM ▶ ▶ 1 RECUR ENTER	PROGRAM:RECUR
3 ENTER	*** :3
PGRM 4 ALPHA N , 1 , 6) ENTER	*** :For(N,1,6)
PGRM ▶ 3 2nd Ans ENTER	:Disp Ans
ENTER	:
2 2nd Ans ENTER	*** :2Ans
PGRM 7 2nd QUIT	:End

Here is an explanation of how the program works:

PROGRAM: RECUR

:3	Sets initial term at 3.
:For(N,1,6)	The sequence is u_1 to u_6.
:Disp Ans	Displays calculated terms.
:	A blank line.
:2Ans	The recursive routine.
:End	That's all folks!

By pressing PGRM 1 (RECUR) ENTER you can execute the program. You should see the sequence 3, 6, 12, 24, 48, 96 displayed on the calculator screen, or you may get an error message if one or more of the commands have been entered incorrectly. The three lines marked with *** will need to be altered when you work with a different sequence. Use PRGM EDIT 1 (RECUR) to edit and 2nd [QUIT] to save.

Later you can add Pt-On(N,Ans) to display the points in an appropriate graphing window. The first point will have coordinates (1, seed value). This new command can take the place of the original blank line in the program. For real-world applications, you may prefer to see the original or initial value on the y-axis. If you start with For(N,0,6), this will produce u0, u1, u2, . . . u6.

The second alternative is to use the sequence mode.

Set the MODE menu to Seq, Dot and Simul. In Y= you will find that you can define two sequences, Un and Vn. To enter a recursive sequence use U$n-1$ in place of Ans, for example Un = 2U$n-1$

On the WINDOW screen, you must set a value for Ustart and *n*Start. For this example

UStart = 3   and *n*Start = 1

In 2nd [TblSet] use TblMin = 1,   ΔTbl = 1,
     Indpnt: Auto   Depend: Auto

```
WINDOW FORMAT
 Ustart=3
 Ustart=0
 nStart=1
 nMin=1
 nMax=6
 Xmin=0
↓Xmax=9.4
```

```
TABLE SETUP
 TblMin=1
 ▵Tbl=1
Indpnt: Auto  Ask
Depend: Auto  Ask
```

Now press 2nd [TABLE] to see the values. You may also set the dimensions of the graphing window and press GRAPH to see a discrete graph of the sequence. You will probably want to turn off any stat plots before you graph a sequence.

APPENDIX 1C85: The Recursive Routine

The TI-85 is a hand-held computer. As with all computers, routines can be written or edited, stored, and executed when needed. The calculator stores many programs. Commands maybe entered from a menu. (For example, if you want the command Goto, you will find it in a menu. You may also type the word with the alpha keys but spelling, spacing, and capitalization must be identical to the commands built in to the calculator. Many new commands can be accessed while writing or editing a program by pressing the PRGM key. Here is the listing of some commands that are available.

```
PAGE↓ PAGE↑  I/O    CTL   IN:>
 Input Promp  Disp  DispG  Outpt▶
 InpSt getKy  ClLCD PrtSc    "
```

```
PAGE↓ PAGE↑  I/O    CTL   IN:>
  If   Then  Else   For   End ▶
 While Repea  Menu   Lbl   Goto▶
  IS>   DS<  Pause  Retur  Stop
```

As written here, the RECUR program will seed 3 as the starting term, generate exactly six terms, and display the results. The display can be a listing of the terms and/or points plotted. Include the blank line in your program. Enter the code on the left-hand column, and you will see what's in the right-hand column displayed on your calculator screen. (To enter a word like RECUR, press 2nd [ALPHA] to "lock" the alpha mode. Unlock the alpha mode by pressing the 2nd key twice.

What you enter:	What you see:
	PROGRAM: RECUR

PRGM F2 RECUR ENTER   *** :3

3 ENTER   *** :For(N,1,6)

F4 F4 ALPHA N , 1 , 6) ENTER   :Disp Ans

2nd F3 F3 2nd Ans ENTER   :

ENTER

2 2nd Ans ENTER   *** :2Ans

2nd F4 F5   :End

2nd QUIT

Following is an explanation of how the program works.

PROGRAM: RECUR

:3	Sets initial term at 3.
:For(N,1,6)	The sequence is u_1 to u_6.
:Disp Ans	Displays calculated terms.
:	A blank line.
:2Ans	The recursive routine.
:End	That's all folks.

Press PGRM F1 (NAMES) F1 (RECUR) to execute the program. You should see the sequence 3, 6, 12, 24, 48, 96 displayed on the calculator screen, or you may get an error message if one or more of the commands have been entered incorrectly. The loop defined by the pair of commands For and End allows the display of several terms. The For(N,1,6) command adds 1 to the value of N, and if N is more than 6, the looping is stopped.

The three lines marked with *** will need to be altered when you work with a different sequence. Press PRGM F2 (EDIT) F1 (RECUR) to edit and 2nd [QUIT] to save.

Later you can add PTON(N,Ans) in place of the blank line to display the points in an appropriate graphing window. The first point will have coordinates (1, seed value). This new command can take the place of the original blank line in the program. For real-world applications, you may prefer to see the original or initial value on the y-axis. If you start with For(N,0,6), this will produce u0, u1, u2, . . . u6.

APPENDIX 1D80: The Series Routine

The SERIES program uses the variable U for term value, S for partial sum, and N for the number of the term. Enter the following program in your calculator.

What you enter:		What you see:
PRGM ▶ ▶ 1 SERIES ENTER		PROGRAM: SERIES
0 STO ALPHA S ENTER		:0->S
7 STO ALPHA U ENTER	***	:7->U
PGRM 4 ALPHA N, 1, 47) ENTER	***	:FOR(N,1,47)
ALPHA S+ ALPHA U STO ALPHA S ENTER		:S+U->S
PGRM ▶ 3 ALPHA N, ALPHA U, ALPHA S,		:DISP N,U,S," "
2nd ALPHA "" ENTER		:
ENTER	***	:U+3->U
ALPHA U + 3 STO ALPHA U ENTER		:END
PGRM 7 2nd QUIT		

The following steps explain how the SERIES program works.

PROGRAM: SERIES	
:0->S	Initializes the sum at 0.
:7->U	The first term is 7.
:FOR(N,1,47)	Establishes a loop for 47 terms.
:S+U->S	Computes the new sum (Old Sum + Term = New Sum).
:DISP N,U,S," "	Displays the number of the term, the value of the term, and the sum.
:	A blank line.
:U+3->U	Adds 3 to the term.
:END	

This program adds the first 47 terms of the series 7, 10, 13, 16, ... The lines marked with *** will need to be changed for another series. The blank line is for plotting the partial sums or slowing the program down so you can read the numbers. To plot the points, insert Pt-On(N,S). You can also insert a Pause command to slow down the display. Be sure to set the window before you run the program.

APPENDIX 1D81: The Series Routine

The SERIES program uses the variable u for term value, S for partial sum, and n for the number of the term. Enter the following program in your calculator.

What you enter:		What you see:
PRGM ▸ 2 SERIES ENTER		PRGM 2:SERIES
0 STO S ENTER		:0→S
1 STO N ENTER	***	:1→N
7 STO U ENTER	***	:7→U
PRGM 1 1 ENTER		:Lbl 1
PGRM ▸ 1 ALPHA U ENTER		:Disp U
ALPHA U + ALPHA S STO S ENTER		:U+S→S
PGRM ▸ 1 ALPHA " ALPHA " ENTER		:Disp S
PGRM ▸ 1 ENTER		:Disp " "
ENTER		:
ENTER		:
ALPHA U + 3 STO U ENTER		:U+3→U
PRGM 4 ALPHA N ALPHA , 47) ENTER	***	:IS>(N,47)
PRGM 2 1 ENTER		:Goto 1
2nd QUIT		

Here's how the SERIES program works:

PRGM 2:SERIES

:0→S	Initializes the sum at 0.
:1→N	Sets the term counter to 1.
:7→U	The first term is 7.
:Lbl 1	Marks the beginning of a loop.
:Disp U	Prints out the term value.
:U+S→S	Computes new sum (Term + Old Sum = New Sum).
:Disp S	Prints out the partial sum.
:Disp " "	Provides a blank line.
:	For later addition of Pt-On(N,U) or Pause.
:	For later addition of Pt-On(N,S) or Pause.
:U+3→U	For an arithmetic series (Old Term + d = New Term).
:IS>(N,47)	Provides first 47 terms & partial sums.
:Goto 1	As long as N ≤ 47.

This program adds the first 47 terms of the series 7, 10, 13, 16, ... The lines marked with *** will need to be changed for another series. The blank line is for plotting the partial sums or slowing the program down so you can read the numbers. To plot the points, insert Pt-On(N,S). You can also insert a Pause command to slow down the display. Be sure to set the window before you run the program.

APPENDIX 1D82: The Series Routine

There are a number of ways to sum a sequence on the TI-82. Some have limitations and some are a little abstract. One choice is to write a short program that has no limitation and follows the form that was presented in the text. Enter the commands in the left-hand column, and you should see what appears in the right-hand column.

What you enter:	What you see:
PRGM ▶ ▶ 1 SERIES ENTER	PROGRAM:SERIES
0 STO ALPHA S ENTER	:0→S
7 STO ALPHA U ENTER	*** :7→U
PGRM 4 ALPHA N , 1 , 47) ENTER	*** :For(N,1,47)
ALPHA S + ALPHA U STO ALPHA S ENTER	:S+U→S
PGRM ▶ 3 ALPHA N , ALPHA U , ALPHA S , 2nd ALPHA	
" " ENTER	:Disp N,U,S," "
ENTER	:
ALPHA U + 3 STO ALPHA U ENTER	*** :U+3→U
PGRM 7 2nd QUIT	:End

Here's how the SERIES program works:

PROGRAM:SERIES

:0→S	Initializes the sum at 0.
:7→U	The first term is 7.
:For(N,1,47)	Establishes a loop for 47 terms.
:S+U→S	Computes the new sum (Old Sum + Term = New Sum).
:Disp N,U,S," "	Displays the number of the term, the value of the term, and the sum.
:	A blank line.
:U+3→U	Adds 3 to the term.
:End	

This program adds the first 47 terms of 7, 10, 13, 16, ... The lines marked with *** will need to be changed for another series. The blank line is for plotting the partial sums or slowing the program down so you can read the numbers. To plot the points, insert Pt-On(N,S). You can also insert a Pause command to slow down the display. Be sure to set the window before you run the program.

As an alternative, if you are comfortable with the sequence mode, you can use this procedure. With the sequence defined in Un, define $Vn = Vn - 1 + Un - 1$. You know that $S_n = S_{(n-1)} + u_n$, not $u_{(n-1)}$, but the calculator will not let us define it that way because of the way that it evaluates sequences. So you have to remember that if you are looking for S_{100}, you need to find V_{101}. Be sure to set VnStart = 0 on the WINDOW screen.

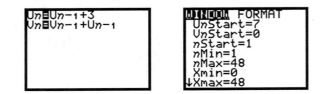

APPENDIX 1D85: The Series Routine

There are a number of ways to sum a sequence on the TI-85. Some have limitations and some are a little abstract. One choice is to write a short program that has no limitation and follows the form that was presented in the text. Type the commands in the left-hand column, and you should see the result in the right-hand column.

What you enter:

	What you see:
PRGM F2 SERIES ENTER	PROGRAM:SERIES
0 STO S ENTER	:0→S
7 STO U ENTER	*** :7→U
F4 F4 ALPHA N , 1 , 47) ENTER	*** :For(N,1,47)
ALPHA S + ALPHA U STO S ENTER	:S+U→S
2nd F3 F3 ALPHA N , ALPHA U , ALPHA S , MORE	
F5 F5 " " ENTER	:Disp N,U,S," "
ENTER	:
ALPHA U + 3 STO U ENTER	*** :U+3→U
2nd F4 F5 2nd QUIT	:End

Following is an explanation of how the SERIES program works.

```
PROGRAM:SERIES
```

`:0→S`	Initializes the sum at 0.
`:7→U`	The first term is 7.
`:For(N,1,47)`	Establishes a loop for 47 terms.
`:S+U→S`	Computes the new sum (Old Sum + Term = New Sum).
`:Disp N,U,S," "`	Displays the number of the term, the value of term, and the sum.
`:`	A blank line.
`:U+3→U`	Adds 3 to the term.
`:End`	

This program adds the first 47 terms of 7, 10, 13, 16, ... The lines marked with *** will need to be changed for another series. The blank line is for plotting the partial sums or slowing the program down so you can read the numbers. To plot the points, insert Pt-On(N,S). You can also insert a Pause command to slow down the display. Be sure to set the window before you run the program.

APPENDIX 1E80, 81, 82, 85: Gingerbread Man

These programs will iterate 500 points based on input values. The TI-81 version is on the left. The program on the right will work for the TI-80, TI-82 and TI-85 calculators. You may wish to clear the screen before you start some parts of the investigation. In the DRAW menu on the TI-81 and TI-82, select choice 1 to clear the drawings (ClrDraw). Enter this command on the HOME screen before running the program. For the TI-85 it is easiest to find this command (ClDrw) in the CATALOG.

```
Prgm2:GMAN
:Input A
:Input B
:0→K
:Lbl 1
:PT-On(A,B)
:1-B+abs A→N
:A→B
:N→A
:K+1→K
:IS>(K,500)
:Goto 1
```

```
Program:GMAN
Input A
Input B
For(K,1,500)
Pt-On(A,B)
1-B+abs A→N
A→B:N→A
End
```

APPENDIX 1F80, 81, 82, 85: Chaos Game

Set your window to [0, 10, 0, 0, 7, 0]. Then edit the stat set and enter the three vertices (1, 0.5), (8, 0.5), and (4.5, 6.5). This program will plot forever, so when you think it is complete you should press [ON] [2] (Quit). Press [GRAPH] to view the points that were plotted.

The program on the left is for the TI-81, the center one is for the TI-80 and TI-82, and the one on the right is for the TI-85.

```
Prgm3:CHAOS
:{x}(1)→A
:{y}(1)→B
:Lbl 1
:Int (3Rand+1)→P
:(A+{x}(P))/2→A
:(B+{y}(P))/2→B
:PT-On(A,B)
:Goto 1
```

```
Program:CHAOS
L₁(1)→A
L₂(1)→B
Lbl 1
int(3rand+1)→P
(A+L₁(P))/2→A
(B+L₂(P))/2→B
Pt-On(A,B)
Goto 1
```

```
Program:CHAOS
xStat(1)→A
yStat(1)→B
Lbl C
int(3rand+1)→P
(A+xStat(P))/2→A
(B+yStat(P))/2→B
PtOn(A,B)
Goto C
```

Chapter Two Appendices

APPENDIX 2A80: Explicit Series

(See **APPENDIX 2A82**.) Oftentimes, the appendix for the TI-80 will be the same as the one for the TI-82. If you don't see an appendix for the TI-80 listed first, look at the appendix for the TI-82.

APPENDIX 2A81: Explicit Series

This explicit version of the Series program sums the terms of a sequence.

Original SERIES program	Modified SERIES program for explicitly defined functions		
PRGM2:SERIES	PRGM2:SERIES		
:0→S	:0→S		
:1→N	:1→N		
:7→U		***	You no longer need to seed the sequence.
:Lbl 1	:Lbl 1		
	:5N–3→U	***	This should be an expression in terms of *n*.
:Disp U	:Disp U		
:U+S→S	:U+S→S		
:Disp S	:Disp S		
:Disp " "	:Disp " "		
:U+3→U	:		Add PT-On(N,Ans) for a graph.
:IS>(N,47)	:IS>(N,47)	***	Control the sequence length with the
:Goto 1	:Goto 1		second entry in the parenthesis.

This example will sum the first 47 terms of the sequence defined by $U_n = 5n - 3$.

APPENDIX 2A80, 82: Explicit Formulas

To use the series program to sum a sequence defined explicitly you no longer need to seed the starting value, but you do need to move the formula before the summing command. The program below will sum the first 47 terms of the sequence defined by $Un = 5n - 3$.

Original SERIES program	Modified SERIES program for explicitly defined functions		
PROGRAM:SERIES :0→S :7→U :For(N,1,47) :S+U→S :Disp N,U,S," " :U+3→U :End	PROGRAM:SERIES :0→S : :For(N,1,47) :5N-3→U :S+U→S :Disp N,U,S," " :End	* * * * * *	You no longer need to seed the sequence. This should be an expression in terms of *n*.

On the TI-82, you can also use the sequence mode of the calculator to evaluate and plot explicit formulas. Enter the equation into Y= in terms of *n* (2nd 9). You must also calculate the starting term, and input it in the WINDOW values as Ustart or Vstart. Set the rest of the window values and press GRAPH. Be sure you are in DOT mode.

APPENDIX 2A85: Explicit Formulas

To use the series program to sum a sequence defined explicitly you no longer need to seed the starting value, but you do need to move the formula before the summing command. The program below will sum the first 47 terms of the sequence defined by $Un = 5n - 3$.

Original SERIES program	Modified SERIES program for explicitly defined functions		
PROGRAM:SERIES :0→S :7→U :For(N,1,47) :S+U→S :Disp N,U,S," " :U+3→U :End	PROGRAM:SERIES :0→S : :For(N,1,47) :5N-3→U :S+U→S :Disp N,U,S," " :End	* * * * * *	You no longer need to seed the sequence. This should be an expression in terms of *n*.

Chapter Three Appendices

APPENDIX 3A80: Entering 1-Variable Data

Six lists of one-variable data can be stored in the TI-80 using the following procedure. Each list can hold up to 99 data values. With this calculator, frequently there are several different methods to accomplish the same result.

EXAMPLE: Enter the list 25, 67, 38, 47, 55, 37, 49, 31, 41, 38 in the calculator.

Press [STAT] [1] (Edit).

(If a list needs to be cleared, move the cursor on top of the list name and press [CLEAR] [ENTER].)

Enter the data starting with L1(1). After entering each data value, press [ENTER].

When finished, press [2nd] [QUIT].

APPENDIX 3A81: Entering 1-Variable Data

The TI-81 will store one set of one-variable data.

EXAMPLE: Enter the list 25, 67, 38, 47, 55, 37, 49, 31, 41, 38 in the calculator.

i. Clear the data file.

    Press [2nd] [STAT] DATA [2] (ClrStat) [ENTER].

ii. Enter the data values.

    Press [2nd] [STAT] DATA [1] (Edit).

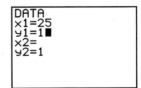

Enter each number in the list as an x-value. Press [ENTER] after each entry accepting 1 for the y-value. (The y-value tells you how many of each x-value there are.) Keep going. When you're finished entering the data, press [2nd] [QUIT].

Your list should look like the following:

$x1 = 25$	$x3 = 38$	$x5 = 55$	$x7 = 49$	$x9 = 41$	$x11 =$
$y1 = 1$	$y3 = 1$	$y5 = 1$	$y7 = 1$	$y9 = 1$	$y11 = 1$
$x2 = 67$	$x4 = 47$	$x6 = 37$	$x8 = 31$	$x10 = 38$	
$y2 = 1$	$y4 = 1$	$y6 = 1$	$y8 = 1$	$y10 = 1$	

APPENDIX 3A82: Entering 1-Variable Data

Six lists of one-variable data can be stored in the TI-82 using the following procedure. Each list can hold up to 99 data values. With this calculator, frequently there are several different methods to accomplish the same result.

EXAMPLE: Enter the list 25, 67, 38, 47, 55, 37, 49, 31, 41, 38 in the calculator.

Press $\boxed{\text{STAT}}$ $\boxed{1}$ (Edit).

(If a list needs to be cleared, move the cursor on top of the list name and press $\boxed{\text{CLEAR}}$ $\boxed{\text{ENTER}}$.)

Enter the data starting with L1(1). After entering each data value, press $\boxed{\text{ENTER}}$.

When finished, press $\boxed{\text{2nd}}$ [QUIT].

APPENDIX 3A85: Entering 1-Variable Data

Lists of one-variable data can be stored in the TI-85 using the following procedure. The working set of data is called xStat and yStat. Usually data is entered into these lists and analyzed. If you wish to keep the data for later use, you can store these lists using a name of your choice. With this calculator frequently there are several different methods to accomplish the same result.

EXAMPLE: Enter the list 25, 67, 38, 47, 55, 37, 49, 31, 41, 38 in the calculator.

Press $\boxed{\text{STAT}}$ $\boxed{\text{F2}}$ (Edit)$\boxed{\text{ENTER}}$ $\boxed{\text{ENTER}}$.

(If the list needs to be cleared, press $\boxed{\text{F5}}$.)

Enter the data starting with x_1. After entering each data value, press $\boxed{\text{ENTER}}$. Accept 1 for the y-value by pressing $\boxed{\text{ENTER}}$. (The y-value tells you how many of each x-value there are.) Keep going. When finished, press $\boxed{\text{2nd}}$ [QUIT].

APPENDIX 3B81: Finding the Median and the Mean

To find the median, use the sorting feature of the calculator. (This appendix uses the same data list as given in **APPENDIX 3A**.)

Press $\boxed{\text{2nd}}$ [STAT] DATA $\boxed{3}$ (xSort) $\boxed{\text{ENTER}}$.

The calculator will say DONE. Look at the list of data again. Data will now be in order of increasing x-values.

$x1 = 25$	$x4 = 38$	$x7 = 47$	$x10 = 67$
$y1 = 1$	$y4 = 1$	$y7 = 1$	$y10 = 1$
$x2 = 31$	$x5 = 38$	$x8 = 49$	$x11 =$
$y2 = 1$	$y5 = 1$	$y8 = 1$	$y11 = 1$
$x3 = 37$	$x6 = 41$	$x9 = 55$	
$y3 = 1$	$y6 = 1$	$y9 = 1$	

```
xSort
                    Done
■
```

If there are an odd number of values, the median will be the middle number in the list. In this example there are 10 values so the median will be the mean of the 5th and 6th values, or 39.5.

The mean of the stored data can be found by the following command sequence.

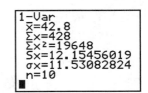

```
1-Var
x̄=42.8
Σx=428
Σx²=19648
Sx=12.15456019
σx=11.53082824
n=10
■
```

Press $\boxed{\text{2nd}}$ [STAT] CALC $\boxed{1}$ (1–Var) $\boxed{\text{ENTER}}$.

In addition, several other values will be displayed.

$\bar{x} = 42.8$	the **mean**
$\Sigma x = 428$	the sum of the x-values
$\Sigma x^2 = 19648$	the sum of the squares of the x-values
$Sx = 12.15456019$	the sample standard deviation
$\sigma x = 11.53082824$	the population standard deviation
$n = 10$	the number of data values

APPENDIX 3B80, 82: Finding the Median and the Mean

Both the TI-80 and the TI-82 will automatically calculate the median and mean of a data set. The command below assumes that you have stored the data in L1, but you can replace L1 with any of the lists L2 through L6. (This appendix uses the same data list as given in **APPENDIX 3A**.)

Press 2nd [STAT] CALC 1 (1–Var) 2nd [L1] ENTER.

A list of values will be displayed.

$\bar{x} = 42.8$	the **mean**
$\sum x = 428$	the sum of the x-values
$\sum x^2 = 19648$	the sum of the squares of the x-values
$Sx = 12.15456019$	the sample standard deviation
$\sigma x = 11.53082824$	the population standard deviation
$n = 10$	the number of data values

Arrow down in the display to find the **median** listed as Med = 39.5.

Another alternative for finding the median is to sort the list, and look for the middle value(s). You can sort a list in ascending order using the following command.

Press STAT EDIT 2 (SortA) 2nd [L1] ENTER.

The median will be the middle number in the list, or if there are an even number of values, the median will be the average of the two middle values. (If you choose 3 (SortD) instead of 2, you can sort the list in descending order.)

An alternative method for finding the mean of a data set is to use the following command, which employs the definition of the mean.

Press 2nd [LIST] MATH 5 (Sum) 2nd [L1] ENTER.

The calculator display will show the sum of the list. Divide this answer by the number of data values, n, to get the mean.

APPENDIX 3B85: Finding the Median and the Mean

To find the median, use the sorting feature of the calculator. The command below assumes that you have stored the data in xStat, but you can replace xStat with the name of any list. (This appendix uses the same data list as given in **APPENDIX 3A**.)

Press $\boxed{\text{STAT}}$ $\boxed{\text{EDIT}}$ (CALC) $\boxed{\text{ENTER}}$ $\boxed{\text{ENTER}}$ $\boxed{\text{F3}}$ (SORTX).

If there are an odd number of values, the median will be the middle number in the list. In this example there are 10 values so the median will be the mean of the 5th and 6th values, or 39.5.

You can find the mean of a stored list using this command. Again the calculator is assuming the list you're interested in is stored in xStat.

Press $\boxed{\text{STAT}}$ $\boxed{\text{F1}}$ (CALC) $\boxed{\text{ENTER}}$ $\boxed{\text{ENTER}}$ $\boxed{\text{F1}}$ (1-Var Stats).

A list of values will be displayed.

$\bar{x} = 42.8$	the **mean**
$\sum x = 428$	the sum of the x-values
$\sum x^2 = 19648$	the sum of the squares of the x-values
$Sx = 12.15456019$	the sample standard deviation
$\sigma x = 11.53082824$	the population standard deviation
$n = 10$	the number of data values

An alternative method for finding the mean of a data set, is to use the following command, which employs the definition of the mean.

Press $\boxed{\text{2nd}}$ [LIST] $\boxed{\text{F5}}$ (OPS) $\boxed{\text{MORE}}$ $\boxed{\text{F1}}$ (Sum) $\boxed{\text{2nd}}$ $\boxed{\text{F3}}$ (NAMES) $\boxed{\text{F?}}$ (xStat).

The calculator display will show the sum of the list. Divide this answer by the number of data values, n, to get the mean.

APPENDIX 3C81: Creating a Box Plot

The TI-81 will not graph a box plot unless you enter a program, and to enter the program may be too complicated or time-consuming (because you probably have not had the experience necessary at this point in the course to do this efficiently.) If this is the case, then graph all box plots on graph paper.

This optional program (It is not required!) will create up to three simple box plots on the TI-81. The data for each plot must be entered into the x-values of the STAT menu. Keep each y-value at 1. If you want to make more than one box plot, enter the data for the first data set, and run the program. Then clear the first data set, enter the second data set, and run the program. Do this process again if you have another data set.

Set the graphing window before running the program. The Xmin and Xmax values are the only important window values. A Ymin value of zero works well because it eliminates the x-axis, which may interfere with the box plot. The plots will always be the same height regardless of the 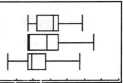 Ymax value. If you wish to change the window, even if you have already graphed one or more of the box plots, simply press GRAPH . The five-point summary is stored in matrix [A] for all three box plots. Press TRACE and read the five-point summary (minimum, first quartile, median, third quartile, and maximum) from the x-values. Just ignore the y-value on the trace.

```
PrgmB:BOXPLOTS
:Dim{x}→N
:3→ARow
:5→ACol
:Disp "PLOT 1,2, OR 3"
:Input P
:(N+1)/2→A
:Int (A+.6)/2→B
:xSort
:Function
:"({x}(Int X)+{x}(-Int -X))/2"→Y₁
:A→X
:Y₁→[A](P,3)
:B→X
:Y₁→[A](P,2)
:N-B→X
:Y₁→[A](P,4)
:{x}(1)→[A](P,1)
```

```
:{x}(N)→[A](P,5)
:Param
:Connected
:Simul
:-5.5→Tmin
:5.5→Tmax
:.5→Tstep
:"[A](1,abs IPart T+(IPart
    T=0))"→X₁ₜ
:"Ymax/4+.1Ymax((abs T=1)+(abs
    T=2.5)+(abs T=3)-(abs T=3.5)-(abs
    T=4)+(abs T=5.5))T/abs T"→Y₁ₜ
:"[A](2,abs IPart T+(IPart
    T=0))"→X₂ₜ
:"Ymax/4+Y₁ₜ"→Y₂ₜ
:"[A](3,abs IPart T+(IPart
    T=0))"→X₃ₜ
:"Ymax/2+Y₁ₜ"→Y₃ₜ
:DispGraph
```

APPENDIX 3C80, 82: Creating a Box Plot

Assuming a set of data has been entered in a list, up to three box plots can be drawn. Clear any equations in the Y= menu. Then set the graphing window values appropriately so that Xmin to Xmax will contain the entire range of values in the list or lists. The Ymin and Ymax values are not important because they have no effect on the height of the graph. However, you may want to set Ymin = 0 so that the x-axis doesn't interfere with the display. It is assumed that the data in L1 will be plotted, but you can select any of the six lists.

Press [2nd] [STAT PLOTS] [1] (Plot1 . . .).

Select On, Box plot, L1, 1.

Press [GRAPH].

The TRACE option allows you to see the five summary values for the box plot as you arrow left and right. If you press the up and down arrows, you can move from one box plot to another. The trace option will always start with the Stat Plots and then the Y= menu. It is a good idea to turn off any plots you aren't interested in seeing in the current graphing window.

APPENDIX 3C85: Creating a Box Plot

The TI-85 will not graph a box plot unless you enter a program, and to enter the program may be too complicated or time-consuming because you probably have not had the experience necessary at this point in the course to do this efficiently. If this is the case, then graph all box plots on graph paper.

This optional program (It is not required!) will create up to three simple box plots on the TI-85. The data for each plot must be entered into the xStat list. Keep each y-value at 1. If you want to make more than one box plot, enter the data for the first data set, and run the program. Then clear the first data set, enter the second data set, and run the program. Do this process again if you have another data set.

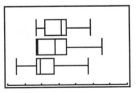

The five-point summary is stored in matrix BP for all three box plots. Press [TRACE] and read the five-point summary (minimum, first quartile, median, third quartile, and maximum) from the x-values. Just ignore the y-values on the trace.

```
PROGRAM:BOX
Disp "Enter 0 to initialize"
Lbl TOP
Input "Plot 1,2, or 3? ",D
If D:Then
dimL xStat→N
Sortx xStat,yStat
(N+1)/2→A
int (A+.6)/2→B
N-B+1→C
[xStat(1),(xStat(int B)+xStat(-int
  -B))/2,(xStat(int A)+xStat(-int
  -A))/2,(xStat(int C)+xStat(-int
  -C))/2,xStat(N)]→BP(D)
OneVar xStat
ClLCD
Disp x̄
Disp sum (abs (xStat-x̄))/N
Disp σx
Disp BP(D,3)
Disp BP(D,4)-BP(D,2)
Disp BP(D)
Outpt(1,1,"mean")
Outpt(2,1,"m.a.d.")
Outpt(3,1,"std dev")
Outpt(4,1,"median")
Outpt(5,1,"IQR")
PARAM
RcGDB BPGDB
.1+1/max({1/(BP(1,1)-.1),1/(BP(2,1)-
  .1),1/(BP(3,1)-.1)})→xMin
max({BP(1,5),BP(2,5),BP(3,5)})→xMax
DispG
Else
Disp "done"
0randM(3,5)→BP
Goto TOP
```

Enter the equations and the range given below, and save as a graph data base. To do this, press GRAPH MORE F4 BPGDB. You have to do this before you run the program.

```
BPGDB          Graph Database
   (Parametric)
xt1 = BP(1, int abs t + (int abs t
   ==0))
yt1 = yMax/4+.1yMax((abs t
   ==5.5)+(abs t==4)+(abs t==3.5)-
   (abs t==3)-(abs t==5.5)+(abs
   t==1))sign t
xt2 = BP(2,int abs t+(int abs t==0)
yt2 = yt1+yMax/4
xt3 = BP(3,int abs t+(int abs t==0)
yt3 = yt2+yMax/4
```

Ranges
```
tMin = -5.5
tMax = 5.5
tStep = .5
xMin = 0
xMax = 90
yMin = 0
yMax = 10
yScl = 2.5
```

Format Settings
```
RectGC
CoordOn
DrawLine
SeqG
GridOff
AxesOn
LabelOff
```

APPENDIX 3D81: Finding the Mean Absolute Deviation.

Rather than calculate the mean absolute deviation (MAD) value by hand, you may choose to enter this program to automate the calculations.

In this program, J will count the values in the stat set and S will hold the sum. The key line is line 5. The command `:Abs(⟨x⟩⟨J⟩-x̄⟩)→D` will give you a list of deviations. In instances where you use y-values as frequencies (greater than one), it will multiply a deviation by its corresponding y-value and add the product to the sum of the mean absolute deviations in line 6. The mean is calculated in line 9 when this sum is divided by the number of data values.

```
PrgmA:MAD
:1-Var
:0→S
:1→J
:Lbl 1
:Abs(⟨x⟩⟨J⟩-x̄⟩)→D
:S+⟨y⟩⟨J⟩D→S
:IS>⟨J,n⟩
:Goto 1
:S/n→M
:Disp M
```

APPENDIX 3D80, 82: Finding the Mean Absolute Deviation

There are several ways to calculate the mean absolute deviation (MAD) value. On the LIST screen you can create new lists based on other lists. Many of the commands used here are found in the LIST menus (above the STAT key). To create a list of deviations of L1 in L2, move the cursor on top of L2, and enter the command, L1−mean(L1). To create a list of absolute deviations enter abs(L1−mean(L1)) for L2 and press ENTER.

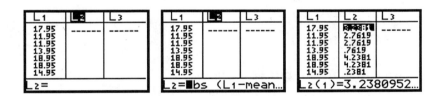

Return to the HOME screen to find the mean of L2. Here are three options.

1. Press 2nd [LIST] MATH 3 (mean) 2nd [L2] ENTER.

2. Press STAT CALC 1 (1-Var Stats) 2nd [L2] ENTER.

3. Press 2nd [LIST] MATH 5 (sum) (2nd [ABS] (2nd [L1] − 2nd [LIST] MATH 3 (mean) 2nd [L1])) ÷ 2nd [LIST] 3 (dim) 2nd [L1] ENTER.

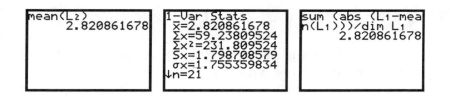

APPENDIX 3D85: Finding the Mean Absolute Deviation

You can create a list of the deviations or of the absolute value of the deviations. First do a one-variable analysis on the data. Then on the HOME screen, store the differences between the *x*-values and the mean to a list called DEV. Now find the mean of that list.

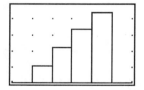

APPENDIX 3E81: Creating a Histogram

After a set of data has been entered, set the RANGE values appropriately. The value of Xscl determines the width of the histogram bars. The data values in the bars contain the left endpoint, but not the right endpoint. This means that you will sometimes need to extend your range one bar-width beyond what you think it should be. For example, in drawing a histogram to represent toothpaste tube size, 6.0 oz will be part of the bar in the 6.0–6.5 interval rather than 5.5–6.0 interval. Warning: You will get an error message if you try to create a histogram with more than 40 intervals. Experiment with different values for Xscl to see what effect they have on the graph.

Press 2nd [STAT] DRAW 1 (Hist) ENTER.

You will not be able to trace the graph, but you can approximate the frequencies in each bar by moving around the screen with the arrow keys. It may be possible to fix the values of Ymin and Ymax so that the numbers are "friendlier."

You can use the second coordinate of the data pairs to indicate frequencies other than one. In the example below, *y*3=83 means there were 83 times when a total of 4 was rolled with the two dice.

$x1 = 2$	$x2 = 3$	$x3 = 4$	$x4 = 5$
$y1 = 26$	$y2 = 56$	$y3 = 83$	$y4 = 110$

APPENDIX 3E80, 82: Creating a Histogram

After a set of data has been entered, set the window values appropriately. The value of Xscl determines the width of the histogram bars. The data values in the bars contain the left endpoint and up to, but not including, the right endpoint. This means that you will sometimes need to extend your range one bar-width beyond what you think it should be. For example, in drawing a histogram to represent toothpaste tube size, 6.0 oz will be part of the bar in the 6.0–6.5 interval rather than 5.5–6.0 interval. Warning: You will get an error message if you try to create a histogram with more than 40 intervals. Experiment with different values for Xscl to see what effect they have on the graph.

Press $\boxed{\text{2nd}}$ [STATPLOT] $\boxed{1}$ (Plot1 . . .).

Select On, Histogram, L1, 1.

Press $\boxed{\text{GRAPH}}$.

The trace option will always start with the STAT menu and then the Y= menu. *It is a good idea to turn off* any plots you aren't interested in seeing in the current graphing window.

You can use a second list to indicate frequencies other than one. In the example below, L2(3) = 83 means there were 83 times when a total of 4 was rolled with the two die. Set the Frequency in $\boxed{\text{STATPLOTS}}$ to L2.

APPENDIX 3E85: Creating a Histogram

After a set of data has been entered, set the $\boxed{\text{RANGE}}$ values appropriately. The value of xScl determines the width of the histogram bars. The data values in the bars contain the left endpoint and up to, but not including, the right endpoint. This means that you will sometimes need to extend your range one bar-width beyond what you think it should be. For example, in drawing a histogram to represent toothpaste tube size, 6.0 oz will be part of the bar in the 6.0–6.5 interval rather than 5.5–6.0 interval. Warning: You will get an error message if you try to create a histogram with more than 60 intervals. Experiment with different values for Xscl to see what effect they have on the graph.

Press $\boxed{\text{STAT}}$ $\boxed{\text{F3}}$ (DRAW) $\boxed{\text{F1}}$ (HIST) $\boxed{\text{CLEAR}}$.

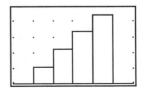

You will not be able to trace the graph, but you can get an approximation for the frequencies in each bar by moving around the screen with the arrow keys. It may be possible to fix the values of yMin and yMax so that the numbers are friendlier.

You can use the second coordinate of the data pairs to indicate frequencies other than one. In the example below, $y3 = 83$ means there were 83 times when a total of 4 was rolled on the two dice.

$x1 = 2$	$x2 = 3$	$x3 = 4$	$x4 = 5$
$y1 = 26$	$y2 = 56$	$y3 = 83$	$y4 = 110$

Chapter Four Appendices

APPENDIX 4A81: Plotting Data

Clear or turn off all functions in Y= . Select Grid Off in the MODE menu.

1. Clear any old data. Press 2nd [STAT] DATA 2 (ClrStat) ENTER .

2. Press 2nd [STAT] 1 (EDIT) to enter the data.

3. Input appropriate window values in the RANGE menu.

4. Press 2nd [STAT] DRAW 2 (Scatter) ENTER to plot the points.

APPENDIX 4A80, 82: Plotting Data

Clear or turn off all functions in Y= . Select GridOff in the WINDOW FORMAT menu. The calculator should be set in Func mode.

1. Press STAT 1 (EDIT) to enter the data. Decide which two of the six lists you will use for storing your data.

2. Clear any old data from these lists. (If a list needs to be cleared, move the cursor on top of the list name and press CLEAR ENTER .) Then enter the data in the chosen lists.

3. To display the data, press 2nd [STATPLOT] and choose one of the three plots. Then position the cursor over On and press ENTER . Next choose the type of plot. In this chapter you will want the first type, a scatter plot. Then highlight the list that holds the x-values and the list that holds the y-values. Finally choose a mark type to indicate the data points.

4. Input appropriate window values on the WINDOW screen.

5. Press GRAPH to display the data points.

APPENDIX 4A85: Plotting Data

Clear or turn off all functions in Y= . Select GridOff in the FORMT menu.

1. Input appropriate window values in the RANGE menu.
2. Press STAT F2 (EDIT) ENTER ENTER to locate the lists.
3. Press F5 (CLRxy) to clear any old data.
4. Enter the data.
5. Press STAT F3 (DRAW) F2 (Scatter) to plot the points.

APPENDIX 4B81: Plotting an Equation and Data

To add the graph of an equation to data presently displayed, use DrawF and type the equation. Then press ENTER (not GRAPH). This will draw the graph over the points.

To graph an equation and data simultaneously, enter the equation into Y= . Then plot the data as in **APPENDIX 4A**. This will draw the points over the graph.

Example: Graph the line $y = 1.3x + 12$ with the data (2, 14.7), (6, 19.1), and (9, 24.2).

What you enter:

2nd [DRAW] 6 1.3 X|T + 12 ENTER

---or---

Y= 1.3 X|T + 12

2nd [STAT] 2 ENTER

What you see:

DrawF 1.3X+12

:Y1=1.3X+12

Scatter

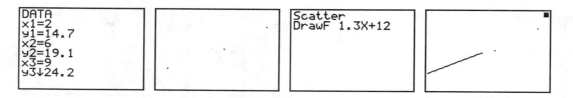

APPENDIX 4B80, 82: Plotting an Equation and Data

To add the graph of an equation to data presently displayed, simply enter it in the Y= menu and press GRAPH . When you press TRACE , you will first be tracing on the data set. Press the down arrow to trace the equation. Note the label in the upper right corner of the screen. The labels P1, P2, and P3 indicate that you are tracing a data plot. The labels 1, 2, 3, . . . (without the P) indicate that you are tracing one of the functions.

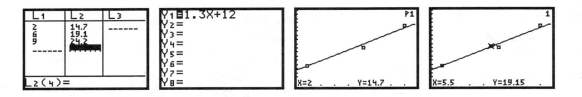

APPENDIX 4B85: Plotting an Equation and Data

To add the graph of an equation to data presently displayed, use DrawF and type the equation. Then press ENTER (not GRAPH). This will draw the graph over the points.

To graph an equation and data simultaneously, enter the equation into Y= . Then plot the data as in **APPENDIX 4A**. This will draw the points over the graph.

Example: Graph the line $y = 1.3x + 12$ with the data (2, 14.7), (6, 19.1), and (9, 24.2).

What you enter:	What you see:
STAT F3 (DRAW) MORE F1 1.3 x-VAR + 12 ENTER	DrawF 1.3x+12

---or---

GRAPH F1 (Y=) 1.3 x-VAR + 12	:y1=1.3x+12
STAT F3 (DRAW) F2 (SCAT)	Scatter

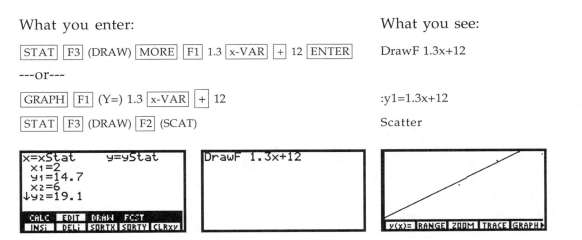

APPENDIX 4C80: The Median-Median Line

You can program the calculator to determine the equation of the median-median line. First you must enter the data. When the program is executed it will store the three summary points in (Q, R), (S, T), and (U, V). It will also overwrite any equations you have in Y1 and Y2. This is a long program, and because you should also know how to do this procedure by hand, you will have to decide if you want to enter the program.

```
PROGRAM:MEDMED
DISP "DATA IN L1,L2"
DIM L1->N
ROUND(N/3,0)->C
C+1->D
N-C+1->E
SORTA(L1,L2)
MAX(L2)->M
"(L1(INT X)+L1(-INT-X))/2"->Y1
"(L6(INT X)+L6(-INT-X))/2"->Y2
L2->L6
FOR(J,D,N)
L6(J)+M->L6(J)
END
FOR(J,E,N)
L6(J)+M->L6(J)
```

```
END
SORTA(L6)
Y1(D/2)->Q
Y2(D/2)->R
Y1((D+E-1)/2)->S
Y2((D+E-1)/2)-M->T
Y1((N+E)/2)->U
Y2((N+E)/2)-2M->V
(U-R)/(U-Q)->A
R-AQ->G:T-AS->H
(2G+H)/3->B
"AX+B"->Y1
""->Y2
DISP "MEDIAN-MEDIAN"
DISP "SLOPE",A
DISP "Y-INTERCEPT",B
```

APPENDIX 4C81: The Median-Median Line

You can program the calculator to find the equation of the median-median line. First you must enter the data. When the program is executed it will store the three summary points in (Q, R), (S, T), and (U, V). It will also overwrite any equation in Y_1. This is a long program, and because you should also know how to do this procedure by hand, you will have to decide if you want to enter the program.

```
PrgmM:MEDMED            :D→J                   :K-2→K
:Dim{x}→N               :Lbl 2                 :DS<((K,-1)
:Round(N/3,0)→C         :K+K(J=E)→K            :Goto 1
:C+1→D                  :{y}(J)+MK→{y}(J)      :(U-R)/(U-Q)→A
:N-C+1→E                :IS>(J,N)              :R-AQ→G
:ySort                  :Goto 2                :T-AS→H
:{y}(N)→M               :D/2→X                 :(2G+H)/3→B
:xSort                  :Y₁→R                  :"AX+B"→Y₁
:"({x}(Int X)+{x}(-     :(D+E-1)/2→X           :Disp "MEDIAN-MEDIAN"
    Int -X))/2"→Y₁      :Y₁→T                  :Disp A
:1→K                    :(N+E)/2→X             :Disp B
:Lbl 1                  :Y₁→U
:R→Q                    :"({y}(Int X)+{y}(-
:T→S                        Int -X))/2"→Y₁
:U→U                    :ySort
```

This program does not handle the special case where multiple data points with the same x-value occur at the boundary of a grouping. The procedure states that data points with the same x-value should not be split up, so this program will not give the correct answer. As this situation happens only rarely, and requires an even longer program, we have chosen to leave it out. If you need to deal with data sets with repeating x-values, you can insert a command above the ninth line (:1→K) that calls a subprogram :PrgmN and enter the following code.

```
PrgmN:SUBMED           :J+1→J                 :Goto 3
:{x}(D)→X              :If {x}(J)=X           :J→E
:D→C                   :Goto 2                :Lbl 4
:0→J                   :If C-D>J-1-C          :J+1→J
:Lbl 1                 :J-1→D                 :If {x}(J)=X
:J+1→J                 :{x}(E)→X              :Goto 4
:If {x}(J)<X           :E→C                   :If C-E>J-1-C
:Goto 1                :Lbl 3                 :J-1→E
:J→D                   :J+1→J
:Lbl 2                 :If {x}(J)<X
```

APPENDIX 4C82: The Median-Median Line

The calculator will automatically determine the equation of the median-median line. With the *x*-values in L1 and the *y*-values in L2, the steps are as follows:

Press ⎡STAT⎤ CALC ⎡4⎤ (Med-Med) ⎡2nd⎤ [L1] ⎡,⎤ ⎡2nd⎤ [L2].

The calculator will display the equation form and the values for the slope and *y*-intercept.

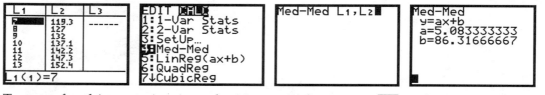

To transfer this equation into the Y= menu first press ⎡Y=⎤ and move to an open equation (or clear one). Then press ⎡VARS⎤ ⎡5⎤ (Statistics) EQ ⎡7⎤ (ReqEQ).

APPENDIX 4C85: The Median-Median Line

You can program the calculator to find the equation of the median-median line. First you must enter the data. When the program is executed it will store the three summary points in (Q, R), (S, T), and (U, V). It will also overwrite any equation in y1. This is a long program, and because you should also know how to do this procedure by hand, you will have to decide if you want to enter the program.

```
Program:MedMed
Disp "data in xStat, yStat"
dimL xStat→N
round(N/3,0)→C
N+1-C→G
While xStat(C)==xStat(C+1)
C+1→C:End
While xStat(G)==xStat(G-1)
G-1→G:End
(C+1)/2→D:(C+G)/2→E
(G+N)/2→F:Sortx
max(yStat)→M
MEDX=(xStat(int x)+xStat(-int
-x))/2
MEDY=(YPLUS(int x)+YPLUS(-int
-x))/2
```

```
yStat→YPLUS
For(J,C+1,N)
YPLUS(J)+M+M(J)N-C)→YPLUS(J):End
sortA YPLUS→YPLUS
D→x:MEDX→Q:MEDY→R
E→x:MEDX→S:MEDY-M→T
F→x:MEDX→U:MEDY-2M→U
(U-R)/(U-Q)→A
R-A*Q→G:T-A*S→H
(2G+H)/3→B
y1=A*x+B
Disp "Median-median line"
Disp "slope",A
Disp "y-intercept",B
```

APPENDIX 4D81: Residuals

This program has been provided because the TI-81 does not have a built-in function to find the residuals. It will plot the residuals of the data stored in the data set compared to the function in Y1 and store the largest positive and negative residual values in Ymax and Ymin. It will also store the sum of the residuals in the variable T. Enter the program into one of the program slots in your calculator.

You could use PT-Chg in place of PT-On if you want to see points on the *x*-axis. In order to replot the original data, you must first restore the range values and SCATTER the data. There is another program that may save you time while setting ranges. (See **APPENDIX 4G**.)

```
PrgmR:RESIDUAL
:0→T
:1→J
:0→Ymin
:0→Ymax
:Lbl 1
:{x}(J)→X
:{y}(J)-Y₁→Y
:Y+T→T
:If Ymin>Y
:Y→Ymin
:If Ymax<Y
:Y→Ymax
:IS>(J,Dim{x})
:Goto 1
:Disp T
:AllOff
:1→J
:Lbl 2
:{x}(J)→X
:PT-On(X,{y}(J)-Y₁)
:IS>(J,Dim{x})
:Goto 2
```

APPENDIX 4D80, 82: Residuals

You can create a third list that contains the residuals for each point. Position the cursor on the name of the list. Subtract the function containing the best-fit line from the list of *y*-values.

Example: Suppose the *x*-values are in L1, the *y*-values are in L2, and the best-fit line is in Y1. Enter the residuals in L3 by placing the cursor on the L3 at the top of the list and entering L2–Y1(L1).

[2nd] [L2] [–] [2nd] [Y-vars] [1] (Function) [1] (Y1) [(] [2nd] [L1] [)] [ENTER]

The residuals for each point will be displayed in the new list. To graph the residuals plot, choose L1 as the *x*-list and L3 as the *y*-list. Set an appropriate window and turn the function off in [Y=] before you graph. See **APPENDIX 4G** for assistance in setting the window quickly.

This is a procedure that you will repeat often. A short program automates these steps. This program will not work for the TI-80 because the TI-80 has no ZoomStat command. You can only use this program if the data and equations are stored in the given locations. Otherwise, you must change the program.

You can create a third list which contains the residuals for each point. This list will be the difference between the function containing the best-fit line and the list of y-values.

```
:Disp "X VALUES IN L1"
:Disp "Y VALUES IN L2"
:Disp "EQUATION IN Y1"
:Pause
:L2-Y1(L1)→L3
:Plot1(Scatter,L1,L3,▫)
:PlotsOn1
:FnOff
:ZoomStat
:DispGraph
```

APPENDIX 4D85: Residuals

Example: Suppose the x-values are in xStat and the y-values are in yStat and the best-fit line is in y1. Enter the residuals in a list called RESID by entering the command, xStat→x:yStat – y1→RESID.

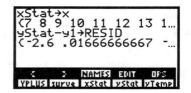

The residuals for each point will be stored in the new list. To graph the residuals, plot xStat as the x-list and RESID as the y-list. Set an appropriate window and deselect the function before you graph. See **APPENDIX G** for assistance in setting the window quickly.

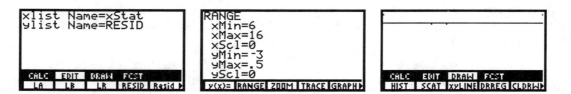

APPENDIX 4E80: Finding and Graphing the Least-Squares Line

The data set should be entered as in **APPENDIX 4A**. To calculate the least-squares line, press ⌐STAT⌐ CALC.

There are two choices for the linear regression or least-squares line. Either choice 3 or choice 5 will work. In choice 3, the slope is named *a* and the *y*-intercept is named *b*. In choice 5, the *y*-intercept is named *a* and the slope is named *b*. In order to be consistent with some of the other regressions which you will study later in the book, and also to be consistent with other calculator models, it is recommended that you use choice 5. The third number displayed is the coefficient of correlation, *r*.

After choosing the type of regression, enter the two list names separated by a comma. Be sure to enter the *x*-list first.

Press [2nd] [STAT] CALC [5] (LinReg) [2nd] [L1] [,] [2nd] [L2].

   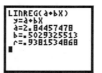

To transfer this equation into the Y= menu, first press [Y=] and move to an open equation (or clear one). Then press [VARS] [2] (STATISTICS) EQ [5] (REGEQ).

APPENDIX 4E81: Finding and Graphing the Least-Squares Line

The data set should be entered as in **APPENDIX 4A**. When the calculator performs the linear regression it will display three figures. The first is the intercept of the line (*a*), the second is the slope of the line (*b*), and the third is the coefficient of correlation (*r*). You may then add the least-squares line to the graph by either of the two methods given in **APPENDIX 4B**. The equation can be entered directly from the LR menu in the VARS menu. Once the data is entered, use the following instructions.

What you enter:	What you see:
[2nd] [STAT] [2] [ENTER]	LinReg
	a=###########
	b=###########
	r=###########
[2nd] [DRAW] [6] [VARS] [▶] [▶] 4 [ENTER]	DrawF ########+########X
---or---	
[Y=] [VARS] [▶] [▶] 4	:Y₁=########+########X
[2nd] [STAT] [▶] 2 [ENTER]	Scatter

APPENDIX 4E82: Finding and Graphing the Least-Squares Line

The data set should be entered as in **APPENDIX 4A**. To calculate the least squares line, press $\boxed{\text{STAT}}$ CALC.

There are two choices for the linear regression (or least-squares) line. Either choice 5 or choice 9 will work. In choice 5, the slope is named a and the y-intercept is named b. In choice 9, the y-intercept is named a and the slope is named b. In order to be consistent with some of the other regressions which you will study later in the book, and also to be consistent with other calculator models, it is recommended that you use choice 9. The third number displayed is the coefficient of correlation, r.

After choosing the type of regression, enter the two lists separated by a comma. Be sure to enter the x-list first. Press $\boxed{9}$ (LinReg) $\boxed{\text{2nd}}$ [L1] $\boxed{,}$ $\boxed{\text{2nd}}$ [L2].

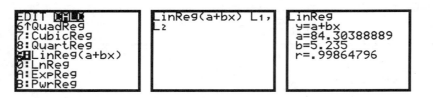

See **APPENDIX 4C**, which explains how to enter and graph the equation.

APPENDIX 4E85: Finding and Graphing the Least-Squares Line

The data set should be entered as in **APPENDIX 4A**. When the calculator performs the linear regression it will display three values. The first is the y-intercept of the line (a), the second is the slope of the line (b), and the third is the coefficient of correlation (r). You can add the least-squares line to the graph of the data points by either of the two methods given in **APPENDIX 4B**, or by pressing $\boxed{\text{STAT}}$ $\boxed{\text{F3}}$ (DRAW) $\boxed{\text{F4}}$ (DRREG). The equation can also be entered directly from the CALC menu in the STAT menu. Once the data is entered, use the following instructions.

What you enter:

$\boxed{\text{STAT}}$ $\boxed{\text{F1}}$ $\boxed{\text{ENTER}}$ $\boxed{\text{ENTER}}$ $\boxed{\text{F2}}$

$\boxed{\text{MORE}}$ $\boxed{\text{F4}}$ $\boxed{\text{2nd}}$ $\boxed{\text{ALPHA}}$ $\boxed{y}$ $\boxed{\text{ALPHA}}$ $\boxed{\text{ALPHA}}$ 1 $\boxed{\text{ENTER}}$

$\boxed{\text{2nd}}$ $\boxed{\text{F3}}$ $\boxed{\text{F2}}$

What you see:

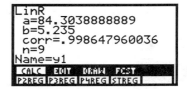

APPENDIX 4F81: Accuracy Measure, Mean Absolute Residual

The mean absolute residual can be calculated with the residual program. You will need to change one line and insert another line.

Replace the eighth line (:Y+T→T) of your residual program with :abs Y + T → T. This line will sum the absolute values of the residuals. Then insert the line T/Dim{x} → T before Disp T to calculate the mean of the absolute values of the residuals.

APPENDIX 4F80, 82: Accuracy Measure, Mean Absolute Residual

If the residuals have been calculated (See **APPENDIX D**) and are in list L3, then the mean absolute residual can be readily determined on the HOME screen with the command mean(abs L3). Press [2nd] [LIST] MATH [3] (MEAN) [2nd] [ABS] [2nd] [L3].

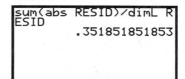

```
a=84.30388889
b=5.235
r=.99864796

mean(abs L₃)
        .3518518519
■
```

APPENDIX 4F85: Accuracy Measure, Mean Absolute Residual

If the residuals have been calculated (See **APPENDIX D**) and are in list RESID, then the mean absolute residual can be readily determined on the HOME screen using the command sum (abs RESID)/dimL RESID.

```
sum(abs RESID)/dimL R
ESID
        .351851851853
```

APPENDIX 4G80: Automating the Window Setting

By choosing ④ (ZDECIMAL) from the ZOOM menu, you will get the basic "friendly" graphing window dimensions for the TI-80. Zooming out or in will maintain the "friendly" nature of the window. The calculator is preset to multiply or divide the range by a factor of 4. To change this factor, you can store a new value into XFACT, YFACT, or both. They are located in choices 9 and 0 after pressing VARS ① (WINDOW). Now select ZOOM ③ (ZOOM OUT) and press ENTER.

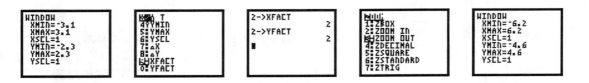

This program will create a window that will fit the data stored in L1 and L2.

```
PROGRAM:ZSTAT                    (MAX(L2)-MIN(L2))/20->X
(MAX(L1)-MIN(L1))/20->X          MIN(L2)-X->YMIN
MIN(L1)-X->XMIN                  MAX(L2)+X->YMAX
MAX(L1)+X->XMAX                  DISPGRAPH
```

APPENDIX 4G81: Automating the Window Setting

This program will automate many chores that you do regularly when dealing with the window. Choice 1 will set the graphing window to a size that gives "friendly" x-values for tracing. Choice 2 will scale the window to 10% larger than the current data set in every direction. Choice 3 and choice 4 will save and return a range. This whole program can be used before and after zooming or plotting residuals.

```
Pr9m7:RANGER           :Lbl 1                 : {x}(1)-W→Xmin
:Disp "1. FRIENDLY"    :Disp "FACTOR"         : {x}(N)+W→Xmax
:Disp "2. AUTO"        :Input X               :End
:Disp "3. KEEP"        : -4.8X→Xmin           :Lbl 3
:Disp "4. RESTORE"     :4.7X→Xmax             :6→Crow
:Input C               : -3.2X→Ymin           :Xmin→[C](1,1)
:If C=1                :3.1X→Ymax             :Xmax→[C](2,1)
:Goto 1                :End                   :Ymin→[C](4,1)
:If C=2                :Lbl 2                  :Ymax→[C](5,1)
:Goto 2                :ySort                  :End
:If C=3                :Dim{x}→N              :Lbl 4
:Goto 3                :({y}(N)-{y}(1))/20→W  [C](1,1)→Xmin
:if C=4                :{y}(1)-W→Ymin         [C](2,1)→Xmax
:Goto 4                :{y}(N)+W→Ymax         [C](4,1)→Ymin
:End                   :xSort                 [C](5,1)→Ymax
                       :({x}(N)-{x}(1))/20→W  :End
```

APPENDIX 4G82: Automating the Window Setting

By choosing 4 (ZDecimal) from the ZOOM menu, you will get the basic "friendly" graphing window dimensions for the TI-82. Zooming out or in will maintain the "friendly" nature of the window. The calculator is preset to multiply or divide the range by a factor of 4. To change this factor, press ZOOM MEMORY 4 (SetFactors). Enter the new factors here. Now select ZOOM 3 (Zoom Out) and press ENTER.

Using ZOOM 9 (ZoomStat) will automatically adjust the window dimensions to be slightly larger than the data that is to be plotted. If you have no data plots turned on, then the calculator will return an error or ignore your command. If you have more than one data plot turned on, ZoomStat will make the window large enough to fit all of them.

A specific setting of window dimensions can be saved for later use by pressing ZOOM MEMORY 2 (ZoomSto) after setting the desired window. To return to this setting later, simply press ZOOM MEMORY 3 (ZoomRcl).

APPENDIX 4G85: Automating the Window Setting

The basic "friendly" graphing window dimensions for the TI-85 can be obtained by entering GRAPH F3 (ZOOM) MORE F4 (ZDECM). This window makes the cursor move in increments of 0.1 units both horizontally and vertically. But because the pixels on this screen are not square, circles will appear more like ellipses. If you follow the above command with F2 (ZSQR), you can "square-up" these dimensions and correct the perspective of your graph.

This program will automate many chores that you do regularly when dealing with two-variable data. Choice 1 will plot the data as small squares in the current window. Choice 2 will scale the window to 10% larger than the current data set in every direction, then plot the data as in choice 1. Choice 3 will calculate the residuals of xStat and yStat based on y1, and choice 4 is useful to remove old plots from the screen before drawing.

```
Program:S1
ClLCD
Disp "Data in xStat, yStat"
Disp "F1-plot data-your range"
Disp "F2-set range for data"
Disp "F3-plot y1 residuals"
Disp "give sum and MAR"
Disp "F4-clear screen"
Disp "F5-to graph menu"
Lbl S:yStat→yTemp
Menu(1,"Plot",P,2,"Zoom",Z,3,"Resid",
    R,4,"Clear",C,5,"Quit",Q)
Lbl R:xStat→x
yStat-y1→Resid
Resid→yStat:ClLCD
Disp "Residuals":Fix 7
Disp "Range ",(min(yStat),max(yStat))
Disp "Sum ",sum (yStat)
Disp "M.A.D. ",sum (abs yStat)/dimL
    yStat
Float
```

```
Lbl Z:min(xStat)→mx:max(xStat)→Mx
min(yStat)→my:max(yStat)→My
(Mx-mx)/20+Mx→xMax
mx-(Mx-mx)/20→xMin
(My-my)/40+My→yMax
my-(My-my)/7→yMin
Lbl C:ClDrw
Lbl P
(xMax-xMin)/127→Dx
(yMax-yMin)/62→Dy
Scatter (xStat-Dx,yStat-Dy)
Scatter (xStat,yStat-Dy)
Scatter (xStat+Dx,yStat-Dy)
Scatter (xStat-Dx,yStat)
Scatter (xStat+Dx,yStat)
Scatter (xStat-Dx,yStat+Dy)
Scatter (xStat,yStat+Dy)
Scatter (xStat+Dx,yStat+Dy)
yTemp→yStat:Goto S
Lbl Q
```

Chapter Five Appendices

APPENDIX 5A80: "Friendly" Graphing Windows

By choosing 4 (ZDECIMAL) from the ZOOM menu, you will get the basic "friendly" graphing window dimensions for the TI-80. Zooming out or in will maintain the "friendly" nature of the window. The calculator is preset to multiply or divide the range by a factor of 4. To change this factor you can store a new value into XFACT, YFACT, or both. They are located in choices 9 and 0 after pressing VARS 1 (WINDOW). Now select ZOOM 3 (ZOOM OUT) and press ENTER.

  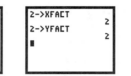

APPENDIX 5A81: "Friendly" Graphing Windows

Below is a **RANGE PROGRAM** to establish a "friendly" graphing window. Range commands like Xmin can be found in the RNG submenu of the VARS menu.

Execute the program and respond with a factor choice. The graphing window values will be [−4.8F, 4.7F, 1, −3.2F, 3.1F, 1].

```
PRGM?:RANGE
:Disp "FACTOR"
:Input F
: -4.8F→Xmin
:4.7F→Xmax
:1→Xscl
: -3.2F→Ymin
:3.1F→Ymax
:1→Yscl
```

APPENDIX 5A82: "Friendly" Graphing Windows

To get a "friendly" graphing window with a zoom factor of 1, press ZOOM 4 (ZDecimal). To get a zoom factor of 2, first set the window to [−9.4, 9.4, 1, −6.2, 6.2, 1]. Then press ZOOM (MEMORY) 2 (ZoomSto). Now each time you want this window enter ZOOM (MEMORY) 3 (ZoomRcl).

.APPENDIX 5A85: "Friendly" Graphing Windows

The basic "friendly" graphing window dimensions for the TI-85 can be obtained by entering GRAPH F3 (ZOOM) MORE F4 (ZDECM). This window makes the cursor move in increments of 0.1 units both horizontally and vertically. But because the pixels on this screen are not square, circles will appear more like ellipses. If you follow the above command with F2 (ZSQR), you can "square-up" these dimensions and correct the perspective of your graph.

APPENDIX 5B80: Lines Program

Set the graphing window at [-6.2, 6.2, 1, -4.6, 4.6, 1]. The program, LINES, will draw a random line for you to match. The program writes the target equation in symbolic form in Y4 and draws a graph that contains two points with integer coordinates. Write your equation for the graph in Y1 and graph it. If you have a match, you can run the program again. Otherwise, rewrite Y1 and graph it again.

```
PROGRAM:LINES
:GRIDON                    Find in 2nd [DRAW] 0 .
:FNOFF 1,2,3               Find in Y-Vars On/Off... .
:"(A/C)X+E"->Y4            Be certain to enter the quote marks.
:RANDINT(-6,6)->A          RANDINT is in the MATH PRB menu.
:RANDINT(1,10)->C
:RANDINT(-6,6)->E
:DISPGRAPH                 Find this in the PRGM I/O commands.
```

APPENDIX 5B81: Lines Program

Set the graphing window at [-9.6, 9.4, 1, -6.4, 6.2, 1]. The program, LINES, will draw a random line for you to match. The program writes the target equation in symbolic form in Y4 and draws a graph that contains two points with integer coordinates. Write your equation for the graph in Y1 and graph it. If you have a match, you can run the program again. Otherwise, rewrite Y1 and graph it again.

```
PRGM?:LINES
:All-Off                   Find this in the Y-VARS menu.
:"(A/C)X+E"→Y₄             Be certain to enter the quote marks.
:Int 13Rand-6→A            Int is in the MATH NUM menu. Rand is in the MATH PRB menu.
:Int 9Rand+1→C
:Int 13Rand-6→E
:DispGraph                 Find this in the PRGM I/O commands.
```

APPENDIX 5B82: Lines Program

Set the graphing window at [⁻9.4, 9.4, 1, ⁻6.2, 6.2, 1]. The program, LINES, will draw a random line for you to match. The program writes the target equation in symbolic form in Y4 and draws a graph that contains two points with integer coordinates. Write your equation for the graph in Y1 and graph it. If you have a match, you can run the program again. Otherwise, rewrite Y1 and graph it again.

```
Program:LINES
:FnOff 1,2,3          Find in Y-Vars On/Off... .
:"(A/C)X+E"→Y4        Be certain to enter the quote marks.
:int 13rand-6→A       Int is in the MATH NUM menu. Rand is in the MATH PRB menu.
:int 9rand+1→C
:int 13rand-6→E
:DispGraph            Find this in the PRGM I/O commands.
```

APPENDIX 5B85: Lines Program

Set the graphing window at [-12.6, 12.6, 1, -7.4, 7.4, 1]. The program, LINES, will draw a random line for you to match. The program writes the target equation in symbolic form in y4 and draws a graph that contains two points with integral coordinates. Write your equation for the graph in y1 and graph it. If you have a match, you can run the program again. Otherwise, rewrite y1 and graph it again.

```
Program:LINES
:FnOff                To find this, press GRAPH F1 (Vars) MORE MORE .
:y4=(A/C)x+E          Be certain to enter lower case x and y.
:int 13rand-6→A       Int is in the MATH NUM menu. Rand is in the MATH PROB menu.
:int 9rand+1→C
:int 13rand-6→E
:DispG                Find this in the PRGM I/O commands.
```

APPENDIX 5C80: Parabola Program

The PARABOLA program will generate a simple parabolic graph. Enter your choice for its equation in Y1 in the form $y = a(x - h)^2 + k$. The program is written for the "friendly" graphing window [−6.2, 6.2, 1, −4.6, 4.6, 1] and will be easier to use with the grid turned on. Press TRACE to see integer coordinate values to help you determine the equation.

```
PRORGAM:PARABOLA
:FNOFF
:"A(X-H)²+K"->Y4
:(-1)^RANDINT(0,1)->A
:RANDINT(-5,5)->H
:RANDINT(-3,3)->K
:DISPGRAPH
```

APPENDIX 5C81: Parabola Program

The PARABOLA program will generate a simple parabolic graph. Enter your choice for its equation in Y1 in the form $y = a(x - h)^2 + k$. The program is written for the "friendly" graphing window [−9.6, 9.4, 1, −6.4, 6.2, 1] and will be easier to use with the grid turned on. Press TRACE to see integral coordinate values to help you determine the equation.

```
PRGM?:PARABOLA
:All-Off
:"A(X-H)²+K"→Y₄
:(-1)^(Int 2Rand)→A
:Int 12Rand-6→H
:Int 8Rand-4→K
:DispGraph
```

APPENDIX 5C82: Parabola Program

The PARABOLA program will generate a simple parabolic graph. Enter your choice for its equation in Y1 in the form $y = a(x - h)^2 + k$. The program is written for the "friendly" graphing window [−9.4, 9.4, 1, −6.2, 6.2, 1] and will be easier to use with the grid turned on. Press TRACE to see integral coordinate values to help you determine the equation.

```
Program:PARABOLA
:FnOff
:"A(X-H)²+K"→Y₄
:(-1)^(int 2rand)→A
:int 12rand-6→H
:int 8rand-4→K
:DispGraph
```

APPENDIX 5C85: Parabola Program

The PARABOLA program will generate a simple parabolic graph. Enter your choice for its equation in Y1 in the form $y = a(x - h)^2 + k$. The program is written for the "friendly" graphing window [-12.6, 12.6, 1, -7.4, 7.4, 1] and will be easier to use with the grid turned on. Press TRACE to see integral coordinate values to help you determine the equation.

```
Program:PARABOLA
:FnOff
:y4=A(x-H)²+K
:(-1)^(int 2rand)→A
:int 12rand-6→H
:int 8rand-4→K
:DispG
```

APPENDIX 5D80, 81, 82, 85: Average-Value Program

This program expects the equation to be in Y1. The lower value must be less than the upper value. The width should be a small value. The smaller the value the greater the accuracy and the slower the speed.

TI-80

```
PROGRAM:AVEVAL
:INPUT "LOWER VALUE ",A
:INPUT "UPPER VALUE ",B
:INPUT "WIDTH ",D
:A->X:0->S
:FOR(N,0,(B-A)/D)
:S+Y1->S
:X+D->X
:END
:S/N->M
:DISP "AVERAGE VALUE",M
```

TI-81

```
Prgm3:AVEVAL
:Disp "LOWER VALUE"
:Input A
:Disp "UPPER VALUE"
:Input B
:Disp "WIDTH"
:Input D
:A→X
:0→S
:0→N
:Lbl 1
:S+Y1→S
:N+1→N
:X+D→X
:If X≤B
:Goto 1
:S/N→M
:Disp "AVERAGE VALUE"
:Disp M
```

TI-82, TI-85

```
Program:AVEVAL
Input "LOWER VALUE ",A
Input "UPPER VALUE ",B
Input "WIDTH ",D
A→X:0→S:0→N
Repeat X>B
S+Y1→S
N+1→N:X+D→X
End
S/N→M
Disp "AVERAGE VALUE",M
```

(Note: For TI-85 use lowercase x and y in the program.)

APPENDIX 5E81: Compositions of Functions

If Y1 = x^2, then you can write Y2 = Y1 + 3 to slide a graph up, or Y3 = 3Y1 to stretch the graph by a factor of 3. This often provides a quick way to write a new function based on a previous function. In effect, Y2 = x^2 + 3 and Y3 = $3x^2$. The TI-81 does not allow you to slide a graph left or right as suggested by $f(x + 4)$.

APPENDIX 5E80, 82: Compositions of Functions

If Y1 = x^2, then you can write Y2 = Y1 + 3 to slide a graph up, or Y3 = 3Y1 to stretch the graph by a factor of 3. This often provides a quick way to write a new function based on a previous function. In effect, Y2 = x^2 + 3 and Y3 = $3x^2$. The TI-82 allows you to slide a graph left or right. For example, Y4 = 3Y1(x + 4) + 3 provides the same results as $3f(x + 4) + 3$ for any defined equation, Y1 = $f(x)$.

APPENDIX 5E85: Compositions of Functions

If y1 = x^2, then you can write y2 = y1 + 3 to slide a graph up, or y3 = 3y1 to stretch the graph by a factor of 3. This often provides a quick way to write a new function based on a previous function. In effect y2 = x^2 + 3 and y3 = $3x^2$. The TI-85 does not allow you to slide a graph left or right as suggested by $f(x + 4)$.

APPENDIX 5F80: Web Graphs

Be sure your calculator is in FUNC mode, and enter the equation for the web graph in Y1. You should set the graphing window before running the program. When you execute the program, it will request a seed value for x. The display will alternate between the graph and the x-values.

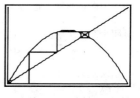

The values are stored in the data set for later reference. For example, with Y1 = $2.8x(1 - x)$, window values of [0, 1, 0, 0, 1, 0], and a seed value of 0.12, the calculator should produce the graph at the right.

```
PROGRAM:WEB
"X"->Y4                          LINE(X,B,X,A)
INPUT "SEED VALUE:",A            A->L1(J)
{A}->L1                          A->B:PAUSE
0->B:DISPGRAPH                   DISP A:PAUSE
FOR(J,1,94)                      LINE(X,A,A,A)
A->X:Y1->A                       END
```

APPENDIX 5F81: Web Graphs

Be sure your calculator is in Function mode, and enter the equation for the web graph in Y1. You should set the graphing window before running the program. When you execute the program, it will request a seed value for x. The display will alternate between the graph and the x-values.

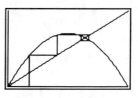

The values are stored in the data set for later reference. For example, with Y1 = $2.8x(1 - x)$, window values of [0, 1, 0, 0, 1, 0], and a seed value of 0.12, the calculator should produce the graph at the right.

```
Prgm8:WEB
:"X"→Y4            :0→K              :A→{y}(J)         :Line(X,A,A,A)
:Disp "SEED VALUE" :DispGraph        :If K=0           :Pause
:Input A           :Lbl 1            :A→{x}(J)         :1-K→K
:ClrStat           :A→X              :A→B              :If K
:A→{x}(1)          :Y1→A             :Pause            :Goto 1
:0→B               :Line(X,B,X,A)    :Disp A           :IS>(J,47)
:1→J               :If K             :Pause            :Goto 1
```

APPENDIX 5F82: Web Graphs

Be sure the calculator is in Seq mode. Define the function recursively in $\boxed{\text{Y=}}$.
Input the seed value in UnStart, and choose Web in the $\boxed{\text{WINDOW}}$ FORMAT.

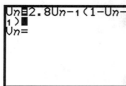  

After you press $\boxed{\text{GRAPH}}$, you can select $\boxed{\text{TRACE}}$ and move through the web with
the right arrow key. You can also get a table of values by pressing $\boxed{\text{2nd}}$ [TABLE].

APPENDIX 5F85: Web Graphs

Be sure your calculator is in Func mode, and enter the
equation for the web graph in y1. You should set the
graphing window before running the program. When you
execute the program, it will request a seed value for x. The
display will alternate between the graph and the x-values.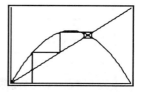
The values are stored in the data set for later reference. For example, with
$y1 = 2.8x(1 - x)$, a window [0, 1, 0, 0, 1, 0], and a seed value of 0.12, the calculator
should produce the graph at the right.

```
Program:WEB
y4=x                          Line(x,B,x,A)
Input "seed value:",A         A→xStat(J)
{A}→xStat                     A→B:Pause
0→B:DispG                     Disp A:Pause
For(J,1,94)                   Line(x,A,A,A)
A→x:y1→A                      End
```

APPENDIX 5G80, 81, 82, 85: Greatest Integer Function

The greatest integer function can be found in the MATH menu as choice 4 under
the NUM submenu. Be sure to put the variable or expression inside parentheses.
When graphing this function, it is best to set the calculator in DOT mode.

TI-80

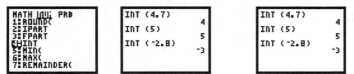

TI-81

```
MATH NUM HYP PRB
1:Round(
2:IPart
3:FPart
4:Int
```

```
Int (4.7)
              4
Int (5)
              5
Int (-2.8)
             -3
■
```

```
Norm Sci Eng
Float 0123456789
Rad Deg
Function Param
Connected Dot
Sequence Simul
Grid Off Grid On
Rect Polar
```

TI-82

```
MATH NUM HYP PRB
1:round(
2:iPart
3:fPart
4:int
5:min(
6:max(
```

```
int (4.7)
              4
int (5)
              5
int (-2.8)
             -3
```

```
Normal Sci Eng
Float 0123456789
Radian Degree
Func Par Pol Seq
Connected Dot
Sequential Simul
FullScreen Split
```

TI-85

```
int (4.7)
              4
int (5)
              5
int (-2.8)■

NUM FROB ANGLE HYP MISC
round iPart fPart int abs ▶
```

```
RectGC PolarGC
CoordOn CoordOff
DrawLine DrawDot
SeqG SimulG
GridOff GridOn
AxesOn AxesOff
LabelOff LabelOn

MATH DRAW FORMT STGDB RCGDB▶
```

Chapter Six Appendices

APPENDIX 6A80, 81: Graphing in Parametric Mode

1. Change the MODE settings to Deg, Param, and Simul.

2. For now, leave the other settings as indicated at the right.

3. Exit from the MODE screen by pressing Clear or 2nd [QUIT].

4. Press Y= , and the parametric function edit screen will appear. The memory for these functions is different from that used for regular functions. This means that whatever functions you had stored in the other Y= menu will still be there when you return to FUNC mode. When entering a function, the calculator now assumes that your variable will be T. When you press X|T , the calculator will automatically give you the variable T. Enter your functions in pairs of X- and Y-equations.

5. The RANGE screen is also slightly different in this mode. You must select the minimum and maximum values for T, and the increment you want for T (the Tstep), as well as the other window values. Plotting will take longer for smaller values of Tstep, but it will be more accurate. If the T-values are set as indicated here, the first values calculated will be the values of X and Y for T = 0. Then it will calculate the values of X and Y for T = 0.5. Next it will use T = 1.0 and so on, up to T = 50. Notice that this has no relationship to the values of Xmin, Xmax, Ymin, and Ymax. These values merely describe the graphing window. If the graph is curved, using a large Tstep will cause the graph to look bent and angular rather than smooth. You will need to choose a Tstep value appropriate to the problem. One method of choosing a reasonable value is to set Tstep equal to about 0.01 times your T-range. For example, if your Tmin is 0 and your Tmax is 100, make the Tstep equal to 1. If your Tmin were -10 and your Tmax were 10, the T-range is 20, so make the Tstep equal to 0.2. This method will usually give a graph in a reasonable amount of time. If you need more detail, make the Tstep smaller. If there are no restrictions on T, use values for Tmin and Tmax that make sense in the situation, or use the same values as Xmin and Xmax.

APPENDIX 6A82: Graphing in Parametric Mode

1. Change the MODE settings to Degree, Par and Simul.

2. For now, leave the other settings as indicated at the right.

3. Exit from the MODE screen by pressing $\boxed{\text{Clear}}$ or $\boxed{\text{2nd}}$ [QUIT].

4. Press $\boxed{\text{Y=}}$, and the parametric function edit screen will appear. The memory for these functions is different from that used for regular functions. This means that whatever functions you had stored in the other Y= menu will still be there when you return to Function mode. When entering a function, the calculator now assumes that your variable will be T. When you press $\boxed{\text{X,T,}\theta}$, the calculator will automatically give you the variable T. Enter your functions in pairs of X- and Y-equations.

5. The WINDOW screen is also slightly different in this mode. You must select the minimum and maximum values for T, and the increment you want for T (the Tstep), as well as the other window values. Plotting will take longer for smaller values of Tstep, but it will be more accurate. If the T-values are set as indicated here, the first values calculated will be the values of X and Y for T = 0. Then the program will calculate the values of X and Y for T = 0.5. Next it will use T = 1.0 and so on, up to T = 50. Notice that this has no relationship to the values of Xmin, Xmax, Ymin, and Ymax. These values merely describe the graphing window. If the graph is curved, using a large Tstep will cause the graph to look bent and angular rather than smooth. You will need to choose a Tstep value appropriate to the problem. One method of choosing a reasonable value is to set Tstep equal to about 0.01 times your T-range. For example, if your Tmin is 0 and your Tmax is 100, make the Tstep equal to 1. If your Tmin were −10 and your Tmax were 10, the T-range is 20, so make the Tstep equal to 0.2. This method will usually give a graph in a reasonable amount of time. If you need more detail, make the Tstep smaller. If there are no restrictions on T, use values for Tmin and Tmax that make sense in the situation, or use the same values as Xmin and Xmax.

APPENDIX 6A85: Graphing in Parametric Mode

Change the MODE settings to Degree, and Param.

Press GRAPH F1 (E(t)=), and the parametric function edit screen will appear. The memory for these functions is different from that used for regular functions. This means that whatever functions you had stored in the other y= menu will still be there when you return to Func mode. When entering a function, the calculator now assumes that your variable will be t. When you press F1 , the calculator will automatically give you the variable t. Enter your functions in pairs of x- and y-equations.

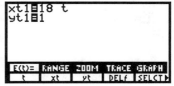

The Range screen is also slightly different in this mode. You must select the minimum and maximum values for t, and the increment you want for t (the tStep), as well as the other window values. Plotting will take longer for smaller values of tStep, but it will be more accurate. If the t-values are set as indicated here, the first values calculated will be the values of x and y for t = 0. Then it will calculate the values of x and x for t = 0.5. Next it will use t = 1.0 and so on up to t = 50. Notice that this has no relationship to the values of xMin, xMax, yMin, and yMax. These values merely describe the graphing window. If the graph is curved, using a large tStep will cause the graph to look bent and angular rather than smooth. You will need to choose a tStep value depending on the problem. One method of choosing a reasonable tStep is to set it equal to about 0.01 times your t-range. For example, if your tMin is 0 and your tMax is 100, make the tStep equal to 1. If your tMin were −10 and your tMax were 10, the t-range is 20, so make the tStep equal to 0.2. This method will usually give a graph in a reasonable amount of time. If you need more detail, make the tStep smaller. If there are no restrictions on t, then use values for tMin and tMax that make sense in the situation, or use the same values as xMin and xMax.

APPENDIX 6B80, 81, 82, 85: Graphing in Both Modes

Even with the calculator in parametric mode, you can use the DrawF command to draw a nonparametric version of a graph. This command, found in the DRAW menu, provides a good way to compare parametric and nonparametric versions of a function. You must use ⎡ALPHA⎤ ⎡X⎤ to type x 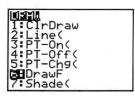 when in parametric mode on the TI-80, TI-81, and TI-82. Remember that to graph a function using the Draw Function command, you must press ⎡ENTER⎤, not ⎡GRAPH⎤, after you have entered the function.

 Press ⎡ENTER⎤.

Chapter Seven Appendices

APPENDIX 7A80: Random Points

Before using either option listed below, you must "seed" your random number generator. If you do not, you will most likely get the same sequence of random numbers as at least one other person in your class. To seed the random number generator, choose a number that is unique to you, such as the last 4 digits of your phone number, and use it in the command, [phone number] $\rightarrow$ Rand.

Press [phone number] STO MATH PRB 1 (RAND) ENTER .

a. Here is a recursive routine that produces a list. Each output has three components: {$0 \le number \le 29$, $0 \le number \le 29$, term number}. To enter RANDINT, press MATH PRB 5 . Note: You can enter the braces used in the expression by pressing 2nd (.

```
0->N    ENTER

N+1->N: {RANDINT(0,29),RANDINT(0,29),N}
 ENTER

 ENTER

 ENTER
```

And so on

A sample output, {15 2 1}, {6 21 2}, {26 13 3}, . . . means the first pair is (15, 2), the second pair is (6, 21), and the third pair is (26, 13).

b. A second possibility allows you to save a random list for later reference. On the HOME screen, enter the following command.

```
SEQ(RANDINT(0,29),X,1,50,1)->L1
```

This will generate 50 random numbers, which will be stored in L1. To store a list in L2, press 2nd [ENTRY] and edit the command to change L1 to L2.

APPENDIX 7A81: Random Points

Before doing either option listed below, you must "seed" your random number generator. If you do not, you will most likely get the same sequence of random numbers as at least one other person in your class. To seed the random number generator, choose a number that is unique to you, such as the last 4 digits of your phone number, and use it in the command, [phone number] →Rand.

Here are two possibilities for generating fifty random pairs of numbers as required in the activity. Each number generated is $0 \le number \le 29$.

Press [phone number] STO MATH PRB 1 (RAND) ENTER.

a. This recursive routine will produce the needed pairs.

0 ENTER

```
100Int 30Rand+Int 30Rand+fPart Ans+.01
```

ENTER

ENTER

ENTER

And so on

The sample output, 2104.01, 2712.02, 2027.03, . . . means the first pair is (21, 4), the second pair is (27, 12), and the third pair is (20, 27).

b. The following program displays random integer pairs (for locating points within a square) from (0, 0) to (29, 29). If you want to generate the same list of numbers a second time, be sure you input the same seed number *before* running the program. If each group wants to obtain a different random number sequence during this activity, then each group will need to use a different seed number. After the coordinates of a point are printed, there is a pause until you press ENTER to continue. The message "DONE" appears when fifty points have been displayed.

```
Prgm?:DECAY
```

`:1→Arow`	Sets dimensions for a point.
`:2→Acol`	
`:1→X`	Sets the counter for recording.
`:Lbl 1`	
`:Int 30Rand→[A](1,1)`	Chooses the first number.
`:Int 30Rand→[A](1,2)`	Chooses the second number.
`:Disp [A]`	Displays the point.
`:Pause`	Waits until enter is pressed.
`:IS>(X,50)`	Repeats for 50 points.
`:Goto 1`	

APPENDIX 7A82: Random Points

Before using either option listed below, you must "seed" your random number generator. If you do not, you will most likely get the same sequence of random numbers as at least one other person in your class. To seed the random number generator, choose a number that is unique to you, such as the last 4 digits of your phone number, and use it in the command, [phone number] → Rand.

Press [phone number] [STO] [MATH] PRB [1] (RAND) [ENTER].

a. Here is a recursive routine that produces a list. Each output has three components: {0 ≤ *number* ≤ 29, 0 ≤ *number* ≤ 29, term number}. Note: You can enter the braces used in the expression by pressing [2nd] [(].

```
0→N    ENTER

N+1→N: {int 30rand, int 30rand, N}

ENTER

ENTER

ENTER
```

And so on

A sample output, {15 2 1}, {6 21 2}, {26 13 3}, . . . means the first pair is (15, 2), the second pair is (6, 21), and the third pair is (26, 13).

b. A second possibility allows you to save a random list for later reference. On the HOME screen, enter the command,

```
seq(int 30rand, X, 1, 50, 1)→L1
```

to generate 50 random numbers, which will be stored in list L1. To store a list in L2, press [2nd] [ENTRY] and edit the command changing L1 to L2.

APPENDIX 7A85: Random Points

Before using either option listed below, you must "seed" your random number generator. If you do not, you will most likely get the same sequence of random numbers as at least one other person in your class. To seed the random number generator, choose a number that is unique to you, such as the last 4 digits of your phone number, and use it in the command, [phone number] $\rightarrow$ Rand.

Press [phone number] [STO] [2nd] [MATH] [F2] (PROB) [F4] (rand) [ENTER].

a. Here is a recursive routine that produces a list. Each output has three components: {$0 \leq number \leq 29$, $0 \leq number \leq 29$, term number}. Note: You can enter the braces used in the expression by pressing [2nd] [(].

```
0→N     ENTER
```

```
N+1→N: {int 30rand, int 30rand, N}
```

```
ENTER
ENTER
ENTER
```

And so on.

A sample output, {15 2 1}, {6 21 2}, {26 13 3}, . . . means the first pair is (15, 2), the second pair is (6, 21), and the third pair is (26, 13).

b. A second possibility allows you to save a random list for later reference. On the HOME screen, enter the following command.

```
seq(int 30rand, X, 1, 50, 1)→xStat
```

This will generate 50 random numbers, which will be stored in list xStat. To store a list in yStat, press [2nd] [ENTRY] and edit the command to change xStat to yStat

APPENDIX 7B81: A List of Values of (x, $x^{0.5}$)

Enter and execute the following program that will create a list as long as your calculator memory will allow.

View the (x, y) pairs listed in [STAT] DATA. As the investigation develops, you might consider changing the fourth line in the program to $\lceil X \rightarrow \{x\}(X)$.

```
PROGRAM: LIST
:ClrStat
:1→X
:Lbl 1
:X→{x}(X)
:X^.5→{y}(X)
:IS>(X, 99)
:Goto 1
```

APPENDIX 7B80, 82: A List of Values of $(x, x^{0.5})$

Edit the lists so that `seq(x,x,1,99,1)→L1` and `L1^0.5→L2`. You can do this directly in the lists or from the HOME screen. Plot the points (L_1, L_2).

As the investigation develops you might consider $\sqrt{L_1}\rightarrow L_3$ for the comparison with L_2.

APPENDIX 7B85: A List of Values of $(x, x^{0.5})$

Edit the lists so that `seq(x,x,1,99,1)→xStat` and `xStat^0.5→yStat`. You can do this directly in the lists or from the HOME screen. Plot the points (xStat, yStat).

As the investigation develops, you might consider $\sqrt{xStat}\rightarrow xStat$ for the comparison with yStat.

APPENDIX 7C81: Radicals and the Calculator

What is the value of $4096^{1/4}$?

$$4096^{1/4} = \sqrt[4]{4096} = 8$$

This is because $8^4 = 4096$. The TI-81 has dedicated square root and cube root functions. For other roots, use the fractional exponent form. For example, $4096\wedge(1/4)$. In general, to find $\sqrt[x]{n}$, use $n\wedge(1/x)$.

APPENDIX 7C80, 82, 85: Radicals and the Calculator

What is the value of $4096^{1/4}$?

$$4096^{1/4} = \sqrt[4]{4096} = 8$$

This is because $8^4 = 4096$. You can arrive at the answer by using the $\wedge$ function, $4096\wedge(1/4) = 8$. These calculators also have a dedicated x-root function in the MATH menu. To find the fourth root of 4096, enter $4\sqrt[x]{4096}$. In general, to find $\sqrt[a]{n}$, use $a\sqrt[x]{n}$.

APPENDIX 7D81: Tables

This program will calculate the value of Y1 at your choice of x. Smart guessing allows you to find a very good approximation rather quickly.

```
PrgmD:Value
:Disp "YOUR CHOICE OF X"
:Input X
:Disp "Y1 IS"
:Disp Y1
```

APPENDIX 7D80, 82: Tables

If a function is selected in the Y= menu, you can build a table by determining the starting value for x and the increment for x.

For example, if Y1 = 125^x, press [2nd] [TblSet]. Set TblMin = 0 and ΔTbl = 0.1. Then press [2nd] [TABLE]. Input a new TblMin and ΔTbl, and repeat the process until you have the accuracy desired.

APPENDIX 7D85: Tables

You can find a single value for a function by entering the following command.

4→x:y1 (Use the [x-VAR] key and [2nd] [ALPHA] Y for a lower case y.)

You can also create a list of values for a function by entering {1,2,3,4,5,6}→x:y1.

The list displayed by the calculator will match the order of the values entered for x. You may need to scroll to the right with the arrow key to see all of the values.

APPENDIX 7E80, 81, 82, 85: Squaring the Graphing Window

The Square option in the ZOOM menu adjusts Ymin and Ymax so that the window is "square." This means the ratio of the height of the window to its width has been adjusted. Perpendicular lines will look perpendicular, circles will look like circles, 45° angles will look like 45° angles, and so on.

APPENDIX 7F80, 81, 82, 85: Functions in Parametric Mode

While in the parametric mode, you can use the DrawF command from the DRAW menu. DrawF $(x - 2)^2$ will produce the graph of $y = (x - 2)^2$ in Func mode. This is a draw command, however, and the figure cannot be traced.

APPENDIX 7G80: Values for Composite Functions

Enter the two equations Y1 = 1.8x + 32 and its inverse Y2 = (x − 32)/1.8. Use these steps to evaluate $f(x)$, $f^{-1}(x)$, and $f^{-1}(f(x))$.

Y1(65)	This is $f(x)$.	
Y2(65)	This is $f^{-1}(x)$.	

```
Y1(65)
          149
Y2(65)
      18.33333333
■
```

Y1(65)	The value of $f(x)$.	
Y2(ANS)	This is $f^{-1}(f(x))$.	

```
Y1(65)
          149
Y2(ANS)
           65
■
```

Record the values for x and $f^{-1}(f(x))$ in a table. You may either plot these points by hand or on your calculator.

To calculate $f(f^{-1}(x))$ execute the following steps.

Y2(65)	The value of $f^{-1}(x)$.	
Y1(ANS)	This is $f(f^{-1}(x))$.	

```
Y2(65)
      18.33333333
Y1(ANS)
           65
■
```

APPENDIX 7G81: Values for Composite Functions

Enter the equation Y1 = 1.8x + 32 and its inverse Y2 = (x − 32)/1.8. Use these steps to evaluate $f(x)$, $f^{-1}(x)$, and $f^{-1}(f(x))$.

65→X	Stores a value in X.	
Y1	This is $f(x)$.	
Y2	This is $f^{-1}(x)$.	

```
65→X
          65
Y1
         149
Y2
  18.33333333
```

Y1→X	Stores the value of $f(x)$ as X.	
Y2	This is $f^{-1}(f(x))$.	

```
Y1→X
         149
Y2
          65
```

Record the values for x and $f^{-1}(f(x))$ in a table. You may either plot these points by hand or on your calculator.

To calculate $f(f^{-1}(x))$ follow these steps:

65→X	Stores a value in X.	
Y2→X	Stores the value of $f^{-1}(x)$ as X.	
Y1	This is $f(f^{-1}(x))$.	

```
65→X
          65
Y2→X
  18.33333333
Y1
          65
■
```

APPENDIX 7G82: Values for Composite Functions

Enter the equation Y1 = 1.8x + 32 and its inverse
Y2 = (x – 32)/1.8. Use these steps to evaluate $f(x)$, $f^{-1}(x)$, and
$f^{-1}(f(x))$.

Set your table to ask for x-values.

Enter a choice for x and the table will show the value for
$f(x)$ and $f^{-1}(x)$.

To find the value for $f^{-1}(f(x))$, enter the value of $f(x)$ for x and
look in the $f^{-1}(x)$ column.

To find the value for $f(f^{-1}(x))$, enter the value of $f^{-1}(x)$ for x
and look in the $f(x)$ column.

APPENDIX 7G85: Values for Composite Functions

Enter the equation y1 = 1.8x + 32 and its inverse y2 = (x – 32)/1.8. Use these steps
to evaluate $f(x)$, $f^{-1}(x)$, and $f^{-1}(f(x))$.

| 65→x: y1 | Stores a value in x, and displays $f(x)$. |
| y2 | This is $f^{-1}(x)$. |

y1→x: y2   Stores the value of $f(x)$ as x, and
                            displays $f^{-1}(f(x))$.

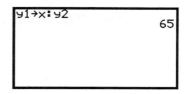

Record the values for x and $f^{-1}(f(x))$ in a table. You may either plot these points by hand or on your calculator. To directly plot the entire function, $f^{-1}(f(x))$, enter y3 = (y1 – 32)/1.8.

To calculate $f(f^{-1}(x))$ follow these steps:

65→x: y2→x: y1   Stores a value in x, calculates and
                        stores the value of $f^{-1}(x)$ as x,
                        displays $f(f^{-1}(x))$.

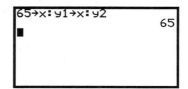

APPENDIX 7H81: Graphing Composite Functions

To graph composite functions on the TI-81, begin with two functions, for example, $f(x) = x^2 + 3$ and $g(x) = \sqrt{x - 3}$.

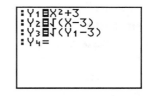

To graph $g(f(x))$ in Y3, replace all the x's that you entered in the second equation with Y1.

Press [2nd] [Y–VARS] [1] (Y1).

APPENDIX 7H80, 82: Graphing Composite Functions

To graph composite functions on the TI-82, begin with two functions, for example, $f(x) = x^2 + 3$ and $g(x) = \sqrt{x - 3}$.

To graph $g(f(x))$, enter Y3 = Y2 (Y1 (X)). To do this, press

[2nd] [Y–VARS] [1] (FUNCTION) [2] (Y2) [(] [2nd] [Y–VARS] [1] (FUNCTION) [1] (Y1) [(] X [)].

APPENDIX 7H85: Graphing Composite Functions

To graph composite functions on the TI-85, begin with two functions, for example, $f(x) = x^2 + 3$ and
$g(x) = \sqrt{x - 3}$.

To enter $g(f(x))$ in y3, replace all the x's that you entered in the second equation with y1. (Press F2 1 to get y1.)

APPENDIX 7I81: Data Altering

At times you may be working with nonlinear data, and frequently you won't discover this until after you have entered it. In order to alter the data in a consistent way, you will need to perform some mathematical operation on each value, and replace the original data set. With only a few points this is not usually a problem. But as the number of points increases, the probability of making a mistake grows combinatorially. (This means fast. You will learn what that word means later on this year.) To alter data efficiently, you can enter this short program into your calculator. The third line of the program, {y}(J)-40→{y}(J), is the critical line. It will subtract 40 from each y-value of the data.

When finished, this program will print the word "Done," and, if you return to the data, you should find the first point changed to (0, 119.5). You can use the same program to alter the y-values again. Change the third line of the program to log {y}(J)→{y}(J),

```
PrgmD:ALTER
:1→J
:Lbl 1
:{y}(J)-40→{y}(J)
:IS>(J,Dim{x})
:Goto 1
```

and run the program again. WARNING! If the program gives an error, it may be because you have asked for something impossible, such as the log of zero or the square root of a negative number. Return to the data set, and find the largest and smallest y-values, and eliminate any entries that will cause an error. To restore the data to its original values, change the third line of the program to
10^{y}(J)+40→{y}(J).

Note: The program can be reworked to alter x-values, y-values, or both, by altering line 3. The program will produce residuals if you alter it to read
Y₁-{y}(J)→{y}(J).

APPENDIX 7I80, 82: Data Altering

You can alter data directly on the LIST screen. If L1 contains the x-values and L2 the y-values, define log L2 → L3. A plot of (L1, L3) provides the graph of (x, log y).

APPENDIX 7I85: Data Altering

You can alter data directly on the HOME screen. To access a list name, press 2nd
[LIST] F3 (NAMES), or you can just enter the name of the list by typing the letters.
If xStat contains the x-values and yStat the y-values, enter the command
log yStat→ALT. A plot of (xStat, ALT) provides the graph of $(x, \log y)$.

APPENDIX 7J80, 81, 82, 85: Other Regressions

You can calculate the least-squares fit to an altered set of data for four types of
curves. They are the line (LinReg), the log curve (LnReg), the exponential curve
(ExpReg), and the power curve (PwrReg). In the TI-85, they are called LINR, LNR,
EXPR, and PWRR.

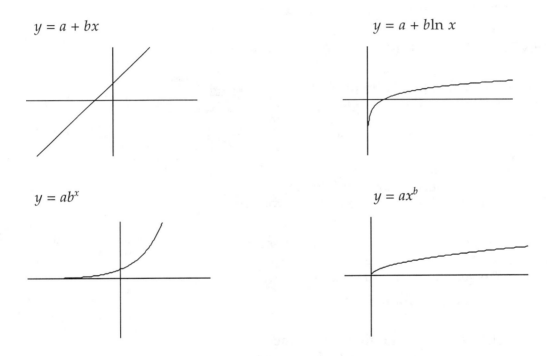

$y = a + bx$

$y = a + b\ln x$

$y = ab^x$

$y = ax^b$

WARNING! These curve regressions work by fitting a line to the logarithms of
the x-data set, the y-data set or both. If you have zero or negative values in the
data, you may get an error.

Chapter Eight Appendices

APPENDIX 8A80, 81, 82, 85: Random Numbers

Refer to **APPENDIX 7A** if you don't remember how to find Rand or how to seed your random number generator.

```
MATH NUM HYP PRB
1:Rand
2: nPr
3: nCr
```

Enter Rand, and press ENTER repeatedly. Each time you press ENTER a new ten-digit decimal number appears on the screen.

```
Rand
              .6709239598
```

Example 1 in Section 1 uses a seed of 1. $1 \to$ Rand.

APPENDIX 8B81: A Random Number Generator Routine

This program will generate 99 random numbers and display the corresponding histogram. You will need ample memory in your calculator for this program and others in this chapter. To be able to store 99 numbers in your data set, you may have to delete programs. Check your calculator to see if it has less than 800 bytes of memory left for programs.

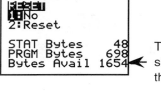

```
RESET
1:No
2:Reset

STAT Bytes    48
PRGM Bytes   698
Bytes Avail 1654
```
This number should be more than 800.

The graphing window [0, 1, 0.1, −5, 26.5, 5] accommodates 99 numbers. Move around the graphing screen with the arrow keys to see the individual results.

To Generate Random Numbers 1 – 6

```
Prgm?: GENERATE
 :All-Off
 :ClrDraw
 :ClrStat
 :1→N
 :Lbl 1
 :Rand→{x}(N)
 :IS>(N,99)
 :Goto 1
 :Hist
```

Alter the GENERATE Program. Change the line Rand→{x}(N) to Int 6Rand+1→{x}(N). The program will now generate 99 random numbers from 1 through 6, and display the corresponding histogram. Use [1, 7, 1, −5, 26.5, 5] as a good graphing window for the display. Move around the graphing screen with the arrow keys to see the individual results.

APPENDIX 8B80, 82: A Random Number Generator Routine

To store 99 random numbers in a list, enter the command
seq(rand,X,1,99,1)→L1. Then, with a graphing window of [0, 1, 0.1, ⁻5, 26.5, 5], set
plot 1 to graph a histogram of L1 using a frequency of 1.

To Generate Random Numbers 1 – 6

Alter the command above to seq(int 6rand+1,X,1,99,1)→L1, which will generate
99 random numbers from 1 through 6. Use [1, 7, 1, ⁻5, 26.5, 5] as a graphing
window, and display the corresponding histogram. Trace to see the individual
results. With the TI-80 you can also use SEQ(RANDINT(1,6),X,1,99,1)->L1.

APPENDIX 8B85: A Random Number Generator Routine

To store 99 random numbers in a list enter the commands,
seq(rand,x,1,99,1)→xStat and seq(1,x,1,99,1)→yStat. Then with a graphing
window of [0, 1, 0.1, ⁻5, 26.5, 5], enter STAT F3 (DRAW) F1 (HIST) to graph a
histogram of the random numbers with a frequency of 1.

To Generate Random Numbers 1 – 6

Alter the first command to seq(int 6rand+1,X,1,99,1)→xStat, to generate 99
random numbers from 1 through 6. Use [1, 7, 1, ⁻5, 26.5, 5] as a graphing window,
and display the corresponding histogram. Move around the graphing screen
with the arrow keys to see the individual results.

APPENDIX 8C80: Dot Graphing

Select DOT rather than CONNECTED in the
MODE menu. Make sure the grid is turned off in
the DRAW menu. Input a graphing window of
[0, 6.4, 0, -5.75, 5.75, 1].

APPENDIX 8C81: Dot Graphing

Select DOT rather than CONNECTED in the MODE menu. Make sure the grid is turned off. Input a graphing window of [0, 9.5, 0, -6.2, 6.4, 1].

APPENDIX 8C82: Dot Graphing

Selected DOT rather than CONNECTED under WINDOW [FORMAT]. Make sure the grid is turned off. Input a graphing window of [0, 9.4, 0, -6.2, 6.2, 1].

APPENDIX 8C85: Dot Graphing

Selected DrawDot rather than DrawLine under GRAPH MORE F3 (FORMT). Make sure the grid is turned off. Input a graphing window of [0, 12.6, 0, -6.2, 6.2, 1].

APPENDIX 8D81: Ratio of Success

The program below will plot a user-defined number of points in a one-by-one-unit square, and count the number of those points that fall under the curve defined in line 2 of the program. When the simulation is finished, the calculator will display the fraction of the total points that were plotted under the curve.

```
Prgm?:RATIO
 :All-Off                 ■:Rand→X            N–the number of points
■:"√(1-X²)"→Y₁            ■:Rand→B            C–the point counter
 :Y₁-On                    :PT-On(X,B)        S–the points under the curve
 :DispGraph                :If B<Y₁           X–the x-value of the point
 :Disp"HOW MANY PTS?"      :S+1→S             B–the y-value of the point
 :Input N                  :IS>(C,N)          F–the fraction of points
 :1→C                      :Goto 1
 :0→S                      :S/N→F
 :Lbl 1                    :Disp F
```

APPENDIX 8D80, 82: Ratio of Success

The program below will plot a user-defined number of points in a one-by-one-unit square, and count the number of those points that fall under the curve defined in line 2 of the program. When the simulation is finished, the calculator will display the fraction of the total points that were plotted under the curve.

```
PROGRAM?:RATIO
 :FnOff                      ■:rand→X
■:"√(1-X²)"→Y₁               ■:rand→B
 :FnOn 1                      :Pt-On(X,B)
 :DispGraph                   :If B<Y₁:S+1→S
 :Input"HOW MANY PTS?",N      :End
 :0→S                         :S/N→F
 :For(C,1,N)                  :Disp F
```

N–the number of points
C–the point counter
S–the points under the curve
X–the x-value of the point
B–the y-value of the point

APPENDIX 8D85: Ratio of Success

The program below will plot a user-defined number of points in a one-by-one-unit square, and count the number of those points that fall under the curve defined in line 2 of the program. When the simulation is finished, the calculator will display the fraction of the total points that were plotted under the curve.

```
PROGRAM?:RATIO
 :FnOff                      ■:rand→x
■:y1=√(1-x²)                 ■:rand→B
 :FnOn 1                      :PtOn(x,B)
 :DispG                       :If B<y1:S+1→S
 :Input"HOW MANY PTS?",N      :End
 :0→S                         :S/N→F
 :For(C,1,N)                  :Disp F
```

N–the number of points
C–the point counter
S–the points under the curve
x–the x-value of the point
B–the y-value of the point

APPENDIX 8E80, 81, 82, 85: Modification to Find Areas

To find areas, modify the program in **APPENDIX D**. Set the graphing window so that you enclose the necessary region within a rectangle. Change the three commands marked with the ■ to fit the function and the dimensions of the rectangle.

```
 :"√X"=Y1          :10Rand→X          :4Rand→B
```

APPENDIX 8F80: The Gumball Simulation

```
PROGRAM:GUMBALLS
:{1,1,0,0,0,0,0,0}->L1          :LBL 1
:0->T                           :G+1->G:END
:INPUT "NUMBER OF TRIALS",N     :IF L1(G)=0
:FOR(J,1,N)                     :GOTO 1
:SEQ(RAND,X,1,8,1)->L2          :T+G->T:END
:SORTA(L2,L1)                   :T/N->E
:0->G                           :DISP E
```

L1 is gumballs (1=purple, 0=not).
 L2 is random for sorting L1.
T is total gumballs.
G is the # each time until purple.
N is the # of trials.
E is the expected value.

APPENDIX 8F81: The Gumball Simulation

```
Prgm5:GUMBALLS
:ClrStat             :1→J              :Lbl 3
:1→K                 :Lbl 1            :G+1→G
:Lbl 0               :1→K              :If {x}(G)=0
:(K≤2)→{x}(K)        :Lbl 2            :Goto 3
:IS>(K,8)            :Rand→{y}(K)      :T+G→T
:Goto 0              :IS>(K,8)         :IS>(J,N)
:0→T                 :Goto 2           :Goto 1
:Disp "NUMBER OF TRIALS"  :ySort       :T/N→E
:Input N             :0→G              :Disp E
```

x-data is gumballs
 (1=purple, 0=not).
y-data is random for
 sorting x-data.
T is total gumballs.
G is the number each
 time until purple.
N is the # of trials.
E is the expected value.

APPENDIX 8F82: The Gumball Simulation

```
Program:GUMBALLS
:{1,1,0,0,0,0,0,0}→L₁            :1→G
:0→T                            :While L₁(G)=0
:Input "NUMBER OF TRIALS",N     :G+1→G:End
:For(J,1,N)                     :T+G→T:End
:seq(rand,X,1,8,1)→L₂           :T/N→E
:SortA(L₂,L₁)                   :Disp E
```

L₁ is gumballs (1=purple, 0=not).
L₂ is random for sorting L₁..
T is total gumballs.
G is the # each time until purple.
N is the # of trials.
E is the expected value.

APPENDIX 8F85: The Gumball Simulation

```
Program:Gumballs
:{1,1,0,0,0,0,0,0}→xStat
:0→T
:Input "Number of trials",N
:For(J,1,N)
:seq(rand,x,1,8,1)→yStat
:Sorty

:1→G
:While xStat(G)==0
:G+1→G:End
:T+G→T:End
:T/N→E
:Disp E
```

xStat is gumballs (1=purple, 0=not).
yStat is random for sorting xStat..
T is total gumballs.
G is the # each time until purple.
N is the # of trials.
E is the expected value.

APPENDIX 8G80, 81, 82, 85: A Simulated Die

Enter the command Int 6Rand+1. Each time you press ENTER, the output will be a random integer from 1 through 6.

APPENDIX 8H81: The Protection Simulation

This program counts the number of successes before a failure. It takes some time to gather results (several minutes). Even if it crashes because it runs out of memory, you still can analyze the results that were collected.

```
Prgm6:PROTECT
:ClrStat              :Goto 2              J is the counter for trials.
:1→J                  :S→{x}(J)            S is the counter until failure.
:Lbl 1                :IS>(J,99)           x-data is where S is stored for
:0→S                  :Goto 1                   each trial.
:Lbl 2                :1-Var               0.98 is the probability of success.
:S+1→S                :x̄                   99 is the number of trials.
:If Rand<0.98         :Disp x̄              x̄ is the expected value.
```

APPENDIX 8H80, 82, 85: The Protection Simulation

This program counts the number of successes before a failure. It takes some time to gather results (several minutes). See the list of variables in **APPENDIX 8H81** to find what each letter represents.

```
PROGRAM:PROTECT (80)    Program:PROTECT (82)    PROGRAM:Protect (85)
:CLRLIST L1             :ClrList L₁             :{0}→xStat
:FOR(J,1,99)            :For(J,1,99)            :For(J,1,99)
:0->S                   :0→S                    :0→S
:LBL 1:S+1->S           :Repeat rand≥0.98       :Repeat rand≥0.98
:IF RAND≥0.98:GOTO 1    :S+1→S:End              :S+1→S:End
:S->L1(J):END           :S→L₁(J):End            :S→xStat(J):End
:1-VAR STATS L1         :1-Var Stats L₁         :OneVar xStat
:x̄                      :x̄                      :x̄
:DISP x̄                 :Disp x̄                 :Disp .x̄
```

APPENDIX 8I80: Matrices

The TI-80 does not have built-in matrix operations. You can use matrices to solve many different kinds of problems, and often there is no alternative method that works as well. The program in this appendix is quite long. Actually, there is one long program and a shorter subprogram. You can expect to spend almost an hour entering it and finding all the errors. There are two subprograms that will be added to this program in the next chapter.

The program uses all six lists, so you cannot keep any information in a list when you run this program. It does not use the equations or the graph values, but it does use most of the normal variables. It will only work with matrices up to 6×6. If the numbers become too large you will not see the entire matrix on the screen. Sometimes you can change the display accuracy in the MODE menu to help this situation. To see actual values, you will need to go to the LIST screen. Matrix A is in L1, matrix B is in L2, matrix C is in L3, and the answer matrix is in L4. Items 1 and 2 give the number of rows and columns, respectively, of the matrix. The row entries begin at item 7, 13, 19, . . . , $6r+1$. For example, you will find the first row of a two-by-two matrix in ANS at L4(7) and L4(8), and you can find the second-row entries in L4(13) and L4(14).

The program begins with four choices. Choice one is to edit or enter the matrices. You must first select which of the three matrices you want to enter or edit. When entering a new matrix, first enter the number of rows. Then begin entering the elements in the first row. When you are inputting the elements in a row, you *must* remember to begin with a brace and enter a comma between each entry. If you forget, you will "crash" the program, and you will have to quit and restart. However, the program will remember any matrices that were already entered correctly.

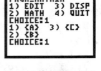

Actually, you can't edit the entries in a matrix from within the program. You can only re-enter the entire matrix. You can, however, edit entries if you exit the program, make your changes directly in the lists, and then restart the program. Be sure to put the same number of values in each row.

The second choice allows you to do matrix operations. First you will be asked to select a matrix followed by an operation. (In this chapter, you will use only addition and multiplication.) Then you must select a second matrix, which can be the same as the first one selected. The result will be displayed after it is calculated. The result is also stored in the matrix ANS. If the two matrices are incompatible for addition or multiplication, you will get a message saying there is a DIMension MISMATCH. In multiplication, this may mean you are trying to multiply the matrices in the wrong order. Try reversing the order, and see if it works.

The third option on the main menu allows you to DISPlay any of the three matrices you have entered, or to look again at the last answer. If you will need to refer to a solution later, you must exit the program and record the result. To store ANS in matrix [C], you should store L4 in L3.

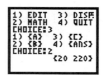

When you select choice four on the main menu, you exit the program, but all the data is saved. Unless you go to the LIST screen and edit or delete any of the first four lists, all of the matrices will still be stored the next time you run the program.

```
Program:MATRIX              If Z≥3:Prgm_MXDET       Else:0->L₅(1)
43->Dim L₁:43->Dim L₃      If Z≥3:Goto 3           Disp "DIM MISMATCH"
43->Dim L₂:43->Dim L₄      L₅->L₆                   End:Goto 3
Lbl 1                       Prgm_MXPICK             Lbl 3
Disp "1) EDIT 3) DISP"     If Z=2:Goto 4           L₅(2)->Dim L₆
Disp "2) MATH 4) QUIT"     If (L₅(1)=L₆(1))        For(J,1,L₅(1))
Input "CHOICE:",X            (L₅(2)=L₆(2))          For(K,1,L₅(2))
If X≥4:Stop                Then:L₅+L₆->L₄           L₅(6J+K)->L₆(K)
Prgm_MXPICK                L₅(1)->L₄(1)            End:Disp L₆
If X=2:Goto 2             L₅(2)->L₄(2)            End:Pause
If X=3:Goto 3             L₄->L₅                   Goto 1
Input "ROWS? ",Z          Else:0->L₅(1)
For(J,1,Z)                Disp "DIM MISMATCH"
Input L₆                  End:Goto 3               Program:MXPICK
Dim L₆->L                 Lbl 4                    Disp "1) {A} 3) {C}"
For(K,1,L)                If L₅(1)=L₆(2):Then      If X=1:Then
L₆(K)->L₅(6J+K)           For(J,1,L₆(1))           Disp "2) {B}"
End:End                   For(K,1,L₅(2))           Else
J->L₅(1):L->L₅(2)         0->U                     Disp "2) {B} 4) {ANS}"
If Y=1:L₅->L₁             For(L,1,L₆(2))           End
If Y=2:L₅->L₂             U+L₆(6J+L)L₅(6L+K)->U    Input "CHOICE:",Y
If Y=3:L₅->L₃             End:U->L₄(6J+K)          If Y=1:L₁->L₅
Goto 1                    End:End                  If Y=2:L₂->L₅
Lbl 2                     L₆(1)->L₄(1)             If Y=3:L₃->L₅
Disp "1) ADD 3) DET"      L₅(2)->L₄(2)             If Y=4:L₄->L₅
Disp "2) MULT 4) INVRS"   L₄->L₅                   Return
Input "CHOICE:",Z
```

APPENDIX 8I81: Matrices

The MATRX EDIT menu allows you to store and use up to three matrices. Matrices [A], [B], and [C] can each have up to six rows and six columns.

Enter 1 to edit the dimensions of [A] to the needed size. For this example, be sure the dimensions of [A] are 1×2. Then input the matrix elements.

  $1,1 = 20$

  $1,2 = 220$

Press MATRX EDIT 2 to edit matrix [B]. If necessary, change the dimensions of [B] to 2×2. Then input the matrix elements.

$1, 1 = \mathbf{0.90}$

$1, 2 = \mathbf{0.10}$

$2, 1 = \mathbf{0.05}$

$2, 2 = \mathbf{0.95}$

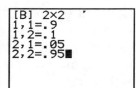

By pressing 2nd [[A]] ENTER , you can display the matrix
[20 220]. Enter 2nd [[B]] ENTER to display the
matrix $\begin{bmatrix} .90 & .10 \\ .05 & .95 \end{bmatrix}$. Multiply [A] and [B] by pressing
2nd [[A]] 2nd [[B]] ENTER .

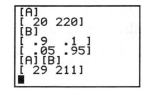

APPENDIX 8I82: Matrices

The MATRX EDIT menu allows you to store and use up to five matrices, [A], [B], [C], [D], and [E]. The dimensions are limited to 99 rows or columns or, more likely, by the memory available.

Enter 1 to edit the dimensions of [A] to
the needed size. For this example, be
sure the dimensions of [A] are $\mathbf{1 \times 2}$.
Then input the matrix elements.

    $1,1 = \mathbf{20}$

    $1,2 = \mathbf{220}$

Press MATRX EDIT 2 to edit matrix [B]. If necessary, change the dimensions of [B] to $\mathbf{2 \times 2}$. Then input the matrix elements.

    $1, 1 = \mathbf{0.90}$

    $1, 2 = \mathbf{0.10}$

    $2, 1 = \mathbf{0.05}$

    $2, 2 = \mathbf{0.95}$

Enter MATRX 1 ENTER to display the matrix [20 220], and
MATRX 2 ENTER to display the matrix $\begin{bmatrix} .90 & .10 \\ .05 & .95 \end{bmatrix}$. Multiply
[A] and [B] by pressing MATRX 1 MATRX 2 ENTER .

APPENDIX 8I85: Matrices

The MATRX EDIT menu allows you to store matrices. The dimensions are limited by the memory available.

Press [2nd] [MATRX] [F2] (EDIT) and enter a name such as MA. Press [ENTER] and edit the dimensions to the needed size, **1 x 2**. Enter the matrix elements. Press [ENTER] after entering each element.

```
MATRX
Name=MA




 BP   MA   MB
```

MATRX:MA **1 × 2**

1,1 = **20**

1,2 = **220**

```
MATRX:MA          1×2
 1,2=220




◄COL  COL►  INSr  DELr  INSc ►
```

Then press [2nd] [MATRX] [F2] (EDIT) and enter another name such as
MB. Press [ENTER] and edit the dimensions to the needed size, **2 x 2**. Then enter the elements.

1,1 = **0.90**

1,2 = **0.10**

2,1 = **0.05**

2,2 = **0.95**

```
MATRX:MB          2×2
 1,2=.1
 2,2=.95■



◄COL  COL►  INSr  DELr  INSc ►
```

Enter MA [ENTER] to display the matrix [20 220] and

MB [ENTER] to display the matrix $\begin{bmatrix} .90 & .10 \\ .05 & .95 \end{bmatrix}$.

Multiply [A] and [B] by pressing MA • MB [ENTER].

```
MA
                 [[20 220]]
MB
                 [[.9  .1 ]
                  [.05 .95]]
MA*MB
                 [[29 211]]
```

Chapter Nine Appendices

APPENDIX 9A80: Zooming

The TI-80 has two routines that redefine the window so that you can more closely view a portion of the current window. The choice between **ZBOX** and **ZOOM IN** is a matter of personal preference. You should try each method and decide which one you prefer. Master the techniques so that you can find points quickly and efficiently.

ZOOM 1: ZBOX Choice 1 from the ZOOM menu allows you to define any two diagonally-opposite corners of a rectangle in the present window. Define a box as small as you can, but be sure that the point you want to view is contained within the box. Start at the point of interest, and press the left (or 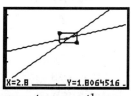 right) arrow two or three times. Then press the down (or up) arrow two or three times. Press ENTER to set one corner of the box. Move to the opposite corner of your box and press ENTER again. If you press ENTER for the first corner too soon, press ZOOM 1 (ZBOX) and start again. If you press ENTER for the second corner too soon, you will have to reset the original window and start the zooming process again.

Sometimes it is helpful to draw a long rectangle to stretch one dimension more than the other. If two functions are very flat near a point of intersection, you can draw a flat rectangle (box) to enhance the vertical change.

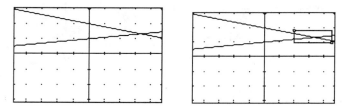

ZOOM 2: ZOOM IN Choice 2 from the ZOOM menu allows you to choose the point on which you want to focus. The zoom size is governed by a pair of numbers that are called the "zoom factors." The calculator default is a zoom factor of 4, which will give $\frac{1}{4}$ of the domain and $\frac{1}{4}$ of the range, or $\frac{1}{16}$ of the area currently shown on the screen. Larger zoom factors, set by storing numbers to XFACT and YFACT, (which can be found in the VARS WINDOW list), will allow a faster zoom. Those who are clever and careful can zoom very quickly with a factor of 20.

Note: The trace command will always follow Y1 when first turned on. Move to the next function that is turned on by pressing the down arrow. The *y*-value of a traced point is the value of the function.

TABLE Zoom in: The TI-80 TABLE feature allows you to find the point of intersection quickly by using a combination of viewing a table and table setup. See **APPENDIX 9A82** for directions on using this method of zooming.

APPENDIX 9A81: Zooming

The TI-81 has two routines that redefine the window to more closely view a portion of the current window. Your choice between **Box** and **Zoom in** is a matter of personal preference. Both methods are presented here for you to try. Master the techniques so that you can find points quickly and efficiently.

ZOOM 1: Box Choice 1 from the ZOOM menu allows you to define any two diagonally-opposite corners of a rectangle in the present window. Define a box to be as small as you can, but be sure that the point you want to view is contained within the box. Start at the point of interest, and press the left (or right) arrow two or three times. Then press the down (or up) arrow two or three times. Press ENTER to set one corner of the box. Move to the opposite corner of your box and press ENTER again. If you press ENTER for the first corner too soon, press ZOOM 1 (Box) and start again. If you press ENTER for the second corner too soon, you will have to manually reset the range, and start the zooming process again.

Sometimes it is helpful to draw a long rectangle to stretch one dimension more than the other. If two functions are very flat near a point of intersection, you can draw a flat rectangle (box) to enhance the vertical change.

ZOOM 2: Zoom In Choice 2 from the ZOOM menu allows you to choose the point on which you want to focus. The zoom size is governed by a pair of numbers that are called the "zoom factors." The calculator default is a zoom factor of 4, which will give $\frac{1}{4}$ of the domain and $\frac{1}{4}$ of the range, or $\frac{1}{16}$ of the area currently shown on the screen. Larger zoom factors, set in the menu choice ZOOM 4, will allow a faster zoom, but you must be careful. Those who are clever and careful can zoom very quickly with a factor of 25. If you do not like the effect of your last "zoom in," then use choice 3 to "zoom out" and try again.

Note: The trace command will always follow Y1 when first turned on. Move to the next function that is turned on by pressing the down arrow. The *y*-value of a traced point is the value of the function.

APPENDIX 9A82: Zooming

The TI-82 has two routines that redefine the window so that you can more closely view a portion of the current window. The choice between Z**Box** and **Zoom In** is a matter of personal preference. You should try each method, and decide which one you prefer. Master the techniques so that you can find points quickly and efficiently.

ZOOM 1: ZBox Choice 1 from the ZOOM menu allows you to define any two diagonally-opposite corners of a rectangle in the present window. Define a box as small as you can, but be sure that the point you want to view is contained within the box. Start at the point of interest, and press the left (or right) 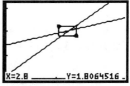 arrow two or three times. Then press the down (or up) arrow two or three times. Press [ENTER] to set one corner of the box. Move to the opposite corner of your box and press [ENTER] again. If you press [ENTER] too soon for the first corner, then press [ZOOM] [1] (ZBox) and start again. If you press [ENTER] for the second corner too soon, you can return to your previous window by pressing ZPrevious from the ZOOM MEMORY menu. Then start again.

Sometimes it is helpful to draw a long rectangle to stretch one dimension more than the other. If two functions are very flat near a point of intersection, you can draw a flat rectangle (box) to enhance the vertical change.

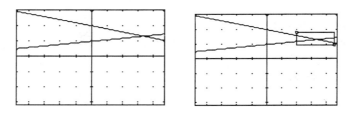

ZOOM 2: Zoom in Choice 2 from the ZOOM menu allows you to choose the point that you wish focus on. The zoom size is governed by a pair of numbers that are called the "zoom factors." The calculator default is a zoom factor of 4, which will give $\frac{1}{4}$ of the domain and the range, or $\frac{1}{16}$ the area. Larger zoom factors, set by the menu choice ZOOM MEMORY 4, will allow a faster zoom but you must be careful. Those who are clever and careful can zoom very quickly with a factor of 25. If you do not like the effect of your last "zoom-in," then ZPrevious and try again.

Note: The trace command will always follow Y1 when first turned on. Move to the next function that is turned on by using the down arrow. The *y*-value of a traced point is the value of the function.

TABLE Zoom in: The TI-82 TABLE feature allows you to find the point of intersection quickly by using a combination of viewing a table and table setup.

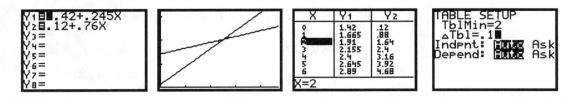

In this example, Y1 > Y2 until somewhere between $2 < x < 3$. Set TblMin to 2 and ΔTbl to 0.1. You will find Y1 > Y2 until somewhere between $2.5 < x < 2.6$. Set TblMin to 2.5 and ΔTbl to 0.01. Continue until you reach the accuracy needed.

APPENDIX 9A85: Zooming

The TI-85 has two routines that redefine the window so that you can more closely view a portion of the current window. The choice between **BOX** and **ZIN** is a matter of personal preference. You should try each method, and decide which one you prefer. Master the techniques so that you can find points quickly and efficiently.

ZOOM F1: BOX Choice F1 from the GRAPH F3 (ZOOM) menu allows you to define any two diagonally opposite corners of a rectangle in the present window. Define a box as small as you can, but be sure that the point you want to view is contained within the box. Start at the point of interest, and

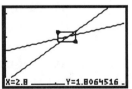

press the left (or right) arrow two or three times. Then press the down (or up) arrow two or three times. Press ENTER to set one corner of the box. Move to the opposite corner of your box and press ENTER again. If you press ENTER too soon for the first
corner, press GRAPH F3 (ZOOM) F1 (BOX) and start again. If you press ENTER too soon for the second corner, you can return to the previous window by pressing F5 (ZPREV). Then start over.

Sometimes it is helpful to draw a long rectangle to stretch one dimension more than the other. If two functions are very flat near a point of intersection, you can draw a flat rectangle (box) to enhance the vertical change.

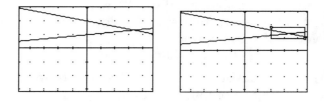

ZOOM 2: ZIN Choice 2 from the ZOOM menu allows you to choose the point on which you want to focus. The zoom size is governed by a pair of numbers that are called the "zoom factors." The calculator default is a zoom factor of 4, which will give $\frac{1}{4}$ of the domain and $\frac{1}{4}$ of the range, or $\frac{1}{16}$ of the area of the current calculator screen. Larger zoom factors, set by pressing GRAPH F3 (ZOOM) MORE MORE F1 (ZFACT), will allow a faster zoom, but you must be careful. Those who are clever and careful can zoom very quickly with a factor of 25. If you do not like the effect of your last "zoom-in" then choose ZPREV and try again.

Note: The trace command will always follow y1 when first turned on. Move to the next function that is turned on by using the down arrow. The *y*-value of a traced point is the value of the function.

APPENDIX 9B80: Matrix Inverse and Determinant

You will need to enter the two subprograms MXDET and MXINV to allow the program MATRIX to find determinants and inverses. After you have entered the programs, test them with the examples here to make sure that most of the errors have been found.

These two options on the MATH menu work much like the rest of the program. They only require one matrix, and it must be a square matrix (with the same number of rows as columns). If you try either determinants or inverses with an unsuitable matrix, you will get a NONSQUARE matrix error. You can only find the inverse of a matrix that does not have a determinant of zero. If you try to find the inverse of such a matrix, you will get a SINGULAR MATRIX error. The determinant is not stored, but the inverse becomes ANS.

The number of steps necessary to calculate determinants and inverses grows very fast as the size of the matrix grows. This program works relatively quickly when finding information for a two-by-two matrix. It could take up to 30 minutes to find the inverse of a six-by-six matrix.

```
Program:MXDET
If L5(1)=L5(2):Then
L5(1)->N:0->D
{1,2,3,4,5,6,7}->L6
0->S
For(J,1,N!)
(-1)^S->P
For(K,1,N)
L5(6K+L6(K))P->P
End:D+P->D:1->L
For(K,2,N)
L+(Fpart(J/K!)=0)->L
End
For(K,1,L)
L6(1)->X
For(M,1,K)
```

```
L6(M+1)->L6(M)
End:X->L6(K+1)
End:S+.5L(L+1)->S
End
If Z=3:Then
Disp "DET=",D
0->L5(1)
Else:If D≠0
Then:Prgm_MXINV
L4->L5
Else:0->L5(1)
Disp "SINGULAR MATRIX"
End:End
Else:0->L5(1)
Disp "NONSQUARE"
End:Return
```

```
Program:MXINV
L5(1)->N:L5->L4
For(J,1,N)
For(K,1,N)
(J=K)->L4(6J+K)
End:End
For(J,1,N)
J->K
Lbl 1
For(L,1,N)
L5(6J+L)+L5(6K+L)->L5(6J+L)
L4(6J+L)+L4(6K+L)->L4(6J+L)
End:K+1->K
If L5(7J)=0:Goto 1
L5(7J)->P
For(L,1,N)
L5(6J+L)/P->L5(6J+L)
```

```
L4(6J+L)/P->L4(6J+L)
End
For(K,J+1,N)
L5(6K+J)->P
For(L,1,N)
L5(6K+L)-PL5(6J+L)->L5(6K+L)
L4(6K+L)-PL4(6J+L)->L4(6K+L)
End:End:End
For(J,N,2,-1)
For(K,1,J-1)
L5(6K+J)->P
For(L,1,N)
L5(6K+L)-PL5(6J+L)->L5(6K+L)
L4(6K+L)-PL4(6J+L)->L4(6K+L)
End:End:End
Return
```

APPENDIX 9B81: Matrix Inverse and Determinant

Refer to **APPENDIX 8I81** and enter [A].

$$[A] = \begin{bmatrix} 1/3 & 1 & 2 \\ -3 & 2 & -1 \\ 5 & 4 & 6 \end{bmatrix}$$

To find the inverse of [A], press 2nd [[A]] x^{-1} ENTER.

To find the determinant of [A], press MATRIX 5 (det) 2nd [[A]] ENTER.

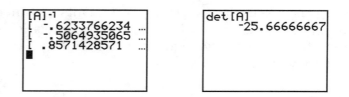

APPENDIX 9B82: Matrix Inverse and Determinant

Refer to **APPENDIX 8I82** and enter [A].

$$[A] = \begin{bmatrix} 1/3 & 1 & 2 \\ -3 & 2 & -1 \\ 5 & 4 & 6 \end{bmatrix}$$

To find the inverse of [A], press $\boxed{\text{MATRIX}}$ $\boxed{1}$ (A) $\boxed{x^{-1}}$ $\boxed{\text{ENTER}}$.

To find the determinant of [A], press $\boxed{\text{MATRIX}}$ MATH $\boxed{1}$ (det) $\boxed{\text{MATRIX}}$ $\boxed{1}$ (A) $\boxed{\text{ENTER}}$.

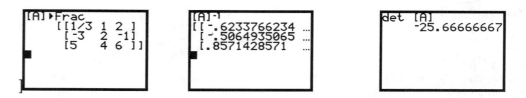

APPENDIX 9B85: Matrix Inverse and Determinant

Refer to **APPENDIX 8I85** and enter [MA].

$$[MA] = \begin{bmatrix} 1/3 & 1 & 2 \\ -3 & 2 & -1 \\ 5 & 4 & 6 \end{bmatrix}$$

To find the inverse of [MA], press $\boxed{\text{ALPHA}}$ M $\boxed{\text{ALPHA}}$ A $\boxed{x^{-1}}$ $\boxed{\text{ENTER}}$.

To find the determinant of [MA],
press $\boxed{\text{2nd}}$ [MATRX] $\boxed{\text{F3}}$ (MATH) $\boxed{\text{F1}}$ (det) $\boxed{\text{ALPHA}}$ M $\boxed{\text{ALPHA}}$ A $\boxed{\text{ENTER}}$.

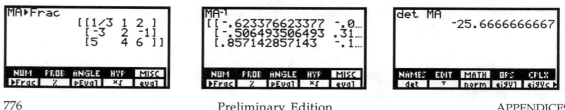

APPENDIX 9C80: Graphing Inequations

You will find three shade commands in the TI-80 DRAW menu. Choice 6 (SHADE_Y>) allows you to shade above a function, choice 7 (SHADE_Y<) allows you to shade below a function, and choice 8 (SHADE) allows you to shade between two functions.

Here are some examples for graphing a linear inequation. Try each of these, using the standard window, with your calculator.

$y \leq 2x - 3$ SHADE_Y<2X–3

$y \geq 0.5x + 2$ SHADE_Y>.5X+2

The calculator will not draw dashed lines to show a strict inequation such as $y > 1.2x + 2$.

This is a different approach. Instead of shading the true side of the line, shade the false side. If this is done for each inequation in a system, then the portion left unshaded will be the solution to the system.

Example: $2x + y \geq 6$ $x + 2y \leq 10$ $4x - 3y \leq 9$

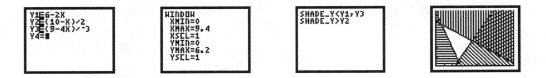

For directions on the **shade between** command see APPENDIX 9C82.

APPENDIX 9C81: Graphing Inequations

The command Shade(is choice 7 in the DRAW menu. It is used to shade between two boundaries. The command has the following structure.

Shade(lower boundary, upper boundary, resolution)

Here are some examples for graphing a linear inequation. Try each of these, using the standard window, with your calculator.

$y \leq 2x - 3$ Shade (−1000, 2X–3,1)

$y \geq 0.5x + 2$ Shade (.5X+2, 1000, 2)

The calculator will not draw dashed lines to show a strict inequation such as $y > 1.2x + 2$.

When you wish to find the intersection of two inequations, graph them with different resolutions. (Use numbers that are mutually prime, such as 2 and 3.) It is usually difficult see the intersection when you have more than three inequations.

This is a different approach. Instead of shading the true side of the line, shade the false side. If this is done for each inequation in a system, then the portion left unshaded will be the solution to the system.

Example: $2x + y \geq 6 \ x + 2y \leq 10 \ 4x - 3y \leq 9$

Enter the following into Y= $Y_1 = 6-2X$

$Y_2 = (10-X)/2$

$Y_3 = (9-4X)/-3$

Set the range to (0, 9.5, 1, 0, 6.3, 1).

Enter   Shade (-1,Y_1)

Shade (Y_2,10)

Shade (-1,Y_3)

APPENDIX 9C82: Graphing Inequations

The command Shade(is choice 7 in the DRAW menu. Use this command to shade between two boundaries. The command has the following structure.

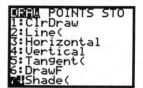

Shade(lower boundary, upper boundary, resolution)

Here are some examples for graphing a linear inequation. Try each of these, using the standard window, with your calculator.

$y \leq 2x - 3$ Shade (-1000, 2X–3,1)

$y \geq 0.5x + 2$ Shade (.5X+2, 1000, 2)

The calculator will not draw dashed lines to show a strict inequation such as $y > 1.2x + 2$.

When you want to show the intersection of two inequations, you can graph each with different resolution. (Use numbers that are mutually prime such as 2 and 3.) It is usually difficult see the intersection when you have more than three inequations.

This is a different approach. Instead of shading the true side of the line, shade the false side. If this is done for each inequation in a system, then the portion left unshaded will be the solution to the system.

Example: $2x + y \geq 6 \quad x + 2y \leq 10 \quad 4x - 3y \leq 9$

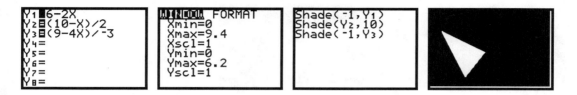

APPENDIX 9C85: Graphing Inequations

Press GRAPH MORE F2 (DRAW) F1 (Shade) to access the Shade(command. This command is used to shade between two boundaries. It has the following structure:

Shade(lower boundary, upper boundary, resolution)

Here are some examples for graphing a linear inequation. Try each of these, using the standard window, with your calculator.

$y \leq 2x - 3$ Shade (−1000, 2x−3,1)

$y \geq 0.5x + 2$ Shade (.5x+2, 1000, 2)

The calculator will not draw dashed lines to show a strict inequation such as $y > 1.2x + 2$.

When you wish to find the intersection of two inequations you can graph each with different resolution (use numbers that are mutually prime such as 2 and 3). It is usually difficult see the intersection when you have more than three inequations.

This is a different approach. Instead of shading the true side of the line, shade the false side. If this is done for each inequation in a system, then the portion left unshaded will be the solution to the system.

Example:

$2x + y \geq 6$ $x + 2y \leq 10$ $4x - 3y \leq 9$

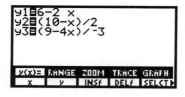

```
y1∎6-2 x
y2∎(10-x)/2
y3∎(9-4x)/-3

y(x)=  RANGE  ZOOM  TRACE  GRAPH
  x  |  y  | INSf | DELf |SELCT▶
```

```
RANGE
 xMin=0∎
 xMax=6.3
 xScl=1
 yMin=0
 yMax=6.2
 yScl=1
y(x)= RANGE ZOOM TRACE GRAPH▶
```

```
Shade(-1,y1)
Shade(y2,10)
Shade(-1,y3)
∎
```

Chapter Ten Appendices

APPENDIX 10A80: Root Finding

(You will need this program again in **APPENDIX 13A**, so don't delete it unless you have to in order to make more memory available.)

Begin by entering an equation in Y1. Graph the equation, and enter boundaries that you are sure lie on either side of a root.

```
PROGRAM:ROOT
:INPUT "ROOT BETWEEN",A          Guess on one side of root.
:INPUT "AND",B                   Guess on the other side of root.
:Y₁(A)->Y                        Find the Y-value at A.
:LBL 1
:(A+B)/2->X                      Average the two ends.
:IF Y₁Y>0:X->A                   If the Y's have the same sign, then replace A.
:IF Y₁Y<0:X->B                   If the Y's have different signs, then replace B.
:IF ABS Y₁≥E-10:GOTO 1           If the Y-value is not close to 0, go back and average
                                     again.
:DISP X                          Otherwise print answer.
```

If the program runs for a long time without giving you an answer, you may have entered two guesses on the same side of a root, or you may have to adjust the accuracy of the solution by changing the command `:IF ABS Y₁≥E-10` to `:IF ABS Y₁≥E-9` or `:IF ABS Y₁≥E-8`.

An alternative would be to move the DISP X line up one line and place it inside the loop. This will give you a continuous display of the progress the program is making. You can press the ON key to stop the program.

APPENDIX 10A81: Root Finding

(You will need this program again in **APPENDIX 13A**, so don't delete it unless you have to in order to make more memory available.)

Begin by entering an equation in Y1. Graph the equation, and enter boundaries that you are sure lie on either side of a root.

```
Prgm3:ROOT
:Disp "ROOT BETWEEN"
:Input A                    Guess on one side of root.
:Disp "AND"
:Input B                    Guess on the other side of root.
:A→X                        Store first guess in X
:Y1→Y                              to find the Y-value.
:Lbl 1
:(A+B)/2→X                  Average the two ends.
:If Y1Y>0                   If the Y's have the same sign,
:X→A                              then replace A.
:If Y1Y<0                   If the Y's have different signs,
:X→B                              then replace B.
:If abs Y1≥E⁻10            If the Y-value is not close to 0,
:Goto 1                           go back and average again.
:Disp X                     Otherwise print answer.
```

If the program runs for a long time without giving an answer, you may have entered two guesses on the same side of a root, or you may have to adjust the accuracy of the solution by changing the command :**If abs Y1≥E⁻10** to :**If abs Y1≥E⁻9** or :**If abs Y1≥E⁻8**.

An alternative would be to move the Disp X line up two lines and place it inside the loop. This will give you a continuous display of the progress the program is making. You can press the ON key to stop the program when you wish.

APPENDIX 10A82: Root Finding

Begin by putting the equation into the Y= menu. Graph the equation, and press 2nd [CALC] 2 (root). If more than one equation is graphed, use the up or down arrow to select the equation for which you wish to find the root. Next use the right or left arrow to trace to a point to the left of the root. Press ENTER. Then trace to a point to the right of the root. Press ENTER again. The last step is to trace along the curve to a point near the root. Press ENTER once more. In a moment, the calculator will give the value of the root. Sometimes this value will be exact, and sometimes it will be an approximation.

APPENDIX 10A85: Root Finding

Begin by putting the equation into the Y= menu. Graph the equation, and press MORE F1 (MATH) F3 (root). If more than one equation is graphed, use the up or down arrow to select the equation for which you wish to find the root. If more than one root exists, move closest to the root you want, and press ENTER. In a moment, the calculator will give the value of the root. Sometimes this value will be exact, and sometimes it will be an approximation.

APPENDIX 10B81: Synthetic Division Program

Using this program, you can use synthetic division to divide any polynomial with real coefficients by a single root. First you enter the root. Next enter the degree of the polynomial. Then enter the coefficients in order of degree. Remember to enter 0 for missing terms. If you have run the program, and wish to repeat with the same polynomial, enter 0 for the degree. When the remainder is zero, the stored polynomial is replaced with its reduced form.

```
PrgmS:SYNDIV           :Input {x}(N)
:Disp "ROOT"           :If Z=0
:Input R               :{y}(N)→{x}(N)
:Disp "DEGREE"         :{x}(N)+XR→X
:Input D               :X→{y}(N)
:0→X                   :IS>(N,L)
:1→N                   :Goto 1
:If D+Z=0              :IPart 10000X→Z
:L-1→L                 :1→N
:If D                  :Lbl 2
:D+1→L                 :Disp {y}(N)
:Disp "COEFFICIENTS"   :IS>(N,L-1)
:Lbl 1                 :Goto 2
:If D>0                :Disp "REMAINDER"
                       :Disp X
```

APPENDIX 10B80, 82, 85: Synthetic Division Program

Using this program, you can use synthetic division to divide any polynomial with real coefficients by a single root. First you enter the root. Next enter the degree of the polynomial. Then enter the coefficients in order of degree. Remember to enter 0 for missing terms. If you have run the program, and wish to repeat it with the same polynomial, enter 0 for the degree. When the remainder is zero, the stored polynomial is replaced with its reduced form.

```
Program:SYNDIV
:Input "ROOT:",R
:Input "DEGREE (0=SAME)",D
:0→X
:If D+Z=0:Then
:L-1→L:L₂→L₁
:Else
:If D:D+1→L:End
:ClrList L₂
:Disp "COEFFICIENTS"
:For(N,1,L)
:If D>0:Then
:Input C:Else
:L₁(N)→C:End
:C+XR→X:C→L₁(N)
:X→L₂(N)
:End
:iPart 10000X→Z
:L-1→dim L₂
:Disp L₂
:Disp "REMAINDER",X
```

```
Program:SynDiv
:Input "Root:",R
:Input "Degree (0=same)",D
:0→x
:If D+Z==0:Then
:L-1→L:yStat→xStat
:Else:If D>0
:D+1→L:End
:Disp "Coefficients"
:For(N,1,L)
:If D>0:Then
:Input C:Else
:xStat(N)→C:End
:C+x*R→x:C→xStat(N)
:x→yStat(N)
:End:L-1→dimL yStat
:iPart 1000x→Z
:Disp yStat
:Disp "Remainder",x
```

APPENDIX 10C80: Quadratic Formula Program

Enter the coefficients of a quadratic equation written in the form $ax^2 + bx + c = 0$. The program will display two values if there are two real roots. It will display the same value twice if the equation has two equal roots. If the roots are complex, it will display the roots in the form $a \pm bi$.

```
PROGRAM:QUADFORM
:INPUT "A",A
:INPUT "B",B
:INPUT "C",C
:B²-4AC→D
:IF D≥0:THEN
:(-B+√D)/2A→X
:(-B-√D)/2A→R
:DISP X,R
:ELSE: -B/2A→R
:√-D/2A→I
:DISP R
:DISP "+/-I*",I
:END
```

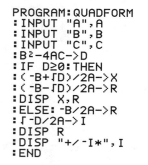

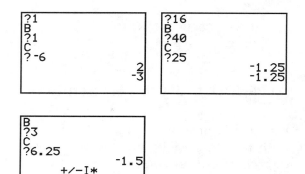

APPENDIX 10C81: Quadratic Formula Program

Enter the coefficients of a quadratic equation written in the form $ax^2 + bx + c = 0$. The program will display two values if there are two real roots. It will display the same value twice if the equation has two equal roots. If the roots are complex, it will display the roots in the form $a \pm bi$.

```
Prgm3:QUADFORM
:Disp "A"
:Input A
:Disp "B"
:Input B
:Disp "C"
:Input C
:B²-4AC→D
:If D<0
:Goto 1
:(-B+√D)/2A→X
:(-B-√D)/2A→R
:Disp X
:Disp R
:End
:Lbl 1
:-B/2A→R
:√-D/2A→I
:Disp R
:Disp "+/-I*"
:Disp I
```

APPENDIX 10C82: Quadratic Formula Program

Enter the coefficients of a quadratic equation written in the form $ax^2 + bx + c = 0$. The program will display two values if there are two real roots. It will display the same value twice if the equation has two equal roots. If the roots are complex, it will display the roots in the form $a \pm bi$.

```
Program:QUADFORM
:Prompt A,B,C
:B²-4AC→D
:If D≥0:Then
:(-B+√D)/2A→X
:(-B-√D)/2A→R
:Disp X,R
:Else: -B/2A→R
:√-D/2A→I
:Disp R
:Disp "+/-I*",I
:End
```

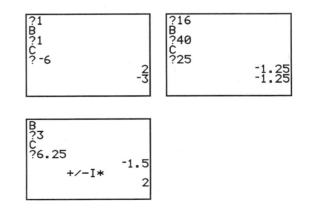

APPENDIX 10C85: Quadratic Formula Program

Enter [2nd] [POLY] and type 2 for order. Enter the coefficients a, b, and c of a quadratic equation, written in the form $ax^2 + bx + c = 0$, when the calculator asks for a2, a1, and a0. Then press [F5], and the calculator will solve the equation. It will display complex numbers such as $-1.5 + 2i$ as $(-1.5, 2)$.

APPENDIX 10D81: Polynomial Fit

```
Pr9m6:POLYFIT
:Disp "DEGREE?"
:Input D
:D+1→ARow
:D+1→ACol
:D+1→BRow
:1→BCol
:0[A]→[A]
:0[B]→[B]
:1→N
:Lbl 1
:1→R
:Lbl 2
:[B](R,1)+{y}(N){x}(N)^(R-1)→[B](R,1)
:1→C
:Lbl 3
:[A](R,C)+{x}(N)^(R+C-2)→[A](R,C)
:IS>(C,D+1)
:Goto 3
:IS>(R,D+1)
:Goto 2
:IS>(N,Dim{x})
:Goto 1
:[A]⁻¹[B]→[C]
:Disp [C]
:If D=2
:"[C](1,1)+[C](2,1)X+[C](3,1)X^2"→Y₁
:If D=3
:"[C](1,1)+[C](2,1)X+[C](3,1)X^2+[C](
4,1)X^3"→Y₁
:If D=4
:"[C](1,1)+[C](2,1)X+[C](3,1)X^2+[C](
4,1)X^3+[C](5,1)X^4"→Y₁
```

Before running the program, enter the data into the stat set. Enter the degree of the fit you want; 2, 3, or 4 for quadratic, cubic, or quartic fitting, respectively. The displayed results will be in order from lowest degree to highest. The example screen here is read as

$y = 10.86 + -2.34x + 0.28x^2 + -0.01x^3$

```
Pr9m6
DEGREE?
?3
[ 10.86]
[ -2.34]
[ .28  ]
[ -.01 ]
```

APPENDIX 10D80, 82, 85: Polynomial Fit

Polynomial regression is built into all of these calculators as part of the STAT CALC menu. Do the analysis as you would do a linear analysis except select 6 for QuadReg, 7 for CubicReg, or 8 for QuartReg on the TI-82, or P2REG, P3REG, or P4REG for the respective regressions on the TI-85. The TI-80 does not have cubic and quartic regressions.

APPENDIX 10E81: Coefficient of Fit

Before running the program, enter the data into the stat set and the equation into Y1. The output will be ρ^2 (rho squared), the square of the coefficient of fit.

```
Prgm7:RHO
:0→S
:1→N
:Lbl 1
:{x}(N)→X
:({y}(N)-Y₁)²+S→S
:IS>(N,Dim{x})
:Goto 1
:S/Dim{x}→S
:LinReg
:(σy²-S)/σy²→R
:Disp "RHO²="
:Disp R
```

APPENDIX 10E80, 82: Coefficient of Fit

Before running the program, enter the x-data in L1, the y-data in L2, and the equation in Y1. The output will be rho squared, or the square of the coefficient of fit.

```
Program:RHO
mean(((L₂-Y₁(L₁))²)→S
2-Var Stats L₁,L₂
(σy²-S)/σy²→R
Disp "RHO²=",R
```

APPENDIX 10E85: Coefficient of Fit

Before running the program, enter the x-data in xStat, the y data is in yStat, and the equation in y1. The output will be rho squared or the square of the coefficient of fit.

```
Program:RHO
xStat→x
sum ((yStat-y1)²)/dimL xStat→S
LinR xStat,yStat
(σy²-S)/σy²→ρ
Disp "ρ²=",ρ
```

APPENDIX 10F81: Mandelbrot Graph

This program will draw the Mandelbrot set for the area contained within the window settings. To create a graph that is proportioned correctly, you need to "square up" the window after you have set the range. Do this by entering ZOOM 5 (Square). It is a slow program because it must check up to 50 iterations on almost 6000 points to find which points "explode." The program uses the fact that if a point gets more than two units from the origin, it will never come back, and if it is still within two units after 50 iterations, then it will likely stay in.

```
Prgm8:MANDELBR
    :Xmin→A              :Lbl 3               :Lbl 4
    :(Xmax-Xmin)/95→U    :X²-Y²+A→Z           :B+U→B
    :(Ymax-Ymin)/63→U    :2XY+B→Y             :If B≤Ymax
    :Lbl 1               :Z→X                 :Goto 2
    :Ymin→B              :If abs X>2          :A+U→A
    :Lbl 2               :Goto 4              :If A≤Xmax
    :1→N                 :IS>(N,50)           :Goto 1
    :0→X                 :Goto 3
    :0→Y                 :PT-On(A,B)
```

APPENDIX 10F80, 82: Mandelbrot Graph

This program will draw the Mandelbrot set for the area contained within the window settings. To create a graph that is proportioned correctly you should "square up" the window after you have set the range. Do this by entering ZOOM 5 (ZSquare). It is a slow program because it must check up to 50 iterations on almost 6000 points to find which points "explode." The program uses the fact that if a point gets more than two units from the origin, it will never come back, and if it is still within two units after 50 iterations, then it will likely stay in.

```
Program:MANDELBR
For(A,Xmin,Xmax,(Xmax-Xmin)/94)
For(B,Ymin,Ymax,(Ymax-Ymin)/62)
0→X:0→Y:1→N
For(N,1,50)
X²-Y²+A→Z
2XY+B→Y:Z→X
If abs X>2:99→N
End
If N=51:Pt-On(A,B)
End:End
```

APPENDIX 10F85: Mandelbrot Graph

This program will draw the Mandelbrot set for the area contained within the window settings. To create a graph that is proportioned correctly you should "square up" the window after you have set the range. Do this by entering $\boxed{\text{GRAPH}}$ $\boxed{\text{ZOOM}}$ $\boxed{\text{MORE}}$ $\boxed{\text{F2}}$ (ZSQR). It is a slow program because it must check up to 50 iterations on almost 8000 points to find which points "explode." The program uses the fact that if a point gets more than two units from the origin, it will never come back, and if it is still within two units after 50 iterations, then it will likely stay in.

```
Program:MANDELBR

For(A,xMin,xMax,(xMax-xMin)/126)
For(B,yMin,yMax,(yMax-yMin)/62)
0→Z:1→N
Lbl A
Z²+(A,B)→Z
If abs Z>2:Goto B
IS>(N,50):Goto A
PtOn(A,B)
Lbl B:End:End
```

Chapter Eleven Appendices

APPENDIX 11A81: Permutations and Combinations

To calculate permutations and combinations, enter the total number of elements, press MATH PRB 2 for permutations or MATH PRB 3 for combinations, and then enter the number to be selected or used.

```
MATH NUM HYP PRB
1:Rand
2: nPr
3: nCr
```

```
5 nPr 3
              60
5 nCr 3
              10
■
```

APPENDIX 11A80, 82: Permutations and Combinations

To calculate permutations and combinations, enter the total number of elements, press MATH PRB 2 for permutations or MATH PRB 3 for combinations, and then enter the number to be selected or used.

```
MATH NUM HYP PRB
1:rand
2:nPr
3:nCr
4: !
```

```
5 nPr 3
              60
5 nCr 3
              10
■
```

APPENDIX 11A85: Permutations and Combinations

To calculate permutations and combinations, enter the total number of elements, press 2nd [MATH] F2 (PROB) 2 for permutations or 2nd

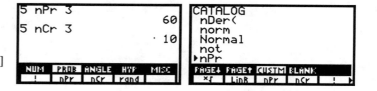

[MATH] F2 (PROB) 3 for combinations, and then enter the number to be selected or used. You may want to move these functions to your custom menu.

APPENDIX 11B80, 81, 82, 85: Free Throw Simulation

Enter your experimental probability, and the program will output the results of 250 trials of a ten-shot basketball experiment.

TI-81

```
PRGM1:FREETHRO          :IS>(B,10)        :If Rand<P         :0→Xmin
:Input "P",P            :Goto 1           :B+1→B             :11→Xmax
:ClrStat                :1→N              :IS>(S,10)         :1→Xscl
:0→B                    :Lbl 2            :Goto 3            :0→Ymin
:Lbl 1                  :1→S              :{y}(B+1)+1→{y}(B+1) :100→Ymax
:B→{x}(B+1)             :0→B              :IS>(N,250)        :All-Off
:0→{y}(B+1)             :Lbl 3            :Goto N            :Hist
```

TI-80, TI-82

```
Program:FREETHRO
:Input "P=",P
:{0,1,2,3,4,5,6,7,8,9,10}→L₁
:{0,0,0,0,0,0,0,0,0,0,0}→L₂
:For(N,1,250)
:0→B
:For(S,1,10)
:If rand<P:B+1→B
:End
:L₂(B+1)+1→L₂(B+1)
:End
:0→Xmin:11→Xmax
:0→Ymin:100→Ymax
:1→Xscl:FnOff
:Plot1(Histogram,L₁,L₂)
:PlotsOff :PlotsOn 1
:DispGraph
```

TI-85

```
Program:FREETHRO
:Prompt P
:{0,1,2,3,4,5,6,7,8,9,10}→xStat
:{0,0,0,0,0,0,0,0,0,0,0}→yStat
:For(N,1,250)
:0→B
:For(S,1,10)
:If rand<P:B+1→B
:End
:yStat(B+1)+1→yStat(B+1)
:End
:0→xMin:11→xMax
:0→yMin:100→yMax
:1→xScl:FnOff
:Hist xStat,yStat
```

APPENDIX 11C80, 81, 82, 85: Binomial Sum

This program will sum terms *A* through *B* of a binomial expression. You need to enter the equation for the term of a binomial expression into the Y= menu. If you enter the generic form of this expression, then you should store the correct values of your variables (N and P) before you run the program. For example, to sum the 47th through 94th terms of $(0.28 + 0.72)^{100}$, enter

$Y1 = (N \text{ nCr } X)(P^{\wedge}(N - X))(1 - P)^{\wedge}X$. Then store $100 \to N$ and $0.28 \to P$ and run the program. Enter 47 for A and 94 for B when prompted.

```
Prgm6:SUMBI---81      Program:SUMBI-80,82      Program:SUMBI---85
:Disp "A"             :Input "A",A             :Prompt A,B        A is the 1st term.
:Input A              :Input "B",B                                B is the last term.
:Disp "B"
:Input B
:A→X
:0→S                  :0→S                     :0→S               S is the sum.
:Lbl 1                :For(X,A,B)              :For(x,A,B)
:S+Y₁→S               :S+Y₁→S                  :S+y1→S            Y1 is the equation.
:IS>(X,B+1)           :End                     :End
:Goto 1
:Disp S               :Disp S                  :Disp S
```

APPENDIX 11D80: Graphing Binomial Curves

The equation $Y1 = (N \text{ nCr } X)(P^{\wedge}(N - X))(1 - P)^{\wedge}X$ will only graph for integer values of X. You can see this graph using a window of [20, 82, 0, −0.02, 0.1, 0.025]. You may have to shift the Xmin and Xmax, but always keep them 62 pixels apart.

APPENDIX 11D81: Graphing Binomial Curves

The equation $Y1 = (N \text{ nCr } X)(P^{\wedge}(N - X))(1 - P)^{\wedge}X$ will only graph for integer values of X. This graph can be seen using a window of [0, 95, 0, −0.02, 0.1, 0.025].

APPENDIX 11D82: Graphing Binomial Curves

The equation $Y1 = (N \text{ nCr } X)(P^{\wedge}(N - X))(1 - P)^{\wedge}X$ will only graph for integer values of X. This graph can be seen using a window of [0, 94, 0, −0.02, 0.1, 0.025].

APPENDIX 11D85: Graphing Binomial Curves

The equation $y1 = (N \text{ nCr } x)(P^{\wedge}(N - x))(1 - P)^{\wedge}x$ will only graph for integer values of x. This graph can be seen using a window of [0, 126, 0, −0.02, 0.1, 0.025].

APPENDIX 11E81, 85: 1-Variable Statistics

To calculate the mean and standard deviation of a set of data in which each data value only appears once, enter each value in the data set as an x-value and set the corresponding y-value to 1. If your calculator stops advancing, then you have run out of memory, and you will have to delete a program before you can continue to enter data. Once all the data has been entered, enter the appropriate command depending on which calculator you are using.

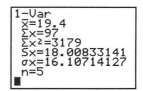

TI-81: [2nd] [STAT] [1] (1-Var) [ENTER]

TI-85: [STAT] [F1] (CALC) [ENTER] [ENTER] [F1] (1-VAR)

The screen shot shows the values for the data set 4, 7, 11, 28, 47. The mean is 19.4 and the standard deviation is 16.10714127.

If the data set has values that appear more than once, then for each x-value you can enter the frequency as the corresponding y-value. The frequency must always be a positive-integer value or the calculator will give you an error message.

APPENDIX 11E80, 82: 1-Variable Statistics

To calculate the mean and standard deviation of a set of data in which each data value only appears once, enter each value in the data set as an x-value and set the corresponding y-value to 1. Once all the data is into a list (for example, L1), enter [STAT] CALC [1] (1-Var Stats) [2nd] [L1] [ENTER]. The screen shot shows the values for the data set 4, 7, 11, 28, 47. The mean is 19.4 and the standard deviation is 16.10714127.

If the data set has values that appear more than once, then for each data value entered in L1, enter the corresponding frequency in L2. However, a frequency cannot be greater than 99. Consider the following data set.

Mass (L1)	2.7 g	2.8 g	2.9 g	3.0 g	3.1 g	3.2 g	3.3 g	3.4 g
Frequency (L2)	2	15	57	111	138	109	54	14

This data set would have to be entered as follows.

Mass (L1)	2.7	2.8	2.9	3	3	3.1	3.1	3.2	3.2	3.3	3.4
Frequency (L2)	2	15	57	99	12	99	39	99	10	54	14

In this way, no frequency value in the second list is greater than 99. If the data values are placed in L1 and the frequencies in L2, then you will enter the command $\boxed{\text{STAT}}$ CALC $\boxed{1}$ (1-Var Stats) $\boxed{\text{2nd}}$ [L1] $\boxed{,}$ $\boxed{\text{2nd}}$ [L2] $\boxed{\text{ENTER}}$.

APPENDIX 11F80: Two-Die Simulation

Enter the command SEQ(RANDINT(1,6)+RANDINT(1,6),X,1,99,1)->L1. The command will place all 99 sums into L1.

APPENDIX 11F81: Two-Die Simulation

Enter the program below and run it. The program will place all 99 sums into the x-values of the data set. If the program gives you an error message, you may be out of memory, in which case you will need to delete a program.

```
Prgm:TWODIE
:ClrStat
:1→N
:Lbl 1
:Int 6Rand+1+Int 6Rand+1→{x}(N)
:IS>(N,99)
:Goto 1
```

APPENDIX 11F82: Two-Die Simulation

Enter the command seq(int 6rand+1+int 6rand+1,X,1,99,1)→L1. The command will place all 99 sums into L1.

APPENDIX 11F85: Two-Die Simulation

Enter the commands seq(int 6rand+1+int 6rand+1,x,1,99,1)→xStat and seq(1,x,1,99,1)→yStat. It will place the 99 sums into xStat and the corresponding frequencies, 99 ones, into yStat.

APPENDIX 11G81: Binomial Data

Enter the binomial distribution function in Y1. Then enter and run the program. This program will enter the numbers from 0 to 90 as x-values and the y-values will be the corresponding integer frequencies from the equation stored in Y1.

```
Prgm:BINOM
:ClrStat
:0→N
:Lbl 1
:N→{x}(N+1)
:Round(1000Y₁,0)→{y}(N+1)
:IS>(N,90)
:Goto 1
```

APPENDIX 11G80, 82: Binomial Data

Place the binomial distribution function in Y1. Then enter the commands `seq(X,X,0,90,1)→L₁` and `seq(round(1000Y₁,0),X,0,90,1)→L₂`. These commands will place the numbers 0 to 90 into L1 and corresponding integer frequencies in L2.

APPENDIX 11G85: Binomial Data

Place the binomial distribution function in y1. Then enter the commands `seq(x,x,0,90,1)→xStat` and `seq(round(1000y1,0),x,0,90,1)→yStat`. These commands will place the numbers 0 to 90 into xStat and corresponding integer frequencies into yStat.

APPENDIX 11H81: Area Under a Curve

This program will calculate the area under a curve by finding the average height of the curve and multiplying this height by the length of the interval. The value of N will determine how many points are used to find the average. The larger the value of N, the more accurate the average will be. However, it will take a long time for the calculator to find this average if N is very large.

```
Prgm6:AREA---81
:Disp "A"          :0→S          A is the left value.
:Input A           :Lbl 1        B is the right value.
:Disp "B"          :A+JD→X       N is the # of values.
:Input B           :S+Y₁→S       D is the width.
:Disp "N"          :IS>(J,N)     S is the sum.
:Input N           :Goto 1       J is the value counter.
:(B-A)/N→D         :(B-A)S/(N+1)→S   Y1 is the equation.
:0→J               :Disp S       The area.
```

APPENDIX 11H80, 82, 85: Area Under a Curve

The program will calculate the area under a curve by finding the average height of the curve and multiplying this height by the length of the interval. The value of N will determine how many points are used to find the average. The larger the value of N, the more accurate the average will be. However, it will take a long time for the calculator to find this average if N is very large.

```
Prgm6:AREA---80        Program:AREA---82        Program:AREA---85
:INPUT "A",A           :Prompt A,B,N            :Prompt A,B,N          A is the left value.
:INPUT "B",B                                                           B is the right
                                                                         value.
:INPUT "N",N                                                           N is the # of
                                                                         values.
:(B-A)/N→D             :(B-A)/N→D               :(B-A)/N→D             D is the width.
:0→S                   :0→S                     :0→S                   S is the sum.
:FOR(J,0,N)            :For(J,0,N)              :For(J,0,N)            J is the value
                                                                         counter.
                                                :A+J*D→x
:S+Y₁(A+JD)→S          :S+Y₁(A+JD)→S            :S+y1→S                Y1 is the equation.
:END                   :End                     :End
:DISP (B-A)S/(N+1)     :Disp (B-A)S/(N+1)       :Disp (B-A)S/(N+1)          The  area.
```

APPENDIX 11I81: Normal-Curve Data Entry

Enter the equation $Y1 = 21(0.991)^{\wedge}(X{-}82)^2$ and the program below. This program will evaluate the function for all x-values from 62 to 102 and round them to integers. These become the frequencies and are stored as the y-values of the data set. You may now do one-variable calculations on the data set to find the mean and standard deviation.

```
Prgm:NORM
:ClrStat
:62→X
:Lbl 1
:X→{x}(X-61)
:Round(Y₁,0)→{y}(X-61)
:IS>(X,102)
:Goto 1
```

APPENDIX 11I80, 82: Normal-Curve Data Entry

Enter the equation $Y_1 = 21(0.991)^{\wedge}(X-82)^2$ and the commands
`seq(X,X,62,102,1)→L₁` and `seq(round(Y₁,0),X,62,102,1)→L₂`. The first command
stores the numbers from 62 to 102 in L1. The second command evaluates the
function for each x-value from 62 to 102. The values are rounded to integer
values and stored in L2 as frequencies. Now you can do one-variable calculations
on L1, L2 to find the mean and standard deviation.

APPENDIX 11I85: Normal-Curve Data Entry

Enter the equation $y_1 = 21(0.991)^{\wedge}(x-82)^2$ and the commands
`seq(x,x,62,102,1)→xStat` and `seq(round(y1,0),x,62,102,1)→yStat`. The first
command stores the numbers from 62 to 102 in the xStat list. The second
command evaluates the function for each x-value from 62 to 102. The values are
rounded to integer values and stored in yStat as frequencies. Now you can do
one-variable calculations on xStat, yStat to find the mean and standard
deviation.

APPENDIX 11J80: Probability and the Normal Curve

The program in **APPENDIX 11H** will find the area or probability of an event given
the interval and the equation of the normal curve. The program in this appendix
will give the interval when you supply the probability. The program will request
the mean, the standard deviation and a probability. It will then find the upper
endpoint of the range with the given probability. See the examples in Section 6
that explain how to use this program.

```
PROGRAM:AREA2
:"1/S√2π*(1-1/2S²)^(X-M)²"→Y₄          :M→X:END
:INPUT "MEAN",M                        :S/50→W
:INPUT "STD DEV",S                     :LBL 1
:INPUT "PROB",P                        :X+W→X
:S/50→W                                :A+WY₄→A
:IF P<.5:THEN                          :IF A<P
:0→A:M-4S→X                            :GOTO 1
:ELSE:0.5→A                            :DISP X
```

APPENDIX 11J81: Probability and the Normal Curve

The program in **APPENDIX 11H** will find the area or probability of an event given the interval and the equation of the normal curve. The program in this appendix will give the interval when you supply the probability. The program will request the mean, the standard deviation and a probability. It will then find the upper endpoint of the range with the given probability. See the examples in Section 6 that explain how to use this program.

```
Prgm:AREA2
:"1/S√2π*(1-1/2S²)^(X-M)²"→Y₄          :If P<.5
:Disp "MEAN"                           :Goto 1
:Input M                               :0.5→A
:Disp "STD DEV"                        :M→X
:Input S                               :Lbl 1
:Disp "PROB"                           :X+W→X
:Input P                               :A+WY₄→A
:0→A                                   :If A<P
:M-4S→X                                :Goto 1
:S/50→W                                :Disp X
```

APPENDIX 11J82, 85: Probability and the Normal Curve

The program in **APPENDIX 11H** will find the area or probability of an event given the interval and the equation of the normal curve. The program in this appendix will give the interval when you supply the probability. The program will request the mean, the standard deviation and a probability. It will then find the upper endpoint of the range with the given probability. See the examples in Section 6 that explain how to use this program.

```
Program:AREA2   ---  82              Program:Area2   ----  85
:"1/S√2π*(1-1/2S²)^(X-M)²"→Y₄         :y4=1/S√2π*(1-1/2S²)^(x-M)²
:Prompt M,S,P                         :Prompt M,S,P
:S/50→W                               :S/50→W
:If P<.5:Then                         :If P<.5:Then
:0→A:M-4S→X                           :0→A:M-4S→x
:Else:0.5→A                           :Else:0.5→A
:M→X:End                              :M→x:End
:Repeat A≥P                           :Repeat A≥P
:X+W→X:A+WY₄→A                        :x+W→x:A+W*y4→A
:End:Disp X                           :End:Disp x
```

APPENDIX 11K80, 81, 82,85: Sample Standard Deviation

APPENDIX 11E explains how to calculate one-variable statistics. Appearing in the screen list just above the population standard deviation, σx, you will find the sample standard deviation, Sx. It should always be the larger of the two numbers.

Chapter Twelve Appendices

There are no appendices for Chapter Twelve.

Chapter Thirteen Appendices

APPENDIX 13A80: Root Finding

(You may have already entered this program, which is also found in **APPENDIX 10A**.)

Begin by entering an equation in Y1. Graph the equation, and enter boundaries that you are sure lie on either side of a root.

```
PRPGRAM:ROOT
:INPUT "ROOT BETWEEN",A        Guess on one side of root.
:INPUT "AND",B                 Guess on the other side of root.
:Y₁(A)->Y                      Find the Y-value at A.
:LBL 1
:(A+B)/2->X                    Average the two ends.
:IF Y₁Y>0:X->A                 If the Y's have the same sign, then replace A.
:IF Y₁Y<0:X->B                 If the Y's have different signs, then replace B.
:IF ABS Y₁≥E-10:GOTO 1         If the Y-value is not close to 0, go back and average
                                    again.
:DISP X                        Otherwise print answer.
```

If the program runs for a long time without giving you an answer, you may have entered two guesses on the same side of a root, or you may have to adjust the accuracy of the solution by changing the command `:IF ABS Y₁≥E-10` to `:IF ABS Y₁≥E-9` or `:IF ABS Y₁≥E-8`.

An alternative would be to move the DISP X line up one line and place it inside the loop. This will give you a continuous display of the progress the program is making. You can press the ON key to stop the program.

APPENDIX 13A81: Root Finding

(You may have already entered this program, which is also found in **APPENDIX 10A**.)

Begin by entering an equation in Y1. Graph the equation, and enter boundaries that you are sure lie on either side of a root.

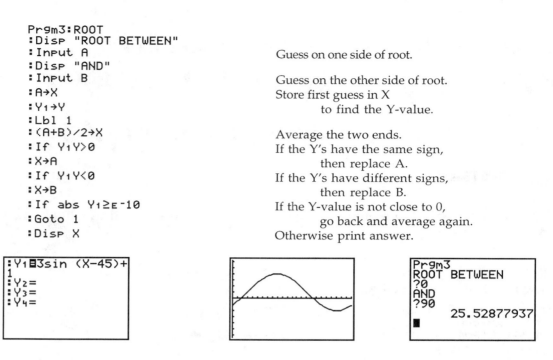

```
Prgm3:ROOT
:Disp "ROOT BETWEEN"
:Input A                          Guess on one side of root.
:Disp "AND"
:Input B                          Guess on the other side of root.
:A→X                              Store first guess in X
:Y₁→Y                                  to find the Y-value.
:Lbl 1
:(A+B)/2→X                        Average the two ends.
:If Y₁Y>0                         If the Y's have the same sign,
:X→A                                   then replace A.
:If Y₁Y<0                         If the Y's have different signs,
:X→B                                   then replace B.
:If abs Y₁≥E‾10                   If the Y-value is not close to 0,
:Goto 1                                go back and average again.
:Disp X                           Otherwise print answer.
```

If the program runs for a long time without giving an answer, you may have entered two guesses on the same side of a root, or you may have to adjust the accuracy of the solution by changing the command :If abs Y₁≥E‾10 to :If abs Y₁≥E‾9 or :If abs Y₁≥E‾8.

An alternative would be to move the Disp X line up two lines and place it inside the loop. This will give you a continuous display of the progress the program is making. You can press the [ON] key to stop the program when you wish.

APPENDIX 13A82: Root Finding

Begin by putting the equation into the Y= menu. Graph the equation, and press [2nd] [CALC] [2] (root). If more than one equation is graphed, use the up or down arrow to select the equation for which you wish to find the root. Next use the right or left arrow to trace to a point to the left of the root. Press [ENTER]. Then trace to a point to the right of the root. Press [ENTER] again. The last step is to trace along the curve to a point near the root. Press [ENTER] once more. In a moment, the calculator will give the value of the root. Sometimes this value will be exact, and sometimes it will be an approximation.

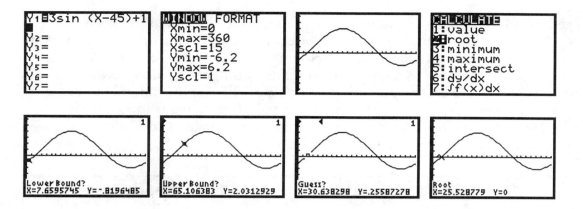

In addition, the calculator has a solve command that will find the variable value that will make an expression equal to zero. Press MATH 0 (Solve). Enter the three parameters for this function–the expression, the variable, and the guess–in that order. The function will then find a root, if one exists, nearest to the guess.

APPENDIX 13A85: Root Finding

Begin by putting the equation into the Y= menu. Graph the equation, and press MORE F1 (MATH) F3 (root). If more than one equation is graphed, use the up or down arrow to select the equation for which you wish to find the root. If more than one root exists, move closest to the root you want, and press ENTER . In a moment, the calculator will give the value of the root. Sometimes this value will be exact, and sometimes it will be an approximation.

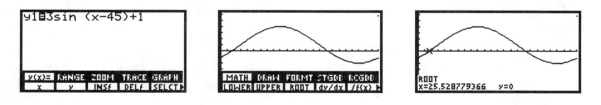

There is also a built-in equation solver routine in the calculator. Press
2nd [SOLVER] and enter the expression or equation. If it is an equation, then you
must give a value for each variable including a guess for the variable for which
you are solving. If it is an expression, you must also give a value for the
expression. With the blinking cursor on the same line as the variable to be
solved for, press F5 (SOLVE). The calculator will display the solution closest to
your guess. It will also calculate the error between the actual root and your guess,
and display the error on the last line.

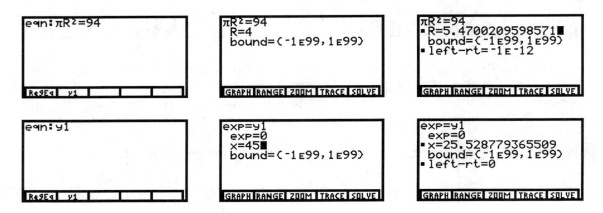

APPENDIX 13B80: Tracing in Polar Coordinates

The TI-80 will not trace in polar coordinates.

APPENDIX 13B81: Tracing in Polar Coordinates

In the MODE menu, select Polar to change the coordinate
type in tracing. The cursor moves the same as in rectangular
mode, but the display will give the polar coordinates of the
point. The r-value is the distance from the origin, and the
θ-value will range between -180 and 180 if the calculator is in
degree mode.

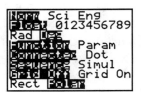

APPENDIX 13B82: Tracing in Polar Coordinates

Press WINDOW FORMAT and select PolarGC to change the coordinate type for tracing. The cursor moves the same as in rectangular mode, but the display will give the polar coordinates of the point. The r-value is the distance from the origin, and the θ-value will range between -180 and 180 if the calculator is in degree mode.

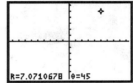

APPENDIX 13B85: Tracing in Polar Coordinates

Press GRAPH MORE F3 (FORMT), and select PolarGC to change the coordinate type in tracing. The cursor moves the same as in rectangular mode, but the display will give the polar coordinates of the point. The r-value is the distance from the origin, and the θ-value will range between -180 and 180 if the calculator is in degree mode.

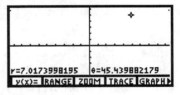

APPENDIX 13C80, 81: Graphing Polar Equations

The TI-80 and the TI-81 do not have a polar graphing mode, but it is fairly simple to use the parametric mode to graph polar equations. The following method will work to graph true polar equations. Enter an equation in the form of $r = f(\theta)$ such as $r = 4 \cos(7\theta)$ into X1T as a function of T. Then enter X2T = X1T cos T and Y2T = X1T sin T. You never need to change these last two entries. Simply change the function in X1T and press GRAPH.

If you want to graph two polar curves, enter X3T = Y1T cos T and Y3T = Y1T sin T, and enter the second function in Y1T. Don't forget to turn off Y1T. Whenever you change either equation, you will need to turn off X1T and Y1T.

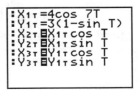

APPENDIX 13C82: Graphing Polar Equations

In the MODE menu, select Pol. The Y= menu will now give you six equations
(r1 through r6) and the X,T,θ key will display θ as the independent variable. On
the WINDOW screen, you must input θmin, θmax, and θstep as well as the
normal dimensions of the graphing window.

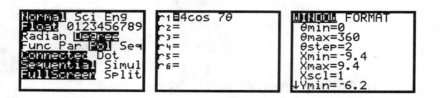

APPENDIX 13C85: Graphing Polar Equations

In the MODE menu you should select Polar. The Y= menu will now give you
equations r1 through r99 and GRAPH F1 will give θ as the independent variable.
In the RANGE menu, you must set θmin, θmax, and θstep as well as the normal
dimensions of the graphing window.

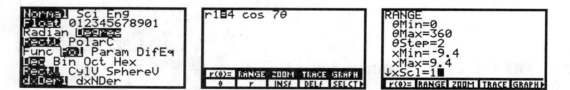

APPENDIX 13D81: Converting to Polar Coordinates

Press MATH 1 (R>P()). Then on the HOME screen enter the
x-coordinate, a comma, and the y-coordinate. The calculator
will display the r-value. It will also store that r-value in R
and the θ-value in θ. Enter ALPHA [θ] to find the angle
(between −180° and 180°). To convert from polar coordinates
to rectangular coordinates, press MATH 2 (P>R(), and enter
the radius, a comma, and the angle (no restrictions). The
calculator will display the x-value, and, at the same time, it
will store the coordinates in X and Y. Enter ALPHA [Y] to see
the y-coordinate.

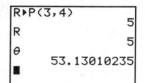

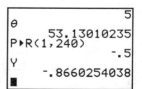

To square a number such as $0.3 - 0.2i$, you could first change it to polar form, square it, then change it back. (See the sample display that shows this process.) The coordinates are converted and stored by the R>P command. Then using DeMoivre's theorem, convert the squared polar form back to rectangular form for plotting.

```
0.3→X
            .3
-0.2→Y
           -.2
P►R(R►P(X,Y)²,2θ
)
            .05
Y■
```

APPENDIX 13D80, 82: Converting to Polar Coordinates

Press [2nd] [ANGLE] [5] (R>Pr( ). Then on the HOME screen enter the x-coordinate, a comma, and the y-coordinate. The calculator will display the r-value. Then press [2nd] [ANGLE] [6] (R>Pθ( ). On the HOME screen enter the x-coordinate, a comma, and the y-coordinate. The calculator will display the θ value (between $-180°$ and $180°$). To convert from polar to rectangular coordinates, press [2nd] [ANGLE] [7] (P>Rx(), and enter the radius, a comma, and the angle (no restrictions). The calculator will display the x-value. Press [2nd] [ANGLE] [8] (P>Ry(), and enter the radius, a comma, and the angle (no restrictions) to display the y-value.

```
R►Pr(3,4)
               5
R►Pθ(3,4)
        53.13010235
```

```
R►Pθ(3,4)
        53.13010235
P►Rx(1,240)
             -.5
P►Ry(1,240)
       -.8660254038
```

To square a number such as $0.3 - 0.2i$, first change it to polar form, square it, then change it back. You can do this all in one step although it is very long. (See the sample screen at the right that shows this process.) The coordinates are converted and stored by the R>P command. Then using DeMoivre's theorem, convert the squared polar form back to rectangular form for plotting.

```
           (.3  -.2)
(P►Rx(R►Pr(Ans(1
),Ans(2))²,2R►Pθ
(Ans(1),Ans(2)))
,P►Ry(R►Pr(Ans(1
),Ans(2))²,2R►Pθ
(Ans(1),Ans(2)))
)
```

APPENDIX 13D85: Converting to Polar Coordinates

In the MODE menu, select PolarC. Then, on the HOME screen, enter the x- and y-coordinates, separated by a comma. The calculator will display the r-value and θ-value (between $-180°$ and $180°$). To convert from polar to rectangular coordinates, select RecC in the MODE menu. On the HOME screen, enter the radius, $\angle$, and the angle (no restrictions). (Press [2nd] [,] for $\angle$.) The calculator will display the x-value and the y-value.

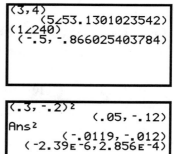

To square a number such as $0.3 - 0.2i$, simply enter it in ordered pair notation and square it.

APPENDIX 13E80, 81, 82, 85: Julia Set Graphs

Enter the program. Before running it, set the window to $[-1.25, 1.25, 0, -1.2, 1.2, 0]$. The program will ask you to input coefficient values, a and b, of a complex number. Only some values will create interesting pictures. The rest represent points that are escapees or prisoners.

```
Prgm5:JULIA   81
:Disp "A"
:Input A
:Disp "B"
:Input B
:0→X
:0→Y
:Lbl 1
:X-A→X
:Y-B→Y
:R►P(X,Y)
:P►R(√R,θ/2+180(Rand>.5))
:PT-On(X,Y)
:Goto 1
```

```
PROGRAM:JULIA 80,82
 Input "A",A
 Input "B",B
 0→X:0→Y
 For(N,1,5000)
 X-A→X:Y-B→Y
 √R►Pr(X,Y)→R
 R►Pθ(X,Y)/2→θ
 θ+180(rand>.5)→θ
 P►Rx(R,θ)→X
 P►Ry(R,θ)→Y
 Pt-On(X,Y)
 End
```

```
PROGRAM:Julia 85

 Prompt C
 (0,0)→Z
 For(N,1,10000)
 √(Z-C)*(-1)^int 2rand→Z
 PtOn(real Z,imag Z)
 End
```

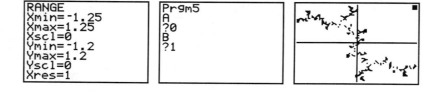

SELECTED ANSWERS

Contents

Chapter 0 808

Chapter 1 809

Chapter 2 812

Chapter 3 816

Chapter 4 819

Chapter 5 826

Chapter 6 834

Chapter 7 840

Chapter 8 848

Chapter 9 855

Chapter 10 862

Chapter 11 868

Chapter 12 871

Chapter 13 879

Chapter Zero Selected Answers

Problem Set 0.1

1. a. 10.63014581 . . .   b. 1.95   c. 30

2. a. $(-4)^2 = 16$, $-4^2 = -16$. In the first   d.
    expression -4 is being squared.
    In the second, only the 4 is being
    squared. The squaring is done
    first (the order of operations),
    and then the multiplication by
    -1 causes the sign change.

    ```
    17→X
                    17
    X²
                   289
    -X²
                  -289
    ■
    ```

3. a. i. 8   ii. 0.8

4. a. i. 268.755   ii. 1.70154
        area of a triangle
    b. i. 87.39   ii. 1358.8416
        height of an object in free fall
    c. i. −1.221428571   ii. undefined
        slope of a line given two points

Problem Set 0.2

1. a. i. $1.23439632 \cdot 10^7$ ii. $8.164967851 \cdot 10^{-5}$
    b. i. $6.63466666 \cdot 10^{-34}$ ii. $1.116 \cdot 10^{-33}$

2. a. 347,895,000   b. 0.000 000 000 008 247   c. 140,000

4. $2 \cdot 10^{18}$ neurons

6. c. i. 64 m   ii. 63.18 m   iii. approximately 1%

7. a. 14,496,768 lb or 7,248.384 T   b. yes

Problem Set 0.3

1. a. x-minimum = -2 or less, x-maximum = 3 or more, x-scale = 1 or less,
        y-minimum = 5 or less, y-maximum = 21 or more, y-scale = 1 or more
    b. x-minimum = 0 or less, x-maximum = 3 or more, x-scale = 1 or less,
        y-minimum = -4 or less, y-maximum = 27 or more, y-scale = 1 or more

2. a.   b.

    c.   d.

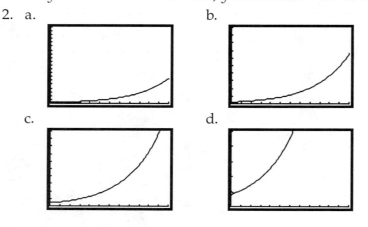

3. a.

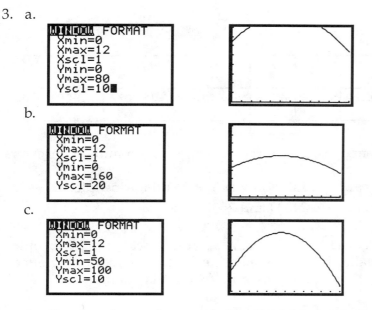

b.

c.

d. Graph c shows the graph for all of the *x*-values and shows the *y*-range as well.

4. Answers will vary.
   a. Range of −25 to 35 for *y*-values is good.
   b. Range of −50 to 300 for *y*-values is good.
   c. Range of −10 to 50 for *y*-values is good.

5. a. i. 14.4   ii. 33.76
   b. i. 0.0030448   ii. $3.43232 \cdot 10^{-6}$

Chapter One Selected Answers

Problem Set 1.1

1. $6, 9, 13.5, \ldots$; geometric; $u_{10} = 230.66015625$

2. 6 [ENTER] seeds the sequence. Ans + 3.2 [ENTER] can be repeated to generate many terms; $u_{10} = 34.8$

3. a. 2 [ENTER] seeds the sequence. 3Ans [ENTER] $\ldots$; $u_{15} = 9{,}565{,}938$
   b. 0.4 [ENTER] .1Ans [ENTER] $\ldots$; $u_{10} = 4E{-}10$ (or $4 \cdot 10^{-10}$).
   c. 1.56 [ENTER] 3.29 + Ans [ENTER] $\ldots$; $u_{14} = 44.33$.

4. a. between 12 and 13 min   b. between 28 and 29 min   c. Ans − 3.1 + 2.4

7. a. $60.00   b. $33.75   c. 9 weeks

Problem Set 1.2

1. a. $1, 2, 4, 8, 16, 32, \ldots$

Generations back	0	1	2	3	4	17	n
Ancestors in a generation	$u_0 = 1$	$u_1 = 2$	$u_2 = 4$	$u_3 = 8$	$u_4 = 16$	$u_{17} = 131{,}072$	$u_n = 2u_{(n-1)}$

   b. Multiply by 2.
   c. 4,194,304. About 22 generations back there were almost 5 million ancestors.
   d. 550 years
   e. The fifteenth century earth population was not 5 million people.
3. About 25 time periods or between 24000 and 25000 years
5. a. 25,098   b. $\approx 64.07\%$ c. 3.2%
   d. Using $u_1 = 39175$ and $u_n = (1 + 0.032) \cdot u_{(n-1)}$ you will get too many people. You need to find a smaller rate to compensate for the compounding effect.
   e. 0.025   f. 50,147; Not halfway, it is nonlinear.

Problem Set 1.3

1. a. 747.45, 818.04
   c. The sequence levels out at 840.
2. a. $1, 2, 6, 24, 120, 720$

3. a. $u_n = \begin{cases} 49.06 & \text{if } n = 1 \\ 1.18 + u_{(n-1)} & \text{if } n > 1 \end{cases}$

4. a. $u_1 = 24{,}000$ and $u_n = (1 + \frac{0.064}{12}) \cdot u_{(n-1)} - 100$
   b. \$24,000; \$24,028; \$24,056.15; \$24,084,45; \$24,112.90
   c. the balance after 4 months
   d. \$24,345.03; \$25,108.03
6. $u_1 = 20$ and $u_n = (1 - 0.25) \cdot u_{(n-1)}$; between 10 and 11 days

9. a. $u_1 = 11000$ and $u_n = (1 + \frac{0.096}{12}) \cdot u_{(n-1)} - 274$
   b. \$11,000; \$10,814; \$10,626.51; \$10,437.52; \$10,247.02
   c. 49 months with a final payment of \$167.73
   d. \$13,319.73

Problem Set 1.4

1. a. $(1, 2.5); (2, 4); (3, 5.5); (4, 7);$
      $(5, 8.5); (6, 10)$
   b. Answers will vary. One possible window is $[0, 7, 1, 0, 11, 1]$.
   d. The sketch will look like the graph for Problem 1c.

   c.

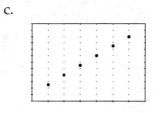

2. a. (0, 3929000); (1, 4871960); (2, 6041230); (3, 7491126); (4, 9288996); (5, 11518355)
   b. the initial population
   c. 24%
   d. geometric
   e.

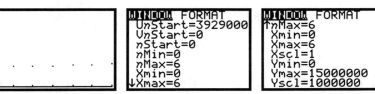

5. [0, 50, 5, 0, 8000, 1000]
   Discrete points will be on this curve.

6. a. The slime takes over during the seventh day.
   b. The concentration increases to 3 1/3 ppm. The pool will never be pure chlorine.

Problem Set 1.5

1. $u_{10} = 56$; $u_{20} = 116$; $u_{30} = 176$

2. a. 1905.56   b. $3631.15   c. $6919.38

3. a. $u_0 = 7000$; $u_n = (1 - 0.12) \cdot u_{(n-1)} + 600$;
      [0, 10, 1, 0, 8000, 1000]; $u_{11} = 5557$ trees (after 10 years)

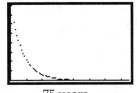

10 years

   b.

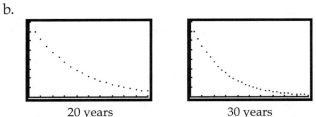

20 years   30 years

   c. In the long run, the number of trees stabilizes at 5000.
      $u_{75} = 5000$.

75 years

5. a. $u_0 = 5000$, $u_n = (1 + 0.85/12) \cdot u_{(n-1)}$;   b. [0, 550, 50, 0, 1100000, 100000]
    $123.98 is the smallest amount.

7. a. 2 million   b. 11 million   c. 29 million
8. a. 1, 1, 2, 3, 5, 8, 13, 21, 34, 55
    b. The ratios are 1, 2, 1.5, 1.6, 1.625, ... ; They are approaching 1.618033989.

Problem Set 1.6

1. a. 2, 8, 18, 32, 50
3. a. 0.3333333333   b. 0.333333333333333
    c. The sum is still listed as 0.3333333333 because the calculator cannot display
        more digits; 0. $\overline{3}$ or 1/3.

4. a. 144   b. 400
5. 1200 min (20 hr); 4550 min (75.8 hr)
7. First plan; $38,373,180,000
    Second plan; $45,035,996,273,704
    The second plan is more profitable by $44,997,623,093,704.

8. 0.3939393939

Chapter Review
Problem Set 1.7

1. a. 3, 6, 9, . . . , 30   b. $u_n = \begin{cases} 3 & n=1 \\ u_{n-1} + 3 & n>1 \end{cases}$
    c. 3384 cans   d. 13 rows
2. a. 511   b. 40   c. 79   d. 820
3. a. 34.171875   b. 10th   c. 45.5625   d. 887.3125
4. a. $657.03   b. $4083.21
5. 5299 students; 5208 students
6. 359 payments of $637.96 and one payment of $620.46
7. a. −3, −1.5, 0, 1.5, 3   b. 2, 4, 10, 28, 82

Chapter Two Selected Answers

Problem Set 2.1

1. a. $\frac{5}{3}$, 7, 18, $36\frac{2}{3}$, 65   b. neither

3. a.
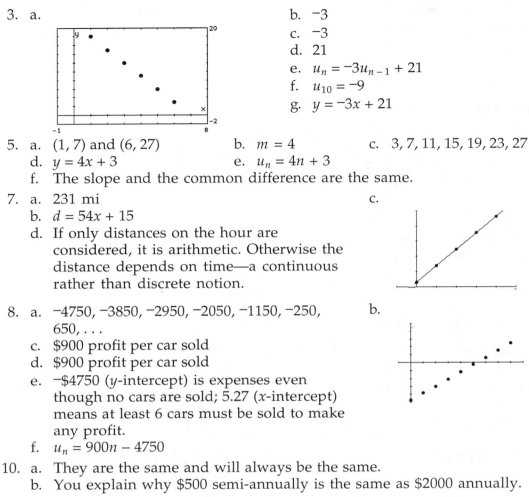

b. −3
c. −3
d. 21
e. $u_n = -3u_{n-1} + 21$
f. $u_{10} = -9$
g. $y = -3x + 21$

5. a. $(1, 7)$ and $(6, 27)$ b. $m = 4$ c. $3, 7, 11, 15, 19, 23, 27$
    d. $y = 4x + 3$ e. $u_n = 4n + 3$
    f. The slope and the common difference are the same.

7. a. 231 mi   c.
    b. $d = 54x + 15$
    d. If only distances on the hour are considered, it is arithmetic. Otherwise the distance depends on time—a continuous rather than discrete notion.

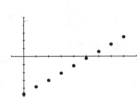

8. a. −4750, −3850, −2950, −2050, −1150, −250, 650, . . .   b.
    c. $900 profit per car sold
    d. $900 profit per car sold
    e. −$4750 ($y$-intercept) is expenses even though no cars are sold; 5.27 (x-intercept) means at least 6 cars must be sold to make any profit.
    f. $u_n = 900n - 4750$

10. a. They are the same and will always be the same.
     b. You explain why $500 semi-annually is the same as $2000 annually.

Problem Set 2.2

1. $S_{50} = 7650$
3. a. $u_{75} = 149$ b. $S_{75} = 5625$
4. $S_{67} = -6639.7$
5. a. 229   b. $u_n = 5n - 1$ c. 5359
7. a sequence with positive slope (line a)
    a sequence with negative slope (line b)
    a sequence with zero slope (line c)

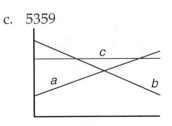

Problem Set 2.3

1. 9565938
2. $2302.03; after 23 years the balance is $5139.23

3. a. the value of $4000 after 10 years of compounded interest at 7.2%
   b. the value of $4000 after 4 years of interest compounded monthly
   c. $1500(1 + 0.055)^8$

6. a. ii   b. i   c. iii

7. a. ≈ 10.74 in.   b. 21st rebound; 31st rebound

Problem Set 2.4

1. a. 3069   b. 22   c. 2.8   d. 0.95

3. a.

n	1	2	3	4	5	6	7
S_n	5	15	35	75	155	315	635

   b. no
   c. when $r = 1$

4. a. $S_5 = 92.224$ b. $S_{15} = 99.9529815$ c. $S_{25} = 99.9997157$

6. a. $1^2 + 2^2 + 3^2 + 4^2 + 5^2 + 6^2 + 7^2 = 140$
   b. $3^2 + 4^2 + 5^2 + 6^2 + 7^2 = 135$

7. a. $9.22 \cdot 10^{18}$ or 2^{63} b. $2^{64} - 1 = 1.84 \cdot 10^{19}$ c. $\sum_{n=1}^{64} 2^{(n-1)}$

Problem Set 2.5

1. $S_{10} = 60$; $S_n = 6n$; infinite

2. a. $S_{10} \approx 12.96$; $S_{40} \approx 13.33$
   b. $S_{10} \approx 170.48$; $S_{40} \approx 481572$
   c. $S_{10} \approx 40$; $S_{40} \approx 160$
   d. The inequality $r > 1$ gives the top graph; $r = 1$ gives the middle graph; $0 < r < 1$ gives the bottom graph.
   e. when $|r| < 1$

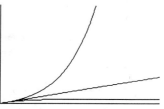

3. $600/0.12 = 5000$ trees

4. a. 0.149382716   b. ≈ 0.1499974597 c. 0.15

8. At age 30, Prudence has $35,120.59 and Charity has $2,000; at age 65, Prudence has $716,950.60 and Charity has $472,249.45.

9. a. $P_{10} = 1.414$ b. $A_{10} = 0.125$
   c. P approaches 109.25 and A approaches 128

Problem Set 2.6

1. Geome Tree

		1	2	3	4	. . . n	. . . ∞
a.	Length of last segment	1	0.5				
b.	Length of path	1	1.5				
c.	Total segments	1	3				
d.	Length of all segments	1	2				

e.	Height of tree	1	1.354				
f.	Width of tree	0	0.7.7				

2. Koch Snowflake.

		1	2	3	4	. . . n	. . . ∞
a.	Length of each segment	1	$\frac{1}{3}$				
b.	Total number of segments	3	12				
c.	Perimeter	3	4				
d.	Area	0.433	0.577				

3. Sierpiński Triangle

		1	2	3	4	. . . n	. . . ∞
a.	Length of last side	1	$\frac{1}{2}$				
b.	Number of triangles	1	3				
c.	Perimeter of each	3	$\frac{3}{2}$				
d.	Area of each	$\frac{\sqrt{3}}{4}$	$\frac{\sqrt{3}}{16}$				
e.	Sum of perimeters	3	4.5				
f.	Sum of areas	$\frac{\sqrt{3}}{4}$	$\frac{\sqrt{3}}{4}$				

Chapter Review
Problem Set 2.7

1. a. $3, 6, 9, \ldots, 30$ b. $u_n = \begin{cases} 3 & n=1 \\ u_{(n-1)} + 3 & n>1 \end{cases}$

   c. $u_n = 3n$ d. 3384 cans   e. 13 rows

2. a. 511   b. 40   c. 79   d. 820

3. a. 144, 1728, 20736, 4.3E8   b. $u_n = \begin{cases} 12 & n=1 \\ 12 \cdot u_{(n-1)} & n>1 \end{cases}$

   c. $u_n = 12^n$ d. 9.7E12 bugs

4. a. 34.171875   b. 10th   c. 45.5625   d. 887.3125
   e. The sum approaches 1024.

5. a. $648.12   b. $3879.87

6. a. 5327 students   b. 5208 students

7. a. ≈ 139.667 cm   b. ≈ 1206.65 cm   c. 4000 cm

8. ≈ 55.786 ft; 60 ft

9. 359 payments of $637.95 and 1 payment of $638.38

10. a. 2, 4, 8, 14, 22   b. 2, 4, 10, 28, 82

11. a. $\left(\frac{2}{3}\right)^0, \left(\frac{2}{3}\right)^1, \left(\frac{2}{3}\right)^2, \left(\frac{2}{3}\right)^3$, and so on

b. $C_n \to 0$

Chapter Three Selected Answers
Problem Set 3.1

1. The median is 84 and the mean is 84 for both Connie and Ozzie. Neither measure separately or combined indicate the larger test variation for Ozzie.

3. a.

     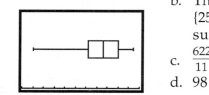

    b. The box plot has {25, 51, 58, 65, 72} as the five summary values.

    c. $\frac{622}{11} \approx 56.55$

    d. 98

4. a. for Connie: below 77.5 or above 89.5
        for Ozzie: below 49 or above 121
    b. for Homer: below 30 or above 86; one outlier; 25 < 30

6. a. {74,300, 87,959, 105,000, 153,900, 246,900}

    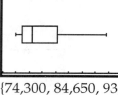

    b. {74,300, 84,650, 93,600, 105,750, 116,800}

    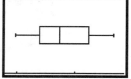

10. a. Tube price median is $2.01 and mean is $2.13; cleaning median rank is 66.5 and mean rank is 67.25.

    b.

    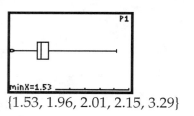 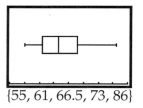

    {1.53, 1.96, 2.01, 2.15, 3.29}   {55, 61, 66.5, 73, 86}

Problem Set 3.2

1. This implies than no CDs can be shipped that measure more than 12.12 cm or less than 11.88 cm.

4. a. 47.1, 45.9, 47.9, 47.4, 45.1, 46.0, 45.7, 45.3
    b. mean absolute deviation is 0.875 cm
    c. 47.9, 47.4, 45.1, 45.3

5. a. First period; because it has the smallest mean absolute deviation.
    b. Not really. First period rates are pretty consistent around the mean of 79.4. sixth period must have some very high rates and some very low rates.
    c. Answers will vary. Lower MAD values will have a shorter box.

8. Juneau has more consistent temperatures; ranging from 22°F to 56°F compared to New York temperatures ranging from 32°F to 77°F. The mean absolute deviation for Juneau is 10.08°F and for New York 14.08°F.

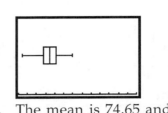

9. a. The median is 75 and interquartile range is 19.
    b. The mean is 80.88 and mean absolute deviation is 15.9.
    c. The outliers are below 39 or above 115. Therefore, 147 and 158 are outliers.

    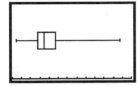

    d.
    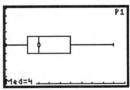

    e. i. The mean is 74.65 and mean absolute deviation is 9.3.
        ii. The median is 74 and interquartile range is 15.

    f. The mean is more affected than median; the mean absolute deviation is more than interquartile range. This is because the mean absolute deviation involves the mean and the interquartile range involves the median.

Problem Set 3.3

1. a. The graph should look exactly like the graph in the problem.
        [1, 13, 1, 0, 200, 50]
    b. It is mound shaped because 7 is the most likely dice total, then 6 and 8, then 5 and 9, and so on.
    c. The median can be found by counting in from the left or right. The median will be the average of the 500th and 501st roll total. The mean can be computed by evaluating $\dfrac{2*26+3*56+\ldots+12*21}{1000}$.

2. a. It means this population of 95 farmers tends to plant two to five acres of sweet corn. The frequencies are on the left.
    b.

    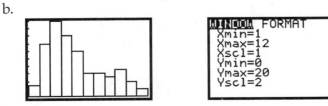

c. There are 95 acres in this distribution. The mean number of acres planted is 4.8 with a mean absolute deviation of 2.6. The median number of acres planted is 4.

5. a. HW { 4, 27.5, 40.5, 49, 65}; TV {5, 26, 36.5, 58, 95}; TV has the larger spread. Mean absolute deviation for HW is 12.78 min. Mean absolute deviation for TV is 20.56 min.

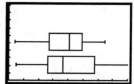

b.

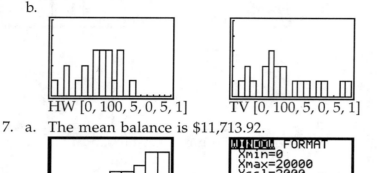

HW [0, 100, 5, 0, 5, 1]   TV [0, 100, 5, 0, 5, 1]

7. a. The mean balance is $11,713.92.

| WINDOW FORMAT |
| Xmin=0 |
| Xmax=20000 |
| Xscl=2000 |
| Ymin=-1 |
| Ymax=11 |
| Yscl=1000 |

c. The unpaid balance is higher for more months than it is lower.
d. $14,302
e. Multiply the mean unpaid balance times 0.075 times 2 yr.

Chapter Review
Problem Set 3.4

1. Plot B, because the data is much more spread out.

2. a. Answers will vary, but the graph for A should be much higher. Shapes should take into account the scale on the horizontal axis and the way values are compacted between the quartiles.
   b. Six in each one.
   c. Because the range of data values is much bigger.

3. The mean of the extreme highs is 118°F with a MAD of 17°F. The mean of the extreme lows is −60°F with a MAD of 38°F. Antarctica is two MADs from the mean high and *almost* two MADs from the extreme low.

4. a. Answers will vary, but the mean absolute deviation near 0 means a tall, skinny graph.
   b. Answers will vary, but the mean absolute deviation of about 5 means a shorter but longer graph.

Preliminary Edition

5. a. The mean value is 127 hr and the median value is 95 hr
    b. Soviet; United States; Both scale: [0, 600, 25, 0, 7, 1]

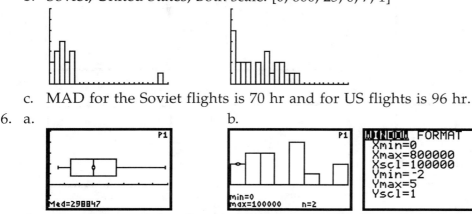

    c. MAD for the Soviet flights is 70 hr and for US flights is 96 hr.
6. a.   b.

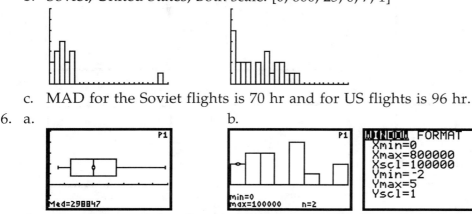

    Answers for c and d will vary. The shape really depends on how the
    additional sales are distributed.

Chapter Four Selected Answers

Problem Set 4.1

1. Answers will vary, here are some examples.
    a. Too many points are above the line.
    b. Most of the points at the left are below the line.
    c. Doesn't follow the tendency of the data from first to last point.
    d. Points on the left are above the line.
    e. This is the best of the lot.
    f. There are no points below the line.
2. For Problems 1–6, answers will vary. Possible answers are given.
    a. y-intercept is about 1.1; point (4, 4)
    b. y-intercept is about 1.8; point (3, 4)
    c. y-intercept is about 7.5; point (2, 6)

3.

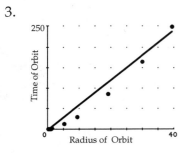

6. a. Window: [0, 22, 2, 20, 45, 5]

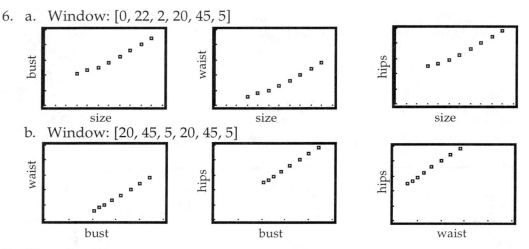

b. Window: [20, 45, 5, 20, 45, 5]

Problem Set 4.2

1. a. 3/2   b. −2/3

2. a. 3   b. −2.8   d. +2.4

3. a. $y = \frac{3}{2}(x - 4)$ or $y = \frac{3}{2}x - 6$

    b. $y = -1.124(x + 4.33) + 7.51$ or $y = -1.124x + 2.643$

In each of Problems 5 and 6, the equation of the line should be close to that of the median-median line, whose equation is given.

5. $y = 5.59x - 8.03$ 6. $y = 0.32x - 1820$

Problem Set 4.3

1. a.

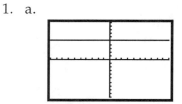

b. Answers will vary, but the y-coordinate should always be 5.

c. Slope = 0

3. $x = 3, y = 1000(3 - x)$, Line(3, Ymin, 3, Ymax)

5. a. For each additional story, the building height increases by about 13 ft.

    b. The stories of a building are often not all the same height, the first floor or two are usually taller. The intercept of about 20 represents this difference in height of the initial stories.

    c. domain $0 \leq x \leq 80$, range $0 \leq y \leq 1100$

Note: Most of the equations in the following answers are the median-median lines. Any line that fits the data "by eye" should be considered acceptable. You may have slightly different equations. This is acceptable, as long as you can justify your choice of an answer.

8. a. $y = -1.71x + 578.5$
    b. years after 1900
    c. There has been a 1.71 point decrease per year in the average verbal score.
    d. 421 points for 1992, 419 for 1993
    e. 441 points
    f. There is a limit to the extrapolation in this model. Using it to predict very far beyond the given data is very unreliable.

9. These answers will vary depending on how the x-values are determined. The answers given are based on mid-range x-values.
    a.
    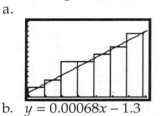
    b. $y = 0.00068x - 1.3$
    c. As family incomes increase by $1000 the percent of students in grades 9–12 using computers at home increases by 0.068%.
    d. 42.1%

10. a. $y = -5.07x + 181.3$
    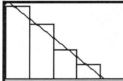
    b. percent of men not married
    c. About 5% of the total male population gets married each year.
    d. -21.4%
    e. The model does not extrapolate very well or it becomes nonlinear after age 30.

Problem Set 4.4

1. a. 10, 11, 10   b. 17, 16, 17
2. a. $y = -0.674x + 21.2$ b. $y = 2.47x + 39.6$
3. $y = 0.75x - 9.9$
4. $y = -1.8x + 72.97$
7. a. 5–5–5   b. (30, 58.1), (55, 66.2), (80, 70)
    c. 0.238; Each year the life expectancy of a male child increases by 0.238 years.
    d. $y = 0.238x + 50.96$ e. $y = 0.238x + 53.11$
    f. $y = 0.238x + 51.68$ g. 70.24

h. 73.34, 64.53   i. the year 2019

10. a. $y = -0.344x + 912$ b. a drop of 0.344 sec each year
     c. 3:46.8
     d. Eventually the record would be 1 mi in 0 sec.
     e. The negative value for percent of married men is not possible. This means
         that the equation does not extrapolate very well or that the model becomes
         nonlinear after 30–34 years of age.

Problem Set 4.5

1. a. −0.2   b. −0.4   c. 0.6

2. a. mostly high, down on the right   c. A better fitting line
                                                    might be
    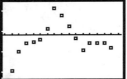 $y = 0.268x + 50.95$.

                                                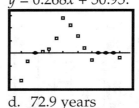

    b. Raising the intercept would lower the
        residuals, but because the four on the right
        are already too low you should decrease the   d. 72.9 years
        slope to bring them more in line with the
        rest.

3. a. $y = 5.08x + 86.3$ c. ages 7 and 15
                                   d. Answers may vary. At age
    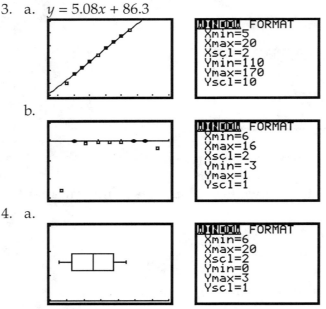   7, you are at the end of the
                                       initial growth of a child
                                       and at age 15 you are at the
                                       end of the secondary
    b.   growth of a child.

4. a.

    b. The residuals are not evenly divided. There are more negative values
        than positive ones and the most negative is an outlier indicating that this
        point does not fit the model well at all.

7. a. Not a good model.
    b. A good model.
    c. A good model, but it needs to be adjusted a bit.

Problem Set 4.6

1. The three summary points remain the same, so the median-median line will be the same. The outliers could change the summary points if they affect the medians of the groups.

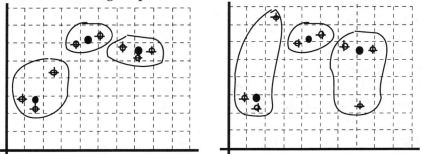

3. It is now much more like the median-median line. Because the median-median line uses only the median x and median y for each of the three groups, it will not be affected by outliers. Adding or subtracting one or two points will have little effect on the median-median line. This is not true of the least-square line. One "bad" data point, and outlier, will have a dramatic effect on the equation of the least-square line.

4. If you minimize the sum of the squares of the residuals, then the vertical distance from the line to any point should be minimized. Answers will vary.

5. a. $y = 5.235x + 84.3$
   c. The median-median line is better in this problem because it ignores the very large residuals at both ends of the line. (See the residual plot for Problem Set 2.5, problem 2.)

7. a. $(400, 113394.27)$, $(500, 42201.91)$, $(600, -28990.44)$, $(700, -100182.80)$
   b. Answers will vary. $y = 398163.69 - 711.92356x$
   c. $\approx \$559.27$

8. The deviations are the differences between the mean and the data values. The residuals are the differences between the data values and the predicted values from the equation. The equation is giving a sort of average by summarizing the data. This is similar to the mean.

Problem Set 4.7

1. 12

2. $y = -1.5(x - 4)$

4. a. $y = 59.2 - 0.536x$ b. $r = -0.9966$
   c. The data has a negative correlation (as x increases, y decreases) and the model is about 99.3% accurate.
   d. 20.6%   e. about 9 or 10 out of ten.

5. a. Volumes versus Cost; $r = 0.60458$, $r^2 = 37\%$: Circulation versus Cost; $r = 0.5826$, $r^2 = 34\%$

   b. Volume versus Cost seems to have a better correlation than Circulation versus Cost.

   c. Interestingly enough there are two outliers on the first plot each with very high numbers of volumes (Boston and Buffalo). If these two are disregarded, then the r-values rises to 0.9111 with r^2 jumping from 37% to 83%. By the same token, an attempt to remove outliers (Detroit) from the Circulation vs Cost plot only raises the r-value to 0.6888 with r^2 changing from 39% to 47%. In our opinion, we believe that the number of books contributes more to the cost than the number of people that use the library.

8. a. student to faculty: $y = {}^-14.8 + 0.08x$
   faculty to student: $y = 3448.75 + 9.54x$

   b. $r = 0.85$ for both equations

Problem Set 4.8

1. a. First. The points lie more on a curve than on a line.

   b. Second. These points are closest to a line.

   c. Second. The slope is negative, or as x increases, y decreases.

2. a. $y = {}^-5.693 + 7.250x$

x	4	7	11	12.9	16	18.5
y	22	47	74	87	111	128
$f(x)$	23.3	45.1	74.1	87.8	110.3	128.4
residuals	−1.31	1.94	−0.06	−0.83	0.69	−0.43
residuals^2	1.710	3.772	0.003	0.694	0.478	0.188

   b. −1.3 to 1.9   c. $\sum |r| = 5.27$

   d. $|x|$ to$(|r|) = 0.88$ e. $\sum r^2 = 6.85$

   f. The residuals are all close to the line, with the mean absolute residual only 0.88 from the line. If you find the mean of the squares of the residuals, you get 1.14, which again is rather close to the line. The line is a good fit.

5. a. 91.73

   b. $r = 0.94$ so $r^2 = 0.88$, which means that all data should be within 88% of the predicted value.

7. a. $y = 46.3 + 0.00323x$ b. 103 g

   c. $r = 0.984$, $r^2 = 96.8\%$, the mean residual is 33 g, and the greatest residual is 68 g.

   d. Use only the data around the animal in the same weight group, discarding the smaller animals and the very large animal.

Chapter Review
Problem Set 4.9

1. −51.316

2. 22.45

3. $x = 19.94$

4. Answers will vary.
   a. [1500, 3500, 250, 40, 80, 10]
   b. [0, 110, 10, 0, 200, 20]
   c. [0, 110, 10, 0, 110, 10]

5. $m \approx 0.024$

6. $y = 0.024x - 1.68$

7. Answers will vary.

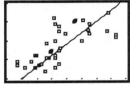

8. The domain is all nonnegative numbers. (1667 ≤ daily calorie supply ≤ 3336) The units of the domain are calories.

9. The units of slope are years of life expectancy per number of calories.

10. For each calorie you would expect your life expectancy to increase by 0.024 yr.

11. 2445 calories

12. 44.4 yr

13. 55.5 yr

14. (34, 48), (57, 53), (88, 69)

15. $m \approx 0.33$

16. $y = 0.34x + 37.4$

17. [0, 110, 10, −20, 15, 5]

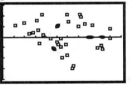

The residuals seem to be evenly distributed above and below the line. There is no pattern in the residuals, which indicates a line is a good model.

18. The residual for Ethiopia is −2.09.

19. Central African Republic

20. $y = 166.7 - 1.26x$

21. For every one percent increase in the availability of health services, the number of infant deaths decreases by 1.26.

22. $y = -1.31x + 176.23$

    least-square   median-median

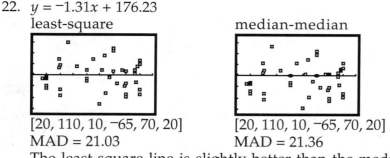

    [20, 110, 10, −65, 70, 20]   [20, 110, 10, −65, 70, 20]
    MAD = 21.03   MAD = 21.36

    The least-square line is slightly better than the median-median line if you compare the MADs.

23. least-square model: 97.33
    median-median model: 104.45

24. $r \approx -0.77$, $r^2 \approx 0.6$; 60% of the points lie in a narrow band on either side of the least-square line.

25. $y = 165.41 - 1.25x$; $r \approx -0.86$, $r^2 \approx 0.74$; 74% of the points will lie in a narrow band on either side of the least-square line.

Chapter Five Selected Answers

Problem Set 5.1

1. a. Answers will vary. The curve, which appears to be a parabola, might describe the relationship between the amount of time the ball is in the air and how far away from the ground it is.
    b. seconds, feet.
    c. domain—60 sec; range—200 ft.
    d. No, the distance is not measured directly.

There will be many different correct answers for Problems 3–21.

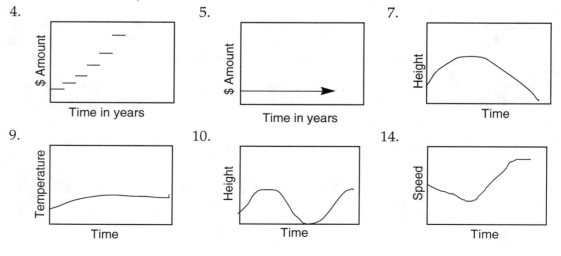

4. 5. 7.

9. 10. 14.

16.

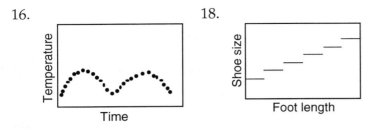

18.

Problem Set 5.2

1. Graph A: (4, 17), (5, 21)
   Graph B: (3, 14.0625), (4, 10.547)
   Graph C: (2, 10), (3, 20), (4, 40), (5, 80), (6, 160)

2. a.   b. $f(x) = x^2$ c.

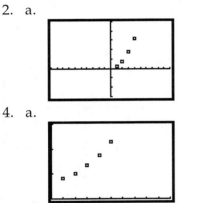

4. a.   b. $4(1.3)^{(x-1)}$ c.

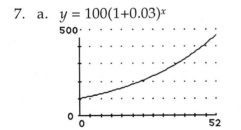

   d.

5. a. 4, $f(4)$) is 4 units right of the origin
      and 8.788 units up from the x-axis.
   b. (7.25, 20.616)
   c. 16.93 is the height of the segment.

7. a. $y = 100(1+0.03)^x$ b. $136.39   c. $465.09

                                                d. Something that starts the year
                                                     costing $100 will cost $465.09 at the
                                                     end of the year.
                                                     e. 36.6 weeks

Problem Set 5.3

1. a and b.   There are many correct answers including (4, 0) (2, −4) (1, −6) and (0, −8).
   c.   Each of the points listed works in both forms of the equation.
   d.   Select another point and demonstrate that it works for both equations.

3. a. $y = \frac{-758}{660}$, $x - 2.7921$

   b. $y = \frac{-758}{660}$, $x - 0.7921$

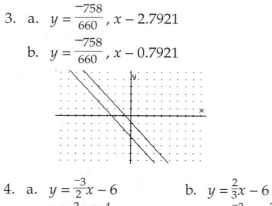

4. a. $y = \frac{-3}{2}x - 6$ b. $y = \frac{2}{3}x - 6$
   c. $y = \frac{2}{3}x + \frac{4}{3}$ d. $y = \frac{-3}{2}x + \frac{27}{2}$
   e.   rectangle

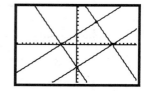

5. a.   Answers will vary with the calculators. For a TI-82, a window would be [−4.7, 4.7, 1, −3.1, 3.1, 1].
   b.   Answers will vary with the calculators. For a TI-82, a window would be [0, 9.4, 1, 0, 6.2, 1].

7. a.   Answers will vary. Possible points are (1, 1.414), (2, 2.828), (3, 4.243), (4, 5.657), and so on. The equation of a best-fit line is $y = 1.414x$.
   b. $k \approx 1.414$ c. $s \approx 9.05$ d. $x \approx 24.25$

8. a. $12,500 is the original value of the equipment.
   b.   After 10 yr, the equipment has no value.
   c.   −1250; each year the value of the equipment decreases by $1,250.
   d. $y = -1250x + 12500$ e. after 4.8 yr

11.   The average value is $6,875.

Year	0	1	2	3	4	5	6	7	8	9	10
Value	12,500	11,250	10,000	8,750	7,500	6,250	5,000	3,750	2,500	1250	0

Problem Set 5.4

1. a. $y = x^2 - 6$ b. $y = x^2 - 3$
   c. $y = x^2 + 2$ d. $y = x^2 + 4$

2. a.   i. $f(x) = x^2 - 6$ ii. $f(x) = x^2 + 2$
   b.   i. $y = x^2 - 5$, down 5 units   ii. $y = x^2 + 4$, up 4 units
   c. $f(x) + c$ is c units p or down from $f(x)$. It goes up if c is positive and down if c is negative.

3. a. $y = (x - 4)^2$ b. $y = (x - 7)^2$ c. $y = (x + 5)^2$

Preliminary Edition   SELECTED ANSWERS

5. a. $y = (x - 2)^2$
   c. $y = (x + 6)^2$
   b. $y = (x - 2)^2 - 5$
   d. $y = (x + 6)^2 + 2$

7. a. $y = -x^2$
   b. $y = -x^2 + 2$

8. $y = -2(x - 2)^2 + 2$

10. a parabola with equation $y = -(x - 25)^2 + 625$

12. a. average height = 40 ft

Time	0	0.5	1	1.5	2
Height	64	60	48	28	0

b. average height = 41.3 ft

Time	0	0.25	0.5	0.75	1	1.25	1.5	1.75	2
Height	64	63	60	55	48	39	28	15	0

c. average height = 42.13

Time	0	0.1	0.2	0.3	0.4	0.5	0.6	0.7	0.8	0.9	1
Height	64	63.8	63.4	62.6	61.4	60	58.2	56.2	53.8	51.0	48

Time	1.1	1.2	1.3	1.4	1.5	1.6	1.7	1.8	1.9	2
Height	44.6	41.0	37.0	32.6	28	23.0	17.8	12.2	6.24	0

d. The ball starts out moving slowly and speeds up as it falls. As you increase the frequency of the measurements, you are adding more large numbers to the list. This makes the average increase.

Problem Set 5.5

1. a. $y = \sqrt{x} + 3$
   b. $y = \sqrt{x} - 4$
   c. $y = \sqrt{x} + 1$
   d. $y = \sqrt{x} - 3$
   e. $y = \sqrt{x + 5}$
   f. $y = \sqrt{x - 2}$
   g. $y = \sqrt{x + 5} + 2$
   h. $y = \sqrt{x - 3} + 1$
   i. $y = \sqrt{x - 1} - 4$

2. a. If x is replaced with $(x - 3)$, the graph moves 3 units to the right; if it is replaced with $(x + 3)$, the graph moves 3 units to the left.
   b. If y is replaced with $(y - 2)$, the graph moves 2 units up; if it is replaced with $(y + 2)$, the graph moves 2 units down.

3. a. $y = -\sqrt{x}$
   b. $y = -\sqrt{x} - 3$
   c. $y = -\sqrt{x + 6} + 5$

6. a. There are x values on each parabola that have more than one y-value.
   b. $y = \pm\sqrt{x + 4}$; $y = \pm\sqrt{x} + 2$
   c. $y^2 = x + 4$; $(y - 2)^2 = x$

7. First, rewrite the parabola into the form $y = \pm\sqrt{x + 3} + 2$

Problem Set 5.6

1. a. $y = |x| + 2$ b. $y = |x| - 5$

2. a. $y = |x + 4|$ b. $y = |x - 3|$

5. a. $y = (x - 5)^2$ b. $y = -|x + 4|$ c. $y = -|x + 4| + 3$

8. a. The graph will move 5 units to the right.
    b. The graph will flip over the y-axis.

9. $(1, 3); (7, 3); 1$ and 7

10. a. $y_1 = |x + 3|, y_2 = 5$; The solutions are $(2, 5)$ and $(-8, 5)$.

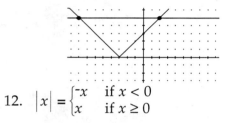

12. $|x| = \begin{cases} -x & \text{if } x < 0 \\ x & \text{if } x \geq 0 \end{cases}$

Problem Set 5.7

1. $y = 2\sqrt{1 - x^2}$

2. a. $y = 3\sqrt{1 - x^2}$ b. $y = 0.5\sqrt{1 - x^2}$

3. a.   b.   c.

6. Graph 1: $y = -5\sqrt{1 - (x + 2)^2} + 3$
    Graph 2: $y = 4\sqrt{1 - (x - 3)^2} - 2$

7. a. $y = \sqrt{1 - x^2} + 2$ b. $y = \sqrt{1 - (x + 3)^2}$

    c. $y = 2\sqrt{1 - x^2}$ d. $y = \sqrt{1 - \left(\frac{x}{2}\right)^2}$

9. a. $y = 2\sqrt{1 - \left(\dfrac{x}{3}\right)^2}$ b. $y = -2\sqrt{1 - \left(\dfrac{x}{3}\right)^2}$

11. a. $y = +3\sqrt{1 - (2x)^2}; \; y = -3\sqrt{1 - (2x)^2}$
    b. $y = \pm 3\sqrt{1 - (2x)^2}$
    c. $y^2 = 9(1 - (2x)^2)$

14. a. average value = 0.546

x	−1	−0.5	0	0.5	1
f(x)	0	0.87	1	0.87	0

    b. average value = 0.690

x	−1	−0.8	−0.6	−0.4	−0.2	0	0.2	0.4	0.6	0.8	1
f(x)	0	0.6	0.8	0.92	0.98	1	0.98	0.92	0.8	0.6	0

    c. For x values spaced 0.1 units apart, the average value = 0.739.
       For x values spaced 0.01 units apart, the average value = 0.781.
    d. The average value will approach 0.785.

Problem Set 5.8

1. a. 4   b. 2   c. −4 and 4
    d. −2, 0, and 3.5   e. $0 \le y \le 4$ f. $-4 \le x \le 4$

2. a.   b.   c.

    d.   e.   f.

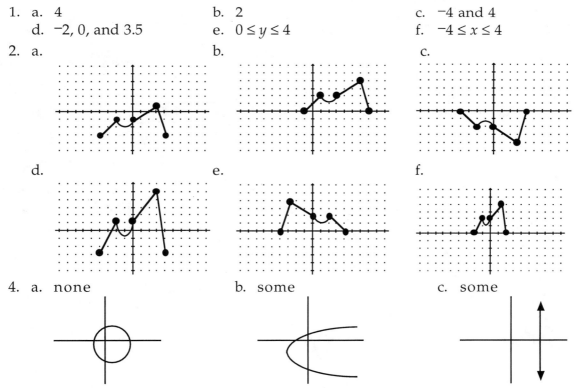

4. a. none   b. some   c. some

5. a. Stretch y-values by 2, and then slide down 3 units.
    b. Slide right 4 units, and then slide down 2 units.
    c. Flip vertical, slide 3 units left and 1 unit up.
    d. Compress y-values by 1/2, slide 2 units right and 3 units down.

8. Evaluate the function at many points. Then average these to find the average value (2). Multiply this average value by the width of the interval (3) to get the area, which is 6.

11. $y = 2(x - 2) + 6$

Problem Set 5.9

1. a. 12 L/min
   b.

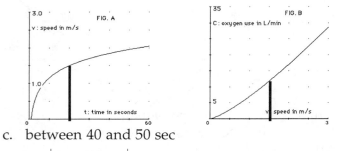

   c. between 40 and 50 sec

2. a. $y = |(x - 3)^2 - 1|$
   b. $f(x) = |x|, g(x) = (x - 3)^2 - 1$

5. a. 2   b. 1

7. a. $g(f(2)) = 2$
   b. $f(g(-1)) = -1$
   c. $g(f(x)) = x$ for all x
   d. $f(g(x)) = x$ for all x
   e. The two functions "undo" the effects of each other, thus giving back the original starting value.

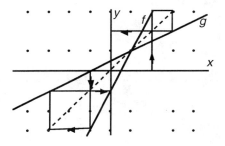

8. a. $f(g(3)) = 4$ b. $f(g(2)) = 3$

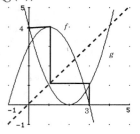
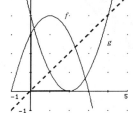

Chapter Review
Problem Set 5.10

1. For a time there are no pops. Then the popping rate begins to slowly increase. When the popping reaches a furious intensity, it seems to nearly level out. Shortly thereafter, it peaks. Then the number of pops per second drops radically to a minimal value and tapers off quickly until the last pop is heard.

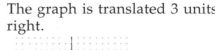

2. a. -7 b. -1 c. 100
   d. $-2x^2 + 11$ e. $(-2x + 8)^2$ f. $(-2x + 7)^2 - 2$

3. a. The graph is translated 3 units down.   b. The graph is translated 3 units right.

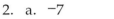 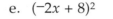

4. a. Slide the graph 2 units left and then 3 units down.
   b. Double all of the x-values. Then reflect the graph over the x-axis, and slide the graph up 1 unit.
   c. Shrink the x-values by dividing by 2, double the y-values, slide the graph 1 unit to the right, and then slide the graph 3 units up.

5. a. $y = \frac{2}{3}x - 2$ b. $y = \pm\sqrt{(x + 3)} - 1$ c. $y = \pm\sqrt{(1 - (x - 2)^2)}$

6. a. Slide the graph down 2 units.
   b. Slide the graph 2 units to the right and then 1 unit up.
   c. Reflect the graph over the x-axis.
   d. Double all the y-values. Then slide the graph 1 unit to the left and 3 units down.
   e. Reflect the graph over the y-axis, and then slide the graph up 1 unit.
   f. Double all the x-values, and then slide the graph 2 units down.
   g. Reflect the graph over the x-axis, slide the graph 3 units to the right, and then slide the graph 1 unit up.
   h. Multiply all the x-values by 1.5. Then multiple all the y-values by -2, and slide the graph 1 unit right and 2 units down.

7. a. $y = 3\sqrt{1 - x^2} - 1$ b. $y = 2\sqrt{1 - \left(\frac{x}{5}\right)^2} + 3$

   c. $y = 4\sqrt{1 - \left(\frac{x - 3}{4}\right)^2} - 1$ d. $y = (x - 2)^2 - 4$
   e. $y = -2(x + 1)^2$ f. $y = -\sqrt{-(x - 2)} - 3$
   g. $y = 0.5|x + 2| - 2$ h. $y = -2|x - 3| + 2$

Chapter Six Selected Answers

Problem Set 6.1

1. a.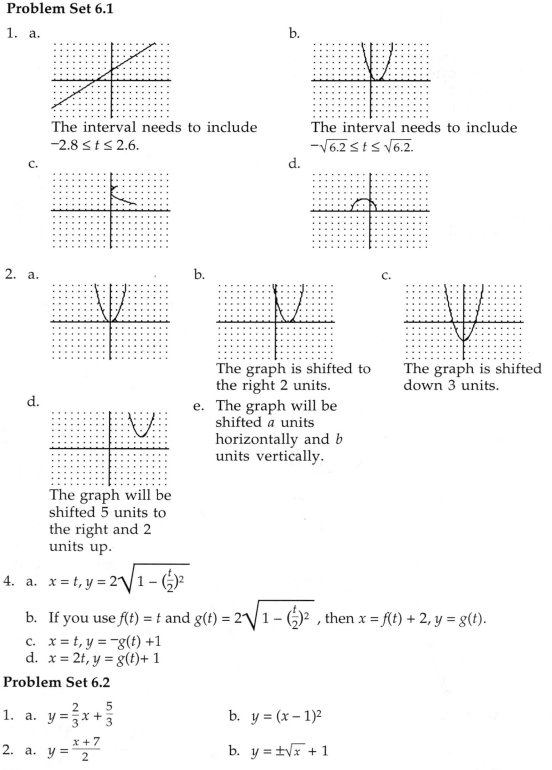

   The interval needs to include
   $-2.8 \le t \le 2.6$.

   b. The interval needs to include
   $-\sqrt{6.2} \le t \le \sqrt{6.2}$.

   c.

   d.

2. a.

   b. The graph is shifted to
   the right 2 units.

   c. The graph is shifted
   down 3 units.

   d. The graph will be
   shifted 5 units to
   the right and 2
   units up.

   e. The graph will be
   shifted a units
   horizontally and b
   units vertically.

4. a. $x = t, y = 2\sqrt{1 - (\frac{t}{2})^2}$

   b. If you use $f(t) = t$ and $g(t) = 2\sqrt{1 - (\frac{t}{2})^2}$, then $x = f(t) + 2, y = g(t)$.

   c. $x = t, y = {}^-g(t) + 1$

   d. $x = 2t, y = g(t) + 1$

Problem Set 6.2

1. a. $y = \frac{2}{3}x + \frac{5}{3}$

   b. $y = (x - 1)^2$

2. a. $y = \frac{x + 7}{2}$

   b. $y = \pm\sqrt{x} + 1$

4. $-\sqrt{6.2} \le t \le \sqrt{6.2}$

5. a. The graph is reflected over the x-axis.

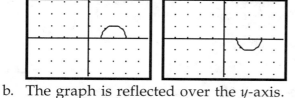

b. The graph is reflected over the y-axis.

c. The graph is reflected over the x-axis and then the y-axis (or over the y-axis and then the x-axis).

7. a. Tanker A: $x = 18t$ and $y = 1$; Tanker B: $x = 22(t - 5)$ and $y = 2$

b. $[0, 50, .5, 0, 900, 100, -1, 3, 1]$ (To get the following graphs, set the Tmax to the hours above each graph.)

after 5 hr after 10 hr after 20 hr

after 30 hr after 40 hr after 50 hr

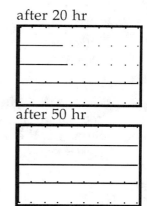

c. $t = 27.5$ hr, $d = 495$ mi

d. Tanker A: $x = 18t$ and $y = 1$; Tanker B: $x = 900 - 22t$ and $y = 2$. The time interval is $21.25 \le t \le 23.75$. The distances are between 382.5 and 427.5 mi out from Corpus Christi.

Problem Set 6.3

1. a. 9.186 b. 57.577 c. 22.780

2. a. 31.19° b. 29.91° c. 37.33°

3. a. 25.297° b. 66.696 cm.

4. a. The graph is a line segment at a 39° angle with the horizontal axis. The initial and end points depend on the interval used for t.

b. Trace and select a point. For example at $T = 1$, $x = 0.7771$ and $y = 0.6293$. These two values become the lengths of the legs.

$$\text{Tan } a = \frac{0.6293}{0.7771}, \ a = \tan^{-1}\left(\frac{0.6293}{0.7771}\right) = 39°$$

6. $x = t \cos 57°$ and $y = t \sin 57°$; an interval that includes $\dfrac{-3.1}{\sin 57°} \le t \le \dfrac{3.1}{\sin 57°}$

9. a. $x = t \cos 47°$, $y = t \sin 47°$; $\dfrac{-3.2}{\sin 47°} \le t \le \dfrac{3.1}{\sin 47°}$

b. $x = t \cos 115°$, $y = t \sin 115°$; $\dfrac{-3.2}{\sin 115°} \le t \le \dfrac{3.1}{\sin 115°}$

10. a. $x = 10t \cos 30°$, $y = 10t \sin 30°$

b. $0 \le t \le 10$

c. The 10 represents 10 mi/hr, t represents time, 30° is the angle with the x-axis, x is the horizontal position at any time and y is the vertical position at any time.

d. Points on the graph are drawn as a simulation of the actual position of the tanker at any time t.

Problem Set 6.4

2. a. $x = 1 \cos t$, $y = 1 \sin t$

b.

Angle A	0°	30°	45°	60°	90°	120°	150°
cos A	1	0.866	0.707	0.5	0	−0.5	−0.707
sin A	0	0.5	0.707	0.866	1	0.866	0.707

c. Cosine A is the x-coordinate of the point where the line extending the central angle A crosses the perimeter of the unit circle.

d. Sine A is the y-coordinate of the point where the line extending the central angle A crosses the perimeter of the unit circle.

3. a. $x = 2 \cos t + 2$, $y = 2 \sin t$ b. $x = 2 \cos t - 3$, $y = 2 \sin t$

4. a. $\cos t = \dfrac{x}{3}$, $\sin t = \dfrac{y}{3}$ b. $(\cos t)^2 = \dfrac{x^2}{9}$, $\sin t)^2 = \dfrac{y^2}{9}$

c. $(\cos t)^2 + (\sin t)^2 = \dfrac{x^2}{9} + \dfrac{y^2}{9}$ d. $1 = \dfrac{x^2}{9} + \dfrac{y^2}{9}$

e. $9 = x^2 + y^2$ or $x^2 + y^2 = 9$ f. 3

6. a. $x = 2 \cos t$ b. $x = 4 \cos t$ c. $x = 2 \cos t$
       $y = 3 \sin t$ $y = \sin t$ $y = 4 \sin t$

8. For Problem 7a

a. $\cos t = \dfrac{x}{2}$, $\sin t = \dfrac{y}{3}$ b. $(\cos t)^2 + (\sin t)^2 = \dfrac{x^2}{4} + \dfrac{y^2}{9}$

c. $1 = \dfrac{x^2}{4} + \dfrac{y^2}{9}$

d. The center is at (0, 0). The lengths of the axes are 4 units and 6 units.

For Problem 7c

a. $\cos t = \dfrac{x}{2.5}$, $\sin t = \dfrac{y-2}{1.5}$ b. $(\cos t)^2 + (\sin t)^2 = \dfrac{x^2}{6.25} + \dfrac{(y-2)^2}{2.25}$

c. $1 = \dfrac{x^2}{6.25} + \dfrac{(y-2)^2}{2.25}$

d. The center is at (0, 2). The lengths of the axes are 5 units and 3 units.

Problem Set 6.5

1. Pat moves at a compass heading of 53.1°; The pilot is on a heading of 265.4°.

2. (Assuming the river flows toward the top of the page and the boat is heading from left to right.)
    a. $y = 2t$ b. $x = 6t$ c.
    d. 0.5 mi downstream
    e. 1.58 mi

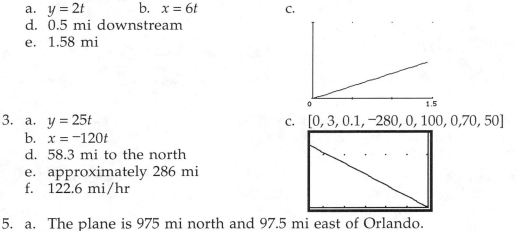

3. a. $y = 25t$ c. $[0, 3, 0.1, -280, 0, 100, 0, 70, 50]$
    b. $x = -120t$
    d. 58.3 mi to the north
    e. approximately 286 mi
    f. 122.6 mi/hr

5. a. The plane is 975 mi north and 97.5 mi east of Orlando.
    b. It actually traveled 979.86 mi.
    c. The speed the plane traveled was 251.2 mi/hr.
    d. The heading at which the plane traveled was 5.71°.

6. a. $x = 1.5t$ c. $[0, 1, 0.01, 0, 2, 0.5, 0, 3, 1]$
    b. $y = -16t^2 + 2.75$
    d. 0.62 ft
    e. 0.41 sec

Problem Set 6.6

1. a. $y = -4t \sin A$ b. $y = 3t$ c. 48.59°
    d. $x = 4t \cos 48.59°$ (for the boat) and $x = 0$ (for the river)
    e. $x = 4t \cos 48.59°$ and $y = 4t \sin 48.59° + 3t$

2. a.

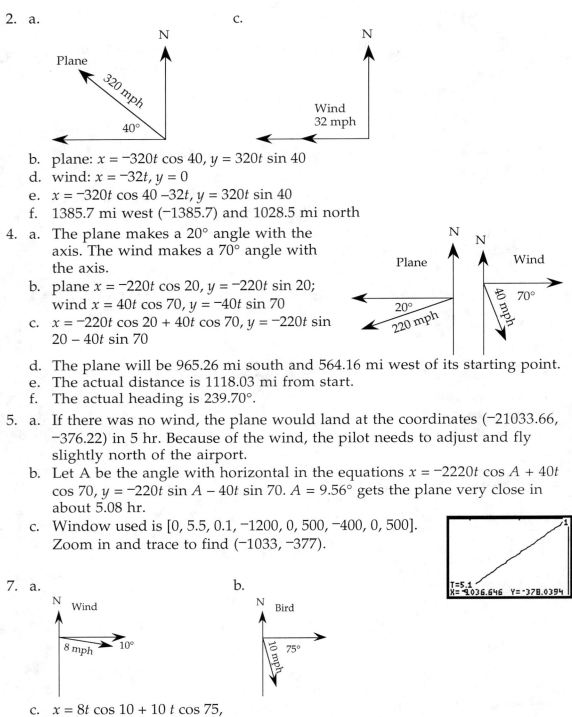

c.

b. plane: $x = -320t \cos 40, y = 320t \sin 40$
d. wind: $x = -32t, y = 0$
e. $x = -320t \cos 40 - 32t, y = 320t \sin 40$
f. 1385.7 mi west (−1385.7) and 1028.5 mi north

4. a. The plane makes a 20° angle with the axis. The wind makes a 70° angle with the axis.
b. plane $x = -220t \cos 20, y = -220t \sin 20$; wind $x = 40t \cos 70, y = -40t \sin 70$
c. $x = -220t \cos 20 + 40t \cos 70, y = -220t \sin 20 - 40t \sin 70$
d. The plane will be 965.26 mi south and 564.16 mi west of its starting point.
e. The actual distance is 1118.03 mi from start.
f. The actual heading is 239.70°.

5. a. If there was no wind, the plane would land at the coordinates (−21033.66, −376.22) in 5 hr. Because of the wind, the pilot needs to adjust and fly slightly north of the airport.
b. Let A be the angle with horizontal in the equations $x = -2220t \cos A + 40t \cos 70, y = -220t \sin A - 40t \sin 70$. $A = 9.56°$ gets the plane very close in about 5.08 hr.
c. Window used is [0, 5.5, 0.1, −1200, 0, 500, −400, 0, 500]. Zoom in and trace to find (−1033, −377).

7. a.

b.

c. $x = 8t \cos 10 + 10t \cos 75$, $y = -8t \sin 10 - 10t \sin 75$, 83.73 mi east and 88.39 mi south
d. 136.6° heading

Chapter Review
Problem Set 6.7

1. a.

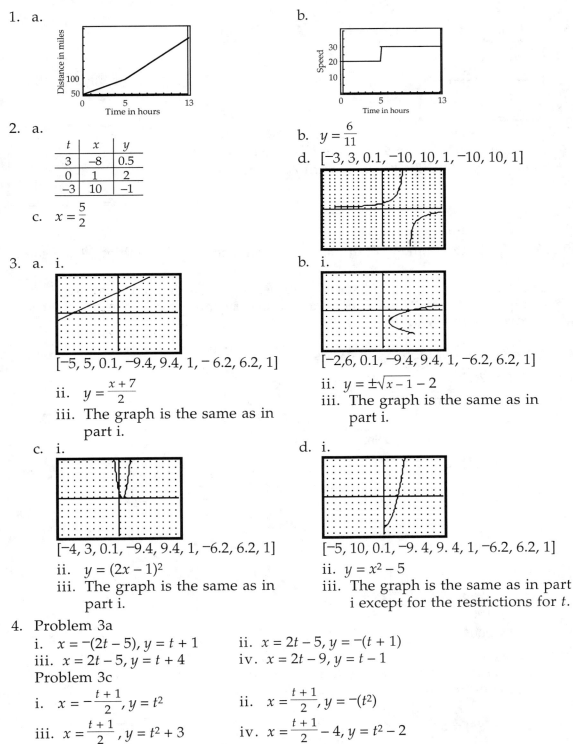

b.

2. a.

t	x	y
3	–8	0.5
0	1	2
–3	10	–1

b. $y = \dfrac{6}{11}$

d. $[-3, 3, 0.1, -10, 10, 1, -10, 10, 1]$

c. $x = \dfrac{5}{2}$

3. a. i.

$[-5, 5, 0.1, -9.4, 9.4, 1, -6.2, 6.2, 1]$

ii. $y = \dfrac{x + 7}{2}$

iii. The graph is the same as in part i.

b. i.

$[-2, 6, 0.1, -9.4, 9.4, 1, -6.2, 6.2, 1]$

ii. $y = \pm\sqrt{x - 1} - 2$

iii. The graph is the same as in part i.

c. i.

$[-4, 3, 0.1, -9.4, 9.4, 1, -6.2, 6.2, 1]$

ii. $y = (2x - 1)^2$

iii. The graph is the same as in part i.

d. i.

$[-5, 10, 0.1, -9.4, 9.4, 1, -6.2, 6.2, 1]$

ii. $y = x^2 - 5$

iii. The graph is the same as in part i except for the restrictions for t.

4. Problem 3a

i. $x = -(2t - 5), y = t + 1$

ii. $x = 2t - 5, y = -(t + 1)$

iii. $x = 2t - 5, y = t + 4$

iv. $x = 2t - 9, y = t - 1$

Problem 3c

i. $x = -\dfrac{t + 1}{2}, y = t^2$

ii. $x = \dfrac{t + 1}{2}, y = -(t^2)$

iii. $x = \dfrac{t + 1}{2}, y = t^2 + 3$

iv. $x = \dfrac{t + 1}{2} - 4, y = t^2 - 2$

5. a. $A = 42.83°$
    b. $B = 28.30°$
    c. $c = 22.98$
    d. $d = 12.86$
    e. $e = 21.36$
    f. $f = 17.11$

6. $[-10, 10, 0.1, -9.4, 9.4, 1, -6.2, 6.2, 1]$; Angle is 28°.

7. Using the edge of the pool as the point $(0, 0)$, the x-equation would be $x = 4t + 1.5$ and the y-equation would be $y = -4.9t^2 + 10$. She hits at a point 7.2 m from the edge.

8. 1.43 ft/sec

9. No, he will miss the monkey.

10. He will hit the monkey. Both the monkey and the dart are falling at the same rates.

11. Flying at a heading of 107.77° will take her to her destination if the wind averages 25 mi/hr. If the wind were 30 mi/hr continuously, she could miss her destination by as much as 8 mi.

Chapter Seven Selected Answers

Problem Set 7.1

1. a. $y = 1151(1 + .015)^x$
    b.

Year	China
1991	1151
1992	1168
1993	1186
1994	1204
1995	1222
1996	1240
1997	1259
1998	1277
1999	1297
2000	1316

    c. 2063
    d. Answers will vary. (The dangers involved in this long range prediction are enormous.)

2. a. 5th day; 250: 6th day; 625
    b. $2.56(2.5^{3.5}) = 63.25$

c. $2.56(2.5^{(6+4/24)}) = 728$ cm

d. $2.56(2.5^{11.539}) = 100{,}000$ or 11 days 13 hr ; 9 p.m. on day 11

4. The actual value is approximately 2056.

Problem Set 7.2

1 a. $49^{5/2}$ is the square root of 49 raised to the fifth power = 16807.

   b. $16^{3/4}$ is the fourth root of 16 raised to the third power = 8.

   c. $64^{5/3}$ is the cube root of 64 raised to the fifth power = 1024.

   d. $32^{2/5}$ is the fifth root of 32 squared = 4.

2. a. 16 Kg   b. 25 Kg   c. 91.125 cm

3. a. $x^{1/4}$ b. $x^{3/5}$

4. a. 128   b. 81

6. a. $\sqrt[3]{x^2}$ b. $\sqrt[4]{x^{11}}$ or $x^2 \sqrt[4]{x^3}$

8. a. $b(x) = \begin{cases} 1 & x = 0 \\ b(x-1) \cdot 1.04 & x > 0 \end{cases}$ b. $b(x) = 1.04^x$ c. about 100 yr

10. a. the amount invested

   b. the annual interest rate

   c. the amount compounded monthly

   d. the x-value used to calculate the amount after 1 mo

   e. the x-value used to calculate the amount in the account at the present

   f. the x-value used to calculate the amount in the account 1 mo ago

   g. $x \approx 115.9$

Problem Set 7.3

1. a. $1/27 = 0.\overline{037}$ b. $1/5 = 0.2$

   c. −216   d. $1/144 = 0.0069\overline{4}$

2. a. $\dfrac{1}{8x^3}$ b. $\dfrac{2}{x^3}$ c. $x^{7/6}$ d. $2x^{3/2}$

5. a. −2   b. −3   c. −5   d. 0

6. As the base increases, the graph becomes steeper. They all intersect the y-axis at (0, 1). The graph of $y = 6^x$ should be the steepest one. It will contain the points (0, 1) and (1, 6).

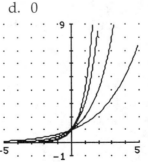

7. As the base increases, the graph flattens out. They all intersect the y-axis at (0, 1). All of these equations involve raising a number between 0 and 1 to a power. The graph of the equation $y = 0.1^x$ should be steeper than any of these given. It will contain the points (0, 1) and (−1, 10).

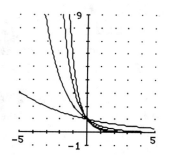

8. Each equation in Problem 6 involves a base larger than one. In Problem 7 each base is less than one.

   a. $y = 2.5^x$ b. $y = 0.35^x$

Problem Set 7.4

1. Graph a is the original and graph b is the inverse.

   a. $x = t + 2, y = 2t − 3$ b. $x = t + 1, y = t^2$

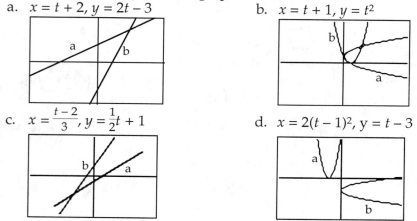

   c. $x = \dfrac{t-2}{3}, y = \dfrac{1}{2}t + 1$ d. $x = 2(t − 1)^2, y = t − 3$

   e. The original and its inverse are symmetric with respect to the line $y = x$.
   f. $x = t, y = t$

2. Graph c is the inverse because the coordinates are switched.

3. a. $y = 2x − 11$ b. $x = 2t − 1$ and $y = t + 5$ c. $x = 2y − 11$
   d. The equations are both linear, but the variables x and y are switched.

5. Answers will vary; $t ≥ 3$ works and so does $t ≤ 3$.

7. a. Answers will vary. One possibility is for $x = t$ and $y = (t + 1)^2 − 2$.
   b. $x = (t + 1)^2 − 2$ and $y = t$
   c. $x = (y + 1)^2 − 2$ or $y = ±\sqrt{x + 2} − 1$
   d. $f(x) = (x + 1)^2 − 2$. The inverse is not a function, so it will take two equations to write it $f^{-1}(x) = \sqrt{x + 2} − 1$ and $f^{-1}(x) = −\sqrt{x + 2} − 1$.

8. a. $f(x) = 2x − 3$ and $f^{-1}(x) = \dfrac{x + 3}{2}$ b. $f(x) = \dfrac{4 - 3x}{2}$ and $f^{-1}(x) = \dfrac{4 - 2x}{3}$

   c. $f(x) = \dfrac{-1}{2}x^2 + \dfrac{3}{2}$; the inverse isn't a function, so $f^{-1}(x)$ notation doesn't apply.

Problem Set 7.5

1. a. 2.187   b. 29.791   c. no solution

    d. 625   e. 1

2. a. $9x^4$ b. $8x^6$

3. 0.109 or 10.9%

4. a. $P = 4 \cdot 1.02^t$ where t is number of years since 1975.

    b. Answers will vary. In 1993 the population is about 5.7 billion.

    c. 1993 population was 5.5 billion or 3.6% error.

6. a.   b.   c.   d.

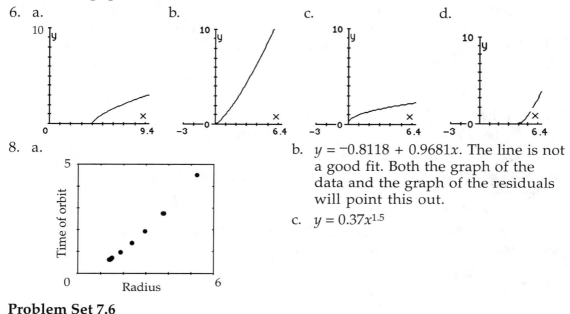

8. a.   b. $y = -0.8118 + 0.9681x$. The line is not a good fit. Both the graph of the data and the graph of the residuals will point this out.

                                               c. $y = 0.37x^{1.5}$

Problem Set 7.6

1. a. $10^x = 1000$ b. $5^x = 625$ c. $7^x = \sqrt{7}$

    d. $8^x = 2$ e. $5^x = \dfrac{1}{25}$ f. $6^x = 1$

4. a. The graph is shifted two units to the left of the log curve.   b. The graph is stretched vertically to three times the size of the log curve.   c. The graph is flipped and shifted two units down from the log curve.

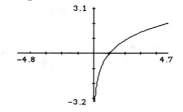

5. in about 25 min (24.66 min)

7. a. $C_1 = 32.7$, $C_2 = 65.4$, $C_3 = 130.8$, $C_6 = 106.4$, $C_7 = 2092.8$, $C_8 = 4185.6$
    b. $y = 32.7 \cdot 2^x$
    c. Answers will vary, but string lengths are related to the frequencies. Longer lengths have smaller frequencies.

8. a. $y = 100(0.999879)^x$
    b. $x \approx 6025$ years ago or the current year $- 6025$. (In 1993, the year would be 4032 BC, in 1994, the year would be 4031 BC, and so on.)

Problem Set 7.7

1. a. log 10   b. log 100   c. log 900   d. log 200
    e. To get the answer, multiply the arguments together.
    f. Answers are the same as parts 1a through 1d.
    g. $\log a + \log b = \log ab$
    h. Logs are exponents. When your multiply numbers of the same base you add the exponents.

3. a. 0.3, 0.9   b. $\log 2^3 = 3 \log 2$ c. 1.7, 3.4
    d. $\log 50^2 = 2 \log 50$ e. Answers are the same.   f. $\log a^b = b \log a$
    g. yes   h. $\frac{1}{2} \log a$

5. Answers will vary. For example, the log of a product is the sum of the logs. The log of a quotient is the difference of the logs. The log of a number raised to a power if the power times the log of the number.

6. Answers will vary. For example, if a horizontal line will intersect f in more than one point, its inverse is not a function.

9. a. $x + y$ b. $z - x$

10. a. 4   b. ≈ 1.292

11. a.   b.   c.

    d. The domain of $f(f^{-1}(x))$ is all positive real numbers, while the domain of $f^{-1}(f(x))$ is all real numbers. The difference is because the inside function in $f(f^{-1}(x))$ is a logarithm that uses only positive values, while in $f^{-1}(f(x))$ the inside function is an exponential that can accept any real number as an input.

12. a. true   b. false   c. true
     d. true   e. true   f. true

Problem Set 7.8

1. about 195.9 mo

2. a. $x = \dfrac{\log 12.85}{\log 4.2} = 1.779$

   b. By definition $12.85 = 4.2^x$ is $\log_{4.2} 12.85 = x$. Use the change of base property.

3. a. 2.903   b. 11   c. $^-4$

4. a. 1.606 m²   b. 153 lb

6. a. 30 dB   b. 65 dB   c. $5 \cdot 10^{-6}$ W/cm³

   d. $\sqrt{10} \approx 3.16$ times louder

Problem Set 7.9

1. $y = 0.21\sqrt{x}$

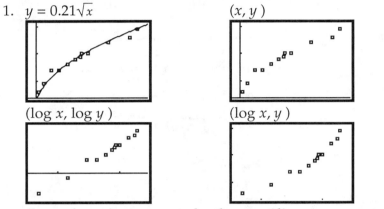

(x, y) $(x, \log y)$

$(\log x, \log y)$ $(\log x, y)$

$(\log x, \log y)$ appears to be the most linear.

$y \approx 0.303x^{0.417}$ (Answers will vary depending on the points used to find the slope, and the accuracy of the numbers. Be sure to check your answer graphically to make sure it appears to fit.)

2. a.

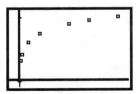

     b. $(\log x, y)$

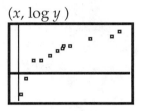

    c. Answers will vary, but the equation should be close to $y = 21x + 5.5$.

    d.

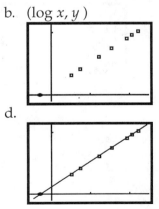

e. $y = 21\log x + 5.5$ (Answers will vary depending on the points used to find the slope, and the accuracy of the numbers. Be sure to check your answer graphically to make sure the graph appears to fit.)

f.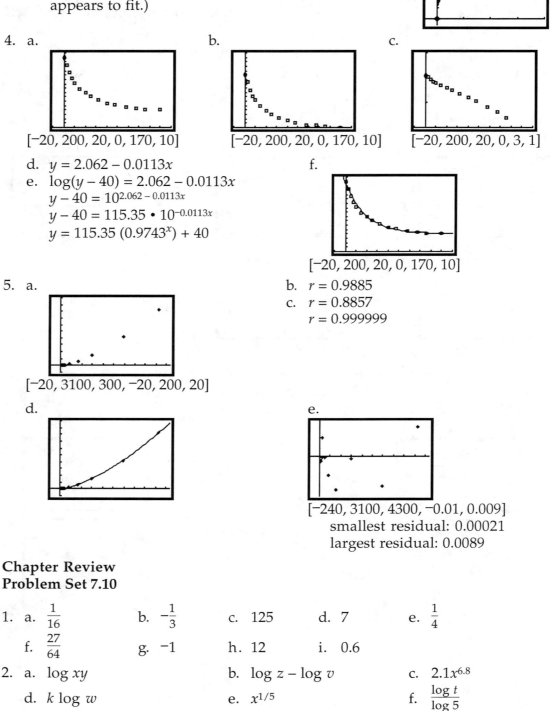

4. a.

$[-20, 200, 20, 0, 170, 10]$

b.

$[-20, 200, 20, 0, 170, 10]$

c.

$[-20, 200, 20, 0, 3, 1]$

d. $y = 2.062 - 0.0113x$

e. $\log(y - 40) = 2.062 - 0.0113x$
$y - 40 = 10^{2.062 - 0.0113x}$
$y - 40 = 115.35 \cdot 10^{-0.0113x}$
$y = 115.35 (0.9743^x) + 40$

f.

$[-20, 200, 20, 0, 170, 10]$

5. a.

$[-20, 3100, 300, -20, 200, 20]$

b. $r = 0.9885$

c. $r = 0.8857$
$r = 0.999999$

d.

e.

$[-240, 3100, 4300, -0.01, 0.009]$
smallest residual: 0.00021
largest residual: 0.0089

Chapter Review
Problem Set 7.10

1. a. $\frac{1}{16}$ b. $-\frac{1}{3}$ c. 125   d. 7   e. $\frac{1}{4}$

   f. $\frac{27}{64}$ g. -1 h. 12   i. 0.6

2. a. $\log xy$ b. $\log z - \log v$ c. $2.1x^{6.8}$

   d. $k \log w$ e. $x^{1/5}$ f. $\frac{\log t}{\log 5}$

3. a. 2.153   b. 2.231   c. 2.344
    d. $3.1^{47} = 1.242\text{E}23$ e. 3.041   f. 45.897
    g. 5902   h. $47^{5/3} = 612$

4. a. $a = 0.50$ b. 2.4998
    c. 0.63 (The first 0.63 min is free.)
    d. \$4.19   e. 3.98 min

5. a. [80, 90, 1, 0, 12000, 1000]

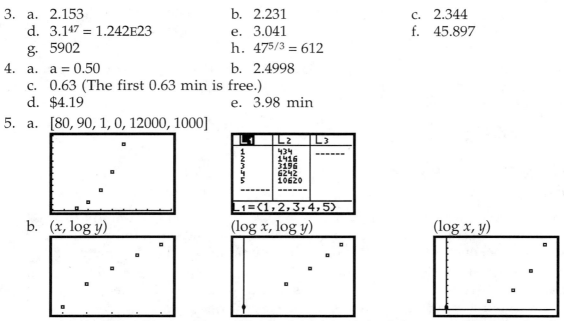

    b. $(x, \log y)$ $(\log x, \log y)$ $(\log x, y)$

    c. The graphs of $(x, \log y)$ and $(\log x, \log y)$ both look linear indicating that
        the best fit for the original data is either a power regression or an
        exponential regression. The equation of the line for $(x, \log y)$ is
        $0.342x - 2.396$ with an $r = 0.988$. The equation of the line for $(\log x, \log y)$ is
        $2.6x + 1.979$ with $r = 0.997$.

    d. The ExpReg on the calculator gives you $249.159(2.20)^x$ with $r = 0.988$. The
        PwrReg gives you $398.14x^{1.98}$ with $r = 0.997$. To determine which is the best
        fit for the original data, you need to calculate the residuals.

        PwrReg   Residuals

        ExpReg   Residuals

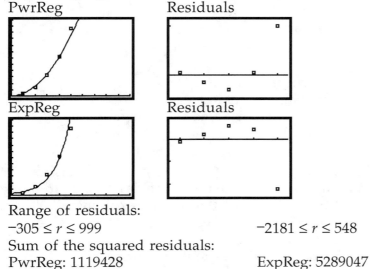

        Range of residuals:
        $-305 \le r \le 999$ $-2181 \le r \le 548$
        Sum of the squared residuals:
        PwrReg: 1119428   ExpReg: 5289047

        Because the sum of the squared residuals is less for the PwrReg, this is
        probably a better choice for the model.
        Using the ExpReg: 1990 = 136046; 1995 = 6,989,589; 2000 = 359,101,100

Using the PwrReg: 1990 = 24,386; 1995 = 63,737; 2000 = 121,357
  e. PwrReg: 52.2 yr
     ExpReg: 10.5 yr
6. a. $y \approx 1.3592 \cdot 10^{-6}x^{3.3185}$, using (55, 0.75) as the first value. Because the sum of the squared residuals is less for the PwrReg, this is probably a better choice for the model.
   b. $5.89 in 2000, $8.08 in 2010, and $10.79 in 2020
   c. The model predicts $0.24 in 1938.

Chapter Eight Selected Answers

Problem Set 8.1

Many of the questions in this problem set ask you to devise a method to randomly select an outcome or to generate a set of random numbers. In this solution set, one example is given but it is by no means the only method.

2. a. Roll a die for each student. If a 1 is rolled, that student gets on bus 1, if a 2 is rolled, that student gets on bus 2, and so on. If a 6 is rolled, roll the die again.

   b. Theoretically, $\frac{1}{5}$ of the students or 20 should be assigned to each bus.

   c. You could alter the Generate routine to *seq* (*int 5rand* + 1, X, 1,99,1)→L_1. (See **Appendix 8B**.) Note: You can only put 99 numbers in a list, so to obtain bus assignments for 100 students, you could have to do the list twice. Using 5 rand results in numbers from 1 to 5 and eliminates the need to roll again if you get a 6. In L_1, you will have a list of 99 random rolls of the die. Plot this data in a histogram to see the total number of rolls for each number from 1 to 6. You will need to do one more roll to get 100 rolls. Use trace to determine the number of students that are on each bus.

   d. For this simulation, there are 23 students on bus 1.

3. Each one of these procedures for producing random numbers has shortcomings.
   a. Middle numbers (3–7) occur more commonly than 1, 2, 8, or 9.
   b. Very few pencils will be 0 in. or 1 in. in length.
   c. Books tend to open to pages that are used more than others.
   d. Answers will vary. You could alter the Generate routine to *seq* (*int 5rand* + 1, X, 1,99,1)'L_1. (See **Appendix 8B**.)

5. b. Assign each of the letters in the word CHAMPION a number from 1 to 8. Look at the first digit in the Random Number Table. If the first digit is a 0 or a 9, which would not represent a letter in the cereal, then look at the next digit until you get a digit from 1 to 8. Count down the table until you have at least one of each number.

   e. Answers will vary. Average numbers should tend towards 21.7 boxes.

7. a. i. $-2 < x < 4$ ii. $\{1, 2, 3\}$

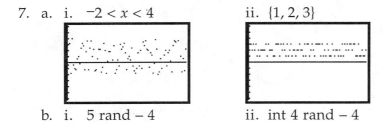

b. i. 5 rand − 4   ii. int 4 rand − 4   iii. int 3 rand + 2

Problem Set 8.2

1. a. 36 different outcomes
   b. 6 different outcomes, all in column Green 4
   c. 12 different outcomes, all in rows White 2 and 3
   d. 3 different outcomes

2. a. $x + y = 9$ gives points at $(3, 6)$, $(4, 5)$, $(5, 4)$, and $(6, 3)$.
   b. $x + y = 6$ gives points at $(1, 5)$, $(2, 4)$, $(3, 3)$, $(4, 2)$, $(5, 1)$.
   c. $x - y = 1$ or $y - x = 1$ gives points at $(1, 2)$, $(2, 3)$, $(3, 4)$, $(4, 5)$, $(5, 6)$, $(2, 1)$, $(3, 2)$, $(4, 3)$, $(5, 4)$, $(6, 5)$.
   d. $x + y = 6$ and $x - y = 2$ gives point $(4, 2)$.
   e. $x + y \le 5$ gives points $(1, 1)$, $(2, 1)$, $(1, 2)$, $(2, 2)$, $(2, 3)$, $(3, 2)$, $(3, 1)$, $(1, 3)$, $(4, 1)$, $(1, 4)$.

3. a. $4; \dfrac{4}{36}$ b. $5; \dfrac{5}{36}$ c. $10; \dfrac{10}{36}$ d. $1; \dfrac{1}{36}$ e. $10; \dfrac{7}{36}$

5. a. 144   b. 44   c. $\dfrac{44}{144} = 0.306$

   d. $\dfrac{44}{144} = 0.306$ e. 0.694   f. 0; 0

7. a. $x + y \le 6$
   b.

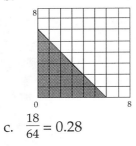

   c. $\dfrac{18}{64} = 0.28$

Problem Set 8.3

1. a. 24   b. $\dfrac{1}{4}$ c. $\dfrac{2}{24}$ or $\dfrac{1}{12}$

   d. $\dfrac{1}{24}$ e. $\dfrac{23}{24}$ f. $\dfrac{12}{24}$ or $\dfrac{1}{2}$

2. a.

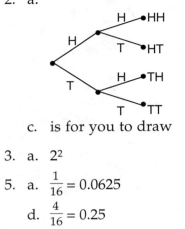

c. is for you to draw

b.

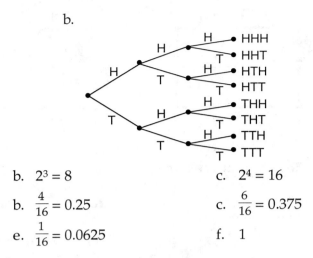

3. a. 2^2 b. $2^3 = 8$ c. $2^4 = 16$

5. a. $\frac{1}{16} = 0.0625$ b. $\frac{4}{16} = 0.25$ c. $\frac{6}{16} = 0.375$

d. $\frac{4}{16} = 0.25$ e. $\frac{1}{16} = 0.0625$ f. 1

g. $\frac{5}{16} = 0.313$

7.

	Liberal	Conservative	Totals
Age under 30	210	145	355
Age 30–45	235	220	455
Age over 45	280	410	690
Totals	725	775	1500

a. $\frac{280}{1500} = 0.187$ b. $\frac{775}{1500} = 0.517$

c. $\frac{145}{355} = 0.408$ d. $\frac{145}{775} = 0.187$

8. a.

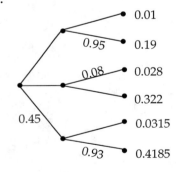

b. 0.08
c. 0.0695
d. $\frac{0.028}{0.0695} = 0.4029$

9.

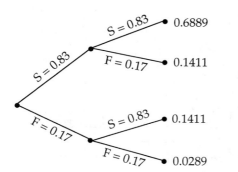

a. 0.0289
b. 0.9711
c. 0.6889

Problem Set 8.4

1. d. −0.25
   e. Answers will vary. One possible answer is 7 points if Sly wins and 5 points if Les wins.

   $$\left(\frac{15}{36} \cdot 7 + \frac{21}{36} \cdot -5 = 0\right)$$

   c.
   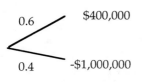

3. a.

   b. −160,000
   c. Answers will vary. He is better off, now knowing the weather report, to cancel the concert and lose $100,000 because this is less than his expected loss of $160,000.

4. a. 4.9%   b. 7.9%   c. 1.88 birds

6. b. $P(\text{testing positive}) = \dfrac{\text{number of positive tests}}{\text{number of people tested}}$

   c. P(having disease if tested positive) =
   $$\frac{\text{number of diseased people testing positive}}{\text{number of people testing positive}}$$

   d.
   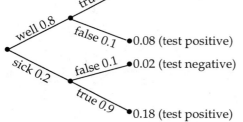

Problem Set 8.5

1. 3

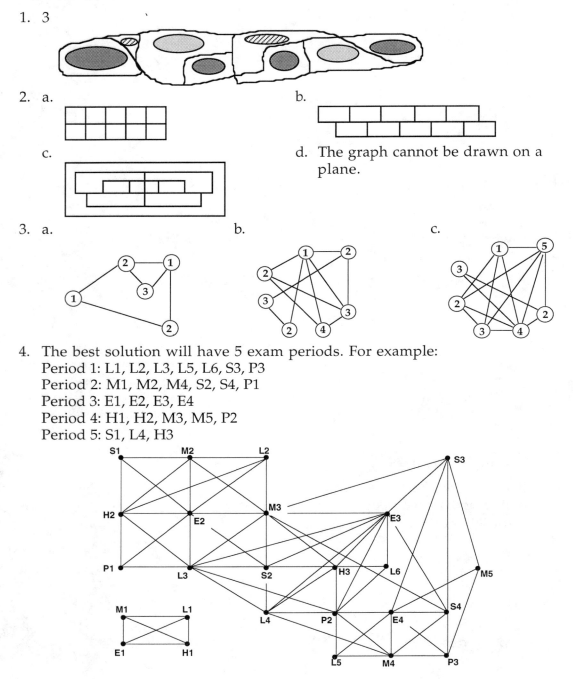

2. a.

   b.

   c.

   d. The graph cannot be drawn on a plane.

3. a.

   b.

   c.

4. The best solution will have 5 exam periods. For example:
   Period 1: L1, L2, L3, L5, L6, S3, P3
   Period 2: M1, M2, M4, S2, S4, P1
   Period 3: E1, E2, E3, E4
   Period 4: H1, H2, M3, M5, P2
   Period 5: S1, L4, H3

Problem Set 8.6

1. 4360 mi

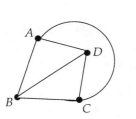

2. a.

b.

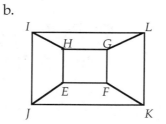

5. a.

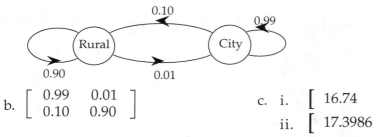

b. $\begin{bmatrix} 0.99 & 0.01 \\ 0.10 & 0.90 \end{bmatrix}$

c. i. $\begin{bmatrix} 16.74 & 8.26 \end{bmatrix}$

   ii. $\begin{bmatrix} 17.3986 & 7.6014 \end{bmatrix}$

   iii. $\begin{bmatrix} 17.984754 & 7.015246 \end{bmatrix}$

Problem Set 8.7

1. $\begin{bmatrix} 43.1525 & 196.84 \end{bmatrix}$

4. a. $\begin{bmatrix} 7 & 54 \end{bmatrix}$

   b. $\begin{bmatrix} 0.815 & 0.185 \\ 0.0925 & 0.9075 \end{bmatrix}$

   c. $\begin{bmatrix} 15.6 & -10.8 \\ 10.7 & 42.2 \end{bmatrix}$

   d. $\begin{bmatrix} 180 & -230 \\ 54 & 322 \end{bmatrix}$

5. a. $\begin{bmatrix} 29 & 211 \end{bmatrix}$

   b. $\begin{bmatrix} 36.65 & 203.35 \end{bmatrix}$

   c. $\begin{bmatrix} 43.1525 & 196.84 \end{bmatrix}$

   d. $\begin{bmatrix} 80 & 160 \end{bmatrix}$

6. a. $\begin{bmatrix} 0.815 & 0.185 \\ 0.0925 & 0.9075 \end{bmatrix}$

   b. $\begin{bmatrix} 0 & 0 & 0 \\ 0 & 4 & 0 \\ 0 & 0 & 0 \end{bmatrix}$

7. a.

	Low	Ave	High
Low	0.5	0.45	0.05
Ave	0.25	0.5	0.25
High	0.3	0.3	0.4

b. after one generation $[0.32 \quad 0.4575 \quad 0.2225]$

after two generations $[0.341125 \quad 0.4395 \quad 0.219375]$

after three generations $[0.34625 \quad 0.43906875 \quad 0.21468125]$

in the long run $[0.3474903475 \quad 0.4401544402 \quad 0.2123552124]$

Chapter Review
Problem Set 8.8

2. Answers will vary.
   a. Look for well shuffled full deck after each draw.
   b. A painfully slow method if you need many numbers. Will randomness depend upon who is called?
   c. This depends on randomness involved in falling off and besides, the numbers 1–12 aren't equally likely.

3. a. int 10 rand + 3   b. int 10 rand – 7   c. 5 rand – 2

4. a. $\frac{1}{2}$ b. 17.765

5. a. 64 possible outcomes   b. 10 possible outcomes

   c. 10/64 = 0.156   d. 49/64 = 0.766

6. a. There are 32 branches.

   b. 10 ways   c. $\frac{3}{8} = 0.375$

7. a.

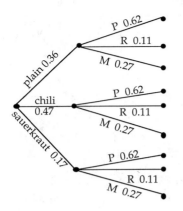

b. 0.0517

c. 0.8946

d. 0.3501

8. a.

	9th grade	10th grade	11th grade	12th grade	Total
Ice Cream	18	37	85	114	**254**
Whipped Cream	5	18	37	58	**118**
Total	**23**	**55**	**122**	**172**	372

b. $\frac{37}{55} = 0.673$

c. $\frac{37}{122} = 0.303$

d. $\frac{18}{254} = 0.071$

e. $\frac{118}{372} = 0.317$

9. $20 \cdot 0.3 + 10 \cdot 0.4 + 5 \cdot 0.2 + 1 \cdot 0.05 + 0 \cdot 0.05 = 11.05$

10. $\begin{bmatrix} 439 & 561 \end{bmatrix}$; $\begin{bmatrix} 400 & 600 \end{bmatrix}$

Chapter Nine Selected Answers

Problem Set 9.1

1. a. (0.000, 1.000), (1.000, 2.000), (5.000, 26.000)
   b. When $x < 0$ or when $1 < x < 5$; when $0 < x < 1$ or $x > 5$
2. b. 1.25, 1.176470588, 0.0735294118; Y_3 is the difference between Y_1 and Y_2.
   c. $Y_3 = 0$
   d. It does not.   e. The equations do not intersect.
4. a. when 48.57 g have been added
   b. when 120 g are added
   c. Answers will vary. The spring that is longer without any attached mass has less stretch than the other for additional amounts of added mass.
7. a. Answers will vary according to the model selected. If least-square lines are used, they intersect in the year 2023 (approximately).
   b. Answers will vary. The least-square lines are $y = 2.12 - 0.009x$ for men and $y = 2.41 - 0.014x$ for women if 1964 is listed as $x = 0$.
   d. For the 1994 Olympics, the time $x = 30$. Using the men's model, the predicted time would be $y = 2.12 - 0.009(30) = 1.85$ min or 1:51. The model is off $1:51.29 - 1:51 = 0:00.29$ min. Using the women's model, the predicted

time would be $y = 2.41 - 0.014(30) = 1.99$ min or 1:59.4. the model is off $2:02.19 - 1:59.4 = 0:02.79$ min. The actual times are close to the predicted times of the models. The residual for the 1994 men's time is 0.005 min and for the 1994 women's time is 0.0465 min.

Problem Set 9.2

1. a. $(-4.7, 29.57)$ b. $(6.66\ldots, 1.4\ldots)$ c. $3.1x + 2(4.7x + 25.1) = 8.2$
$12.5x + 50.2 = 8.2$
$12.5x = -42$
$(-3.36, 9.308)$

2. $(6\sqrt{5}, 2\sqrt{5}), (-6\sqrt{5}, -2\sqrt{5})$ b. $(\sqrt{2}, \sqrt{2} - 4)$ and $(-\sqrt{2}, -\sqrt{2} - 4)$

4. a. $\approx (-0.53297, 2.71429)$ b. $(8, \frac{-5}{2})$

5. a.

c. $1.8y = 8.46x - 7.2$

$4.7y = -8.46x + 32.9$

b.

d. $y = \dfrac{25.7}{6.5} \approx 3.954$

6. a. multiply by 3, $y \approx 2.475$ b. multiply by -3, $y \approx -6.786$
$\approx (-0.9088, 2.4746)$ $\approx (6.286, -6.786)$

11. $u_{31} = v_{31}$ when they are both 21

Problem Set 9.3

1. a. ii and iii   b. They graph as parallel lines.

c. ii. $\frac{3}{4}x - 4 = .75x + 3$ iii. $12x + 18y = 27$
$0 = 7$ $12x + 18y = 47$
$0 = -20$

In both cases the statements are false.
d. The lines have the same slope.

2. Answers will vary. Samples are given below.
a. $y = 2x + b$ where b is any number except 4

b. $y = \frac{-1}{3}x + b$ where b is any number except -3
c. $2x + 5y = b$ where b is any number except 10
d. $x - 2y = b$ where b is any number except -6

3. a. ii, iii   b. They are the same lines.

c. ii. $\frac{1}{4}(2x - 1) = 0.5x - .25$ iii. $12x + 18y = 27$

$\frac{1}{2}x - \frac{1}{4} = 0.5x - .25$ $3x + 2y = 15$

$$0 = 0 \qquad\qquad\qquad 0 = 0$$

You get a true statement.

    d. They have the same slope and the same intercept; or they are multiples of each other.

4. Answers will vary. Samples are given below.
    a. $2y = 4x + 8$ or multiply the original equation by any other number
    b. $3y = {}^-x - 9$ or multiply the original equation by any other number

5. a. $t = 0.25, x = 1.75, y = {}^-1.5$ b. no solution

7. $a = 100$ and $b = 0.7$

10. a. Answers will vary. If a least-square model is used for both populations, the lines intersect in approximately in the year 1996.
    b. 903,635 people
    c. Least-square lines are $y \approx 72579.4 + 18052x$ and $y \approx 1875016 - 21100x$.

Problem Set 9.4

1. a. $\begin{bmatrix} 15 & -19 \\ 22 & -27 \end{bmatrix}$ b. $\begin{bmatrix} 7 & -18 & -7 \\ 12 & -27 & 42 \\ 1 & -4 & -21 \end{bmatrix}$

    c. This is not possible because you need the same number of rows in the second matrix as you have columns in the first matrix.

2. a. $\begin{bmatrix} 1a + 5c & 6a + 2c \\ 1b + 5d & 6b + 2d \end{bmatrix}$ b. $\begin{bmatrix} 1a + 5c & 6a + 2c \\ 1b + 5d & 6b + 2d \end{bmatrix} = \begin{bmatrix} 1 & 0 \\ 0 & 1 \end{bmatrix}$

    $= \begin{bmatrix} -7 & 33 \\ 14 & -26 \end{bmatrix}$ $a = -0.071428 = \frac{-1}{14}, b = 0.1785714 = \frac{5}{28},$

    $a = 3, b = -7, c = -2, d = 8$ $c = 0.21428 = \frac{3}{14}, d = -0.035714 = \frac{-1}{28}$

3. a. $\begin{bmatrix} 5 & 2 \\ 7 & 3 \end{bmatrix}\begin{bmatrix} 3 & -2 \\ -7 & 5 \end{bmatrix} = \begin{bmatrix} 1 & 0 \\ 0 & 1 \end{bmatrix}$ c. Answers will vary. Two matrices are inverses if when you multiply them together you get the identity matrix as the answer.

    Yes, it's an inverse.

4. a. $\begin{bmatrix} 4 & 3 \\ 5 & 4 \end{bmatrix}^{-1} = \begin{bmatrix} 4 & -3 \\ -5 & 4 \end{bmatrix}$ b. $\begin{bmatrix} 6 & 4 & -2 \\ 3 & 1 & -1 \\ 0 & 7 & 3 \end{bmatrix}^{-1} = \begin{bmatrix} -0.5555 & 1.4444 & 0.1111 \\ 0.5 & -1 & 0 \\ -1.1666 & 2.3333 & 0.3333 \end{bmatrix}$

5. a. $\begin{bmatrix} 5.2 & 3.6 \\ -5.2 & 2 \end{bmatrix}\begin{bmatrix} x \\ y \end{bmatrix} = \begin{bmatrix} 7 \\ 8.2 \end{bmatrix}$

6. a. $\begin{bmatrix} 8 & 3 \\ 6 & 5 \end{bmatrix}^{-1}\begin{bmatrix} 41 \\ 39 \end{bmatrix} = \begin{bmatrix} 4 \\ 3 \end{bmatrix}$ b. $\begin{bmatrix} 11 & -5 \\ 9 & 2 \end{bmatrix}^{-1}\begin{bmatrix} -38 \\ -25 \end{bmatrix} = \begin{bmatrix} -3 \\ 1 \end{bmatrix}$

8. a. The three equations are:
    $7t + 3a + 9s = 19.55$
    $9t + 10a = 13$
    $8t + 7a + 10s = 24.95$
    Rides for the timid cost $0.50.
    Rides for the adventurous cost $0.85.
    Rides for the thrill seekers cost $1.50.
  b. $28.50
  c. Carey would have been better off buying a ticket book for $28.50 because it cost her $24.95 + $5.00 or $29.95.

Problem Set 9.5

1. $y \geq 2.4x + 2$ and $y \leq -x^2 - 2x + 6.4$

2. $(0, 2), (0, 5), (2.752, 3.596), (4, 1.6)$

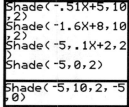

$[-1, 12, 1, -1, 8, 1]$

3. $(1, 0), (1.875, 0), (3.307, 2.2914), (0.2087, 0.7913)$

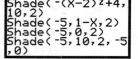
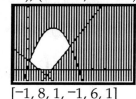

$[-1, 8, 1, -1, 6, 1]$

6. a. $xy \geq 200; xy \leq 300$
    $x + y \geq 33; x + y \leq 40$
  b.

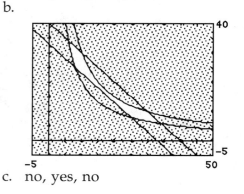

  c. no, yes, no

8. a. First, substitute the given point values in for x and y in the generic equation. There will be 3 equations in 3 variables a, b, and c. Set up a matrix equation in the form $[A] [X] = [B]$ and find $[X]$.

   b. The parabola is $3x^2 + 16x - 12$.

Problem Set 9.6

1. Change the window format to Grid On in order to see the integers in the feasibility region.

   i. a. $[-1, 4, 1, -1, 4, 1]$ b. $(0, 0), (1.5, 0), (1.2, 1.2), (0, 2)$

   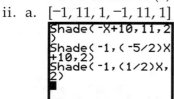

   c. Possible integer points are $(0, 0), (0, 1), (0, 2), (1, 0), (1, 1)$. The maximum value occurs at $(1, 1)$: $5x + 2y = 5(1) + 2(1) = 7$.

   ii. a. $[-1, 11, 1, -1, 11, 1]$ b. $(3.3333, 1.6667), (6.6667, 3.3333), (0, 10)$

   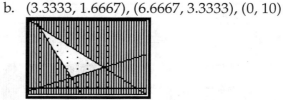

   c. Possible integer points are $(1, 8), (2, 6), (2, 7), (3, 3), (3, 4), (3, 5), (3, 6),$ $(4, 3), (4, 4), (4 ,5), (5, 3), (5, 4)$. The minimum value occurs at $(4, 2)$: $x + 3y = 4 + 3(2) = 10$.

   iii. a. $[-1, 15, 1, -1, 15, 1]$ b. $(2, 5), (5.6667, 5), (6.75, 8.25), (2, 13)$

   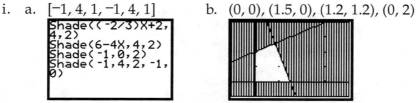

   c. The maximum value occurs at $(6, 8)$: $2x + y = 2(6) + 8 = 20$.

   iv. a. $[-1, 15, 1, -1, 15, 1]$ b. $(4.6667, 2.6667), (8.6667, 0.6667)$

   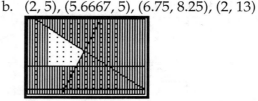

   c. The minimum value occurs at $(4, 4)$: $3x + 2y = 3(4) + 2(4) = 20$.

2. i.   4; 7.5; 8.4; 0   ii.   30; 8.33 . . . ; 16.66 . . .
   iii. 9; 21.75; 16.33 . . . ; 17   iv.   24; 19.33 . . . ; 27.33 . . .
   The optimal value is always located at a vertex of the region.

3. a. [−1000, 50000, 10000, −1000, 50000, 10000]

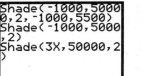 

The solution is the portion of the line $x + y = 40,000$ that lies between the shaded portions of the graph.

   b. The integer point providing the maximum value is (10000, 30000). The maximum value is $0.08(10000) + 0.10(30000) = 3800$.

Problem Set 9.7

1.

	Shawls (x)	Afghans (y)	Constraining value
Spinning hours	1	2	≤ 8
Dyeing hours	1	1	≤ 6
Weaving hours	1	4	≤ 14
Profit	$16	$20	

$x + 2y \leq 8$; $x + y \leq 6$; $x + 4y \leq 14$; $x \geq 0$; $y \geq 0$; profit $= 16x + 20y$

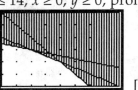

[0, 8, 1, 0, 6, 1]

Vertices: (0, 0), (6, 0), (4, 2), (2, 3)
The maximum profit occurs at (4, 2) or $16(4) + 20(2) = \$104$.
They should make 4 shawls and 2 afghans.

2.

	Siberians (x)	Poodles (y)	Constraining value
Poodles		y	≤ 20
Siberians	x		≤ 15
Food	6	2	≤ 100
Training	250	1000	≤ 10000
Profit	80	200	

$y \leq 20$; $x \leq 15$; $6x + 2y \leq 100$; $250x + 1000y \leq 10000$; $x \geq 0$; $y \geq 0$;
Profit $= 80x + 200y$

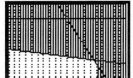

[0, 20, 1, 0, 25, 1]

Vertices are (0, 0), (15, 0), (15, 5), (14.5455, 6.3636), (0, 10).
To maximize profits, raise 14 Siberians and 6 poodles:
$80(14) + 200(6) = \$2320$.

Preliminary Edition   SELECTED ANSWERS

Problem Set 9.8

1. Only 1b and 1d have solutions, all other coefficient matrices have determinant of zero. (The calculator may show 1.74×10^{-10} for 1f.)

2. a. Dependent, the point $(16, -5.333333)$ works in both equations.
   c. Dependent, the point $(21, -17, 1)$ works in all equations.
   e. Inconsistent, the point $(16, 15.667, -3.862)$ does not work in the first equation but does work in the other two.
   f. Inconsistent, the point $(1, 1.209, 1.116, 0.256)$ does not work in the first equation but does work in the other three.

3.

	True/false (w)	Fill in (x)	Matching (y)	Essay (z)	Constraints
Points	2	4	6	10	= 100
Time	1	2	5	6	= 60
Lines	4	3	15	9	= 110

The inequalities are: $2w + 4x + 6y + 10z = 100$, $1w + 2x + 5y + 6z = 60$, and $4w + 3x + 15y + 9z = 110$.

Because there are four variables and only three equations, there are many solutions. The question is, is there is an integer solution? You can simply try numbers for one of the variables. Create a new equation such as $w = 1$. Use this to create a 4 by 4 system. This will give a solution $(1, 7.667, 2.333, 5.333)$. Try this with $w = 2$, and you find a solution with integers $(2, 6, 2, 6)$. There is another solution with $w = 5$: $(5, 1, 1, 8)$.

Chapter Review
Problem Set 9.9

1. $(0.634, -0.598)$ and $(2.366, 4.598)$

2. a.   b.

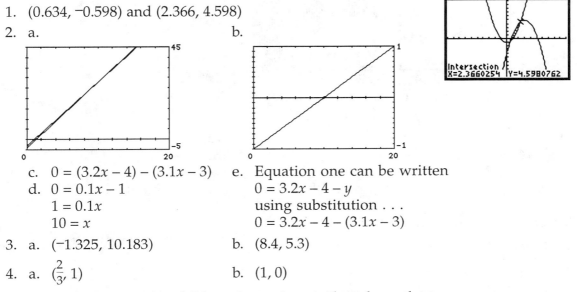

   c. $0 = (3.2x - 4) - (3.1x - 3)$ e. Equation one can be written
   d. $0 = 0.1x - 1$ $0 = 3.2x - 4 - y$
        $1 = 0.1x$ using substitution . . .
       $10 = x$ $0 = 3.2x - 4 - (3.1x - 3)$

3. a. $(-1.325, 10.183)$ b. $(8.4, 5.3)$

4. a. $\left(\frac{2}{3}, 1\right)$ b. $(1, 0)$

5. 5a is consistent; 5c and 5d are inconsistent; 5b is dependent.

6. a. $\begin{bmatrix} 0.8 & -0.6 \\ 0.2 & -0.4 \end{bmatrix}$
    b. $\approx \begin{bmatrix} -0.0353 & 0.1882 & -0.0235 \\ 0.2118 & -0.1294 & 0.1412 \\ -0.3765 & 0.3412 & 0.0824 \end{bmatrix}$

    c. none
    d. $\begin{bmatrix} -0.08929 & 0.1429 & 0.125 \\ -0.0536 & 0.2857 & -0.125 \\ -0.5179 & 0.4286 & 0.125 \end{bmatrix} = \begin{bmatrix} \frac{-5}{56} & \frac{1}{7} & \frac{1}{8} \\ \frac{-3}{56} & \frac{2}{7} & \frac{-1}{8} \\ \frac{-29}{56} & \frac{3}{7} & \frac{1}{8} \end{bmatrix}$

7. a. $\begin{bmatrix} \frac{233}{62} \\ \frac{81}{31} \end{bmatrix}$
    b. $\begin{bmatrix} \frac{-274}{7} \\ \frac{1205}{49} \\ \frac{432}{49} \\ \frac{-1688}{49} \end{bmatrix}$

8. a. $[0, 10, 1, 0, 6, 1]$

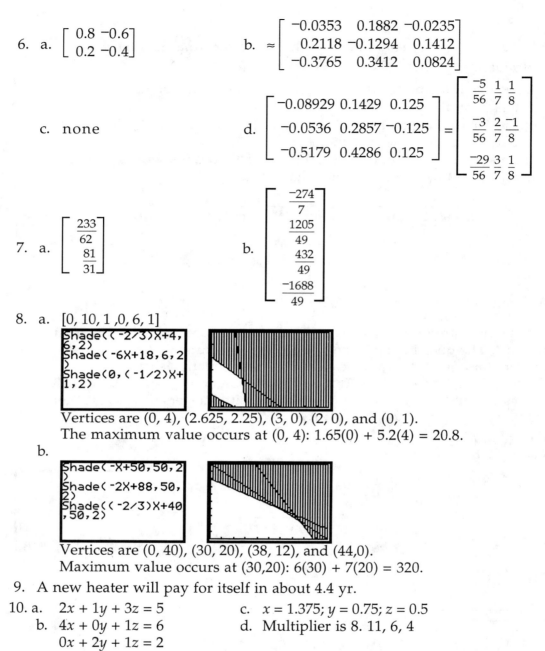

Vertices are (0, 4), (2.625, 2.25), (3, 0), (2, 0), and (0, 1).
The maximum value occurs at (0, 4): 1.65(0) + 5.2(4) = 20.8.

    b.

Vertices are (0, 40), (30, 20), (38, 12), and (44, 0).
Maximum value occurs at (30, 20): 6(30) + 7(20) = 320.

9. A new heater will pay for itself in about 4.4 yr.

10. a. $2x + 1y + 3z = 5$ c. $x = 1.375; y = 0.75; z = 0.5$
    b. $4x + 0y + 1z = 6$ d. Multiplier is 8. 11, 6, 4
        $0x + 2y + 1z = 2$
    e. 11 parts of mixture 1, 6 parts of mixture 2, 4 parts of mixture 3

Chapter Ten Selected Answers

Problem Set 10.1

1. a. $y = 10000x^4 + 5000x^2 + 2000$
    c. 1.006
    d. 7.2%

2. a. $(1 - p)$ because p is a percent decrease.
    b. $30x^3$ c. 0.55 d. 45%
3. a. $50x^3 + 70x^2 + 90x$ b. 0.3976 c. 60.24%
5. a. $D_1 = 15.1, 5.3, -4.5, -14.3, -24.1, -33.9$; $D_2 = -9.8, -9.8, \ldots$
    b. $D_1 = 59.1, 49.3, 39.5, 29.7, 19.9, 10.1$; $D_2 = -9.8, -9.8, \ldots$
    c. second degree
    d. $h = -4.9t^2 + 20t + 80$

Problem Set 10.2

1. a. $y = x^2 - 4x + 7$ b. $y = x^2 + 8x + 14$
    c. $y = 2x^2 - 20x + 46$ d. $y = -0.5x^2 - x + 3.5$
    e. $y = -3x^2 + 24x - 48$ f. $y = 1.5x^2 - 3$
    g. $y = -0.5x^2 - Hx + 4 - 0.5H^2$ h. $y = Ax^2 - 8Ax + 16A$
    i. $y = Ax^2 - 2AHx + AH^2 + K$

2. a. $y = (x + 3)^2 - 2$ $y = x^2 + 6x + 7$
    b. $y = -(x - 4)^2 + 3$ $y = -x^2 + 8x - 13$
    c. $y = 2(x - 2)^2 - 4$ $y = 2x^2 - 8x + 4$
    d. $y = -0.5(x + 1.5)^2 + 3$ $y = -0.5x^2 - 1.5x + 1.875$
    e. $y = A(x - H)^2 + K$ $y = Ax^2 - 2AHx + AH^2 + K$

3. a. $3, 2, -5$ b. $3, 2+d, 14s^2$

4. a. $A, -2AH, K + AH^2$ b. $a = A$
    c. $b = -2AH; H = \dfrac{-b}{2a}$ d. $c = K + AH^2; K = c - \dfrac{b^2}{4a}$

5. a. $(2.17, -2.08); y = 3(x - 2.17)^2 - 2.08$
    b. $(-3, 2); y = (x + 3)^2 + 2$
    c. $(-1, -9); y = (x + 1)^2 - 9$

6. $T = 0.03w^2 - 2.3w + 37.8$ (37 mi/hr, $-5.2°F$)

7. Sold $= 200, 195, 190, 185, 180$ Income $= 400, 409.50, 418, 425.50, 432$
    b. $D_1 = 9.5, 8.5, 7.5, 6.5$; $D_2 = -1, -1, -1$
    c. $y = -50x^2 + 300x$
    d. $3, \$450$

Problem Set 10.3

1. a. x-intercepts; $7.5, -2.5, 3.2$: y-intercept; 150
    b. $y = 2.5x^3 - 20.5x^2 - 6.875x + 150$
    c. $[-5, 10, 1, -100, 200, 50]$

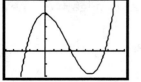

2. a. $y = -4.9(x - 0.7)(x - 2.8)$
   b. $(1.75, 5.40225)$
      At 1.75 second the ball reaches 5.4 m.
   c. -9.604
      The well is 9.6 m deep.
   d. The maximum changes the roots stay the same.

3. a. x-intercepts, -1.5 and -6; y-intercept, -2.25; vertex, $(-3.75, 1.265625)$
   b. x-intercept, 4; y-intercept, 48; vertex, $(4,0)$

5. a. i. $y = 2(x - 2)(x - 4)$ ii. $y = -0.25(x + 6)(x + 1.5)$
   b. i. $y = 2x^2 - 12x + 16$ ii. $y = -.025x^2 - 1.875x - 2.25$
   c. i. $y = 2(x - 3)^2 - 2$ ii. $y = -0.25(x + 3.75)^2 - 1.265625$

7. a. $y = A(x + 5)(x - 3)(x - 6)$ b. $A = 2$
   c. $y = 2(x + 5)(x - 3)(x - 6) + 100$ d. $y = 2(x + 9)(x + 1)(x - 2)$

9. a. $x , 4 , x , 4$ $2x , 6 , 3 , 18$
   b. i. $(x + 4)^2$ $(2x + 6)(x + 3)$
      ii. $x^2 + 8x + 16$ $2x^2 + 12x + 18$

10. a. $(x - 4)(x - 6)$ b. $(x - 3)^2$ c. $(x + 8)(x - 8)$ d. $(x + 10)(x - 12)$

Problem Set 10.4

1. a. $(2x - 3)^2$ b. $\left(x + \dfrac{5}{2}\right)^2$ c. $(x - y)^2$

2. a. $2.3 \pm \sqrt{25} = -2.7, 7.3$ b. $-4.45 \pm \sqrt{12.25} = -7.95, -0.95$
   c. $-\dfrac{1}{2}, 2$

3. a. $3x^2 - 13x - 10 = 0$ b. $x^2 - 5x - 13 = 0$
      $a = 3, b = -13, c = -10$ $a = 1, b = -5, c = -13$

      $\dfrac{-2}{3}, 5$ or $-0.667, 5$ $\dfrac{5 \pm \sqrt{77}}{2}$ or $-1.887, 6.887$
   c. $3x^2 + 5x + 1 = 0$
      $a = 3, b = 5, c = 1$

      $\dfrac{-5 \pm \sqrt{13}}{6}$ or $-1.434, -0.232$

5. Answers will vary. Those listed below are only examples.
   a. $(x - 3)(x + 3) = 0$ b. $(x - 4)(5x + 2) = 0$
   c. $(x - R_1)(x - R_2) = 0$ d. $-4.9(x - 1.1)(x - 4.7) = 0$

6. Answers will vary. The calculator will give an error message or produce an answer in complex form. The value under the radical is negative. The graph does not cross the x-axis. Example: $y = x^2 + 1$

8. $(7 + 0.5\sqrt{300})^2 - 14(7 + 0.5\sqrt{300}) - 26$ $(7 - 0.5\sqrt{300})^2 - 14(7 - 0.5\sqrt{300}) - 26$
   $49 + 7\sqrt{300} + 75 - 98 - 7\sqrt{300} - 26$ $49 - 7\sqrt{300} + 75 - 98 + 7\sqrt{300} - 26$
   $49 + 75 - 98 - 26 + 7\sqrt{300} - 7\sqrt{300}$ $49 + 75 - 98 - 26 - 7\sqrt{300} + 7\sqrt{300}$
   $126 - 126 = 0$ $126 - 126 = 0$

9. a. $y = \sqrt{400 - x^2}$ b. 17.3 ft   c. 8.7 ft
    d. Pythagorean theorem: $a^2 + b^2 = c^2$

Problem Set 10.5

1. $y = -4.9x^2 = 227$ m $y = -16x^2 = 740$ ft

2. a. $H(t) = -4.9t^2 + 100t + 25$ b. height = 25 m, velocity = 100 m/sec
    c. 10.2 sec   d. 535 m
    e. 3.27 sec and 17.1 sec   f. 20.7 sec

3. a. $y = -20x^2 + 332x$
    b. $8.30 each for a total of $1377.80

7. $y = 11000x^2 - Mx - M$

9. a. $L = -4t^2 - 6.8t + 49.2$ b. 49.2 L   c. 2.76 min

Problem Set 10.6

1. a. $y = x - 4$ b. $y = (x - 4)^2$ c. $y = (x - 4)^3$

2. a. $[-6, 6, 1, -150, 500, 100]$ b. $[-6, 6, 1, -700, 100, 100]$

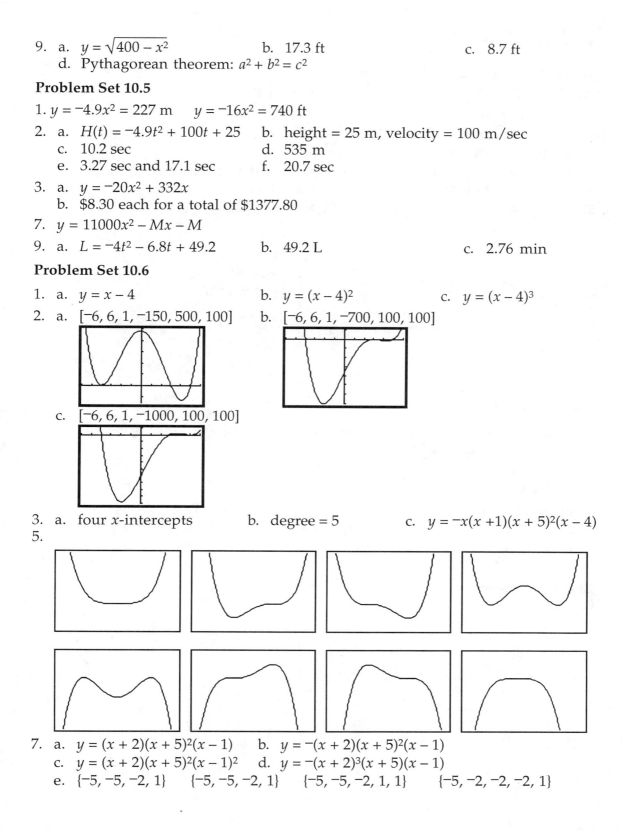

    c. $[-6, 6, 1, -1000, 100, 100]$

3. a. four x-intercepts   b. degree = 5   c. $y = -x(x + 1)(x + 5)^2(x - 4)$

5.

7. a. $y = (x + 2)(x + 5)^2(x - 1)$ b. $y = -(x + 2)(x + 5)^2(x - 1)$
    c. $y = (x + 2)(x + 5)^2(x - 1)^2$ d. $y = -(x + 2)^3(x + 5)(x - 1)$
    e. $\{-5, -5, -2, 1\}$ $\{-5, -5, -2, 1\}$ $\{-5, -5, -2, 1, 1\}$ $\{-5, -2, -2, -2, 1\}$

Problem Set 10.7

1. a. $2 \pm i\sqrt{2}$ or $2 \pm 1.41i$ b. $\pm i$ c. $0.5 \pm 0.866i$

2. a. $x^2 - 2x - 15 = 0$ d. $x^2 - 4x + 5 = 0$

3. a. $y = (x + 4)(x - 5)(x + 2)^2$ b. $y = -2(x + 4)(x - 5)(x + 2)^2$
   c. $y = x(3x - 1)(2x + 5)$ d. $y = -1(x + 1)^3(x - 4)(x^2 + 25)$

4. a. $10.83i, -0.83i$ b. $2i, i$
   c. The solutions do not come in conjugate pairs because the coefficients of the equation are imaginary.

5. a. $b^2 < 4ac$ b. $b^2 \geq 4ac$ c. $b^2 = 4ac$

7. a.

   b. 1
   c. factor the expression
   d. $1.75 \pm 1.56i$

Problem Set 10.8

1. a. $11 \cdot 4 + 3 = 47$ b. $(x - 1)(6x^3 + x^2 + 8x - 4) + 11$ c. $(x - 2)(x^2 + x - 8)$

2. a. $x^4 - 5x^3 + 15x^2 - 45x + 54$ b. $x^3 - 3x^2 + 9x - 27$
   c. $x^2 + 9$ d. $\pm 3i$
   e. (calculator check)

4. a. $\pm 2i, \pm 2, \pm 1$ b. $-7.01107428896, -0.942786970498, 0.453861259465$

5. a. $0, \pm 3.0786423, \pm 4.434 \pm 1.844i$ b. $0, \pm 3.141148, \pm 6.2 \pm 4.5i, \pm 5.7 \pm i$
   c. for degree 15: $0, \pm 3.14159188$ as the degree increases the real roots approach 0 and $\pm\pi$

Chapter Review
Problem Set 10.9

1. $1, 4, 10, 20, 35, \ldots$; the expression for n points is $\frac{1}{6} n^3 - \frac{1}{2} n^2 + \frac{1}{3} n$.

2. a. $y = 2x^2 - 8x - 8$ and $y = 2(x - 4.828)(x + 0.828)$
   b. $y = -3x^2 + 12x + 15$ and $y = -3(x - 2)^2 + 27$
   c. $y = (x + 1)(x + 2)$ and $y = (x + 1.5)^2 - 0.25$
   d. $y = x^3 + 2x^2 - 11x - 12$
   e. $y = 2(x + 3.386)(x - 0.886)$ and $y = 2(x + 1.25)^2 - 9.125$
   f. $y = -x^2 - 14x - 51$

3. a.

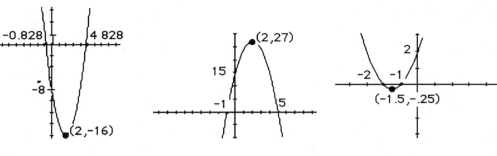

d.   e.

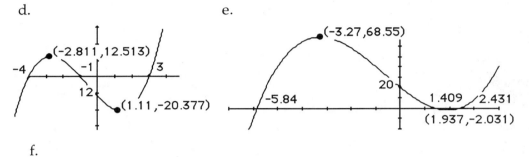

f.

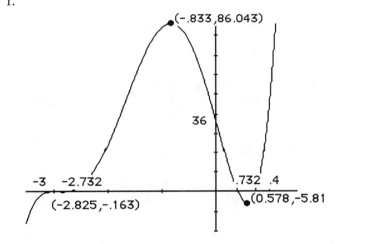

4. a. $y = 2(x + 1)(x - 4)$ b. $y = 2(x + 3)^2(x - 1)$
   c. $y = (x + 2)(x - 3)^3$ d. $y = 0.5(x + 4)(x - 2)(x^2 + 9)$

5. 18 in. × 18 in. × 36 in. = 11,664 in.^{3}

Chapter Eleven Selected Answers

Problem Set 11.1

1. a. $8! = 40,320$ b. $7! = 5040$ c. $\frac{1}{8}$

    e. $\frac{4}{8} = 0.5$; This should occur half the time.

    f. 1   g. $8! - 1$ h. $\frac{8! - 1}{8!}$

2. a. 12   b. 7   c. $n + 1$ d. n
    e. $120(119) = 14,280$ f. $n(n - 1)$ g. $n + 1 = 15$; $n = 14$

5. $8 \cdot 10^6 = 8,000,0006.$

6. $12! = 8$ min; $13! = 1.7$ hr; $15! = 15$ days; $20! = 771$ centuries

Problem Set 11.2

1. a. $2!$; 21   b. $3! = 6$; 35   c. $4! = 24$; 35   d. $7! = 5040$; 1
2. a. 120   b. 35   c. 105   d. 1
3. a. 120   b. 35   c. 105   d. 1

4. a. $_{10}C_4 = \frac{10!}{6! \ 4!}$ b. $_{10}C_4 = {_{10}C_6}$ c. $\frac{10!}{6! \ 4!} = \frac{10!}{4! \ 6!}$

6. a. $_{20}C_6 = 38,760$ b. $_{18}C_4 = 3,060$ c. $\frac{3060}{38760}$

9. a. $_7C_5(0.3)^5(0.7)^2 = 0.0250047$ b. $_7C_6(0.3)^6(0.7)^1 = 0.0035721$
    c. $_7C_7(0.3)^7(0.7)^0 = 0.0002187$ d. $0.0025 + 0.00357 + 0.00022 = 0.2879$

Problem Set 11.3

1. a. HH, HT, TH, TT   b. HH, HT, TH, TT
    c.

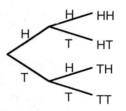

    d. The combination number $_2C_0$ is the number of times you get no tails when two coins are tossed; $_2C_1$ is the number of times you get 1 tail when two coins are tossed; $_2C_2$ is the number of times you get 2 tails when two coins are tossed

    e. The terms represent the long range distribution of 2 heads, 1 head, and 0 heads.

2. a. $x^4 + 4x^3y + 6x^2y^2 + 4xy^3 + y^4$ b. $p^5 + 5p^4q + 10p^3q^2 + 5p^2q^3 + 5pq^4 + q^5$
    c. $8x^3 + 36x^2 + 54x + 27$ d. $81x^4 - 432x^3 + 864x^2 - 678x + 256$

3. a. 1
   b. Answers will vary. On a TI-82, if $L_1 = \{0, 1, 2, \ldots, 8\}$ then $L_2 = y_1(L_1)$ works nicely.

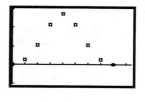

   c. 1
   d. Answers will vary. As p increases, the distributions lose symmetry and become extremely skewed.

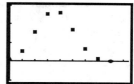

4. a. $0.97^{30} = 0.40$
   b. $\displaystyle\sum_{j=0}^{2} {}_{30}C_j (0.97)^j (0.03)^{30-j} = 0.94$

7. Answers will vary. The horizontal shift can be found by tracing to the highest point of the binomial curve and finding the x-value. It should be $90(1 - p)$. The y-value of the maximum point should be the value of a in the exponential curve. The value of b will be less than 1, but not much less.

Problem Set 11.4

1. a. Answers will vary but the second set has less spread.
   b. In the first set, the mean is 35 and the standard deviation is 19.99; the mean of the second set is 117 and the standard deviation is 3.16.
   c. Both the mean and the standard deviations are ten times the original numbers.

3. a. Both French and German had the lowest mean. The larger standard deviation on the French exam indicates that more people did worse on that test (also more did better).
   b. This is clearly the French exam with the greatest standard deviation.
   c. Pierre $\dfrac{88 - 72}{8.5} = 1.88$ Hans $\dfrac{84 - 72}{5.8} = 2.06$ Juanita $\dfrac{91 - 85}{6.1} = 0.98$

4. a. Answers will vary, but $\bar{x}$ should be close to 7, and σ should be close to 2.4.
   b. about 67   c. 68%   d. about 95%

8. The mean is 31.95 and the standard deviation is 4.51.

Problem Set 11.5

1.   2.   3.

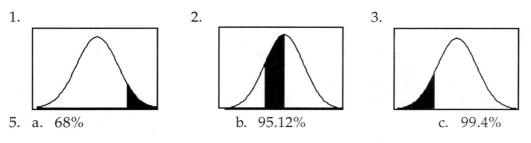

5. a. 68%   b. 95.12%   c. 99.4%

7. a. $\bar{x} = 165$, $\sigma = 5.82$

b.

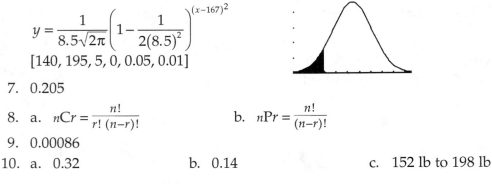

```
WINDOW FORMAT
 Xmin=148
 Xmax=180
 Xscl=2
 Ymin=-5
 Ymax=70
 Yscl=5
```

c. $y = 66(0.9851)^{(x-165)^2}$ where $66 =$ maximum height and $1 - 1/2\sigma^2 = 0.9851$

d. $y = 0.0698(0.9851)^{(x-165)^2}$ where $0.0698 = 66/$(area under curve)

Problem Set 11.6

1. 0.31

2. a. 69.3 g   b. 67.6g   c. 66.2 g

3. a. 0.0127   b. 0.0005

6. a. 0.08655   b. 86 or 87 groups   d. 4.3634   e. 4.3763

Chapter Review
Problem Set 11.7

1. a. $12! = 479{,}001{,}600$ b. $\dfrac{5!\,7!}{12!} = 0.00126$ or 0.13%

2. $\dfrac{1}{_{13}C_{10}} = 0.0035$

3. $\displaystyle\sum_{i=17}^{20} {}_{20}C_i (0.65)^i (0.35)^{20-i} = 0.044$ or 4.4%

4. a. $100 - 800x + 2800x^2 - 5600x^3 + 7000x^4 - 5600x^5 + 2800x^6 - 800x^7 + 100x^8$

   b. $600 + 250x + 41.667x^2 + 3.4722x^3 + 0.14468x^4 + 0.002411x^5$

5. The mean is 67.8 in., and the standard deviation is 3.6 in.

6.

$$y = \frac{1}{8.5\sqrt{2\pi}}\left(1 - \frac{1}{2(8.5)^2}\right)^{(x-167)^2}$$

$[140, 195, 5, 0, 0.05, 0.01]$

7. 0.205

8. a. $_nC_r = \dfrac{n!}{r!\,(n-r)!}$ b. $_nP_r = \dfrac{n!}{(n-r)!}$

9. 0.00086

10. a. 0.32   b. 0.14   c. 152 lb to 198 lb

Chapter Twelve Selected Answers

Problem Set 12.1

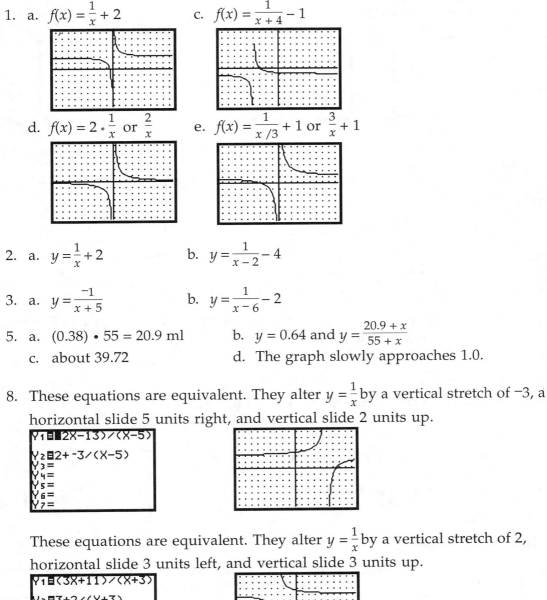

1. a. $f(x) = \frac{1}{x} + 2$

    c. $f(x) = \frac{1}{x+4} - 1$

    d. $f(x) = 2 * \frac{1}{x}$ or $\frac{2}{x}$

    e. $f(x) = \frac{1}{x/3} + 1$ or $\frac{3}{x} + 1$

2. a. $y = \frac{1}{x} + 2$

    b. $y = \frac{1}{x-2} - 4$

3. a. $y = \frac{-1}{x+5}$

    b. $y = \frac{1}{x-6} - 2$

5. a. $(0.38) \cdot 55 = 20.9$ ml

    b. $y = 0.64$ and $y = \frac{20.9 + x}{55 + x}$

    c. about 39.72

    d. The graph slowly approaches 1.0.

8. These equations are equivalent. They alter $y = \frac{1}{x}$ by a vertical stretch of -3, a horizontal slide 5 units right, and vertical slide 2 units up.

    ```
    Y1=(-2X-13)/(X-5)
    Y2=2+-3/(X-5)
    Y3=
    Y4=
    Y5=
    Y6=
    Y7=
    ```

    These equations are equivalent. They alter $y = \frac{1}{x}$ by a vertical stretch of 2, horizontal slide 3 units left, and vertical slide 3 units up.

    ```
    Y1=(3X+11)/(X+3)
    Y2=3+2/(X+3)
    Y3=
    Y4=
    Y5=
    Y6=
    Y7=
    ```

Problem Set 12.2

1. a. The graph has a slant asymptote at $x - 2$. Add $y = x - 2$ to confirm this.

    b. The graph is stretched vertically by a factor of 2 and has a slant asymptote at $-2x + 3$.

    c. The graph has a horizontal asymptote at $y = 3$ with a hole at $(2, 3)$.

2. a. The graph has a value of -1 except for the hole when $x = 5$.

    b. The graph has a value of 3 except for the hole when $x = -2$.

    c. The graph is always $y = x + 3$ except for the hole when $x = 4$.

3. a. $y = 0 + \dfrac{(x + 2)}{x + 2}$

    b. $y = -3 + \dfrac{(x - 3)}{x - 3}$

    c. $y = \dfrac{(x + 2)(x + 1)}{x + 1}$

5. a. The graph has a slant asymptote of $y = x$, vertical asymptote at $x = -2$, and has been vertically stretched by -3.

    b. $y = x$

    c. Answers will vary. One possibility is $y = \dfrac{1}{x + 2}$

    d. Answers will vary. One possibility is $y = (x + 3)(x - 1)$

    e. $y = x + \dfrac{-3}{x + 2}$ or $\dfrac{(x + 3)(x - 1)}{x + 2}$

7. a. The graph has x-intercepts at 1 and -4 and vertical asymptotes at $x = 2$ and $x = -3$.

    b. The graph has a horizontal asymptote at $y = 1$.

Problem Set 12.3

1. a. The unrestricted growth rate is 8%, and the population limit is 500.

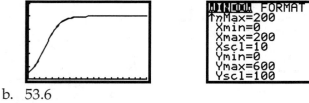

```
WINDOW FORMAT
↑nMax=200
 Xmin=0
 Xmax=200
 Xscl=10
 Ymin=0
 Ymax=600
 Yscl=100
```

    b. 53.6
    c. 70.38, 131.75, 220.44,. . . 476.99
    d. 500

2. After 20 weeks, the bacteria population is at 5000. This is a net rate increase of 9900%.

4. This graph and model are based on 48% unrestricted growth per year and a limiting population of 11,000 grasshoppers.

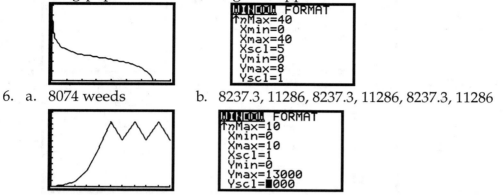

6. a. 8074 weeds   b. 8237.3, 11286, 8237.3, 11286, 8237.3, 11286

d. After about 5 years the weed population vacillates between 8237 and 11286 weeds.

Problem Set 12.4

1. a. The shortest distance occurs when the boat travels directly to point D.

   b. The boat would travel $\sqrt{15^2 + 98^2} \approx 99.1$ mi and the ambulance 0 mil.

   c. The shortest time (2.016 hr) occurs when $x \approx 5.218$. Using this point the boat travels 15.88 mi and the ambulance $98 - 5.218 = 92.782$ mi.

2. a.

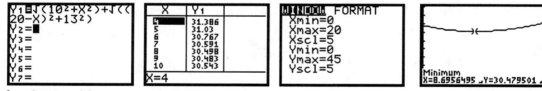

   b. $0 \le x \le 20$

   c. Fasten it at $x \approx 8.7$ m for a minimum wire length of ≈ 30.5 m.

4. a. 64 sec (0.125 mi/sec; time = 8 mi)

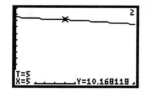

   b. $d = \sqrt{7^2 + (8 - 0.125t)^2}$

Time (sec)	0	1	5	10	20	30	64
Ground distance	8	7.875	7.375	6.75	5.5	4.25	0 mi
Actual distance	10.63	10.536	10.168	9.7243	8.9022	8.1892	7

Problem Set 12.5

1. a. Center at $(0, 0)$ and radius 2.
   b. Center at $(3, 0)$ and radius 1.
   c. Center at $(-1, 2)$ and radius 3.

   d. Center at $(0, 1.5)$ and radius 0.5.
   e. Center at $(1, 2)$ and radius 2.
   f. Center at $(-3, 0)$ and radius 4.

2. a. $x = 5 \cos t + 3$ and $y = 5 \sin t$ or $(x - 3)^2 + y^2 = 25$
   b. $x = 3 \cos t - 1$ and $y = 3 \sin t + 2$ or $(x + 1)^2 + (y - 2)^2 = 9$

3. a. $(2, 0), (-2, 0), (0, 4),$ $(0, -4)$
   b. $(5, -2), (-1, -2), (2, -1),$ $(2, -3)$
   c. $(1, 1), (7, 1), (4, 4),$ $(4, -2)$

4. a. $x = 6 \cos t$ and $y = 3 \sin t$ or $\left(\frac{x}{6}\right)^2 + \left(\frac{y}{3}\right)^2 = 1$

   b. $x = 5 \cos t + 3$ and $y = 5 \sin t$ or $\left(\frac{x - 3}{2}\right)^2 + \left(\frac{y}{5}\right)^2 = 1$

5. a. Answers will vary. The equation $\left(\frac{x - 500}{500}\right)^2 + \left(\frac{y}{65}\right)^2 = 1$ is a good fit.
   b. ± 65 AUs   c. $\approx (1025, 0)$ d. $\approx (1000, 0)$

7. a. The string will be 12 units long.
   b. $(3\sqrt{3}, 0)$ and $(-3\sqrt{3}, 0)$

Problem Set 12.6

1. a. vertex $(0, 5)$, focus $(0, 6)$, directrix $y = 4$
   b. vertex $(-2, -2)$, focus $(-1.75, -2)$, directrix $x = -2.25$
   c. vertex $(-3, 1)$, focus $(-3, 0.5)$, directrix $y = 1.5$

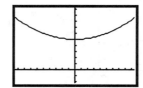
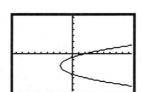
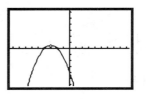

Preliminary Edition

d. vertex (4, 0),
   focus (−4, 0),
   directrix $x = 12$

e. vertex (−1, 3),
   focus (−1, 5),
   directrix $y = 1$

f. vertex (3, 0),
   focus $(\frac{61}{12}, 0)$,

   directrix $x = \frac{35}{12}$

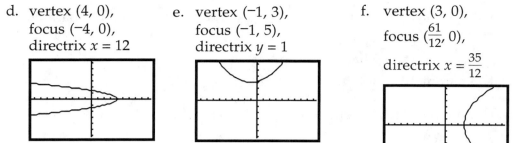

2. a. $x = t^2$ and $y = t + 2$ or $x = (y − 2)^2$
      vertex (0, 2), focus (0.25, 2), and directrix $x = −0.25$
   b. $x = t$ and $y = −t^2 + 4$ or $y = −x^2 + 4$
      vertex (0, 4), focus (0, 3.75), and directrix $y = 4.25$

3. The path will be parabolic. The rock is the focus and the shoreline is the directrix.

4. a. The graph is a parabola with vertex (0, 1),
      focus (0, 3), and directrix $y = −1$.
   b. $y = 0.125x^2 + 1$

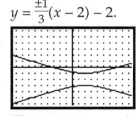

6. $y = −2.4x^2 + 21.12x − 44.164$

Problem Set 12.7

1. a. The vertices are at (±2, 0) and the asymptotes are $y = ±x$.

   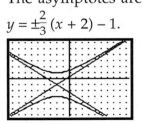

   b. The vertices are at (2, −1) and (2, −3). The asymptotes are
   $y = \frac{±1}{3}(x − 2) − 2$.

   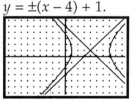

   c. The vertices are at (1, 1) and (7, 1). The asymptotes are $y = ±(x − 4) + 1$.

   d. The vertices are (−2, 1) and (−2, −3). The asymptotes are
   $y = ±\frac{2}{3}(x + 2) − 1$.

   e. The vertices are (−5, 3) and (3, 3). The asymptotes are $y = ±0.5(x + 1) + 3$.

   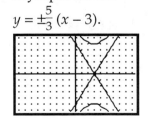

   f. The vertices are (3, 5) and (3, −5). The asymptotes are
   $y = ±\frac{5}{3}(x − 3)$.

2. a. The parametric equations are $x = \dfrac{2}{\cos t}$ and $y = \tan t$. The nonparametric

equation is $\left(\dfrac{x}{2}\right)^2 - \left(\dfrac{y}{1}\right)^2 = 1$. The asymptotes are $y = \pm 0.5x$.

   b. The parametric equations are $x = 2\tan t + 3$ and $y = \dfrac{2}{\cos t} - 3$.

   The nonparametric equation is $\left(\dfrac{y+3}{2}\right)^2 - \left(\dfrac{x-3}{2}\right)^2 = 1$. The asymptotes are

   $y = \pm(x - 3) - 3$.

3. a. $(\pm\sqrt{2}, 0)$ b. $(2, -2 + \sqrt{10})$ and $(2, -2 - \sqrt{10})$

4. $\left|\sqrt{(x+2)^2 + (y-1)^2} - \sqrt{(x-4)^2 + (y-1)^2}\right| = 10$

6.

Value of x	5	10	20	40
Distance	0.4105	0.2462	0.1357	0.0713

Problem Set 12.8

1. a. $1x^2 + 0xy + 0y^2 + 14x - 9y + 148 = 0$
   b. $1x^2 + 0xy + 9y^2 - 14x - 198y + 1129 = 0$

2. a. $a = \dfrac{21}{15}$ or $\dfrac{7}{5}$ b. $b = \dfrac{21}{30}$ or $\dfrac{7}{10}$

   c. $c = \left(\dfrac{7}{10}\right)^2 = \dfrac{49}{100}$ d. $d = \dfrac{147}{20}$ e. $e = \dfrac{7}{10}$

4. a. matches the ellipse (4th graph)
   b. matches hyperbola (2nd graph)
   c. matches the parabola (3rd graph)
   d. matches the circle (1st graph)

6. a. $y = \dfrac{-0 \pm \sqrt{0^2 - 4(4)(-25x^2 - 100)}}{8}$ b. $y = \dfrac{-16 \pm \sqrt{16^2 - 4(4)(-10x + 36)}}{8}$

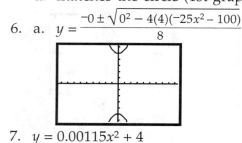 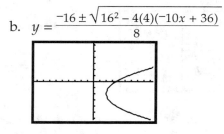

7. $y = 0.00115x^2 + 4$

Problem Set 12.9

1. a. $\begin{bmatrix} 0.866 & -0.5 \\ 0.5 & 0.866 \end{bmatrix}$ b. $\begin{bmatrix} -0.839 & -0.545 \\ 0.545 & -0.839 \end{bmatrix}$

   c. $\begin{bmatrix} 0 & 1 \\ -1 & 0 \end{bmatrix}$ d. $\begin{bmatrix} -0.839 & -0.545 \\ 0.545 & -0.839 \end{bmatrix}$

2. $\begin{bmatrix} 2 & -5 & 2 \\ 1 & 4 & 7 \end{bmatrix}$ If $A = 30°$:

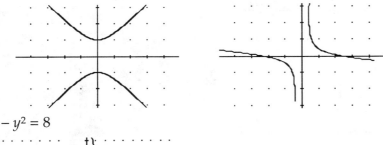

4. a. $\begin{bmatrix} -1 & -7 & -4 \\ -4 & -2 & 1 \end{bmatrix}$

   b. A reflection over the x-axis followed by a reflection over the y-axis (or vice-versa).

6. a. The graph is a unit hyperbola which opens vertically.
   b. The equations for x_2 and y_2 rotate the original hyperbola 50° clockwise.
   c.

7. $x^2 - y^2 = 8$

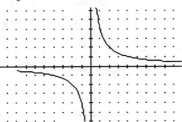

Chapter Review
Problem Set 12.10

1. approximately 10.34 oz
2. a. The slice is perpendicular to the axis.
   b. The slice intersects only one branch of the cone. The angle is not perpendicular to the axis.
   c. The slice intersects only one branch of the cone and is parallel to an edge.
   d. The slice intersects both branches of the cone but does not contain the vertex.
   e. The slice intersects at the vertex.
   f. The slice is along an edge.
   g. The axis is contained in the slice.

3. a. $(\frac{x-5}{3})^2 + (\frac{y+2}{4})^2 = 1$

   b. $x = 3\cos t + 5$ and $y = 4\sin t - 2$

   c. Center is $(5, -2)$. foci are $(5, -2 + \sqrt{7})$ and $(5, -2 - \sqrt{7})$.

   d. $16x^2 + 9y^2 - 160x + 36y + 292 = 0$

   e. $x = (3\cos t + 5)\cos 75 - (4\sin t - 2)\sin 75$
      $y = (3\cos t + 5)\sin 75 + (4\sin t - 2)\cos 75$

   f. $16(x\cos 75 - y\sin 75)^2 + 9(x\sin 75 + y\cos 75)^2 - 160(x\cos 75 - y\sin 75) + 36(x\sin 75 + y\cos 75) + 292 = 0$. The expansion is just too messy.

4. a. $y = \pm 0.5x$ b. $x^2 - 4y^2 - 4 = 0$

   c. distance $= \left| 0.5x - \sqrt{\dfrac{x^2}{4} - 1} \right|$

   d.

x	0	1	2	10...	20
Distance	none	0	1	0.10	0.05

5. a.

   b. $y = 2$ and $x = 5$

   c. distance $= \left| 2 - \dfrac{2x - 14}{x - 5} \right|$

   d.

x	0	3	5	10...	20
Distance	0.8	2	none	0.8	0.27

6. Include $(x + 3)$ as a factor in both the numerator and denominator of the fraction. $y = \dfrac{(2x - 14)(x + 3)}{(x - 5)(x + 3)}$

7. About 23.3 mi/hr and 43.3 mi/hr. One approach is to find the intersection of the two times represented by y_1 and y_2. (x is the rate during the first 2 mi.)
   $y_1 = \dfrac{2}{x} + \dfrac{3.5}{x + 20}$ and $y_2 = \dfrac{10}{60}$

8. a. $y_1 = \dfrac{34}{x + 11} + \dfrac{13}{x}$

b. See the graph and window. The faster Eric runs, the less time it takes for
    the event.

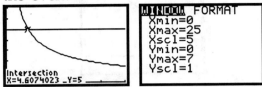

c. Answers will vary depending on how fast of a runner you think Eric is
    (perhaps $2 < x < 10$ and $3 < y < 9$).

d. about 4.6 mi/hr

Chapter Thirteen Selected Answers

Problem Set 13.1

1. a. 0.9962
    b. −0.8387
    c. −0.9848

    d. 0.6428
    e. −0.7314

2. a. $y = \sin x$
    b. The graph will shift up 2 units.

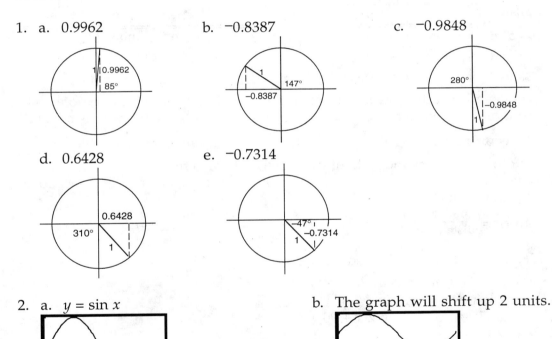

c. The graph will shift right 180°.

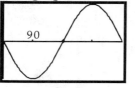

d. The graph will be stretched vertically by a factor of 2, shifted up 3 units and to the right 180°.

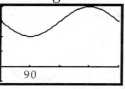

3. a and b.

Angle	0°	30°	60°	90°	120°	150°	180°
x-coord	1	0.8660	0.5	0	−0.5	−0.8660	−1
y-coord	0	0.5	0.8660	1	0.8660	0.5	0
Slope	0	0.5774	1.7321	undefined	−1.7321	−0.5774	0

Angle	210°	240°	270°	300°	315°	330°	360°
x-coord	−0.8660	−0.5	0	0.5	0.7071	0.8660	1
y-coord	−0.5	−0.8660	−1	−0.8660	−0.7071	−0.5	0
Slope	0	1.7321	undefined	−1.7321	−1	−0.5774	0

c. The lengths of the legs of the reference triangle form the same ratio as the ratio of the x and y coordinates because lengths of the sides are the same as the coordinates so the definition of a slope, $\frac{\text{rise}}{\text{run}}$, can be translated to $\frac{y\text{-coord}}{x\text{-coord}}$. Another name for the ratio of the legs is the tangent.

d. The tangents of the angles in the table in a. are the same as the slopes for the angles in the table.

e. $\tan A° = \dfrac{\text{height of lily pad}}{\text{distance of lily pad from center}}$

5. a. 360°   b. 360°   c. 180°   d. 180°   e. 60°

8. a. $y = \sin 2x + 1$ or $y = {}^-\cos 2(x + 45) + 1$
   b. $y = {}^-\cos x$ or $y = {}^-\sin (x + 90)$
   c. $y = \tan 2x - 1$ or $y = \tan 2(x + 90) - 1$
   d. $y = {}^-2 \sin 2x$ or $y = 2 \cos 2(x + 45)$

Problem Set 13.2

1. $y = \sin (x - 90)$
   $y = 1/(\sin (x - 90))$

2. a. $y = 2 \csc (x + 360) + 1$ or $y = 2 \csc (x + 720) + 1$
   b. $y = {}^-\cot \frac{1}{3}(x + 270)$ or $y = {}^-\cot \frac{1}{3}(x - 270)$

Preliminary Edition

3. a. The value of *d* raises or lowers the function; a positive *d* raises the
        function and a negative lowers.
    b. The value of *a* represents the amplitude. A value of 1
        for *a* gives an amplitude of 1 and a value of 5 gives an
        amplitude of 5.
    c. The value of *a* determines the period such that as *a*

        increases the period decreases; $\frac{360}{a}$ = period.

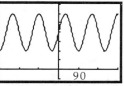

    d. The value of *c* shifts the function; a positive *c* shifts the graph to the left
        and a negative *c* shifts the functions to the right.
5. a. $h = 20 \tan A° + 1.5$ b. 33.5 m
    c. 16 m, 18.3 m   d. 23°
7. a.

    b. $y = 10{,}000 \sin 4x$, the residuals imply that the functions accuracy decreases
        as the angle increases.
    c. $y = 39{,}190 \tan x$, the residuals show that the accuracy is much better than
        the sine function.
    d. The maximum safe speed is ∞.
8. a.

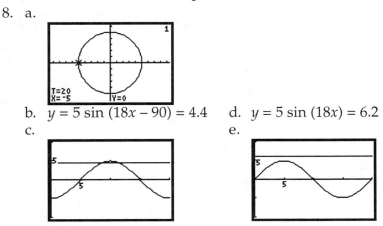

    b. $y = 5 \sin (18x - 90) = 4.4$ d. $y = 5 \sin (18x) = 6.2$
    c.   e.

Problem Set 13.3

1. $y = \sin 8x$; $0° \le x \le 45°$, $-1 \le y \le 1$
2. b. physical, $y = \sin 15.6521x$; emotional, $y = \sin 12.8571x$; intellectual,
        $y = \sin 10.9091x$
    c. The plot depends on where your cycles are starting today.
    d. 21,252 days or 58.22 years
4. a. $y = 10 \sin 18(x + 15) + 12$
    b. $y = 11 \sin 12(x + 22.5) + 22$

c. $y = (10 \sin 18(x + 15) + 12) + (11 \sin 12(x + 22.5) + 22) - 12$
Note: The term '− 12' is so that there is not at total of + 34, but instead only '+ 22'

d. 6 times

7. a. $y = 1 - \sin 2x$

b. $y = (\sin x - \cos x)^2 = \sin^2 x + \cos^2 x - 2 \sin x \cos x = 1 - \sin 2x$

Problem Set 13.4

1. $\triangle ABC$; $AB = 8.35$, $BC = 6.40$, $\angle ABC = 25.5°$
$\triangle DEF$; $DF = 6.46$, $\angle EDF = 81.21$, $\angle EFD = 52.68°$
$\triangle GHI$; $\angle HGI = 66.31°$, $\angle GHI = 84.64°$, $\angle GIH = 29.05°$
$\triangle LKJ$; $\angle LJK = 38.81°$, $\angle JLK = 33.29°$, $JK = 4.76$

3. 1659.844 mi

4.

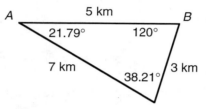

5. 26.549 cm

7. 93° from north

9. The pocket is 3.0 km deep, in a direction of 88.24° from north in relation to C, at a distance of 11.6 km from C.

Problem Set 13.5

1. $\angle A = 73.2°$, $\angle B = 59.55°$

2. a. $-90 \le T \le 90$

b. $-45 \le T \le 45$

c. $-180 \le T \le 180$

d. period = range; that is if period doubles, so does the range

3. $0 \le t \le 6.927$, $11.073 \le t \le 18.927$, $23.073 \le t \le 30.927$, $35.073 \le t \le 42.927$, $47.073 \le t \le 48$

4. a. $y = \sin 432x$

b. 144 times

6. a. not including $t = 0$, 12 times

b. 51.111% of the time

10. a. $y = 5 \sin 25.714x + 11$

b. $0 \le x \le 7.917$, $13.083 \le x \le 21.917$

Problem Set 13.6

1. (−3308, 2) and (210 °, −2)

3. a.

q	0°	5°	10°	15°	20°	25°	30°	35°	40°	45°	50°	55°
r	3	2.90	2.60	2.12	1.5	.45	0	−.78	−1.5	−2.1	−2.6	−2.9

60°	65°	70°	75°	80°	85°	90°	95°	100°	105°	110°	115°	120°
−3	−2.9	−2.6	−2.1	−1.5	−.78	0	.78	1.5	2.12	2.60	2.90	3

125°	130°	135°	140°	145°	150°	155°	160°	165°	170°	175°	180°	185°
2.90	2.60	2.12	1.5	.45	0	−.78	−1.5	−2.1	−2.6	−2.9	−3	−2.9

190°	195°	200°	205°	210°	215°	220°	225°	230°	235°	240°	245°	250°
−2.6	−2.1	−1.5	−.78	0	.78	1.5	2.12	2.60	2.90	3	2.90	2.60

255°	260°	265°	270°	275°	280°	285°	290°	295°	300°	305°	310°	315°
2.12	1.5	.45	0	−.78	−1.5	−2.1	−2.6	−2.9	−3	−2.9	−2.6	−2.1

320°	325°	330°	335°	340°	345°	350°	355°	360°
−1.5	−.78	0	.78	1.5	2.12	2.60	2.90	3

b.

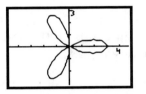

5. a. They are flipped images of each other.
    b. It is the same image rotated 90°.
    c. The width at $y = 0$ is $2a$.

6. a. This is better for audience noise because it only 'listens' to the area in front, where the performers are.
    b. The edge performers are 3 units away. The center is 4, and the others are 3.732 units away.

7. in all cases $0° \leq \theta \leq 360°$
    a. $r = 3 \cos \theta$ b. $r = 3 \cos 2\theta, r = 2 \sin 2\theta$

Problem Set 13.7

1.

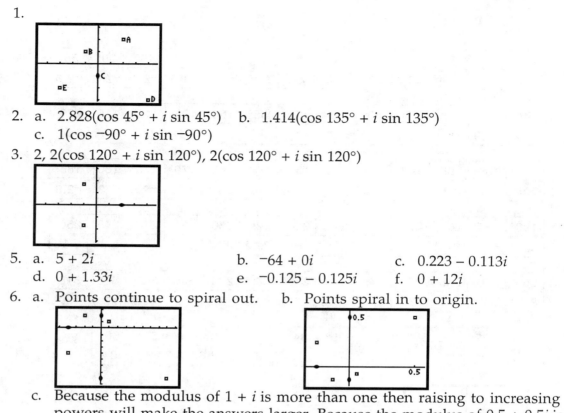

2. a. 2.828(cos 45° + i sin 45°)   b. 1.414(cos 135° + i sin 135°)
   c. 1(cos ⁻90° + i sin ⁻90°)

3. 2, 2(cos 120° + i sin 120°), 2(cos 120° + i sin 120°)

5. a. 5 + 2i b. ⁻64 + 0i c. 0.223 − 0.113i
   d. 0 + 1.33i e. ⁻0.125 − 0.125i f. 0 + 12i

6. a. Points continue to spiral out.   b. Points spiral in to origin.

   c. Because the modulus of 1 + i is more than one then raising to increasing
      powers will make the answers larger. Because the modulus of 0.5 + 0.5i is
      less than one it will shrink as it is raised to larger powers.

10. a. goes to (1, 0)   b. goes to (1, 0)
    c. goes to (1, 0)   d. all points go to (1, 0)

Preliminary Edition   SELECTED ANSWERS

11. The points iterate as shown below. Those colored black iterate to (1, 0). Those left white iterate to (−0.5, 0.866). The others iterate to (−0.5, −0.866).

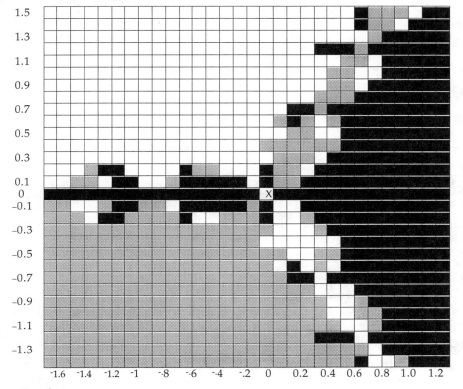

Chapter Review
Problem Set 13.8

1. a. period = 120°, $y = -2 \cos 3(x - 120°)$ b. period = 90°, $y = 3 \sin 4(x - 22.5°)$
   c. period = 90°, $y = \csc 2(x + 45)$ d. not a periodic function

2. a. $y = -2 \sin 2x - 1$ b. $y = 1.5 \sin 0.5(x + 60) + 1$
   c. $y = 0.5 \tan (x - 45)$ d. $y = 0.5 \sec 2x$

3. a. The equation should be similar to $y = 4.21 \sin \frac{360}{374} (x - 63) + 12.2$.
   b. June 5; 16.4 hr of daylight.
   c. March 1 and September 8.

4. a.

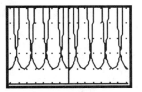

   b. $\tan^2 x = \sec^2 x + 1$

5. $\angle A = 74.51°$, $\angle B = 58.41°$, side c = 10.49 cm
   $\angle E = 52.55°$, $\angle F = 17.45°$, side f = 5.55 cm

6. If the known parts include SAS or SSS, use the Law of Cosines. If the known parts include AAS, use the Law of Sines. If the known parts are SSA, you can use either Law, but be careful if you use the Law of Sines to check whether you want an acute or obtuse angle.

7. $y = 100 \cos \frac{360}{105} (x - 10)$, 82.6 mi from the equator. Passes over the launch site 82 times in three days.

8. $(220°, -5), (400°, 5)$

9. a. $r = -2(\cos \theta + 1)$ b. $r = 2(\sin \theta + 1)$

10.

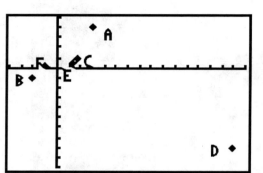

11. Points inside a circle of radius 1 centered at the origin iterate to $(0, 0)$. Points outside the circle become further and further away from the origin as they are iterated. Points on the circle stay on the circle. Some such as $1 + i$ iterate to a single point. Others such as $(\sqrt{0.3}, \sqrt{0.7})$ keep bouncing around the circle hitting various points on the circle.